FOCUS ON ALZHEIMER'S DISEASE RESEARCH

FOCUS ON ALZHEIMER'S DISEASE RESEARCH

EILEEN M. WELSH
EDITOR

Nova Biomedical Books
New York

Senior Editors: Susan Boriotti and Donna Dennis
Coordinating Editor: Tatiana Shohov
Office Manager: Annette Hellinger
Graphics: Wanda Serrano
Editorial Production: Maya Columbus, Vladimir Klestov,
Matthew Kozlowski and Tom Moceri
Circulation: Ave Maria Gonzalez, Vera Popovic, Raymond Davis, Melissa Diaz
Magdalena Nuñez, Marelene Nuñez and Jeannie Pappas
Marketing: Cathy DeGregory

Library of Congress Cataloging-in-Publication Data

Focus on Alzheimer's disease research / [edited by] Eileen M. Welsh.
p. cm.
Includes bibliographical references and index.
ISBN: 1-59033-788-3
1. Alzheimer's disease.
[DNLM: 1. Alzheimer Disease—etiology. 2. Alzheimer Disease—physiopathology. 3. Alzheimer Disease—therapy. 4. Ethics, Research. WT 155 F652 2003] I. Welsh, Eileen M.

RC523.F63 2003
616.8'31'0072—dc21 2003014371

An Imprint of Nova Science Publishers, Inc.
400 Oser Ave, Suite 1600
Hauppauge, New York 11788-3619
Tele. 631-231-7269 Fax 631-231-8175
e-mail: Novascience@earthlink.net
Web Site: http://www.novapublishers.com

Printed in the United States of America

CONTENTS

PREFACE

Dementia is a brain disorder that seriously affects a person's ability to carry out daily activities. The most common form of dementia among older people is Alzheimer's disease (AD), which involves the parts of the brain that control thought, memory, and language. Age is the most important known risk factor for AD. The number of people with the disease doubles every 5 years beyond age 65. AD is a slow disease, starting with mild memory problems and ending with severe brain damage. The course the disease takes and how fast changes occur vary from person to person. On average, AD patients live from 8 to 10 years after they are diagnosed, though the disease can last for as many as 20 years.

Current research is aimed at understanding why AD occurs and who is at greatest risk of developing it, improving the accuracy of diagnosis and the ability to identify those at risk, discovering, developing, and testing new treatments, and discovering treatments for behavioral problems in patients with AD. This new book gathers state-of-the-art research from leading scientists throughout the world which offers important information on understanding the underlying causes and discovering the most effective treatments for Alzheimer's Disease.

Alzheimer's disease (AD) is the most common type of dementia and as humans experience longer life spans AD prevalence is estimated to increase with age. This devastating disease is characterized by memory loss, confusion, and cognitive deficits.

Chapter one discusses aims at improving cerebral metabolism and preventing the occurrence of brain hypometabolism and may represent an effective therapeutic strategy in the battle against AD dementia.

The treatment and prevention of AD in women includes hormone replacement therapy (HRT) due to estrogen's hormonal action on cognitive abilities and the physiological benefits in brain via estrogen receptors. However, the known benefits and more importantly the potentially adverse effects of HRT in postmenopausal women have produced concerns about reproductive, endocrine and brain health issues. These concerns have stimulated a sustained surge of 'natural' alternative therapy usage such as dietary or nutritional supplement products. Since soy foods and nutritional supplements are readily available and contain high levels of natural estrogen-like molecules [produced in plants (phytoestrogens)] consumption of these products has increased dramatically. Specifically a particular group of phytoestrogens, namely isoflavones principally derived from soy foods, has gained increased usage. Given the recognized importance of estrogen hormone action in brain and its link to dementia such as AD justifies further research to investigate the neurobehavioral aspects of phytoestrogens. These topics/themes above are covered in chapter 2.

Melatonin administration synchronizes the sleep-wake cycle in blind people and in individuals suffering from delayed sleep phase syndrome or jet lag. The effect of melatonin on sleep is probably the consequence of increasing sleep propensity (by inducing a fall in body temperature) and of a synchronizing effect on the circadian clock (chronobiotic effect); typically the latter takes several days (or weeks) to occur. Daily melatonin production decreases with age, and in several pathologies, attaining its lowest values in Alzheimer's disease (AD) patients. About 45% of AD patients have disruptions in their sleep and sundowning agitation. Based on this evidence, the supplementary administration of melatonin to treat sleep and behavior disorders in AD patients was a logical therapeutic approach. Chapter 3 discusses the use of melatonin in Alzheimer's Disease.

Increasing evidence has placed cytokines prominently in the landscape of Alzheimer's pathology. What remain elusive are the functional roles of cytokines in the brain of Alzheimer patients. It is the hope of chapter 4 to identify both the promises and deficits of the emerging research on cytokines and Alzheimer's disease.

Lysosomes develop a propensity for free radical formation with age and an associated reduction in their protein processing capability. Gradual decay of lysosomal function likely contributes to the aging risk factor that enhances the susceptibility to neurodegenerative conditions. In fact, lysosomal disturbances are common among age-related protein accumulation disorders including Alzheimer's disease. Chapter 5 covers the Implications of the lysosomal system for and against Alzheimer's Disease.

The conversion of soluble, nontoxic amyloid β-protein (Aβ) to aggregated, toxic Aβ rich in β-sheet structures by seeded polymerization is considered to be the key step in the development of Alzheimer's disease. In chapter 6, the formation mechanisms and the properties of GM1-Aβ are reviewed, and the possibility of the lipid raft (lipid microdomain containing gangliosides) as a nidus for the aggregation of Aβ is discussed.

Mutations in the presenilin genes (PS1 and PS2) account for the majority of all autosomal dominant early onset familial Alzheimer's disease (AD) cases. Chapter 7 discusses presenilins and their role in amyloid-β generation.

Alzheimer's Disease (AD), the most common primary neurodegenerative disorder in the elderly, is characterized by protein processing gone haywire and a rising cluster of toxic proteins inside the brain cells and in the intercellular spaces. Chapter 8 discusses these issues.

In chapter 9 the author briefly reviews the type of ethical concerns and the type of research that has appeared over many years from the perspective of professionals involved in dementia care.

In chapter 11 the authors present the risk factors, signs and symptoms of AD, how assessment/diagnosis is determined, the kinds of care available and the impact of the setting on the life and performance of persons with AD.

In chapter 12, the authors introduce 2 commonly used screening tools for dementia in Taiwan. One is an objective test, the Mini-Mental State Examination (MMSE), and the other is a subjective test, the Informant Questionnaire on Cognitive Decline in the Elderly (IQCODE).

Chapter I

ALZHEIMER'S DEMENTIA: A METABOLIC PERSPECTIVE

Miao-Kun Sun and Daniel L. Alkon
Blanchette Rockefeller Neurosciences Institute
9601 Medical Center Drive
Johns Hopkins Academic and Research Building, Third Floor
Rockville. MD 20850-3332 USA

The primary focus of research on Alzheimer's disease (AD), a progressive cognitive decline, has been on the role of amyloid β peptide (Aβ) and τ hyperphosphorylation in the disorder. However, evidence is accumulating that amyloid plaques and neurofibrillary tangles may be only part of the underlying pathology. Impaired metabolic function, on the other hand, occurs pre-clinically and may play a more important role in the pathogenesis and progression of the disease. Cognitive processing in the brain is metabolically expensive and thus highly vulnerable to abnormal dynamic integrity of metabolic function. Impaired brain metabolism forms a fundamental component of AD, leading directly to enhanced formation of Aβ and oxidative species, Ca2+ overloading, and neuronal injury/apoptosis. These molecular cascades result in deficiencies in signaling, both intracellular and extracellular, including synaptic plasticity. Synapses are believed to be the final target for memory-related events to form the long-term memory trace in the brain. Cerebral hypoperfusion/hypometabolism impairs synaptic function and thus compromises memory consolidation. Indeed, synaptic dysfunction is the most reliable correlate of cognitive disturbance and is at the core of AD dementia, at least initially. Aims at improving cerebral metabolism and preventing the occurrence of brain hypometabolism may represent an effective therapeutic strategy in the battle against AD dementia.

INTRODUCTION

Among the neurodegenerative disorders, Alzheimer's disease (AD) represents one of the biggest challenges to life scientists and medical practitioners. Not only does it rob the very nature of humanity and devastate so many human lives, but also its underlying mechanisms are so complicated that agreement on possible therapeutic targets cannot be reached. What is clear, however, is the dramatic social impact of the disorder. AD presently affects four million Americans, a figure that is expected to nearly quadruple within 50 years (de la Torre, 1997a; Selkoe and Schenk, 2003). At the present time, it is estimated that 10% of those aged 65 and 47% of those aged 85 or over will develop AD (Evans *et al.*, 1989). The financial burden is also enormous. AD is the third costliest disorder (after cancer and heart disease) with approximately $82.7 billion (U.S. dollars) being spent presently in total annual costs. Assuming the prevalence for AD remains constant, this figure should easily balloon to US $400 billion annual costs by the year 2040 (Hay and Ernst, 1987; Ernst and Hay, 1994). Yet, these numbers hardly reflect the tragic nature manifested by this dementia. When first discovered or suspected, AD patients have a hard time learning new information and tend to forget day-to-day events. As the disease progresses, long-term memories are compromised. Other intellectual abilities requiring language, abstraction, reasoning, judgment, decision-making, and visuospatial skills are also gradually impaired and lost.

The central problem with AD research is that the cause of late-onset, sporadic AD, the majority of AD cases, remains an enigma. No proposal has been able to integrate the assorted major pieces of the AD puzzle and to provide a cohesive picture that reasonably explains the pathogenesis of this brain disorder. This knowledge gap puts us at a great disadvantage in AD therapy. If the cause of this disease can be found, an essential step in developing an effective remedy for this dementia will naturally follow.

Intensive research in recent decades has been on the pathogenetic role of extracellular senile amyloid plaques and intracellular neurofibrillary tangles, the common pathological hallmarks of AD brains. Several lines of evidence (see below), however, suggest that the neuropathology of AD extends beyond amyloid plaques and neurofibrillary tangles. This view is in fact consistent with the initial description of the pathological findings in the brains of patients suffering from AD by Dr. Alois Alzheimer in 1907, who clearly indicated cerebrovascular damage (Alzheimer, 1907), although the vascular dysfunction in AD brains has not received much attention. Therapies targeting amyloid plaques appear to elicit clearance of Aβ plaques but have not been successful so far relative to cognitive improvements (Nicoll et al., 2003). Effects on cognition of improving cholinergic transmission by inhibiting acetylcholinesterase are rather limited, especially in severe cases. This naturally raises the possibility that something is missing in our therapeutic strategies. Whether the vascular lesions are coincidental or causal in the pathogenetic processes of AD needs to be addressed. This is an important issue because it determines whether AD dementia should be classified and treated as a vascular disorder, i.e., employing vascular-oriented therapeutic interventions to neutralize, reverse or effectively slow down the progressive cognitive meltdown that characterizes AD. Otherwise, treatment efforts will continue to be focused solely on removing neurotoxic Aβ and/or blocking Aβ neurotoxicity. Here, the potential contribution of cerebral hypoperfusion and hypometabolism to AD neurodegeneration and their relation to Aβ neurotoxicity are explored.

AD DEMENTIA: A SYNAPTIC FAILURE

Synaptic plasticity is believed to play a central role in learning and memory. Encoding experiences into memory may involve a diversity of synaptic plasticity (Kornhauser and Greenberg 1997; Brenowitz et al. 1998; Alkon, 1984; Alkon et al., 1998; Paulsen and Moser 1998; Ahrens and Freeman, 2001), including changing the operation of pre-existing synapses and the growth of new synapses. Since explicit memories are the earliest and the most severely affected in AD patients and depend on functions of the hippocampus and related cortex, the discussion of synaptic efficacy will be mainly restricted to those synapses in these structures. The hippocampal formation plays an important role in episodic, declarative, and spatial learning and memory and in the control of autonomic and vegetative functions (adrenocorticotropin secretion; Jacobson and Sapolsky, 1991; Eichenbaum and Otto, 1992) and also is an especially plastic and vulnerable brain structure that is damaged in AD, head trauma, and stroke, and is susceptible to damage during repeated stress and aging (McEwen, 1999 for review).

Synapses are believed to be the sites where the neuro-injury and neurodegenerative processes begin in AD (Tienari *et al.*, 1996; Mattson and Duan, 1999), and thus the key to understanding the pathogenesis of AD (Selkoe, 2002). Synaptic impairment is likely the result of both a reduction of functional synapses and impaired capacity of the synapses to undergo memory-related dynamic changes. Synaptic density has been shown to be markedly reduced in AD (Masliah *et al.*, 1989; Scheff and Price, 1993; Liu *et al.*, 1999), a reduction that is believed to be the most reliable correlate of cognitive disturbances in both the postmortem and biopsied AD brain (Terry *et al.*, 1991; Dekosky *et al.*, 1996). Interestingly, it has been reported that synaptic density in AD brains closely parallels regional cerebral blood flow (rCBF) reduction and the severity of dementia (Liu *et al.*, 1999). Therefore, it has been proposed that glucose hypometabolism in AD may reflect reduced synaptic activity (Salmon *et* al., 1996). Likewise, Parkinson patients with dementia also show a global decrease in glucose metabolism similar to that in AD (Peppard *et al.*, 1992). More importantly, synaptic pathology in the hippocampus is a very early event of AD (Martin *et al.*, 1994) and impaired synaptic efficacy occurs early at the time when mild memory deficit becomes evident (Selkoe, 2002), and years before the occurrence of amyloid plaques and neurofibillary tangles in the brain. Synaptic functional dropout exceeds local neuronal loss in AD and it progresses with time. In AD, as in transgenic AD models, cognitive deterioration is observed initially without apparent neurodegeneration or cell loss (Irizarry et al., 1997; Jellinger and Stadelmann, 2001).

The reason for the extreme sensitivity of synaptic function to hypometabolism is obvious. Information processing is metabolically expensive. It costs 10^4 ATP molecules to transmit an information bit at a synapse and 10^6-10^7 ATP for an action potential or a spike (Laughlin *et al.*, 1998). Synaptic activity is thus reflected by dynamical alterations in regional metabolism as neurons restore their resting ionic gradients via Na/K-ATPase (Kadekaro *et al.*, 1985) and can thus be monitored by positron emission tomography (PET), assuming a close coupling of blood flow to glucose utilization. Altered regional metabolism is required for dynamic functional and structural changes that occur in the neural network. Memory processes, as shown in a variety of memory tasks, are known to require activation of relevant synapses and neurons (Waldvogel et al., 2000; Attwell and Iadecola, 2002). Increased synaptic activity, for instance, is accompanied by movement of mitochondria to the sites of neurotransmitter release (Brodin *et al.*, 1999), the active zones. It has been shown that increased synaptic activity induces increased expression of mitochondrially-encoded genes in the hippocampus (Williams *et al.*, 1998).

In AD, metabolism of glucose and ATP production in the mitochondria of the synapses is dysfunctional (Mecocci *et al.*, 1994). It has been shown that in AD a marked reduction of rCBF and cerebral hemoglobulin oxygenation occur during activation of brain function (Hock *et al.*, 1997), indicating an insufficient perfusion/metabolism to support increased neuronal and synaptic activity. In learning and memory tasks, the increased neuronal activity, such as bursting discharges of the place cells and theta cells in the hippocampal CA1 during spatial memory tasks, is central to the ability of forming a sound memory trace in the brain. The metabolic dysfunction and loss of the dynamic response to increased metabolic demand put a brake on the expression and maintenance of synaptic plasticity and memory.

Consistent with the central role of synaptic dysfunction are also the effects of Aβ on the synapses. Amyloid precursor protein (APP) is transported to presynaptic terminals, with Aβ being released at synapses (Lazarov *et al.*, 2002). Aβ is known to attenuate synaptic efficacy (Ikegaya *et al.*, 2002; Sun and Alkon, 2002b,c). This is consistent with an $A\beta_{1-42}$ accumulation in multivesicular bodies within presynaptic and postsynaptic compartments (Takahashi *et al.*, 2002). The synaptic accumulation is associated with abnormal synaptic pathology, before amyloid plaque pathology. It is not clear, however, whether the impact of Aβ on synapses is one more factor whose effect becomes evident at a late stage of the disorder.

AMYLOID/AMYLOID PLAQUES: JUST ONE OF MANY FACTORS IN AD DEMENTIA

As mentioned above, AD brain is characterized by the common hallmarks of extracellular senile amyloid plaques and intracellular neurofibrillary tangles. Aβ neurotoxicity is believed by many to induce neuritic plaque formation, followed by neurofibrillary tangle formation and ultimately, cell death. According to the amyloid hypothesis, altered APP metabolism involving a reduction in sAPPα and increased levels of Aβ is a common feature of AD (Gasparini *et al.*, 1998). The amyloid hypothesis also views other abnormalities in AD as either leading to Aβ formation/deposition or resulting from it. Intellectually intact subjects who have an adequate number of neuritic amyloid plaques are viewed as "preclinical AD". It has been hypothesized that these patients will develop clinical dementia if they live long enough, even for those who died at age 101 without dementia but with the plaques (Snowdon, 1997). The neurotoxic potency is thus attributed to Aβ, consisting of 40-43 amino acids that are cleaved from a much larger APP, by the sequential action of β- and γ-secretases. Alternatively, cleavage of APP by α-secretase forms a large (~100 kDa) N-terminal fragment (soluble α-secretase-derived N-terminal fragment of APP; sAPPα), which is released into extracellular medium. Thus, the action of the α-secretase pathway not only gives rise to sAPPα, which may have neuroprotective properties, but also precludes the formation of Aβ.

Mutations in the gene encoding APP and in other genes have been proposed to be involved in AD dementia, and lead to overproduction of the amyloidogenic 42 amino acid residue long isoform of Aβ, $A\beta_{1\text{-}42}$. Bilateral injections of $\beta_{25\text{-}35}$+ibotenic acid into the hippocampus (Dornan *et al.*, 1993) or $\beta_{25\text{-}35}$ into hippocampal areas CA1-3 (Chen *et al.*, 1996) impair spatial memory in rats, evaluated by use of a Morris water maze task. Metabolic inhibition has been shown to enhance Aβ toxicity and synapses are particularly sensitive to energy deficits (Arias *et al.*, 2002). Transgenic mice expressing the 695-amino acid isoform of human APP containing a Lys670-->Asn, Met671-->Leu mutation have normal learning and memory in spatial reference and alteration tasks at 3 months of age but show impairment by 9 to 10 months of age and a 5-fold increase in Aβ (1-40) and a 14-fold increase in Aβ (1-42/43) (Hsiao *et al.*, 1996). Transgenic mice expressing the amyloidogenic carboxy-terminal 104 amino acids of APP develop, with aging, extracellular β-amyloid immunoreactivity, increased gliosis and microglial reactivity, as well as cell loss in the CA1 region of the hippocampus (Nalbantoglu *et al.*, 1997). Adult transgenic mice demonstrate spatial (Morris water maze)-learning deficits (Nalbantoglu *et al.*, 1997). In hippocampal slices of transgenic mice expressing C-terminal fragments of APP, recovery of CA1 synaptic transmission after transient hypoxic episodes has been shown to be much slower than that of controls (Ghribi *et al.*, 1999). Similar results are also observed in presymptomatic APP23 transgenic mice (Büchner *et al.*, 2002). This impaired recovery from hypoxia does not appear to be related to alterations in either functional or biochemical properties of glutamate receptors (Ghribi *et al.*, 1999).

Aβ is a neurotoxic peptide, which is believed by many to play a central role in the pathogenesis of AD. Aβ(1-40) (10^{-8} M) has been reported to inhibit high-affinity choline uptake and acetylcholine release in rat hippocampal slices (Kar *et al.*, 1998). Introducing cDNA encoding human APP holoprotein (the membrane-bound form of APP) into rat hippocampal neurons by use of an adenoviral vector in culture has been found to enhance responses to applied glutamate versus the non-expressing control neurons revealed by Ca^{2+} fluorometry (Tominaga *et al.*, 1997). This increased responsiveness is not the result of secreted APP, as confirmed by observations of closely spaced APP-expressing and non-expressing cells in the same culture dish. Aβ is also rapidly transported from brain across the blood brain-barrier by LDL receptor-mediated protein-1 (Shibata *et al.*, 2000). Although the mechanisms by which Aβ causes neuronal injury and death are not fully understood, *in vitro* results suggest that an increase in oxidative stress and destabilization of calcium homeostasis are involved (Mark *et al.*, 1996; Cotman and Su, 1996). Exposure of cultured neurons to Aβ results in oxidative stress and elevations of intracellular calcium levels. Neurons degenerating in AD brains also exhibit an increased level of intracellular calcium, which promotes oxidative stress. The involvement of oxidative species in neurodegenerative disease is proposed to be due to their causing protein oxidation, DNA oxidation and lipid perooxidation, promoting intracellular Aβ accumulation (Misonou et al., 2000). The involvement of the Aβ-oxidative species pathway in AD neurodegeneration, however, remains controversial. On one hand, Aβ-induced increased levels of oxidative stress and impaired energy metabolism can compromise neuronal ability to properly regulate intracellular calcium levels and process information signals. On the other hand, neuronal damage can occur distal to Aβ deposits. The reactive oxygen responsible for most if not all of the damage, the OH radical, has a radius of diffusion of only nanometers, implying that the source of reactive oxygen activity must be in close physical proximity to the damage, leading to the suggestion that Aβ-deposit-mediated damage is insignificant to explain the pattern of oxidative damage to neuronal cell bodies distal to Aβ deposits (Cash *et al.*, 2002). On the contrary, oxidative damage is reduced with increasing senile plaque and neurofibrillary tangle density (Nunomura *et al.*, 1999, 2000, 2001), suggesting that formation of Aβ plaques and neurofibrillary tangles may be a protective response to reduce oxidative damage (Morsch *et al.*, 1999). However, others have reported no increase in oxidative DNA damage in the frontal, occipital, temporal cortex, or hippocampal tissue in AD (Te Koppele *et al.*, 1996). Aggregates of Aβ comprising residue 1-40/42, especially those that assemble into fibrils and are present in large amounts late on in the disease, are also cytotoxic, because they disturb the integrity of the cell membrane and stimulate the production of reactive oxygen intermediates (Hensley *et al.*, 1994), eventually causing cell death (Yankner *et al.*, 1990 Benzi and Moretti, 1995; Cotman and Anderson, 1995). Aggregated Aβ is toxic to cultured neurons of the cerebral cortex or the hippocampus *in vitro* (Mark *et al.*, 1996; Cotman and Su, 1996). But, more importantly, early in the course of Alzheimer's, before abundant large fibrils impinge on the cells, stronger and more specific interactions with cell-surface receptors for Aβ may trigger signal transduction (El-Khoury *et al.*, 1996; Paresce *et al.*, 1996; Yan *et al.*, 1996). Endogenous substances that accelerate the formation of amyloid would thus be risk factors for AD. A therapeutic agent that could slow the rate of its formation could delay the onset of AD symptoms (Lansbury, 1997). The amyloid hypothesis is supported by numerous reports that amyloid plaques are neurotoxic and that appoint gene mutation in the APP gene on chromosome 21 is responsible for some rare familial AD. Soluble β-amyloids are biologically active and have been shown to induce a variety of responses (Etcheberrigaray et al., 1994; Wu et al., 1995; Kar et al., 1996, 1998; Bahr et al., 1998; Itoh et al., 1999; Chen et al., 2000; Wang et al., 2000a,b; Yang et al., 2000; Pittit et al., 2001; Sun and Alkon, 2002c), many of which are neurotoxic responses.

Attention has focused on the mechanisms by which extracellular plaque-associated Aβ exerts its effects on cells. Intracellular accumulation of amyloidogenic Aβ occurs in several cell types (Yoshikawa *et al.*, 1992; Fuller *et al.*, 1995; Frackowiak *et al.*, 1995; Tiernari *et al.*, 1997; Wild-Bode *et al.*, 1997; Xia *et al.*, 1997; Xu *et al.* 1997), probably reflecting cellular processing with excessive amounts of Aβ generated within the cell or from uptake of released Aβ. Generally speaking, however, while there is no question that Aβs are neurotoxic when applied at sufficient concentrations, many data do not fit into the amyloid hypothesis:

1) The vast majority of AD cases (99.5%) are not linked to APP gene mutations or an extra copy of chromosome 21.
2) Amyloid deposition is not the earliest neuropathological event in AD (Braak and Braak, 1996, 1997; Naslund et al., 2000).

3) Amyloid plaques are not an AD-specific feature. They are also found in non-AD neurodegenerative disorders, such as Parkinson's disease, Huntington's disease, stroke patients and patients surviving cardiac arrest, and progressive nuclear palsy.
4) Amyloid plaques exist in a significant proportion of non-demented elderly. In the hippocampus and neocortex, for example, large amounts of amyloid deposits may be present in elderly, non-demented subjects (Crystal *et al.*, 1988; Hardy, 1997; Snowdon, 1997; Chapman *et al.*, 2001; Polvikoski *et al.*, 2001), reaching 80% of subjects in the cortex over 75 years (Davies *et al.*, 1988) and near 100% of subjects in the parahippocampus (DeLaere *et al.*, 1993).
5) In transgenic mice with APP expression, amyloid did not appear to be acutely neurotoxic (Irizarry *et al.*, 1997). APP may be an injury-response protein, with its expression being increased after a variety of insults. Because of the properties of its Met_{35}, AD amyloid peptide is, among other profiles, an antioxidant (Butterfield *et al.*, 1998), though this does not rule out a toxic action of its oxidized form.
6) The amyloid burden has neither been found to correlate with the AD diagnosis (Bouras *et al.*, 1994) nor related to neuronal loss, number of neurofibrillary tangles or duration of the disease (Gòmez-Isla *et al.*, 1997). A reduction of the cerebrospinal fluid levels of Aβ about 30% in AD has also been reported (Maruyama *et al.*, 2001).
7) Since Aβ is known to lead to the production of oxidative species, the interaction between oxidative species and Aβ has been proposed to form a basis for the AD dementia. However, effective antioxidative agents are widely available (in vitamin supplements and food) and can be taken in sufficient doses to maintain effective concentrations. Longitudinal studies have found no difference in AD incidence or memory improvement in long-term users of vitamin C and E supplements (Sano *et al.*, 1997; Masaki et al., 2000; Luchsinger et al., 2003; Selkoe and Schenk, 2003; but see Morris et al., 1998; Engelhart et al., 2002).
8) Endogenous anti-amyloid antibodies do not appear to slow the course of AD (Hyman *et al.*, 2001).

These findings would suggest that amyloid pathophysiology may be insufficient to explain what causes or underlies AD dementia but are not enough to rule out the involvement of amyloid in the disorder. Using neuronal and synaptic activity as indicators, the question remains whether the presence of amyloid plaques and tangles in AD is indeed related to decreased neuronal activity, whether these AD hallmarks would induce a decreased metabolic rate, another early feature of the AD brain (see below), or vice versa, and whether the neuropathological AD changes and decreased metabolic rate would occur independently. Evidence has been provided that the presence of neurofibrillary tangles does not seem to decrease the general metabolic rate of a neuron (Salehi *et al.*, 1995), in addition to their occurrence at the late stage of the dementia. There appears to be no relationship between either the density of neuritic plaques or the distance of each neuritic plaque and the metabolic activity of neighboring neurons (Salehi *et* al., 1998). However, Hatanpää *et al.* (1996) have shown that cytochrome oxidase subunit III mRNA is decreased in tangle-bearing neurons.

Cerebral Hypoperfusion/Hypometabolism: A Reality in AD Brain

Vascular lesions such as cerebral amyloid angiopathy, microvascular degeneration, and periventricular white matter lesions are evident in almost all cases of AD (Kalaria, 2000, 2001). The common presence of amyloid angiopathy in leptomeningeal and cortical blood vessels is in fact the most obvious vascular abnormality in AD. Cerebrovascular amyloidosis or cerebral amyloid angiopathy has therefore been proposed as another marker for AD (Rhodin and Thomas, 2001). The component of cerebrovascular amyloid is thought to be identical with that of senile plaque amyloid. The current state of knowledge, however, does not allow us to determine whether the vascular changes in AD are the cause, a consequence, or an epiphenomenon of the disease. Although both structural and physiological changes have been documented in the elderly and patients with AD, simultaneous studies of structural and physiological measurements in the same individuals to test a causal relationship have been difficult to carry out. Nevertheless, the direct consequence of vascular abnormality is a reduced cerebral perfusion, which can be measured at early stage of AD or preclinically. Normal aging is known to be associated with increased vascular resistance and decreased CBF (Cavestri *et al.*, 1992; Ajmani *et al.* 2000), a hemodynamic process that is proportional to advancing age (Marin *et al.*, 1991; de la Torre, 1997a,b; Dorfler *et al.*, 2000; Scheel *et al.*, 2000). Such changes are more severe in an AD brain (Kalaria, 2000, 2001; Rhodin and Thomas, 2001), at the level of microcirculation. It has been known for a long time that the sites of most resistance to blood flow is in the microcirculation. According to fluid dynamic laws, these capillaries will transform normal laminar flow into disturbed flow at regions where structural changes in the microvessel's cylindrical lumen occur (de la Torre and Mussivand, 1993; de la Torre, 1994). As a result of such 'disturbed' microvascular blood flow, glucose and oxygen fail to reach their neuronal targets in optimal concentrations, eventually creating an energy crisis at the mitochondrial level. The major two questions are, however, what causes these capillary changes in the first place and when do they appear relative to AD symptoms?

While it is not certain whether cerebral hypoperfusion is the cause or the consequence of cerebral metabolism, AD brains clearly show reduced glucose metabolism (Swerdlow *et al.*, 1994), including the early onset type (Sakamoto *et al.*, 2002), changes in regional glucose metabolism (measured by positron emission tomography) correlated with a change of the Mini Mental State Examination score in the patients (Mielke *et al.*, 1994), and decreased activity of hippocampal cells (Salehi, 1995), which are not related to the presence of neurofibrillary tangles. However, values of [^{18}F]fluorodeoxyglucose positron emission tomography and Aβ deposition may not be closely correlated in the temporal lobe of AD brains (Mega *et al.*, 1999). A clear reduction in AD brain metabolism has been shown in several severely affected brain regions, including the nucleus basalis of Meynert (NBM), the CA1 area of the hippocampus (Salehi and Swaab, 1999), areas that play an essential role in memory, especially the explicit memory.

Evidence is accumulating (de la Torre and Stefano, 2000) that supports the premise that AD is a vascular disorder with neurodegenerative consequences rather than a neurodegenerative disorder with vascular consequences.

1) Compelling epidemiological data indicate that conditions that lower CBF during advanced aging are risk factors in the development of AD.
2) Clinical AD dementia essentially never occurs without decreased cerebral metabolism (Blass, 2002). Temporo-parietal CBF reduction is present in AD that correlates positively with cognitive decline.
3) Drugs that have potential to alleviate or delay AD symptoms, such as cholinesterase inhibitors, NSAIDS, ginkgo biloba, vitamin E, estrogen, acetyl-L-carnitine, etc, all improve cerebral perfusion, despite their different pharmacokinetic and pharmacological actions (de la Torre *et al*, 1997; Smith *et al.*, 2000; Weggen *et al.*, 2001). Non-steroidal anti-inflammatory agents reported to lessen AD risk also ameliorate blood flow through their platelet-deaggregating and anti-thrombotic effects.
4) Capillary changes involving basement membrane thickening, endothelial cell distortion, pericyte degeneration and luminal buckling, occur in the vast majority of AD brains.
5) Glucose and oxygen brain metabolism is consistently depressed in AD and depressed values correlate positively with disease severity.
6) Glucose transporter 1, located in the distorted endothelial cells, is markedly deficient in the AD brain, further reducing glucose availability to neurons and glia.
7) Regional mismatched-perfusion develops in AD brains that are reflected by elevation of an oxygen extraction factor, most notably in temporo-parietal lobes where neuropathological changes are most severe.
8) Most importantly, regional vascular changes and hypometabolism measured in AD brains does not appear to result from neurodegenerative changes but appears to precede it (see below).

Hypometabolism in the AD brain is consistent with the evidence that many types of cellular insults can damage mitochondria and brain biopsy samples from AD patients have been found to have abnormal neuronal mitochondria (Hirai *et al.*, 2001). Mitochondria from AD patients exhibit aberrant calcium homeostasis and increased production of oxygen radicals (Sheehan *et* al., 1997).

HYPOMETABOLISM: IMPACT ON NEURONAL FUNCTIONS AND SYNAPTIC EFFICACY

The human brain with less than 2% of the body's mass requires 20-25% of total body oxygen consumption but has no reserved energy source from within. There is no question that neural function and cognition depend on sufficient and continuous energy metabolism and cerebral perfusion. Impaired glucose tolerance has been found to be associated with decreased general cognitive performance, memory impairment, and atrophy of the hippocampus in middle aged and elderly subjects (Convit et al., 2003). Cerebral hypometabolism induces mental impairment that mimics those of dementia in both humans and animals (Blass, 2002). Sodium azide, for instance, has been reported to impair both spatial and nonspatial learning, not secondary to a sensory or motor impairment in rats (Bennett *et al.*, 1992).

Hypometabolism has a dramatic impact on neuronal health and function. Inactivation and the occurrence of degenerative changes are coupled. The question is whether hypoperfusion/ hypometabolism at the levels occurring in the preclinical AD brain would selectively induce synaptic and memory impairments. All mammalian cells can sense changes in O_2 concentrations (Semenza, 1999) and are potentially damaged by a restriction in O_2 and nutrient supplies. Different populations of neurons, however, show very different vulnerability to ischemia/hypoxia *in vivo* (Cervos-Navarro and Diemer, 1991; Lipton, 1999). For instance, 5-minute global ischemia caused delayed death in almost all cornu Ammonis (CA) 1 pyramidal cell neurons with no effects on other cell populations, while 20 minutes of global ischemia are needed to cause cell death in CA3 neurons but had almost no effect on dentate granule cells in the hippocampus (Kirino and Sano, 1984; Kirino *et al.*, 1985) or on interneurons in CA1 (Ferrer *et al.*, 1995). The difference in vulnerability to energy restriction is consistent with functional disturbance centered first at the hippocampal CA1 area in AD. Functions that depend on neurotransmitter synthesis and release are also vulnerable. For instance, acethylcholine synthesis consumes a large number of high-energy molecules and is compromised early when the demand is not dynamically met (Sun and Alkon, 2001). These observations are consistent with the early occurrence of cognitive deficits due to high sensitivity of memory-related networks and molecular cascades to the insult.

The impact of hypoperfusion and hypometabolism on neuronal function and integrity depends on the extent and duration of the insult, ranging from reversible functional interference to irreversible neuronal death. Mild hypoperfusion and hypometabolism put a limit on activity of neurons and impair synaptic plasticity. Under hypoxic conditions, the reduction of O_2 to H_2O by cytochrome oxidase is inhibited, resulting in release of electrons upstream at complex III and generation of O_2^-. Reduced energy production generates free radicals, which blocks glial membrane Na^+, K^+ATPase transport of glutamate and thus its uptake, resulting in buildup of glutamate in the extracellular space to excitotoxic levels. Decreased ATP levels also reduce Na^+, K^+ATPase ion pumping, impair acetylcholine synthesis and Ca^{2+} homeostasis, activate kinases, and promote abnormal protein synthesis. Chronic hypoperfusion thus leads to the formation of reactive oxygen species, cytokine production, and an inflammatory reaction. Reduced ATP activity also leads to down-regulation of Na^+, K^+ATPase. Na^+, K^+ATPase pump consumes approximately 60% of all ATP in the brain to maintain cellular ionic gradients, action potentials, synaptic transmission, and protein synthesis. Its down-regulation results in impairment of Ca^{2+} transport across membranes, axoplasmic flow, and axodendritic synaptic function. Eventually, neurotransmitter dysfunction and synaptic loss result from impaired axonal transport of vesicles, further corrupting the already compromised cognitive status.

Severe and lasting hypoperfusion and hypometabolism can induce apoptosis in neurons. One important mediator that underlies severe neuronal injury and apoptosis is cytochrome *c* (Li *et al.*, 1998; Luo, *et al.*, 1998). Cytochrome *c* can be transformed from a life-sustainer into a life-destroyer. Normally, it is restricted to the intermembrane space of mitochondria. The importance of cytochrome *c* has been well established for oxidative phosphorylation in the electron transport chain in mitochondria, where it assists with production of life-sustaining ATP by participating in electron transport. The first indication that cytochrome *c* could be toxic to cells came when Xiaodong Wang and his colleagues set out to purify factors from the cytosol that induced proteolytic processing and activation of the cell death protease, caspase-3. One of the required factors surprisingly proved to be cytochrome *c* (Liu *et al.*, 1996). Subsequent investigations using both subcellular fractionation methods and confocal immunofluorescence microscopy demonstrated that following exposure of cells to apoptotic stimuli, cytochrome *c* is rapidly released from mitochondria into the cytosol (Kluck *et al.*, 1997; Yang *et al.*, 1997). In apoptosis, an ill-defined mitochondrial lesion, including that induced by hypoxia/ischemia, free radicals (Fujimura *et al.*, 1999) or Aβ, allows it to escape into the cytosol, where it interacts with the cytosolic factors Apaf-1 and procaspase-9, leading to the aggregation and transactivation of the latter (Newmeyer and Green, 1998). Thus far, cytochrome *c* release from mitochondria has been shown to accompany apoptosis in every circumstance and in every cell line where it has been studied.

Aβ is formed at the endoplasmic reticulum and intermediate compartment and can directly induce cytochrome *c* release (Kim *et al.*, 2002). Cytosolic redistribution of cytochrome *c* has also been reported in striatal and cortical neurons 4 hrs after 90 minutes of middle cerebral artery occlusion (Fujimura *et al.*, 1998). Other studies show that cytosolic cytochrome *c* can be detected as early as 1 hr after focal ischemia (Fujimura *et al.*, 1999). Ten minutes of bilateral common carotid artery occlusion and hypotension in rats revealed cytosolic cytochrome *c*-positive cells exclusively in the CA1 subregion, in CA1 neurons and a small number of astrocytes of the hippocampus as early as 2 hr after ischemia. There is a corresponding decrease in the mitochondrial cytochrome *c*, and DNA fragmentation 3-5 d after ischemia (Sugawara *et al.*, 1999). Is cytochrome *c* release from mitochondria the critical first step for cell death or does the downstream activation of caspases represent the point of no return in cell death? Experiments using irreversible pan-caspase-inhibitory peptides have provided evidence that apoptosis induced by growth factor deprivation, anticancer drugs, and Bax overexpression is potently inhibited when caspases are inactivated, but cell death is not prevented. Under these circumstances, cytochrome *c* is still released, $\Delta\psi$ drops, reactive oxygen species are generated, and the cell dies by a caspase-independent mechanism that resembles necrosis. Thus, release of cytochrome *c* from mitochondria has two ways of killing cells:

1) by activating caspases; and
2) by interrupting electron-chain transport, thus preventing oxidative phosphorylation, promoting free-radical production, and eventually depriving the cell of ATP.

For instance, cytochrome *c* activates caspase-9, which has been shown to be an initiator of the cytochrome *c*-dependent caspase cascade (Li *et al.*, 1997; Kuida *et al.*, 1998; Yoshida *et al.*, 1998). Activated caspase-9 directly triggers activation of additional caspases and leads to apoptosis (Liu *et al.*, 1996; Slee *et al.*, 199). Oxidative species may play important roles in regulating synaptic plasticity (Mattson and Liu, 2002), either blocking or inducing long-term potentiation of the glutamatergic inputs onto the hippocampal pyramidal cells. Brief exposures of hippocampal slices to superoxide, for example, results in a long-lasting potentiation of synaptic transmission via activation of protein kinase C (Knapp and Klann,

2002). One important mechanism involves the release of cytochrome *c* from the mitochondria into the cytoplasm, in which cytochrome *c* subsequently causes apoptosis by activation of caspases (Kluck *et al.,* 1997; Reed, 1997; Yang *et al.*, 1997; Kuida *et al.*, 1998; Newmeyer et al., 2003), essential components of the mammalian cell death machinery. Since activated Caspase 3 can directly initiate certain caspase-activated deoxyribonucleases (Liu *et al.,* 1997; Enari *et al.*, 1998), the cytochrome *c*-mediated caspase activation may serve as an amplification mechanism during most forms of apoptosis.

The exquisite sensitivity of cell extracts to cytochrome *c* has led the hypothesis that cells need to regulate apoptosis by controlling the efflux of cytochrome *c* from their mitochondria. However, the full story is not so simple and experiments in which cytochrome *c* was microinjected into cultured cells have shown that to induce a significant neurodegneration, a higher cytosol concentration is needed than that cytochrome *c* release can reach in the cytosol after apoptotic induction (Li *et al.*, 1997; Zhivotovsky *et al.*, 1998). Cell lines were found to vary in their sensitivity to killing by microinjected cytochrome *c*. Even for the sensitive cells, moreover, the intracellular concentrations of cytochrome *c* needed for cell killing (2-10 μM) were an order of magnitude higher than those required to activate caspases in cell extracts (0.2-0.5 μM). Intact cells thus seem to have a way to regulate or suppress the response to cytosolic cytochrome *c*.

It should also be mentioned that the neural networks and synapses that are the earliest and most severely affected in AD are those in the hippocampus and related structures. This sensitivity is consistent with the central role of the brain structures in explicit memory, including spatial memory. It has been known for some time that lesions of the hippocampus impair the ability of the rat to solve spatial tasks (Olton, 1977; O'Keefe and Nadel, 1978; Olton *et al.*, 1979; Morris *et al.*, 1982, 1990; Davis *et al.*, 1986; Barnes, 1988; Squire *et al.*, 1989). Detectable neuronal damage has been hypothesized to be responsible for the severity of the observed behavioral impairment (Squire and Zola, 1996). Animal models of global cerebral ischemia have revealed that pyramidal cells of the CA1 layer of the hippocampus are selectively vulnerable to oxygen and energy deficiency (Pulsinelli and Brierley, 1979; Mudrick and Baimbridge, 1989) and various glutamate and Ca^{2+}-dependent mechanisms have been suggested to explain the acute and the delayed CA pyramidal neuronal death following transient cerebral ischemia (Choi, 1988; Siesjö and Bengtsson, 1989; Siesjö and Asplund, 1991; Zivin and Choi, 1991). Neuronal death in the CA1 subregion after global ischemia is in part caused by apoptosis (MacManus *et al.*, 1993; Nitatori *et al.*, 1995). In a cell-free system, cytochrome *c* activates caspase-3 (CPP32), a cysteine protease of the interleukin-1β-converting enzyme (ICE) family, which triggers apoptosis (Liu *et al.*, 1996). CPP32, an important caspase in the cytochrome *c*-dependent caspase cascade, is overexpressed in the CA1 subregion after transient global ischemia, and administration of a CPP32 inhibitor reduces apoptotic cell death (Chen *et al.*, 1998). The latter result has been questioned by recent morphological data (Colbourne *et al.*, 1999).

Hypoperfusion/Hypometabolism: A Pre-Clinical Feature in AD Dementia

A major difficulty in AD research is that neuronal impairment spreads as AD dementia progresses to multiple neural networks and signal cascades, resulting in a variety of functional and structural abnormalities. That may explain why research often yields overwhelming information about abnormalities in the AD brains but does not reveal the initial and intermediate causes of the disorder. One important question relating to AD pathogenesis is what happens before or at the early stages of AD dementia in those subjects who will develop into AD dementia at a future time.

Increasingly, studies show a reduced cortical and hippocampal perfusion/metabolism in mild demented AD patients and a significant correlation between the cortical and hippocampal perfusion level and the severity of both cognitive deficit and memory impairment (Ouchi *et al.*, 1998; Hoffman *et al.*, 2000; Rodriguez *et al.*, 2000; Chantal *et al.*, 2002; Herholtz *et al.*, 2002). Evidence has been provided that cerebral hypoperfusion/hypometabolism occurs early in the AD brain, before the AD dementia becomes evident and represents the most accurate indicator of probable AD subjects to develop the dementia at a future time. In addition, the regional vascular changes and hypometabolism measured in AD brains do not appear to result from neurodegenerative changes but appears to precede it (Duara *et al.*, 1992; Rhodin and Thomas, 2001). Furthermore, decreased energy metabolites have been found in cognitively normal subjects almost 4 years prior to the onset of dementia (Pettegrew *et al.*, 1995). Changes in membrane phospholipid and high-energy phosphate metabolism occur very early in the molecular pathophysiology of AD (Pettegrew *et al.*, 1997). These early changes may be closely linked to the fundamental pathophysiology of the disease and could provide a molecular basis for Aβ deposition (see below) and synaptic damage that results in cognitive decline. Similarly, in AD transgenic mice, cerebrovascular and metabolic abnormalities are early events, with hypoperfusion (about 30-47% reduction)/hypometabolism occurring before amyloid plaques or neurodegeneration (Büchner *et al.*, 2002; Niwa *et al.*, 2002), suggesting that impaired energy metabolism may partake in initiating the neurodegenerative cascade.

More evidence suggesting an important role for cerebral hypoperfusion/hypometabolism in AD pathogenesis derives from studies on subjects who show mild cognitive impairment (MCI). The concept of MCI is recently recognized as a transitional clinical state between normal aging and AD, a valuable "biomarker" for the diagnosis to monitor cognitive state and progression at an early phase for probable AD patients in the future. These MCI subjects have isolated memory impairment but do not satisfy the criteria for Mental Disorder from the Diagnostic Statistical Manual. They have a significantly higher rate of progression to AD. These preclinical early AD patients have consistently been found to have a decline in blood perfusion in the hippocampal-amygdaloid complex, anterior thalamus, and cingulated gyrus (Johnson *et al.*, 1998). Hypometabolism is often associated with structural atrophy. Average atrophy rates from hippocampus and entorhinal cortices were 5.1% greater in patients than controls using magnetic resonance imaging (MRI), probably occurring several years before the onset of AD dementia (Schott, *et al.*, 2003). Entorhinal cortex atrophy appears to be a better indicator for AD (Du et al., 2003). Furthermore, functional brain imaging studies, including PET and single photon emission computerized tomography (SPECT), have demonstrated a consistent cellular glucose utilization deficit that precedes brain atrophy or mental impairment (de Leon *et al.* 2001; Blass, 2002; de la Torre, 2002), and accompanies the AD process (Munch *et* al., 1998). These techniques are useful when no specific diagnostic information is evident from structural brain imaging techniques such as X-ray computerized tomography (CT) or MRI in patients with milder deficits or in the early stages of AD. Metabolic reductions occur in the posterior cingulate, parietal, temporal, and prefrontal cortices (Reiman *et al.*, 1996; Small *et al.*, 2000; Valla *et al.*, 2001). In fact, measurements of rCBF in humans can accurately identify those subjects with mild memory difficulties who are likely to develop AD at a future time (Celsis *et al.*, 1997; Waldemar *et al.*, 1997; Johnson *et al.*, 1998; Alsop *et al.*, 2000). A longitudinal study using SPECT measurements of regional CBF (rCBF) in elderly individuals with questionable AD (subjects with memory trouble who do not meet NINDS/ADRDA criteria for probable AD) has revealed that only those subjects with significant cerebral hypoperfusion in the amygdaloid-hippocampal region later developed AD within a 2-year follow-up period (Johnson *et al.*, 1998).

HYPOPERFUSION/HYPOMETABOLISM: POSSIBLE CAUSES

Various forms of cerebrovascular/metabolism insufficiency and disrupted microvascular integrity in the cortical regions may represent the initial or intermediate cause in the chain of events ending with cognitive failure in AD. Although it is not clear what causes the early cerebral hypoperfusion and hypometabolism in the memory-related brain structures, clues are starting to emerge. It appears that in AD there is a global down-regulation of the expression of all subunits of the respiratory chains, though the precise underlying mechanisms remain unclear (Chandrasekaran *et al.*, 1996, 1997; Rapoport *et al.*, 1996; Hatanpää *et al.*, 1996). Compared with age-matched controls, there are increased mitochondria DNA deletions in AD (Mecocci *et al.*, 1994). Genetic analysis has provided evidence for associations between mutations in genes encoding mitochondrial proteins including cytochrome *c* oxidase and AD (Davis *et al.*, 1997). AD brains exhibit a biochemical defect of complex IV (cytochrome oxidase, COX) of the mitochondrial electron transport chain (Kish *et al.,* 1992; Multisya *et al.*, 1994; Chagnon *et al.*, 1995; Sheehan *et* al., 1997; Maurer *et al.*, 2000). Freshly prepared AD mitochondria showed a 40% decrease in complex I and a 53% reduction in COX activity (Parker *et al.,* 1994; Parker and Parks, 1995). Significant reductions of COX activity and mRNA expression have been observed in the hippocampus of AD brain (Simonian and Hyman, 1993, 1994). Activity of important enzymes in energy metabolism that are mitochondrial but not part of the respiratory chain is also decreased in AD; these include ATP-synthase (Schagger and Ohm, 1995), pyruvate dehydrogenase (Sheu *et al.*, 1985), and α-ketoglutarate dehydrogenase (Mastrogiacomo *et al.*, 1993; Gibson *et al.*, 1998; Blass, 2001), compared to age-matched controls.

This global reduction and abnormality in the expression of the enzymes involved in the cellular respiration and glucose metabolism has two major impact on the cells: a reduction in the capacity to rapidly increase energy production upon demand and an increase in oxygen radical formation. The COX defect and resulting oxidative stress may activate the release of mitochondrial factors involved in apoptosis (Cassarino *et al.*, 1998). We can expect a close association between the levels of cerebral perfusion and cellular metabolism since they are functionally coupled through a variety of regulatory mechanisms (Reis *et al.,* 1994; Sun, 1995, 1996; Lauritzen, 2001). The question is whether the reduced cerebral perfusion and expression of enzymes critical for energy production and glucose metabolism underlie the development of AD dementia or whether neural network damage would lead to reduced metabolism and cerebral perfusion in particular brain regions. Evidence has been provided that inadequate cerebral perfusion and metabolism may play a more important role than what has been realized, since reduced perfusion will certainly impair synaptic functions and network integrity, while network injury is not likely to lead to reduced perfusion.

The relationship between CBF and apolipoprotein (*APOE*) has been studied by many investigators. *APOE* has 3 common alleles: ε2, ε3, and ε4, resulting in amino acid substitutions at positions 112 and 158 of the protein. *APOE* ε4 allele has been found to increase the risk of AD. An earlier age of onset appears to be a function of the inherited dose of the ε4 allele (Corder *et al.*, 1993). Furthermore, ε4 homozygosity is associated with a faster rate of cognitive decline (Craft *et al.*, 1998; Bennett *et al.*, 2003), although the effect of the *APOE* ε4 allele on the risk of AD differs greatly for white and black subjects (Evans et al., 2003). Many others, however, have reported that the presence of the ε4 allele does not affect clinical progression in AD patients (Gòmez-Isla *et al.*, 1996; Growdon *et al.*, 1996; Slooter *et al.*, 1999).

There are many other ways to induce hypometabolism and less active hippocampal cells. Corticosterone inhibits glucose uptake into the hippocampal neurons and, therefore, might mediate the impact of stress. In addition, AD brains show reduced neuronal glucose transporters GLUT-1 and GLUT-3 (Kalaria and Harik, 1989; Simpson *et al.,* 1994; Mooradian *et* al., 1997). Denervation of hippocampal neurons is another way of inactivation of cell groups. After denervation of dopaminergic and cholinergic inputs, granule cells of rat dentate gyrus displayed abnormally phosphorylated τ (Torack and Miller, 1995). Energy-impaired, less active cells become increasingly vulnerable to endogenous concentrations of excitatory amino acids. Energy impairment would result in decreased high-energy phosphate stores and a deteriorating membrane potential. These conditions reduce the voltage-sensitive Mg^{2+} blockade of *N*-methyl-D-aspartate receptors (NMDAs), allowing them to be overactivated by glutamate.

The contribution of neurotoxic amyloid to the preclinical cerebral hypoperfusion/ hypometabolism cannot be ruled out. $A\beta_{1\text{-}42}$ is the predominant form of amyloid β-protein in the brain of short-term survivors of head-injury (Gentleman *et al.*, 1997). Aβ can rapidly damage vessels (Thomas *et al.*, 1996). Hypoxia or hypoxia/reoxygenation may initiate pathogenesis of amyloid angiopathy (Wang *et al.*, 2002) and enhance Aβ neurotoxicity (Egashira *et al.*, 2002). In PC12 cells, 24-h hypoxic culture leads to Aβ-mediated enhancement of Ca^{2+} channel currents (Green and Peers, 2001). The primary site of the onset of AD and the target of the toxic amyloid, have been proposed to be the small arteries, arterioles, and capillaries of the CNS (Rhodin and Thomas, 2001 for review). These blood vessels show signs of inflammation, amyloid accumulations, and a focal breach of the blood brain barrier. It has been proposed that the blood vessels are damaged first, causing the toxic amyloid to be released and subsequently infiltrate the nerve cells. In addition, there is a narrowing of the vascular lumen, leading to a reduction in CBF, low oxygen tension, and neuronal damage. The typical cerebral cortex capillary from AD patients shows thickened basement membrane, endothelial cell shape distortion, degenerated pericyte, and severe luminal buckling (Mancardi *et al.*, 1980; Zarron *et al.*, 1997), present in virtually all AD brains examined (Kalaria and Hedera, 1995). Another important mechanism of cytotoxicity of Aβ species results from their engagement by intracellular targets. β-amyloid fragment 25-35 (100 μM) has been reported to produce a rapid, dose-dependent decrease in the activity of complex IV, but not on the activities of complex I, II-III, or citrate synthase when incubated with rat brain mitochondria (Canevari *et al.*, 1999). The reverse sequence peptide (35-25) had no effect (Canevari *et al.*, 1999), suggesting that inhibition of mitochondrial complex IV might be a contributing factor to the pathogenesis of AD. Aβ inhibits complex IV activity and its toxicity has been reported to require a functional mitochondria (Canevari *et al.*, 1999; Cardoso *et al.*, 2001), which is simultaneously the source and the target for reactive oxygen species. Aβ, which is deposited prominently in synaptic regions (see above), can induce caspase activation and mitochondrial dysfunction (Mattson, 2002).

The interpretation that cholinergic deficits in AD have pathophysiological cerebrovascular consequences also appears to be justified. Studies on the substantial contribution of the cholinergic pathways to cognitive processes have a long history. A marked deficiency in cholinergic neurotransmission is one of the distinguishing degenerative features of AD and occurs early in AD patients. The loss or shrinkage of cholinergic neurons in the basal forebrain and the medial septum and the disappearance of cholinergic projection fibers from the medial septum to the hippocampus are widely investigated in view of the concomitant memory deficits typically of AD (Gaykema *et al.*, 1992; Muir *et al.*, 1993; Whitehouse, 1998). The capacity of this network to influence CBF has only recently gained more attention. It has been recognized that the activation of the substantia innominata/NBM complex could increase CBF by inducing vasodilation in cortical microvessels (Biesold *et al.*, 1989; Vaucher *et al.*, 1994,1995; Barbelivien *et al.*, 1999). The striking coincidence of a reduced cortical CBF and cholinergic neurodegeneration of the NBM both seen in AD patients has stimulated more intensive research in this field.

The integrity of the cholinergic system is extremely vulnerable to metabolic state, since the synthesis of acetylcholine is metabolically expensive and depends on the availability of acetyl coenzyme A from glucose metabolism (Sun and Alkon, 2001; Melo et al., 2002). Under normal conditions, choline acetyltransferase (ChAT) is probably not rate limiting for acetylcholine synthesis (Marchbanks and Kessler, 1982). The fall in its activity in AD is unlikely to account for the decrease in acetylcholine synthesis. 3-Bromopyruvate acid (BPA), an active-site-directed inhibitor of pyruvate dehydrogenase complex (PDC), reacts irreversibly with PDC in the presence of thiamine pyrophospate (Maldonado *et al.*, 1972; Apfel *et al.*, 1984; Lowe and Perham, 1984). At 2 mM, it causes a 90% drop in acetylcholine tissue content (Arendt *et al.*, 1990), which has been reported to reduce the cholinergic neuronal activity of the cerebral cortex and cortical choline acetyltransferase activity. Dysfunction of the PDC has been well established for a number of neurodegenerative disorders, including AD (Perry *et al.*, 1980; Sorbi *et al.*, 1983; Sheu *et al.*, 1985). In *E. coli*, and one may assume in mammalian brain, BPA is metabolized by the enzyme becoming inactivated once every 40-60 turnovers (Lowe and Perham, 1984). Bilateral injections of the

PDC inhibitor into the basal forebrain have been found to reduce acetylcholine synthesis and produce impairment in retention of passive avoidance (Arendt *et al.*, 1990). The dose corresponding to that impairment produces a 40-80% inhibition of acetylcholine synthesis, seven days after the injections. A recovery was observed 18 days after the injections, suggesting that the inhibition is reversible. The cerebral metabolic rate of glucose remained low 3 weeks after the injections into the basal forebrain (intracranial injection, 0.1 μ 2 mM solution, rat) (Ouchi *et al.*, 1996). The cholinergic system is so sensitive to energy metabolism also because PDC is an intramitichondrial enzyme, whereas ChAT and the last stage of acetylcholine synthesis are located in the cytosol. Thus, there is an impediment in the access of ChAT to the main compartment of acetyl-CoA, which would account for the more sensitive response of the cholinergic system to interruption of the tricarboxylic acid cycle.

The involvement of acetylcholine as a neurotransmitter in the control of rCBF has been demonstrated by the administration of cholinergic drugs such as scopolamine, physostigmine. When a group of human subjects is treated with scopolamine, a non-selective muscarinic acetylcholine receptor blocker, a 20% decrease of CBF in the cortex was detected (Honer *et al.*, 1988). On the other hand, the application of the acetylcholine-esterase inhibitors physostigmaine and eptastigmine, which increase the extracellular level of endogenous acetylcholine, leads to a significant increase of CBF in a wide variety of brain regions in the rat and human (Scremin *et al.*, 1993; Blin *et al.*, 1997; Peruzzi *et al.*, 2000). Although these studies provided convincing evidence for the involvement of acetylcholine in CBF regulation, the origin and exact target structures of the neurotransmitter still remained to be clarified.

Evidence for the direct impact of cholinergic dysfunction on the integrity of synapses and metabolism in the cortex and hippocampus has also been provided. For instance, selective cholinotoxic antibody has been shown to induce synaptic loss, lasting hippocampal (most significant: CA1 by 29.5%, CA3 by 23.7%; dentate gyrus by 21.9%) and cortical (by 11.4-21.0%) hypometabolism, and memory deficits (Browne *et al.*, 2001). The underlying mechanisms may include deafferation and loss of cholinergic cerebral vasodilation. However, whether early cholinergic deficiency is causal and underlies AD is questioned by recent findings. Patients with mild cognitive impairment and moderate AD have been found to have ChAT (the marker for cholinergic neurons) levels that do not differ from those of non-demented, aging patients (Dekosky and Ikonomovic, 2002). ChAT levels in the frontal cortex and hippocampus appear higher in patients with mild cognitive impairment (Morris, 2002). It is unclear whether such an increase may reflect a period of compensation to impaired cholinergic system.

Hypometabolism in AD: Vascular Contribution

The brains of all vertebrates are perfused by a dense microvascular network, approximately 400 miles of capillary in humans, formed by the capillary endothelial cells within the brain (Bar, 1980). The surface area of the human brain microvascular endothelium is approximately 20 m^2 (Pardridge, 2001). No neurons or glial cell is more than 20 μm from a neighboring capillary. Thus, every neuron is virtually perfused by its own microvessel. In addition, increased single neuron activity is associated with an immediate increased oxygen consumption, followed by a rapidly increased blood flow to the activated area (Thompson et al., 2003). The oxygen consumption is sufficient to cause a regional reduction of oxygen level by about 2.5-3 % for 4s of 20 spikes/s. The reduction would be more dramatic if not compensated for by the increased blood flow.

The impact of decreased CBF on brain function and possible contribution of cerebrovascular deficiencies to AD have received increased scientific interest in recent years (de la Torre and Stefano, 2000; Farkas and Luiten, 2001 for review). It has been suggested that cerebrovascular disease and AD coincide more than by chance alone (Leys *et al.*, 1998; Pasquier *et al.*, 1998; Kalaria, 2000). Cerebral hypoperfusion, a hemodynamic microcirculatory insufficiency, when reaching a critical level (de la Torre and Stefano, 2000), will destabilize neurons, synapses, neurotransmission and cognitive ability, eventually evolving into a neurodegenerative state characterized by the formation of senile plaques, neurofibrillary tangles, amyloid angiopathy and in some cases, Lewy bodies. It has been proposed that the critically lowered cerebral hypoperfusion initiates AD by distorting regional brain capillary structure involving endothelial cell shape changes and impairment of nitric oxide release that affects signaling between the immune, cardiovascular and nervous system.

Cerebral vascular abnormality and hypoperfusion can directly lead to hypometabolism. Animal studies have revealed that the hippocampus, and particularly its CA1 area, is selectively vulnerable to the consequences of hypoperfusion (Schmidt-Kastner and Freund, 1991). 'Mild' but 'chronic' cerebral hypoperfusion delivered to aging rats for 1 year has been found to result in nearly identical capillary alterations as described in AD brains (de Jong *et al.*, 1999). In addition, the capillary degeneration initially is found exclusively in the CA1 hippocampal region and is associated with spatial memory deficits, resembling the visuo-spatial memory decline seen at onset of AD (de Jong *et al.*, 1999; Farkas *et al.*, 2000). As mentioned above, the hippocampal CA1 sector is also the site of the initial and severest pathological damage seen in AD brain (West *et al.*, 1994; de Leon *et al.*, 1997). Four weeks of exposure to chronic ischemia (2-vessel occlusion) in aging (20 month-old) rats have been reported to have a reduced cytochrome oxidase activity, most significant (-33%) in the hippocampus, and a reduced spatial learning/ memory (Cada *et al.*, 2000). Two-vessel occlusion surgery in rats leads to a chronic reduction in cerebral blood flow to 70% of the original flow rate, a reduction matching that observed in AD brains. Such hypoperfusion in aged rats has been reported to impair spatial memory in the Morris maze as early as seven days after surgery (Pappas *et al.*, 1996; de la Torre *et al.*, 1997) but not in young animals. The difference is that young adult rats compensate for decreases in blood flow after carotid artery occlusion by dilation of a basilar artery (He *et al.*, 1997). However, aging animals have a substantially increased risk of sclerotic changes, which would prevent the expected dilation of arteries (He *et al.*, 1997). These studies in animals are consistent with the two determinant factors for AD to develop in humans: advanced aging, and the presence of a condition that lowers cerebral perfusion. In younger adults, a more severe cerebral hypoperfusion state is all that is necessary to induce the disorder, indicating the central role of cerebral perfusion. Middle age rats will develop Alzheimer-like pathology when blood flow is reduced to <40% of normal baseline levels (de la Torre *et al.*, 1992a,b; de la Torre and Fortin, 1994). These observations suggest that cerebral hypoperfusion may underlie brain hypometabolism and indicate that the capacity of vascular microcirculation makes a big difference between normal cognition and dementia.

HYPOMETABOLISM/ISCHEMIA: INDUCER OF β-AMYLOID

The accumulation of the small protein β-amyloid into so-called plaques, a hallmark feature of AD, is believed by many to play a major role in dementia. Some of the proteolytic fragments of APP are cytotoxic, causing neuronal dysfunction and death in AD (Yankner *et al.*, 1989; Cai *et al.*, 1993; Haass and Selkoe, 1993; Roses, 1996; Scheuner *et al.*, 1996; Hardy, 1997; Leeuwen *et al.*, 1998). Even though there are many inconsistent findings (see above), one common feature of AD brain is still the accumulation of amyloid plaques in the memory-related structures. If cerebral hypoperfusion and hypometabolism indeed play an important role in AD dementia, their relationship with Aβ needs careful consideration.

There is no question that cerebral hypoperfusion or hypoxia is a powerful inducer of Aβ production. Chronic hypoxia/ischemia induces over-production of Aβ and formation of Ca^{2+}-permeable Aβ channels (Taylor *et al.*, 1999). Hypoxia/ischemia results in cerebral/extracellular APP/Aβ-like fragment accumulation and increased amyloid βA4 precursor gene expression (Kalaria *et al.*, 1993; Wisniewski and Maslinska, 1996; Pappas *et al.*, 1997; Bennett *et al.*, 2000; Kalaria, 2000; Jin *et al.*, 2001). One of the mechanisms may be a chronic hypoxia-induced reduced (by 50%) expression of ADAM 10 (A Disintegrin And Metalloproteinase 10; Webster *et al.*, 2002), a leading candidate for the α-secretase (Lammich *et al.*, 1999). As mentioned above, the action of α-secretase gives rise to sAPPα and precludes the formation of Aβ. This is associated with increased levels of APP by hypoxia/ischemia (Abe *et al.*, 1991; Kalaria *et al.*, 1993; Kogure and Kato, 1993; Tomimoto *et al.*, 1994; Koistinaho *et al.*, 1996; Yakota *et al.*, 1996; Jendroska *et al.*, 1997; Baiden-Amissah *et al.*, 1998), resulting in increased Aβ. Chronic ischemia due to myocardial infarction in middle-aged individuals has been reported to be accompanied with high levels of Aβ deposition (Sparks, 1997). Extra- and intracellular space accumulations of the C-terminal and βA domains of APP and apolipoprotein E have been observed in the rat brain after cardiac arrest (10 minutes) with long-term survival (Pluta *et al.*, 1997, 1998), including extracellular and intracellular accumulation of Aβ (Pluta *et al.*, 1998). A brief episode of global ischemia has also been found to increase production of APP in vulnerable CA1 neurons 24 hours (more intense at 48 hours) after transient global ischemia by 12 minutes of four-vessel occlusion (Gervais *et at.*, 1999).

Again, evidence is available for hypoperfusion/hypometabolism-induced Aβ over-production and for Aβ-induced vascular injury and respiratory inhibition. Alternatively, decreased metabolism and the presence of plaques and tangles could be independent phenomena, as proposed (Salehi and Swaab, 1999).

AD Dementia: Related but Different from Acute Stroke

Stroke may account for as many as 50% of AD cases in older age groups (Kokmen *et al.*, 1996). It is estimated that AD is almost three times more likely to occur in the elderly after a stroke episode or a transient ischemic attack (Kokmen *et al.*, 1996). A number of studies have also documented that about one-quarter of patients who have a stroke develop dementia (Kotila *et al.*, 1986; Tatemichi *et al.*, 1992, 1994; Pederson *et al.*, 1996; van Kooten *et al.*, 1996). Ischemic impairment to spatial memory is progressive (Nelson *et al.*, 1997a), consistent with the notion that ischemic brain damage is not static, but that neuronal degeneration and reorganization persists for some time after an ischemic insult (Onodera *et al.*, 1990; Nakano *et al.*, 1990). Although death of pyramidal cells largely occurs within the first week (Simon *et al.*, 1984), GABAergic interneurons, for example, are still declining in the CA1 sector some 6-8 weeks after global ischemia in gerbils (Fukuda *et al.*, 1993). Although the type of dementia has not been well characterized, a proportion of these individuals develop a slowly progressive dementia suggestive of AD.

Because the brain stores neither oxygen nor glucose, severely reduced or completely blocked cerebral blood flow can lead, within minutes, to irreversible cerebral damage and long-lasting neurological disorders, including memory, motor, and sensory losses. One of the most persistent consequences of ischemia in humans is amnesia. Interruption of CBF, as occurs in heart attack, bypass surgery, or coronary artery occlusion, results in a high incidence (up to 48%) of memory deficits, moderate to profound anterograde memory loss in humans, in the absence of general cognitive or neurological impairment (Nelson *et al.*, 1997a). Memory loss has been observed in patients who suffered focal cerebral ischemia following an occlusion of the posterior cerebral artery (e.g., Brindley and Janora, 1975; De Renzi *et* al., 1987). Memory loss also occurred in a significant proportion (up to 20%) of survivors of transient global cerebral ischemia induced by cardiac arrest or coronary artery occlusion (e.g., Bedell *et* al., 1983; Longstreth *et* al., 1983). Focal cerebral ischemia is associated with infarcts of total tissue loss in the region supplied by the posterior cerebral artery, which includes the posterior part of the hippocampal formation and parahippocampal region, and the occipito-temporal cortex to varying degree. Global ischemia induces widespread changes throughout the hippocampus, including upregulation of heatshock proteins, trophic factors, and receptor binding, and also changes in calcium channel conductance, neurotransmitter levels and second messenger systems including increases in cytosolic inositol phosphate levels (Onodera and Kogure, 1989; Onodera *et al.*, 1987, 1989; Schmedt-Kastner and Freund, 1991; Siekluca *et al.*, 1991). Thus, cognitive deficits may also relate to more subtle neural changes than the death of CA1 cells.

Hippocampal cells, particularly cells in the hilar and CA1 fields, are highly vulnerable to effects of ischemia. Two amnesic patients have been described who, following an ischemic event, had bilateral lesions limited to the CA1 region of the hippocampus (Zola-Morgan *et al.*, 1986; Rempel-Clower *et al.*, 1996). Rats subjected to a controlled period of global ischemia (four vessel occlusion for 10 minutes) showed cell loss confined to the hippocampal CA1 field (Nelson *et* al., 1997b) and significantly retarded rates of learning and impaired recall of the platform position, relative to controls (Nelson *et al.*, 1997a,b). Spatial memory tasks, such as the Morris water maze, are sensitive to ischemic impairment. Global transient cerebral ischemia, such as those produced by 4-vessel occlusion for 8-20 minutes in rats, impairs water maze acquisition and working memory (Olsen *et al.*, 1994; Block and Schwarz, 1997; Nelson *et al.*, 1997a). Thus, it is possible to relate the histological damage of CA1 in the anterior-dorsal hippocampus to impaired memory performance in the Morris water maze performance (Auer *et al.*, 1989; Volpe *et al.*, 1992; Olsen *et al.*, 1994; Sinden *et al.*, 1997). Nevertheless, Nunn *et al.* (1994) have reported that CA1 damage may not be the only determinant of water-maze deficits. Rats with only partial damage to their CA1 region have been reported to exhibit no significant impairments in water maze performance (Olsen *et al.*, 1994). It has been concluded that damage restricted to only 50% of the CA1 cells of the hippocampus exceeded the threshold for production of a spatial memory deficits (Auer *et al.*, 1989). Microsphere (48 μm, 900 in 20% dextran solution; into the right internal carotid artery in rats) embolism-induced multiple small infarctions have been suggested to resemble clinical vascular dementia more closely than the infarction induced by middle cerebral artery occlusion in terms of pathophysiological alterations. These were reported to decrease the acetylcholine concentration and choline acetyltransferase activity in the cerebral cortex and hippocampus and to impair learning functions (passive avoidance task; Takagi *et al.*, 1997).

Spatial memory deficits (Morris water maze) have also been reported in rats subjected to chronic ischemia, such as those induced by permanent bilateral carotid artery ligation (de la Torre *et al.*, 1997) or focal cerebral ischemia with occlusion of the middle cerebral artery (Yonemori *et al.*, 1996). These deficits are believed to be predictable by reduced cytochrome oxidase activity, the terminal enzyme in the electron transport chain, in the CA1 and posterior parietal regions (de la Torre *et al.*, 1997). No such reduced activity has been observed in other brain regions including CA2 and CA3 of the hippocampus, dentate gyrus, presubiculum, dorsal subiculum, ventral subiculum, lateral habenula, medial habenula, parafascicular, lateral posterior and ventral basal-medial thalamic nuclei, caudal caudate-putamen, posteror cingulate, and primary olfactory cortices, for the same insult (de la Torre *et al.*, 1997). Thus, hypometabolism in the hippocampal CA1, induced by cerebral hypoperfusion is sufficient to induce spatial memory deficits. This is consistent with the evidence of reduced cytochrome oxidase (Kish *et al.*, 1992) and Na^+, K^+-ATPase (Liguri *et al.*, 1990) in AD brains.

Although stroke dementia resembles AD dementia in many behavioral and molecular aspects because the same neural structures affected in the AD brain are also sensitive to an acute ischemia, it should be emphasized that stroke involves an acute infarction at the center of the ischemia and an association of a large portion of neuronal necrosis, while AD is mainly a chronic neurodegenerative disorder.

HYPOMETABOLISM: THERAPEUTIC PERSPECTIVES

The validity of a metabolic role in AD pathogenesis would imply that restoration of the activity of neurons, either by pharmacological or non-pharmacological stimuli, would lead to diminished cognitive impairment. Evidence has been provided that reducing cerebral hypoperfusion/ hypometabolism improves cognition in AD (Craft *et al.*, 1993; Mannin *et al.*,

1993; Blass, 2002) and increasing cerebral perfusion leads to cognitive and neurological improvement (Goldsmith, 2002). Furthermore, the increase in glucose metabolism and nicotinic receptors following tacrine (a cholinesterase inhibitor) treatment is paralleled by improvements in neuropsychological performance and EEG (Nordberg 1992, 1995). Consistently, hippocampal metabolism improvement, as measured by PET, sensitively measures the progression of AD and its improvement with rivastigmine (Potkin *et al.*, 2001), a cholinesterase inhibitor. AD patients who have benefited cognitively from the treatment demonstrated significantly increased glucose metabolism, for instance, an increased hippocampal glucose metabolism by 32.5%, while those patients who did not benefit form the treatment did not show a significant increase (Nordberg 1992, 1995; Potkin *et al.*, 2001). These observations argue strongly not only for the therapeutic value of restoration of cerebral perfusion and metabolism in AD therapy but also for a biomarker to monitor the progression of and recovery from AD dementia.

As discussed above, many potentially effective antidementia agents have been shown to increase cerebral perfusion. In addition to efforts to improve cerebral perfusion and metabolism, therapeutic strategies may also include antioxidants, anti-inflammatory agents, anti-excitotoxic agents, anti-Aβ agents, and drugs that stabilize mitochondrial function. Cholinergic therapies in AD improve temporarily the performance of undamaged neurons but do not stop the progressive mental decline (Dominguez and De strooper, 2002). The effects of NMDA receptor agonists on neurological injury would be consistent with the evidence that oxidative damage and mitochondrial abnormalities occur early in AD (Sun and Alkon, 2002b). Some low-affinity NMDA receptor antagonists at the open channel site have been tried in all forms of dementia, including AD, and shown to improve memory in severe dementia (Winblad and Poritis, 1999; Helmuth, 2002; Le and Lipton, 2001; Orgogozo et al., 2002). Ulchino *et al* (1998) reported that cyclosporin A ameliorates the histological damage in the hippocampal CA1 subregion after global ischemia. Because this drug prevents the mitochondrial permeability transition and subsequent DNA fragmentation of the hippocampus after hypoglycemia (Ferrand-Drake *et al.*, 1999), it would be of great interest to evaluate the cytochrome *c* expression after administration of cyclosporin A in the global ischemia model. However, treatment with vitamin E and/or vitamin C antioxidants has been reported to neither stop the progression of AD nor improve memory (Sano *et al.*, 1997; Selkoe and Schenk, 2003). A recent study shows that intake of both for a mean time of 4 years in 980 elderly subjects has been found to have no association with any decreased risk of AD (Luchsinger et al., 2003). Indomethacin seemed to slow the cognitive decline in patients with AD in a placebo-controlled pilot study (Rogers, *et al.*, 1993; Lim *et al.*, 2000). Prednisone, a powerful anti-inflammatory that enters the central nervous system, however, has no effect on AD (Eisen, 2000).

Anti-Aβ agents, including those that reduce Aβ overproduction, remove Aβ from the brain, and reduce Aβ neurotoxicity. Enhancing Aβ cleavage may have therapeutic value since brain structures such as the caudate nucleus and peripheral organs of the body that express high levels of neprilysin, the major enzyme that cleaves Aβ (Iwata *et al.*, 2000, 2001), never develop Aβ deposits (Yasojima *et al.*, 2001), consistent with an aging-related down-regulation of neprilysin (Apelt et al., 2003). Propentoflylline, a xanthine derivative with stimulatory effects on nerve growth factor, has been found to improve learning and memory deficits in rats induced by β-amyloid 1-40 (Yamada *et al.*, 1998). Peripheral administration of agents, such as gelsolin (extracted from bovine plasma) or ganglioside GM1 (extracted from bovine brain), which have high affinity for Aβ can also reduce the level of Aβ in the brain, as shown in transgenic mice (Matsuoka *et al.*, 2003). Inhibition of γ-secretase, on the other hand, may not necessarily be beneficial. γ-Secretase inhibitors have been developed that either inhibit the generation of all Aβ species or show preferential activity against $A\beta_{40}$. Several of these inhibitors have been demonstrated to bind presenilins, leading to the hypothesis that presenilins are actually γ-secretase (Li *et al.*, 2000). Because presenilins not only increase γ-secretase cleavage of APP but also proteolytic processing of the Notch receptor (De Strooper *et al.*, 1999), γ-secretase inhibitors may concomitantly inhibit Notch cleavage, resulting in adverse side effects (Hadland *et al.*, 2001). In addition, treatment with γ-secretase inhibitors leads to the accumulation of high amounts of carboxy-terminal fragments (CTFs) of APP that may be neurotoxic (Yankner *et al.*, 1989; Oster-Granite *et al.*, 1996).

One interesting hormone is estrogen. Estrogen receptors are present throughout the brain, including the hippocampus (Osterlund et al., 2000). Menopause during aging removes women's hormonal protection from AD. A drop in estrogen level decreases CBF and put women at a risk for AD similar to that of men (Resnick *et al.*, 1998). In animals, estrogen protects hippocampal neurons against Aβ neurotoxicity (Behl et al., 1997), improves synaptic formation in the hippocampus (Murphy et al., 1998), and enhances survival of hippocampal neurons (Singh et al., 1995). The CBF decrease and potential risk for AD can be diminished by increasing cerebral perfusion to premenopausal levels with estrogen replacement therapy during menopause. Use of an estrogen patch has been found to result in an improvement in attention and verbal memory on selected tasks but not on global cognitive and functional scales in some studies (Asthana et al., 1999, 2001). However, others have failed to detect cognitive improvement with estrogen replacement (Henderson et al., 2000; Mulnard et al., 2000; Wang et al., 2000c). In a study of older women and men without dementia, higher estrogen levels are not associated with larger hippocampi and better memory performance (den Heijer et al., 2003). Increasing estrogen levels in postmenopausal women does not predict cognitive improvement on a variety of cognitive measures (Thal et al., 2003).

Concluding Remarks

The research and therapy of AD dementia suffers because of the lack of critical insights into AD pathogenesis. As indicated in a recent review (Selkoe and Schenk, 2003), the neurotransmitter deficits of AD are multiple, including cholinergic, glutamatergic, GABAergic, serotoninergic and others. Functional neuroimaging with glucose metabolic PET imaging with fluorodeoxyglucose has been shown to have the potential to detect very early neural dysfunction before abnormal cognitive testing is obtainable and to monitor treatment response (Demetriades, 2002). Hypometabolism correlates with AD neuropathology and indicates the disease progression or severity. The role of hypometabolism in AD dementia lies in its preclinical occurrence in AD and its association with cerebral hypoperfusion and great impact on the synaptic plasticity and functions of the neural network involved in explicit memory. There is also a high correlation between rCBF and power spectrum of EEG in the theta and delta bands (Passero *et al.*, 1995). Thus far, available evidence indicates that recovery of synaptic activity is a good measure of neuronal integrity and function. Its value for a wide use in monitoring the progression of AD dementia and judging the effectiveness of AD therapy remains to be evaluated.

The ultimate goal of AD research and pharmacology is to prevent the onset of the disease process and therefore to allow normal aging without cognitive decline. This will involve a removal of the cause of the disease, in addition to a change of life style for some (Morris et al., 2003; Scarneas et al., 2003). However, if it turns out to be true, as suggested by numerous studies, that AD is a chronic vascular disease that causes neurodegenerative changes in the brain rather than a neurodegenerative process that affects cerebral vascularization, increasing and maintaining CBF would be the major therapeutic goal in AD treatment and prevention. Preventing cerebrovascular damage and hypometabolism may, therefore, provide a new avenue for AD therapy.

REFERENCES

Abe, K.; Tanzi, R.E.; Kogure, K. Selective induction of Kunitztype protease inhibitor domain-containing amyloid precursor protein mRNA after persistent focal ischemia in rat cerebral cortex. *Neurosci. Lett.* **125:** 172–174, 1991.

Ahrens, K.F.; Freeman, W.J. Response dynamics of entorhinal cortex in awake, anesthetized, and bulbotomized rats. *Brain Res.* **911:** 193-202, 2001.

Ajmani, R.S.; Metter, E.J.; Jaykumar, R.; Ingram, D.K.; Spagler, E.L.; Abugo, O.; Rifkind, J.M. Hemodynamic changes during aging associated with cerebral blood flow and impaired cognitive function. *Neurobiol. Aging* **21:** 257-270, 2000.

Alkon, D.L. Calcium-mediated reduction of ionic currents: a biophysical memory trace. *Science* **226:** 1037-1045, 1984.

Alkon, D.L.; Nelson, T.J.; Zhao, W.Q.; Cavallaro, S. Time domains of neuronal Ca^{2+} signaling and associative memory: steps through a calexcitin, ryanodine receptor, K^+ channel cascade. *Trends Neurosci.* **21:** 529-537, 1998.

Alsop, D.C., Detre, J.A. and Grossman, M. Assessment of cerebral blood flow in Alzheimer's disease by spin-labeled magnetic resonance imaging. *Ann. Neurol.* **47:** 93-100, 2000.

Alzheimer, A. Uber eine eigenartige erkrangkung der himrinde. *All. A. Psychiatr.* **64:** 146-148, 1907.

Apelt, J.; Ach, K.; Schliebs, R. Aging-related down-regulation of neprilysin, a putative β-amyloid-degrading enzyme, in transgenic TG2576 Alzheimer-like mouse brain is accompanied by an astroglial upregulation in the vicinity of β-amyloid plaques. *Neurosci. Lett.* **339:** 183-186, 2003.

Apfel, M.A., Ikeda, B.H., Speckhard, D.C. and Frey, P.A. *Escherichia coli* pyruvate dehydrogenase complex: Thiamine pyrophosphate-dependent inactivation by 3-bromopyruvate. *J. Biol. Chem.* **259:** 2905-2909, 1984.

Arendt, T.; Schugens, M.M.; Marchbanks, R.M. Reversible inhibition of acetylcholine synthesis and behavioral effects caused by 3-bromopyruvate. *J. Neurochem.* **55:** 1474-1479, 1990.

Aria, C.; Montiel, T.; Quiroz-Báez, R.; Massieu, L. β-Amyloid neurotoxicity is exacerbated during glycosis inhibition and mitochondrial impairment in the rat hippocampus *in vivo* and in isolated nerve terminals: implications for Alzheimer's disease. *Exp. Neurol.* **176:** 163-174, 2002.

Asthana, S.; Craft, S.; Baker, L.D.; Raskind, M.A.; Birnbaum, R.S.; Lofgreen, C.P.; Veith, R.C.; Plymate, S.R. Cognitive and neuroendocrine response to transdermal estrogen in postmenopausal women with Alzheimer's disease: results of a placebo-controlled, double-blind, pilot study. *Psychoneuroendocrinology* **24:** 657-677, 1999.

Asthana, S.; Baker, L.D.; Craft, S.; Stanczyk, F.Z.; Veith, R.C.; Raskind, M.A.; Plymate, S.R. High-dose estrodiol improves cognition for women with AD: results of a randomized study. *Neurology* **57:** 605-612, 2001.

Attwell, D.; Iadecola, C. The neural basis of functional brain imaging signals. *Trends Neurosci.* **25:** 621-625, 2002.

Auer, R.N.; Jensen, M.L.; Whishaw, I.Q. Neurobehavioral deficit due to ischemic brain damage limited to half the CA1 sector of the hippocampus. *J. Neurosci.* **9:** 1641-1647, 1989.

Bahr, B.A.; Hoffman, K.B.; Yang, A.J.; Hess, U.S.; Glade, C.G.; Lynch, G. Amyloid beta protein is internalized selectively by hippocampal field CA1 and causes neurons to accumulate amyloidogenic carboxyterminal fragments of the amyloid precursor protein. *J. Comp. Neurol. **397:** 139-147, 1998.*

Baiden-Amissah, K.; Joashi, U.; Blumberg, R.; Mehmet, H.; Edwards, A.D.; Cox, P.M. Expression of amyloid precursor protein (β-APP) in the neonatal brain following hypoxic ischaemic injury. *Neuropathol. Appl. Neurobiol.* **24:** 346-352, 1998.

Bar, T. The vascular system of the cerebral cortex. *Adv. Anat. Embryol. Cell Biol.* **59:** 1-62, 1980.

Barbilivien, A.; Bertrand, N.; Besret, L.; Beley, A.; MacKenzie, E.T.; Dauphin, F. Neurochemical stimulation of the rat substantia innominata increases cerebral blood flow (but not glucose use) through the parallel activation of cholinergic and non-cholinergic pathways. *Brain Res.***840:** 115-124, 1999.

Barnes, C.A. Spatial learning and memory processes: the search for their neurological mechanism in the rat. *Trends Neurosci.* **11:** 163-169, 1988.

Bedell, S.E.; Delbanco, T.L.; Cook, E.F.; Epstein, F.H. Survival after cardiopulmonary resuscitation in the hospital. *N. Engl. J. Med.* **309:** 569-576, 1983.

Behl, C.; Skutella, T.; Lezoualch, F.; Holsboer, F. Neuroprotection against oxidative stress by estrogen: structure-activity relationship. *Mol. Pharmacol.* **51:** 535-541, 1997.

Bennett, M.C.; Diamond, D.M.; Stryker, S.L.; Parks, J.K.; Parker, W.D. Jr. Cytochrome oxidase inhibition: a novel animal model of Alzheimer's disease. *J. Geriatr. Psychiatry Neurol.* **5:** 93-101, 1992.

Bennett, D.A.; Wilson, R.S.; Schneider, J.A.; Evans, D.A.; Aggarwal, N.T.; Arnold, S.E.; Cochran, E.J.; Berry-Kravis, E.; Bienias, J.L. Apolipoprotein E ε4 allele, AD pathology and the clinical expression of Alzheimer's disease. *Neurology* **60:** 246-252, 2003.

Bennett, S.A.; Pappas, B.A.; Stevens, W.D.; Davidson, C.M.; Fortin, T.; Chen, J. Cleavage of amyloid precursor protein elicited by chronic cerebral hypoperfusion. *Neurobiol. Aging* **21:** 2000.

Benzi, G.; Moretti, A. Are reactive oxygen species involved in Alzheimer's disease? *Neurobiol. Aging* **16:** 661-674, 1995.

Biesold, D.; Inanami, O.; Sato, A.; Sato, Y. Stimulation of the nucleus basalis of Meynert increases cerebral cortical blood flow in rats. *Neurosci. Lett.* **98:** 39-44, 1989.

Blass, J.P. The mitochondrial spiral. An adequate cause of dementia in the Alzheimer's syndrome. *Ann. NY Acad. Sci.* **924:** 170-183, 2001.

Blass, J.P. Alzheimer's disease and Alzheimer's dementia: distinct but overlapping entities. *Neurobiol. Aging* **23:** 1077-1084, 2002.

Blin, J.; Ivaoiu, A.; Coppens, A.; De Volder, A.; Labar, D., Michel, C.; Laterre, E.C. Cholinergic neurotransmission has different effects on cerebral glucose consumption and blood flow in young normals, aged normals, and Alzheimer's disease patients. *Neuroimage* **6:** 335-343, 1997.

Block, F.; Schwarz, M. Correlation between hippocampal neuronal damage and spatial learning deficit due to global ischemia. *Pharmacol. Biochem. Behav.* **56:** 755-761, 1997.

Bouras, C.; Hof, P.R.; Giannakopoulos, P.; Michel, J.-P.; Morrison, J.H. Regional distribution of neurofibrillary tangles and senile plaques in the cerebral cortex of elderly patients: A quantitative evaluation of a one-year autopsy population from a geriatric hospital. *Cereb. Cort.* **4:** 138-150, 1994.

Braak, H.; Braak, E. Age, neurofibrillary changes, A-beta and onset of Alzheimer's disease. *Neurosci. Lett.* **210:** 87-90, 1996.

Braak, H.; Braak, E. Frequency of stages of Alzheimer-related lesions in different age categories. *Neurobiol. Aging* **4:** 351-357, 1997.

Brenowitz, S.; David, J.; Trussell, L. Enhancement of synaptic efficacy by presynaptic GABA(B) receptor. *Neuron* **20:** 135-141, 1998.

Brindley, G.S.; Janota, I. Observations on cortical blindness and on vascular lesions that cause loss of recent memory. *J. Neurol. Neurosurg.* Psychiatry **38:** 459-464, 1975.

Brodin, L.; Bakeeval, L.; Shupliakov, O. Presynaptic mitochondria and the temporal pattern of neurotransmitter release. *Philos. Trans. R. Soc. Lond. B Biol. Sci.* **354:** 365-372, 1999.

Browne, S.F.; Lin, L.; Mattsson, A.; Georgievska, B.; Sacson, O. Selective antibody-induced cholinergic cell and synaptic loss produce sustained hippocampal and cortical hypometabolism with correlated cognitive deficits. *Exp. Neurol.* **170:** 36-47, 2001.

Büchner, M.; Huber, R.; Sturchler-Pierrat, C.; Staufenbiel, M.; Riepe, M.W. Impaired hypoxic tolerance and altered protein binding of NADH in presympatomatic APP23 transgenic mice. *Neuroscience* **114:** 285-289, 2002.

Butterfield, D.A.; Hensley, K.; Hall, N.; Subramaniam, R.; Howard, B.J.; Cole, P.; Yatin, S.; LaFontaine, M.; Harris, M.E.; Askenova, M.; Askenov, M.; Carey, J.M. β-Amyloid-derived free radical oxidation: a fundamental process in Alzheimer's disease. In: Wasco W, Tanzi RE, editors. Molecular mechanisms of dementia. Totowa, NJ: Humana Press. 1998, pp 87–94.

Cada, A.; de la Torre, J.C.; Gonzalez-Lima, F. Chronic cerebrovascular ischemia in aged rats: effects of brain metabolic capacity and behavior. *Neurobiol. Aging* **21:** 225-233, 2000.

Cai, X.; Glode, T.; Younkin, S. Release of excess amyloid β protein from a mutant amyloid β protein precursor. *Science* **259:** 514-516, 1993.

Canevari, L.; Clark, J.B.; Bates, T.E. β-Amyloid fragment 25-35 selectively decrease complex IV activity in isolated mitochondria. *FEBS Lett.* **457:** 131-134, 1999.

Cardoso, S.M.; Santos, S.; Swerdlow, R.H.; Oliverira, C.R. Functional mitochondria are required for amyloid β-mediated neurotoxicity. *FASEB J.* **15:** 1439-1441, 2001.

Cash, A.D.; Perry, G.; Ogawa, O.; Raina, A.K.; Zhu, X.-W.; Smith, M.A. Is Alzheimer's disease a mitochondrial disorder? *Neuroscientist* **8:** 489-496, 2002.

Cassarino, D.S.; Swerdlow, R.H.; Parks, J.K.; Parker, W.D. Jr.; Bennett, J.P. Jr. Cyclosporin A increases resting mitochondrial membrane potential in SY5Y cells and reverses the depressed mitochondrial membrane potential of Alzheimer's disease cybrids. *Biochem. Biophys. Res. Commun.* **248:** 168-173, 1998.

Cavestri, R.; Radices, L.; Ferrarini, F.; Longhini, M.; Longhini, E. Influence of erythrocyte aggregability and plasma fibrinogen concentration on cerebral blood flow with aging. *Acta Neurol. Scand.* **85:** 292-298, 1992.

Celsis, P.; Agniel, A.; Cardebat, D.; Demonet, J.F.; Qusset, P.; Puel, M. Age related cognitive decline: a clinical entity? A longitudinal study of cerebral blood flow and memory performance. *J. Neurol. Neurosurg. Psychiatry* **87:** 469-480, 1997.

Cervos-Navarro, J.; Diemer, N.H. Selective vulnerability in brain hypoxia. *Crit. Rev. Neurobiol.* **6:** 149-182, 1991.

Chagnon, P.; Betard, C.; Robitaille, Y.; Cholette, A.; Gauvreau, D. Distribution of brain cytochrome oxidase activity in various neurodegenerative disease. *Mol. Neurosci.* **6:** 711-715, 1995.

Chandrasekaran, K.; Hatanpää, K.; Brady, D.R.; Rapoport, S.I. Evidence for physiological down-regulation of brain oxidative phosphorylation in Alzheimer's disease. *Exp. Neurol.* **142:** 80-88, 1996.

Chandrasekaran, K.; Hatanpää, K.; Rapoport, S.I.; Brady, D.R. Decreased expression of nuclear and mitochondrial DNA-encoded genes of oxidative phosphorylation in association neocortex in Alzheimer's disease. *Mol. Brain Res.* **44:** 99-104, 1997.

Chantal, S.; Labelle, M.; Bouchard, R.W.; Braun, C.M.J. Correlation of regional proton magnetic resonance spectroscopic metabolic changes with cognitive deficits in mild Alzheimer disease. *Arch. Neurol.* **59:** 955-962, 2002.

Chapman, P.F.; Falinska, A.M.; Knevett, S.G.; Ramsay, M.F. Genes, models, and Alzheimer's disease. *Trends Genet.* **17:** 254-261, 2001.

Chen, S.Y.; Wright, J.W.; Barnes, C.D. The neurochemical and behavioral effects of beta-amyloid peptides (25-35). *Brain Res.* **720:** 54-60, 1996.

Chen, J.; Nagayama, T.; Jin, K.; Stelter, R.A.; Zhu, R.L.; Graham, S.H.; Simon, R.P. Induction of caspase-3-like protease may mediate delayed neuronal death in the hippocampus after transient cerebral ischemia. *J. Neurosci.* **18:** 4914-4928, 1998.

Chen, Q.-S.; Kagan, B.L.; Hirakura, Y.; Xie, C.-W. Impairment of hippocampal long-term potentiation by Alzheimer amyloid β-peptides. *J. Neurosci. Res.* **60:** 65-72, 2000.

Choi, D.W. Calcium-mediated neurotoxicity: relationship to specific channel types and role in ischemic damage. *Trends Neurosci.* **11:** 465-469, 1988.

Colbourne, F.; Sutherland, G.R.; Auer, R.N. Electron microscopic evidence against apoptosis as the mechanism of neuronal death in global ischemia. *J. Neurosci.* **19:** 4200-4210, 1999.

Convit, A.; Wolf, O.T.; Tarshish, C.; de Leon, M.J. Reduced glucose tolerance is associated with poor memory performance and hippocampal atrophy among normal elderly. *Proc. Natl. Acad. Sci. USA* **100:** 2019-2022, 2003.

Corder, E.H.; Saunders, A.M.; Strittmatter, W.J.; Schmechel, D.E.; Gaskell, P.C.; Small, G.W.; Roses, A.D.; Haines, J.L. Pericak-Vance, M.A Gene dose of apolipoprotein E type 4 allele and the risk of Alzheimer's disease in late onset families. *Science* **261:** 921-923, 1993.

Cotman, C.W.; Su, J.H. Mechanisms of neuronal death in Alzheimer's disease. *Brain Pathol.* **6:** 493-506, 1996.

Cotman, C.; Anderson. A. A potential role for apoptosis in neurodegeneration and Alzheimer's disease. *Mol. Neurobiol.* **10:** 19-45, 1995.

Craft, S.; Dagago-Jack, S.E.; Wiethop, B.V.; Murphy, C.; Nevins, R.T.; Fleischman, S.; Rice, V.; Newcomer, J.W.; Cryer, P.E. Effects of hyperglycemia on memory and hormone levels in dementia of the Alzheimer type – a longitudinal study. *Behav. Neurosci.* **107:** 926-940, 1993.

Craft, S.; Teri, L.; Edland, S.D.; Kukull, W.A.; Schellenberg, G.; McCormick, W.C.; Bowen, J.D.; Larson, E.B. Accelerated decline in apoliopoprotein E-ε4 homozygotes with Alzheimer's disease. *Neurology* **51:** 149-153, 1998.

Crystal, H.; Dickson, D.; Fuld, P.; Masur, D.; Scott, R.; Mehler, M.; Masdeu, J.; Kawas, C.; Aronson, M.; Wolfson, L. Clinico-pathological studies in dementia: nondemented subjects with pathologically conformed Alzheimer's disease. *Neurology* **38:** 1672-1687, 1988.

Davis, H.P; Tribuna, Pulsinelli; W.A.; Volpe, B.T. Reference and working memory of rats following hippocampal damage induced by transient forebrain ischemia. *Physiol. Behav.* **37:** 387-392, 1986.

Davies, L.; Wolska, B.; Hilbich, C.; Multhaup, G.; Martins, R.; Simms, G.; Beyreuther, K.; Masters, C.L. A4 amyloid protein deposition and the diagnosis of Alzheimer's disease: Prevalence in aged brains determined by immunocytochemistry compared with conventional neuropathologic techniques. *Neurology* **38:** 1688-1693, 1988.

Davis, R.E.; Miller, S.; Hernstadt, C.; Ghosh, S.S.; Fahy, E.; Shinobu, L.A.; Galasko, D.; Thal, L.J.; Beal, M.F.; Howell, N.; Parker, W.D., Jr. Mutations in mitochondrial cytochrome c oxidase genes segregate with late-onset Alzheimer's disease. *Proc. Natl. Acad. Sci. USA* **94:** 4526-4531, 1997.

de Jong, G.I.; Farkas, E.; Plass, J.; Keijser, J.N.; de la Torre, J.C.; Luiten, P.G.M. Cerebral hypoperfusion yields capillary damage in hippocampus CA1 that correlates to spatial memory impairment. *Neuroscience* **91:** 203-210, 1999.

DeKosky, S.T.; Ikonomovic, M.D. Upregulation of choline acetyltransferase activity in hippocampus and frontal cortex of elderly subjects with mild cognitive impairment. *Ann. Neurol.* **51:** 145-155, 2002.

DeKosky, S.T.; Scheff, S.W.; Styren, S.D. Structural correlates of cognition in dementia: Quantification and assessment of synapse changes. *Neurodegeneration* **5:** 417-421, 1996.

DeLaere, P.; Yi, H.E.; Fayet, G.; Duychaerts, C.; Hauw, J.-J. βA4 deposits are constant in the brain of the oldest old: an immunohistochemical study of 20 French centenarians. *Neurobiol. Aging* **14:** 191-194, 1993.

de la Torre, J.C. Impaired brain microcirculation may trigger Alzheimer's disease. *Neurosic. Behav. Rev.* **18:** 397-410, 1994.

de la Torre, J.C. Cerebromicrovascular pathology in Alzheimer's disease compared to normal aging. *Gerontology* **43:** 26-43, 1997a.

de la Torre, J.C. Cerebrovascular changes in the aging brain. *Adv. Cell Aging Gerontol.* **2:** 77-107, 1997b.

de la Torre, J.C. Vascular basis of Alzheimer's pathogenesis. *Ann. NY Acad Sci.* **977:** 196-215, 2002.

de la Torre, J.C.; Fortin, T. A chronic physiological rat model of dementia. *Behav. Brain Res.* **63:** 35-40, 1994

de la Torre, J.C.; Mussivand, T. Can disturbed brain microcirculation cause Alzheimer's disease? *Neurol. Res.* **15:** 146-153, 1993.

de la Torre, J.C.; Fortin, T.; Park, G.A.S.; Butler, K.; Kozlowski, P.; Pappas, B.; de Socarraz, H.; Saunders, J.; Richard, M. Chronic cerebrovascular insufficiency induces dementia-like deficits in aged rats. *Brain Res.* **582:** 186-195, 1992a.

de la Torre, J.C.; Fortin, T.; Park, G.A.S.; Saunders, P.; Kozlowski, P.; Butler, K.; de Socarraz, H.; Pappas, B.; Richard, M. Aged but not young rats develop metabolic, memory deficits after chronic brain ischemia. *Neurol. Res.* **14 (Suppl.):** 177-180, 1992b.

de la Torre, J.C.; Cada, A.; Nelson, N.; Davis, G.; Sutherland, R.J.; Gonzalez-Lima, F. Reduced cytochrome oxidase and memory dysfunction after chronic brain ischemia in aged rats. *Neurosci. Lett.* **223:** 165-168, 1997.

de la Torre, J.C.; Stefano, G.B. Evidence that Alzheimer's disease is a microvascular disorder: the role of constitutive nitric oxide. *Brain Res. Rev.* **34:** 119-136, 2000.

de Leon, M.J.; Convit, A.; DeSanti, S.; Bobinoski, M. Contribution of structural neuroimaging to the early diagnosis of Alzheimer's disease. *Int. Psychogeriatr.* **9 (Suppl. 1):** 183-190, 1997.

de Leon, M.J.; Convit, A.; Wolf, O.T.; Tarshish, C.Y.; DeSanti, S.; Rusinek, H.; Tsui, W.; Kandil, E.; Scherer, A.J.; Roche, A.; Imossi, A.; Thorn, E.; Bobinski, M.; Caraos, C.; Lesbre, P.; Schlyer, D.; Poirier, J.; Reisberg, B.; Fowler, J. Prediction of cognitive decline in normal elderly subjects with 2-[(18)F]fluoro-2-deoxy-D-glucose/postron emission tomography (FDG/PET). *Proc. Natl. Acad. Sci. USA* **98:** 10966-10971, 2001.

Demetriades, A.K. Functional neuroimaging in Alzheimer's type dementia. *J. Neurol. Sci.* **203-204:** 247-251, 2002.

De Renzi, E.; Zambolin, A.; Crisi, G. The pattern of neuropsychological impairment associated with left posterior cerebral artery infarcts. Brain **110:** 1099-1116, 1987.

De Strooper, B.; Annaert, W.; Cupers, P.; Saftig, P.; Craessaerts, K.; Mumm, J.S.; Schroeter, E.H.; Schrijvers, V.; Wolfe, M.S.; Ray, W.J.; Goate, A.; Kopan, R. A presenilin-1-dependent γ-secretase-like protease mediates release of Notch intracellular domain. *Nature* **398:** 518-522, 1999.

den Heijer, T.; Geerlings, M.I.; Hofman, A.; de Jong, F.H.; Launer, L.J.; Pols, H.A.P.; Breteler, M.M.B. Higher estrogen levels are not associated with larger hippocampi and better memory performance. *Arch Neurol.* **60:** 213-220, 2003.

Dominguez, D.I.; De Strooper, B. Novel therapeutic strategies provide the real test for the amyloid hypothesis of Alzheimer's disease. *Trends Pharmacol. Sci.* **23:** 324-330, 2002.

Dorfler, P.; Puls, I.; Schliesser, M.; Maurer, M.; Becker, G. Measurement of cerebral blood flow volume by extracranial sonography. *J. Cereb. Blood Flow Metab.* **20:** 269-271, 2000.

Dornan, W.A.; Kang, D.E.; McCampbell, A.; Kang, E.E. Bilateral injections of beta A(25-35)+IBO into the hippocampus disrupts acquisition of spatial learning in the rat. *NeuroReport* **18:** 165-168, 1993.

Du, A.T.; Schuff, N.; Zhu, X.P.; Jagust, W.J.; Miller, B.L.; Reed, B.R.; Kramer, J.H.; Mungas, D.; Yaffe, K.; Chui, H.C.; Weiner, M.W. Atrophy rates of entorhinal cortex in AD and normal aging. *Neurology* **60:** 481-486, 2003.

Duara, R.; Barker, W.W.; Chang, J.; Yoshii, F. Viability of neocortical function shown in behavioral activation state PET studies in Alzheimer's disease. *J. Cereb. Blood Flow Metab.* **12:** 927-934, 1992.

Egashira, N.; Iwasaki, K.; Ishibashi, M.; Hatip-Al-Khatib, I.; Wolozin, B.; Mishima, K.; Irie, K.; Fugiwara, M. Hypoxia enhances β-amyloid-induced apoptosis in rat cultured hippocampal neurons. *Jpn. J. Pharmacol.* **90:** 321-327, 2002.

Eichenbaum, H.; Otto, T. The hippocampus-what does it do? *Behav. Neural Biol.* **57:** 2-36, 1992.

Eisen, P. Anti-inflammatory therapy for Alzheimer's disease: implications of the prednisone trial. *Acta Neurol. Scand. Suppl.* **176:** 85-89, 2000.

El-Khoury, J., Hickman, S.E.; Thomas, C.A.; Cao, L.; Silverstein, S.C.; Loike, J.D. Scavenger receptor-mediated adhesion of microglia to β-amyloid fibrils. *Nature* **382:** 716-719, 1996.

Enari, M.; Sakahira, H.; Yokoyama, H.; Okawa, K.; Iwamatsu, A.; Nagata, S. A caspase-activated DNAase that degrades DNA during apoptosis, and its inhibitor ICAD. *Nature* **391:** 43-50, 1998.

Engelhart, M.J.; Geerlings, M.L.; Ruitenberg, A.; van Swieten, J.C.; Hofman, A.; Witteman, J.C.; Breteler, M.M. Dietary intake of oxidants and risk of Alzheimer's disease. *JAMA* **287:** 3223-3229, 2002.

Ernst, R.L.; Hay, J.W. The US economic and social costs of Alzheimer's disease revisited. *Am. J. Publ. Health* **84:** 1261-1264, 1994.

Etcheberrigaray, R.; Ito, E.; Kim, C.S.; Alkon, D.L. Soluble beta-amyloid induction of Alzheimer's phenotype for human fibroblast K^+ channels. *Science* **264:** 276-279, 1994.

Evans, D.A.; Funkenstein, H.H.; Albert, M.; Schrr, P.A.; Cook, N.R.; Chown, M.; Hebert, L.; Hennekens, C.; Taylor, J. Prevanlence of Alzheimer's disease in a community population of older person: Higher than previously reported. *JAMA* **262:** 2551-2556, 1989.

Evans, D.A.; Bennett, D.A.; Wilson, R.S.; Bienias, J.L.; Morris, M.C.; Scherr, P.A.; Hebert, L.E.; Aggarwal, N.; Beckett, L.A.; Joglekar, R.; Berry-Kravis, E.; Schneider, J. Incidence of Alzheimer disease in a biracial urban community. *Arch Neurol.* **60:** 185-189, 2003.

Farkas, E.; Luiten, P.G.M. Cerebral microvascular pathology in aging and Alzheimer's disease. *Prog. Neurobiol.* **64:** 575-611, 2001.

Farkas, E.; De Vos, R.; Jansen, E.; Steur, J.; Luiten, P.G.M. Are Alzheimer's disease, hypertension and cerebrocapillary damage related? *Neurobiol. Aging* **21:** 235-244, 2000.

Ferrer, I.; Soriano, M.A.; Vidal, A.; Planas, A.M. Survival of parvalbumin-immunoreactive neurons in the gerbil hippocampus following transient forebrain ischemia does not depend on HSP-70 protein induction. *Brain Res.* **692:** 41-46, 1995.

Ferrand-Drake, M.; Friberg, H.; Wieloch, T. Mitochondrial permeability transition induced by DNA fragmentation in the rat hippocampus following hypoglycemia. *Neuroscience* **90:** 1325-1338, 1999.

Frackowiak, J., Mazur-Kolecka, B.; Wisniewski, H.M.; Potempska, A.; Carroll, R.T.; Emmerling, M.R.; Kim, K.S. Secretion and accumulation of Alzheimer's β-protein by cultured vascular smooth muscle cells from old and young dogs. *Brain Res.* **676:** 225-230, 1995.

Fujimura, M.; Morita-Fujimura, Y.; Murakami, K.; Kawase, M.; Chan, P.H. Cytosolic redistribution of cytochrome c after transient focal cerebral ischemia in rats. *J. Cereb. Blood Flow Metab.* **18:** 1239-1247, 1998.

Fujimura, M.; Morita-Fujimura, Y.; Kawase, M.; Copin, J.-C.; Calagui, B.; Epstein, C.J.; Chan, P.H. Manganese superoxide dismutase mediates the early release of mitochondrial cytochrome c and subsequent DNA fragmentation after permanent focal cerebral ischemia in mice. *J. Neurosci.* **19:** 3414-3422, 1999.

Fukuda, T.; Nakano, S.; Yoshiya, I.; Hashimoto, P.H. Persistent degenerative state of non-pyramidal neurons in the CA1 region of the gerbil hippocampus following transient forebrain ischemia. *Neuroscience* **53:** 23-38, 1993.

Fuller, S., Storey, E.; Li, Q.X.; Smith, A.I.; Beyreuther, K.; Masters, C.L. Intracellular production of βA4 amyloid of Alzheimer's disease: modulation by phosphoramidon and lack of coupling to the secretion of the amyloid precursor protein. *Biochemistry* **34:** 8091-8098, 1995.

Gasparini, L.; Racchi, M.; Binetti, G.; Trabucchi, M.; Solerte, S.B.; Alkon, D.; Etcheberrigaray, R.; Gibson, G.; Blass, J.; Paoletti, R.; Govoni, S. Peripheral markers in testing pathophysiological hypotheses and diagnosing Alzheimer's disease. *FASEB J.* **12:** 17-34, 1998.

Gaykema, R.P.; Nyakas, C.; Horvath, E.; Hersh, L.B.; Majtenyi, C.; Luiten, P.G.M. Cholinergic fiber aberrations in nucleus basalis lesioned rat and Alzheimer's disease. *Neurobiol.* Aging **13:** 441-448, 1992.

Gentleman, S.M.; Greenberg, B.D.; Savage, M.J.; Noori, M.; Newman, S.J.; Roberts, G.W.; Griffin, S.T.; Graham, D.I. $A\beta_{42}$ is the predominant form of amyloid β-protein in the brains of short-term survivors of head injury. *NeuroReport* **8:** 1519-1522, 1997.

Ghribi, O.; Lapierre, L.; Girard, M.; Ohayon, M.; Nalbantoglu, J.; Massicotte, G. Hypoxia-induced loss of synaptic transmission is exacerbated in hippocampal slices of transgenic mice expressing C-terminal fragments of Alzheimer amyloid precursor protein. *Hippocampus* **9:** 201-205, 1999.

Gibson, G.E.; Zhang, H.; Aheu, K.F.; Bogdanovich, N.; Lindsay, J.G.; Lannfelt, L.; Vestling, M.; Cowburn, R.F. *Ann. Neurol.* **44:** 676-681, 1998.

Goldsmith, H.S. Treatment of Alzheimer's disease by transposition of the omentum. *Ann. NY Acad. Sci.* **977:** 454-467, 2002.

Gòmez-Isla, T.; West, H.L.; Rebeck, G.W.; Harr, S.D.; Growdon, J.H.; Locascio, J.J.; Perls, T.T.; Lipsitz, L.A.; Hyman, B.T. Clinical and pathological correlates of apolipoprotein E ε4 in Alzheimer's disease. *Ann. Neurol.* **39:** 62-70, 1996.

Gòmez-Isla, T.; Hollister, R.; West, H.L.; Mui, S.; Growdon, J.H.; Petersen, R.C.; Parisi, J.E.; Hyman, B.T. Neuronal loss correlates with but exceeds neurofibrillary tangles in Alzheimer's disease. *Ann. Neurol.* **41:** 17-24, 1997.

Green, K.N.; Peers, C. Amyloid β peptides mediate hypoxic augmentation of Ca^{2+} channels. *J. Neurochem.* **77:** 953-956, 2001.

Growdon, J.H.; Locascio, J.J.; Corkin, S.; Gomez-Isla, T.; Hyman, B.T. Apolipoprotein E genotype does not influence rates of cognitive decline in Alzheimer's disease. *Neurology* **47:** 444-448, 1996.

Haass, C.; Selkoe, D. Cellular processing of β-amyloid precursor protein and the genesis of amyloid β-peptide. *Cell* **75:** 1039-1042, 1993.

Hadland, B.K.; Manley, N.R.; Su, D.; Longmore, G.D.; Moore, C.L.; Wolfe, M.S.; Schroeter, E.H.; Kopan, R. γ-Secretase inhibitors repress thymocyte development. *Proc. Natl. Acad. Sci. USA* **98:** 7487-7491, 2001.

Hardy J. Amyloid, the presenilins and Alzheimer's disease. *Trends Neurosci.* **20:** 154-159, 1997.

Hatanpää, K.; Brady, D.R.; Stool, J.; Rapoport, S.I.; Chandrasekaran, K. Neuronal activity and early neurofibrillary tangles in Alzheimer's disease. *Ann. Neurol.* **40:** 411-420, 1996.

Hay, J.W.; Ernst, R.L. The economic costs of Alzheimer's disease. *Am. J. Publ. Health* **77:** 1169-1175, 1987.

He, Z.; Ibayashi, S.; Sugimori, H.; Sadoshima, K. Age-related ischemia in the brain after carotid artery occlusion – collateral blood flow and brain metabolism. *Neurochem. Res.* **22:** 37-42, 1997.

Helmuth, L. New therapies. New Alzheimer's treatments that may ease the mind. *Science* **297:** 1262-1263, 2002.

Henderson, V.W.; Paganini-Hill, A.; Miller, B.L.; Elble, R.J.; Reyes, P.F.; Shoupe, D.; McCleary, C.A.; Klein, R.A.; Hake, A.M.; Farlow, M.R. Estrogen for Alzheimer's disease in women: randomized, double-blind, placebo-controlled trial. *Neurology* **54:** 295-301, 2000.

Hensley, K.; Carney, J.M.; Mattson, M.P.; Aksenova, M.; Harris, M.; Wu, J.F.; Floyd, R.A.; Butterfield, D.A. A model for β-amyloid aggregation and neurotoxicity based on free radical generation by the peptide: relevance to Alzheimer disease. *Proc. Natl. Acad. Sci. USA* **91:** 3270-3274, 1994.

Herholtz, K.; Schopphoff, H.S.; Schmidt, M.; Mielke, R.; Escher, W.; Scheidhauer, K.; Schicha, H.; Heiss, W.-D.; Ebmeier, K. Direct comparison of spatially normalized PET and CPECT scans in Alzheimer's disease. *J. Nucl. Med.* **43:** 21-26, 2002.

Hirai, K.; Aliev, G.; Nunomura, A.; Fujioka, H.; Russell, R.L.; Atwood, C.S.; Johnson, A.B.; Kress, Y.; Vinters, H.V.; Tabaton, M.; Shimohama, S.; Cash, A.D.; Siedlak, S.L.; Harris, P.L.; Jones, P.K.; Petersen, R.B.; Perry, G.; Smith, M.A. Mitochondrial abnormalities in Alzheimer's disease. *J. Neurosci.* **21:** 3017-3023, 2001.

Hock, C.; Villringer, K.; Müller-Spahm, F.; Wenzel, R.; Heekeren, H.; Schuh-Hofer, S.; Hofmann, M.; Minoshima, S.; Schwaiger, M.; Dirnagl, U.; Villringer, A. Decrease in aprietal cerebral hemoglobin oxygenation during performance of a verbal fluency task in patients with Alzheimer's disease monitored by means of near-infrared spectroscopy (NIRS) – correlation with simultaneous rCBF-PET measurements. *Brain Res.* **651:** 134-142, 1997.

Hoffman, J.M.; Welsh-Bohmer, K.A.; Hanson, M.; Crain, B.; Hulette, C.; Earl, N.; Coleman, R.E. FDG PET imaging in patients with pathologically verified dementia. *J. Nucl. Med.* **41:**1920–1928, 2000.

Honer, W.G.; Prohovnik, I.; Smith, G.; Lucas, L.R. Scoplamine reduces frontal cortex perfusion. *J. Cereb. Blood Flow Metab.* **8:** 635-641, 1988.

Hsiao, K.; Chapman, P.; Nilsen, S.; Eckman, C.; Harigaya, Y.; Younkin, S.; Yang, F.; Cole, G. Correlative memory deficits, Aβ elevation, and amyloid plaques in transgenic mice. *Science* **274:** 99-102, 1996.

Hyman, B.T.; Smith, C.; Buldyrev, I.; Whelan, C.; Brown, H.; Tang, M.X.; Mayeux, R. Autoantibodies to amyloid-β and Alzheimer's disease. *Ann. Neurol.* **49:** 808-810, 2001.

Ikegaya, Y.; Matsuura, S.; Ueno, S.; Baba, A.; Yamada, M.K.; Nishiyama, N.; Matsuki, N. β-Amyloid enhances glial glutamate uptake activity and attenuates synaptic efficacy. *J. Biol. Chem.* **277:** 32180-32186, 2002.

Irizarry, M.C.; McNamara, M.; Fedorchak, K.; Hsiao, K.; Hyman, B.T. APP_{SW} transgenic mice develop age-related deposits and neuropil abnormalities, but no neuronal loss in CA1. *J. Neuropathol. Exp. Neurol.* **56:** 965-973, 1997.

Itoh, A.; Akake, T.; Sokabe, M.; Nitta, A.; Iida, R.; Olariu, A.; Yamada, K.; Nabeshima, T. Impairment of long-term potentiation in hippocampal slices of β-amyloid-infused rats. *Eur. J. Pharmacol.* **382:** 167-175, 1999.

Iwata, N.; Tsubuki, S.; Takaki, Y.; Watanabe, K.; Sekiguchi, M.; Hosoki, E.; Kawashima-Morishima, M.; Lee, H.J.; Hama, E.; Sekine-Aizawa, Y.; Saido, T.C. Identification of the major Aβ-42-degrading catabolic pathway in brain parenchyma: suppression leads to biochemical and pathological deposition. *Nature Med.* **6:** 143-150, 2000.

Iwata, N.; Tsubuki, S.; Takaki, Y.; Shirotani, K.; Lu, B.; Gerard, N.P.; Gerard, C.; Hama, E.; Lee, H.J.; Saido, T.C. Metabolic regulation of brain Aβ by neprilysin. *Science* **292:** 1550-1552, 2001.

Jacobson, L.; Sapolsky, R. The role of the hippocampus in feedback regulation of the hypothalamic-pipuitary-adrenocortical axis. *Endocr. Rev.* **12:** 18-24, 1991.

Jellinger, K.A.; Stadelmann, C. Problems of cell death in neurodegeneration and Alzheimer's disease. *J. Alzheimers Dis.* **3:** 31-40, 2001.

Jendroska, K.; Hoffmann, O.M.; Patt, S. Amyloid b peptide and precursor protein (APP) in mild and severe brain ischemia. *Ann. NY Acad. Sci.* **826:** 401–405, 1997.

Jin, K.; Mao, X.O.; Eshoo, M.W.; Nagayama, T.; Minami, M.; Simon, R.P.; Greenberg, D.A. Microarray analysis of hippocampal gene expression in global cerebral ischemia. *Ann Neurol.* **50:** 93-103, 2001.

Johnson, K.A.; Jones, K.; Holman, B.L.; Becker, J.; Spiers, P.A.; Satlin, A.; Albert, M.S. Preclinical prediction of Alzheimer's disease using SPECT. *Neurology* **50:** 1563-1571, 1998.

Kadekaro, M.; Crane, A.M.; *Sokoloff, L. Proc Natl Acad Sci USA* **82:** 6010-6013, 1985.

Kalaria, R.N. The role of cerebral ischemia in Alzheimer's disease. *Neurol. Aging* **21:** 321-330, 2000.

Kalaria, R.N. Advances in molecular genetics and pathology of cerebrovascular disorders. *Trends Neurosci.* **24:** 392-400, 2001.

Kalaria, R.N.; Harik, S.I. Reduced glucose transporter at the blood-brain barrier and in cerebral cortex in Alzheimer's disease. *J. Neurochem.* **53:** 1083-1088, 1989.

Kalaria, R.N.; Nhatti, S.U.; Lust, W.D.; Perry, G. The amyloid precursor protein in ischemic brain injury and chronic hypoperfusion. *Ann. N.Y. Acad. Sci.* **695:** 190-193, 1993.

Kalaria, R.N.; Hedera, P. Differential degeneration of the cerebral microvasculature in Alzheimer's disease. *NeuroRep.* **6:** 477-480, 1995.

Kar, S.; Seto, D.; Gaudreau, P.; Quirion, R. β-Amyloid-related peptides inhibit potassium-evoked acetylcholine release from rat hippocampal formation. *J. Neurosci.* **16:** 1034-1040, 1996.

Kar, S.; Issa, A.M.; Seto, D.; Auld, D.S.; Collier. B.; Quirion, R. Amyloid beta-peptide inhibits high-affinity choline uptake and acetylcholine release in rat hippocampal slices. *J. Neurochem.* **70:** 2179-2187, 1998.

Kim, H.-S.; Lee, J.-H.; Kim, Lee, J.-P.; E.-M.; Chang, K.-A.; Park, C.H.; Jeong, S.-J.; Wittendorp, M.C.; Seo, J.-H.; Choi, S.-H.; Suh, Y.-H. Amyloid β peptide induces cytochrome c release from isolated mitochondria. *NeuroReport* **13:** 1989-1993, 2002.

Kirino, T.; Sano, K. Selective vulnerability in the gerbil hippocampus following transient ischemia. *Acta Neuropathol.* **62:** 201-208, 1984.

Kirino, T.; Tamura, A.; Sano, K. Selective vulnerability of the hippocampus to ischemia-reversible and irreversible types of ischemic cell damage. *Prog. Brain Res.* **63:** 39-58, 1985.

Kish, S.J.; Bergeron, C.; Rajput, A.; Dozie, S.; Mastrogiacomo, F.; Chang, L.J.; Wilson, J.; Distefano, L.; Nobrega, J. Brain cytochrome oxidase in Alzheimer's disease. *J. Neurochem.* **59:** 776-779, 1992.

Kluck, R.M.; Bossy-Wetzel, E.; Green, D.R.; Newmeyer, D.D. The release of cytochrome c from mitochondria: a primary site for Bcl-2 regulation of apoptosis. *Science* **275:** 1132-1136, 1997.

Knapp, L.T.; Klann, E. Potentiation of hippocampal synaptic transmission by superoxide requires the oxidative activation of protein kinase C. *J. Neurosci.* **22:** 674-683, 2002.

Kogure, K.; Kato, H. Altered gene expression in cerebral ischemia. *Stroke* **24:** 2121–2127, 1993.

Koistinaho, J.; Pyykonen, I.; Keinanen, R.; Hokfelt, T. Expression of b-amyloid precursor protein mRNAs following transient focal ischaemia. *NeuroReport* **7:** 2727–2731, 1996.

Kokmen, E.; Whisnant, J.P.; O'Fallon, W.N.; Chu, C.P.; Beard, C.M., Dementia after ischemic stroke: a population-based study in Rochester, Minesota (1960-1984). *Neurology* **46:** 154-159, 1996.

Kornhauser, JM.; Greenberg, M.E. A kinase to remember: dual roles for MAP kinase in long-term memory. *Neuron* **18:** 839-842, 1997.

Kotila, M.; Waltimo, O.; Niemi, M.-L.; Laaksonen, R. Dementia after stroke. *Eur. Neurol.* **25:** 134-140, 1986.

Kuida, K.; Haydar, T.F.; Kuan, C.-Y.; Gu, Y.; Taya, C.; Karasuyama, H.; Su, M.S.-S.; Rakic, P.; Flavell, R.A. Reduced apoptosis and cytochrome c-mediated caspase activation in mice lacking caspase 9. *Cell* **94:** 325-337, 1998.

Lammich, S.; Kojiro, E.; Postina, R.; Gilbert, S.; Pfeiffer, R.; Jasionowski, M.; Haass, C.; Fahrenholz, F. Constitutive and regulated alpha-secretase cleavage of Alzheimer's amyloid precursor protein by a disintegrin metalloprotease. *Proc. Natl. Acad. Sci. USA* **96:** 3922–3927, 1999.

Lansbury, P.T. Jr. Inhibition of amyloid formation: a strategy to delay the onset of Alzheimer's disease. *Curr. Opin. Chem. Biol.* **1:** 260-267, 1997.

Laughlin, S.B.; de Ruyter van Steveninck, R.R.; Anderson, J.C. The metabolic cost of neuronal information. *Nature Neurosci.* **1:** 36-41, 1998.

Lauritzen, M. Relationship of spikes, synaptic activity, and local changes of cerebral blood flow. *J. Cereb. Blood Flow Metab.* **21:** 1367-1383, 2001.

Lazarov, O.; Lee, M.; Peterson, D.A.; Sisodia, S.S. Evidence that synaptically released β-amyloid accumulates as extracellular deposits in the hippocampus of transgenic mice. *J. Neurosci,* **22:** 9785-9793, 2002.

Le, D.A.; Lipton, S.A. Potential and current use of N-methyl-D-aspartate (NMDA) receptor antagonists in disease of aging. *Drugs Aging* **18:** 717-724, 2001.

Leys, D.; Pasquier, F.; Scheletens, P.; editors, Stroke and Alzheimer's Disease. Current Issues in Neurodegenerative Diseases. **9:** 1998; The Hague- The Netherland: Holland Academic Graphics.

Li, P.; Nijhawan, D.; Budihardjo, I.; Srinivasula, S.M.; Ahmad, M.; Alnemri, E.S.; Wang, X. Cytochrome c and dATP-dependent formation of Apaf-1/caspase-9 complex initiates an apoptotic protease cascade. *Cell* **91:** 479-489, 1997.

Li, H.; Zhu, H.; Xu, C.-J.; Yuan, J. Cleavage of BID by caspase 8 mediates the mitochondrial damage in the Fas pathway of apoptosis. *Cell* **94:** 491-501, 1998.

Li, Y.M.; Xu, M.; Lai, M.T.; Huang, Q.; Castro, J.L.; DiMuzio-Mower, J.; Harrison, T.; Lellis, C.; Nadin, A.; Neduvelil, J.G.; Register, R.B.; Sardana, M.K.; Shearman, M.S.; Smith, A.L.; Shi, X.P.; Yin, K.C.; Shafer, J.A.; Gardell, S.J. Photoactivated γ-secretase inhibitors directed to the active site covalently label presenilin 1. *Nature* **405:** 689-694, 2000.

Liguri, G.; Taddei, N.; Nassi, P.; Latorraca, S.; Nediani, C.; Sorbi, S. Changes in Na^+ K^+-ATPase, Ca^{2+}-ATPase and some soluble enzymes related to energy metabolism in brains of patients with Alzheimer's disease. *Neurosci. Lett.* **112:** 338-342, 1990.

Lim, G.P.; Yang, F.; Chu, T.; Chen, P.; Beech, W.; Teter, B.; Tran, T.; Ubeda, O.; Ashe, K.H.; Frautschy, S.A.; Cole, G.M. Ibuprofen suppresses plaque pathology and inflammation in a mouse model for Alzheimer's disease. *J. Neurosci.* **20:** 5709-5714, 2000.

Lipton, P. Ischemic cell death in brain neurons. *Physiol. Rev.***79:** 1431-1568, 1999.

Liu, X.; Kim, C.N.; Yang, J.; Jemmerson, R.; Wang, X. Induction of apoptotic program in cell-free extracts: requirement for dATP and cytochrome c. *Cell* **86:** 147-157, 1996.

Liu, X.; Zou, H.; Slaughter, C.; Wang, X. DFF, a heterodimeric protein that functions downstream of caspase-3 to trigger DNA fragmentation during apoptosis. *Cell* **89:** 175-184, 1997.

Liu, X.-Y.; Passant, U.; Risberg, J.; Warkentin, S.; Brun, A. Synapse density related to cerebral blood flow and symptomatology in frontal lobe degeneration and Alzheimer's disease. *Dement. Geriat. Cogn. Disord.* **10 (suppl. 1):** 64-70, 1999.

Longstreth, W.T.; Inui, T.S.; Cobb, L.A.; Copass, M. Neurologic recovery after out-of-hospital cardiac arrest. *Ann. Intern. Med.* **95:** 580-592, 1983.

Lowe, P.N.; Perham, R.N. Bromopyruvate as an active-site-directed inhibitor of the pyruvate dehydrogenase multienzyme complex from *Escherichia* coli. Biochemistry **23:** 91-97, 1984.

Luo, X.; Budihardjo, I.; Zou, H.; Slaughter, C.; Wang, X. Bid, a Bcl-2 interacting protein, mediates cytochrome c release from mitochondria in response to activation of cell surface death receptors. *Cell* **94:** 481-490, 1998.

Luchsinger, J.A.; Tang, M.-X.; Shea, S.; Mayeux, R. Antioxidant vitamin intake and risk of Alzheimer disease. *Arch Neurol.* **60:** 203-208, 2003.

MacManus, J.P.; Buchan, A.M.; Hill, I.E.; Rasquinha, I.; Preston, E. Global ischemia can cause DNA fragmentation indicative of apoptosis in rat brain. *Neurosci. Lett.* **164:** 89-92, 1993.

Maldonado, M.E.; Oh, K.-J.; Frey, P.A. Studies on *Escherichia* coli pyruvate dehydrogenase complex. *J. Biol. Chem.* **247:** 2711-2716, 1972.

Mancardi, G.L.; Perdelli, F.; Leonardi, A.; Bugiani, O. Thickening of the basement membrane of cortical capillaries in Alzheimer's disease. *Acta Neuropathol.* **49:** 79-83, 1980.

Manning, C.A.; Ragozzino, M.E.; Gold, P.E. Glucose enhancement of memory in patients with probable senile dementia of the Alzheimer type. *Neurobiol. Aging* **14:** 523-528, 1993.

Marchbanks, R.M.; Kessler, P.D. The independency of choline transport and acetylcholine synthesis. *J. Neurochem.* **39:** 1424-1433, 1982.

Marin, A.J.; Friston, K.J.; Colebatch, J.G.; Frackowiak, R. Decreases in regional cerebral blood flow with normal aging. *J. Cereb. Blood Flow Metab.* **11:** 684-689, 1991.

Mark, R.J.; Blanc, E.M.; Mattson, M.P. *Mol. Neurobiol.* **12:** 211-224, 1996.

Martin, L.J.; Pardo, C.A.; Cork, L.C.; Price, D.L. Synaptic pathology and glial responses to neuronal injury precede the formation of senile plaques and amyloid deposits in the aging cerebral cortex. *Am. J. Pathol.* **145:** 1358-1381, 1994.

Maruyama, M.; Arai, H.; Sugita, M.; Tanji, H.; Higuchi, M.; Okamura, N.; Matsui, T.; Higuchi, S.; Matsushita, S.; Yoshida, H.; Sasaki, H. Cerebrospinal fluid amyloid β1-42 levels in the mild cognitive impairment age of Alzheimer's disease. *Exp. Neurol.* **172:** 433-436, 2001.

Masaki, K.H.; Losonczy, K.G.; Izmirlian, G.; Foley, D.J.; Ross, G.W.; Petrovitch, H.; Havlik, R.; White, L.R. Association of vitamin E and C supplement use with cognitive function and dementia in elderly men. *Neurology* **54:** 1265-1272, 2000.

Masliah, E.; Terry, R.K.; DeTeresa, R.; Hansen, L. Immunohistochemical quantitation of the synapse-related protein synaptophysin in Alzheimer's disease. *Neurosci. Lett.* **103:** 234-239, 1989.

Mastrogiacomo, F.; Bergeron, C.; Kish, S.J. Brain α-ketoglutarate dehydrogenase activity in Alzheimer's disease. *J. Neurochem.* **6:** 2007-2014, 1993.

Matsuoka, Y.; Saito, M.; LaFrancois, J.; Saito, M.; Gaynor, K.; Olm, V.; Wang, L.; Casey, E.; Lu, Y.; Shiratori, C.; Lenere, C.; Duff, K. Novel therapeutic approach for the treatment of Alzheimer's disease by peripheral administration of agents with high affinity to β-amyloid. *J. Neurosci.* **23:** 29-33, 2003.

Mattson, M.P. Contributions of mitochondrial alterations, resulting from *BAD* genes and a hostile environment, to the pathogenesis of Alzheimer's disease. *Internat. Rev. Neurobiol.* **53:** 387-409, 2002.

Mattson, M.P.; Duan, W. "Apoptotic" biochemical cascades in synaptic compartments: Role in adaptive plasticity and neurodegenerative disorders. *J. Neurosci. Res.* **58:** 152-166, 1999.

Mattson, M.P.; Liu, D. Energetics and oxidative stress in synaptic plasticity and neurodegenerative disorders. *NeuroMol. Med.* **2:** 215-231, 2002.

Maurer, I.; Zierz, S.; Moler, H.J. A selective defect of cytochrome c oxidase is present in brain of Alzheimer's disease patients. *Neurobiol. Aging* **21:** 455-462, 2000.

Mecocci, P.; MacGarvey, U.; Beal, M.F. *Ann. Neurol.* **36:** 747-751, 1994.

Mega, M.S.; Chu, T.; Mazziotta, J.C.; Trivedi, K.H.; Thompson, P.M.; Shah, A.; Cole, G.; Frautschy, S.A.; Toga, A.W. Mapping biochemistry to metabolism: PDG-PET and amyloid burden in Alzheimer's disease. *NeuroReport* **10:** 2911-2917, 1999.

Melo, J.B.; Agostinho, P.; Oliveira, C.R. Amyloid β-peptide 25-35 reduces [^{3}H]acetylcholine release in retinal neuros. Involvement of metabolic dysfunction. *Amyloid* **9:** 221-228, 2002.

Mielke, R.; Herholz, K.; Grond, M.; Kessler, J.; Heis,, W.D. Clinical deterioration in probable Alzheimer's disease correlates with progressive metabolic impairment of association areas. Dementia **5:** 36-41, 1994.

Misonou, H.; Morishima-Kawashima, M.; Ihara, Y. Oxidative stress induces intracellular accumulation of amyloid beta-protein in human neuroblastoma cells. *Biochemistry* **39:** 6951-6959, 2000.

Mooradian, A.D.; Chung, H.C.; Shah, G.N. GLUT-1 expression in the cerebra of patients with Alzheimer's disease. *Neurobiol. Aging* **18:** 469-474, 1997.

Morris, J.C. Challenging assumptions about Alzheimer's disease: mild cognitive impairment and the cholinergic hypothesis. *Ann. Neurol.* **51:** 143-144, 2002.

Morris, R.G.M.; Garrud, P.; Rawlins, J.N.P.; O'Keefe, J. Place navigation impaired in rats with hippocampal lesions. *Nature* **297:** 681-683, 1982.

Morris, R.G.M.; Schenck, F.; Tweedie, F.; Jarrad, L.E. Ibotenate lesion of hippocampus and/or subiculum: Dissociating components of allocentric spatial learning. *Eur. J. Neurosci.* **2:** 1016-1028, 1990.

Morris, M.C.; Beckett, L.A.; Scherr, P.A.; Hebert, L.E.; Bennett, D.A.; Field, T.S.; Evans, D.A. Vitamin E and vitamin C supplement use and risk of incident Alzheimer's disease. *Alzheimer Dis. Assoc. Disord.* **12:** 121-126, 1998.

Morris, M.C.; Evans, D.A.; Bienias, J.L.; Tangney, C.C.; Bennett, D.A.; Aggarwal, N.; Schneider, J.; Wilson, R.S. Dietary fats and the risk of incident Alzheimer disease. *Arch Neurol.* **60:** 194-200, 2003.

Morsch, R.; Simon, W.; Coleman, P.D. Neurons may live for decades with neurofibrillary tangles. *J. Neuropathol. Exp. Neurol.* **58:** 188-197, 1999.

Mudrick, L.A.; Baimbridge, K.G. Long-term structural changes in the rat hippocampal formation following cerebral ischemia. *Brain Res.* **493:** 179-184, 1989.

Muir, J.L.; Page, K.J.; Sirinathsinghji, D.J.; Robbins, T.W.; Everitt, B.J. Ectitoxic lesions of basal forebrain cholinergic neurons: effects on learning, memory and attention. *Behav. Brain Res.* **57:** 123-131, 1993.

Mulnard, R.A.; Cotman, C.W.; Kawas, S.; van Dyck, C.H.; Sano, M.; Doody, R.; Koss, E.; Pfeiffer, E.; Jin, S.; Gamst, A.; Grundman, M.; Thomas, R.; Thal, L.J. Estrogen replacement therapy for the Alzheimer's Disease Cooperative Study. Estrogen replacement therapy for treatment of mild to moderate Alzheimer disease: a randomized clinical trial. *JAMA* **283:** 1007-1015, 2000.

Munch, G.; Schinzel, R.; Loske, C.; Wong, A.; Durany, N.; Li, J.J.; Vlassara, H.; Smith, M.A.; Perry, G.; Riederer, P. Alzheimer's disease – synergistic effects of glucose deficit, oxidative stress and advanced glycation endproducts. *J. Neural Transm.* **105:** 439-461, 1998.

Murphy, D.D.; Cole, N.B.; Greenberger, V.; Segal, M. Estrogen increases dendritic spine density by reducing GABA neurotransmission in hippocampal neurons. *J. Neurosci.* **18:** 2550-2559, 1998.

Mutisya, E.M.; Bowling, A.C.; Beal, M.F. Cortical cytochrome oxidase activity is reduced in Alzheimer's disease. *J. Neurochem.* **63:** 2179-2184, 1994.

Nakano, S.; Kogure, K.; Fujikura, H. Ishcemia-induced slowly progressive damage in the rat brain. *Neuroscience* **38:** 115-124, 1990.

Nalbantoglu, J.; Tirado-Santiago, G.; Lahsaïni, A.; Poirier, J.; Goncalves, O.; Verge, G.; Momoli, F.; Welner, S.A.; Massicotte, G.; Julien, J.-P.; Shapiro, M.L. Impaired learning and LTP in mice expressing the carboxy terminus of the Alzheimer amyloid precursor protein. *Nature* **387:** 500-505, 1997.

Naslund, J.; Haroutunian, V.; Mohs, R.; Davis, K.L.; Davies, P.; Greengard, P.; Buxbaum, J.D. Correlation between elevated levels of amyloid beta-peptide in the brain and cognitive decline. *JAMA* **283:** 1571-1577, 2000.

Nelson, A.; Sowinski, P.; Hodges, H. Differential effects of global ischemia on delayed matching- and non-matching-to-position tasks in the water maze and Skinner box. *Neurobiol. Learn. Mem.* **67:** 228-247, 1997a.

Nelson, A.; Lebessi, A.; Sowinski, P.; Hodges, H. Comparison of effects of global cerebral ischaemia on spatial learning in the standard and radial water maze: relationship of hippocampal damage to performance. *Behav. Brain Res.***85:** 93-115, 1997b.

Newmeyer, D.D.; Green, D.R. Surviving the cytochrome seas. *Neuron* **21:** 653-655, 1998.

Newmeyer, D.D.; Ferguson-Miller, S. Mitochondria: releasing power for life and unleashing the machineries of death. *Cell* **112:** 481-490, 2003.

Nicoll, J.A.R.; Wilkinson, D.; Holmes, C.; Steart, P.; Markham, H.; Weller, R.O. Neuropathology of human Alzheimer disease after immunization with amyloid-β peptide: a case report. *Nat. Med.* **in press:** 1-5, 2003.

Nitatori, T.; Sato, N.; Waguri, S.; Karasawa, Y.; Araki, H.; Shibanai, K.; Kiminami, E.; Uchiyama, Y. Delayed neuronal death in the CA1 pyramidal cell layer of the gerbil hippocampus following transient ischemia is apoptosis. *J. Neurosci.* **15:** 1001-1011, 1995.

Niwa, K.; Kazama, K.; Younkin, S.G.; Carlson, G.A.; Iadecola, C. Alterations in Cerebral Blood Flow and Glucose Utilization in Mice Overexpressing the Amyloid Precursor Protein. *Neurol. Aging* **9:** 61-68, 2002.

Nordberg, A.; Lilja, A.; Lundqvist, H.; Hartvig, P.; Amberla, K.; Viitanen, M.; Jobansson, M.; Hellstrom-Lindahl, E.; Bjurling, P.; et al. Tacrine restores cholinergic nicotinic receptors and glucose metabolism in Alzheimer patients as visualized by positron emission tomography. *Neurobiol. Aging* **13:** 747-758, 1992.

Nordberg, A. Long-term treatment with tacrine: Effects on progression of Alzheimer's disease as determined by functional brain studies. In Iqbal, K.; Mortimer, J.A.; Winbland, B.; Wisniewski, H.M. (Eds.) Research Advances in Alzheimer's Disease and Related disorders. John Wiley and Sons, New York, pp. 293-298, 1995.

Nunn, J.A.; LePeillet, E.; Netto, C.A.; Hodges, H.; Gray, J.A.; Meldrum, B.S. Global ischemia: hippocampal pathology and spatial deficits in the water maze. *Behav. Brain Res.* **62:** 41-54, 1994.

Nunomura, A.; Perry, G.; Hirai, K.; Aliev, G.; Takeda, A.; Chiba, S.; Smith, M.A. Neuronal RNA oxidation in Alzheimer disease and Down's syndrome. *Ann. NY Acad. Sci.* **893:** 362-364, 1999.

Nunomura, A.; Perry, G.; Pappolla, M.A.; Fridland, R.P.; Hirai, K.; Chiba, S.; Smith, M.A. Neuronal oxidative stress precedes amyloid-β deposition in Down's syndrome. *J. Neuropathol. Exp. Neurol.* **59:** 1011-1017, 2000.

Nunomura, A.; Perry, G.; Aliev, G.; Hirai, K.; Takeda, A.; Balrai, E.K.; Jones, P.K.; Ghanbari, H.; Wataya, T.; Shimohama, S.; Chiba, S.; Atwood, C.S.; Petersen, R.B.; Smith, M.A. Oxidative damage is the earliest event in Alzheimer disease. *J. Neuropathol. Exp. Neurol.* **60:** 759-767, 2001.

O'Keefe, J.; Nadel, L. Spatial behavior. In: *The Hippocampus as a Cognitive Map*, O'Keefe, J. and Nadel, L. (ed.) Oxford:Clarendon:Press, pp. 62-101, 1978.

Olsen, G.M.; Scheel-Kruger, J.; Moller, A.; Jensen, L.H. Does neuronal damage of CA1 relate to spatial memory performance of rats subjected to transient forebrain ischemia? *Acta Neurol. Scand.* **89:** 204-209, 1994.

Olton, D.S. Spatial memory. *Sci. Am.* **236:** 82-98, 1977.

Olton, D.S.; Papas, B. Spatial memory and hippocampal function. *Neuropsychology* **17:** 669-682, 1979.

Onodera, H.; Kogure, K. Mapping second messenger systems in the rat hippocampus after transient forebrain ishcemia: *in vitro* [^{3}H]forskolin and [^{3}H]inositol, 4,5,-triphosphate binding. *Brain Res.* **487:** 343-349, 1989.

Onodera, H.; Aoki, H.; Yae, T.; Kogure, K. Post-ischemic synaptic plasticity in the rat hippocampus after long-term survival: a histochemical and autoradiographic study. *Neuroscience* **38:** 125-136, 1990.

Onodera, H.; Araki, T.; Kogure, K. Protein kinase C activity in the rat hippocampus after forebrain ischemia: autoradiographic analysis by [^{3}H]phorbal 12,13-dibutyrate. *Brain Res.* **481:** 1-7, 1989.

Onodera, H.; Sato, G.; Kogure, K. Quantitative autoradiographic analysis of muscarinic cholinergic and adenosine A1 binding sites after transient forebrain ischemia in the gerbil. *Brain Res.* **415:** 309-322, 1987.

Orgogozo, J.-M.; Rigaud, A.-S.; Stöffler, A.; Möbius, H.-J.; Forette, F. Efficacy and safety of memantine in patients with mild to moderate vascular dementia: a randomized, placebo-controlled trial (MMM 300). *Stroke* **33:** 1834-1839, 2002.

Oster-Granite, M.L.; McPhie, D.L.; Greenan, J.; Neve, R.L. Age-dependent neuronal and synaptic degeneration in mice transgenic for the terminus of the amyloid precursor protein. *J. Neurosci.* **16:** 6732-6741, 1996.

Osterlund, M.K.; Grandien, K.; Keller, E.; Hurd, Y.L. The human brain has distinct regional expression patterns of estrogen receptor α mRNA isoforms derived from alternative promoters. *J. Neurochem.* **75:** 1390-1397, 2000.

Ouchi, Y.; Fukuyama, H.; Ogawa, M.; Yamauchi, H.; Kimura, J.; Magata, Y.; Yonekura, Y.; Konishi, J. Cholinergic projection from the basal forebrain and cerebral glucose metabolism in rats: a dynamic PET study. J. Cereb. Blood Flow Metab. **16:** 34-41, 1996.

Ouchi, Y.; Nobezawa, S.; Okada, H.; Yoshikawa, E.; Futatsubashi, M.; Kaneko, M. Altered glucose metabolism in the hippocampal head in memory impairment. *Neurology* **51:** 136-142, 1998.

Pappas, B.A.; de la Torre, J.C.; Davidson, C.; Keyes, M.; Fortin, T. Chronic reduction of cerebral blood flow in the adult rat: late emerging CA1 cell loss and memory function. *Brain Res.* **708:** 50-58, 1996.

Pappas, B.A.; Davidson, C.M.; Bennett, S.A.; de la Torre, J.C.; Fortin, T.; Tenniswood, M.P. Chronic ischemia: memory impairment and neural pathology in the rat. *Ann. N.Y. Acad. Sci.* **826:** 498-501, 1997.

Paresce, D.; Ghosh, R.; Maxfirled, F. Microglial cells internalize aggregates of the Alzheimer's disease amyloid β-protein via a scavenger receptor. *Neuron* **17:** 553-565, 1996.

Pardridge, W.M. *Brain Drug Targeting: the Future of Brain Drug Development*, Cambridge, UK: Cambridge University Press, 2001.

Parker, W.D.; Parks, J.K. Cytochrome *c* oxidase in Alzheimer's disease brain. *Neurology* **45:** 482-486, 1995.

Parker, W.D.; Parks, J.K.; Filley, C.M.; Kleinschmidt-Demasters, B.K. Electron transport chain defects in Alzheimer's disease brain. *Neurology* **44:** 1090-1096, 1994.

Pasquier, F.; Leys, D.; Scheltens, P. The influence of coincidental vascular pathology on symptomatology and course of Alzheimer's disease. *J. Neural. Transm.* **54 (Suppl):** 117-127, 1998.

Passero, S.; Rocchi, R.; Vatti, G.; Burgalassi, L.; Battistini, N. Quantitative EEG mapping, regional cerebral blood flow, and neuropsychological function in Alzheimer's disease. *Dementia* **6:** 148-156, 1995.

Paulsen, O.; Moser, E.I. A model of hippocampal memory encoding and retrieval: GABAergic control of synaptic plasticity. *Trends Neurosci.* **21:** 273-278, 1998.

Pederson, P.M.; Jørgensen, H.S.; Nakayama, H.; Raaschou, H.O.; Olsen, T.S. The incidence and consequences of reduced general cognitive function in acute stroke. The Copenhagen stroke study. *Cerebrovasc. Dis.* **6 (Suppl 2):** 17, 1996.

Peppard, R.F.; Martin, W.R.W.; Carr, G.D.; Grochowski, E.; Schulzer, M.; Guttman, M.; McGeer, P.L. Phillips, A.G.; Tsui, J.K.C.; Calne, D.B. Cerebral glucose metabolism in Parkinson's disease with and without dementia. *Arch. Neurol.* **49:** 1262-1268, 1992.

Perry, E.K.; Perry, R.H.; Tomlinson, B.E.; Blessed, G.; Gibson, P.H. Coenzyme A-acetylating enzymes in Alzheimer's disease: possible cholinergic 'compartment' of pyruvate dehydrogenase. *Neurosci. Lett.* **18:** 105-110, 1980.

Peruzzi, P.; von Euw, D.; Lacombe, P. Differential cerebrovascular effects of physostigmine and tacrine in cortical areas deafferented from the nucleus basalis magnocellularis suggest involvement of basalocortical projections to microvessels. *Ann. N.Y. Acad. Sci.* **903:** 394-406, 2000.

Pettegrew, J.W.; Klunk, W.E.; Kanal, E.; Panchalingam, K.; McClure, R.J. Changes in brain membrane phospholipid and high-energy phosphate metabolism precede dementia. *Neurobiol. Aging* **16:** 973-975, 1995.

Pettegrew, J.W.; Klunk, W.E.; Panchalingam, K.; McClure, R.J.; Stanley, J.A. Magnetic resonance spectroscopic changes in Alzheimer's disease. *Ann. N.Y. Acad. Sci.* **826:** 282-306, 1997.

Pettit, D.L.; Shao, Z.; Yakel, J.L. β-Amyloid$_{1-42}$ peptide directly modulates nicotinic receptors in the rat hippocampal slice. *J. Neurosci.* **21:RC120:** 1-5, 2001.

Pluta, R.; Barcikowska, M.; Dębicki, G.; Ryba, M.; Januszewski, S. Changes in amyloid precursor protein and apolipoprotein E immunoreactivity following ischemic brain injury in rat with long-term survival: influence of idebenone treatment. *Neurosci. Lett.* **232:** 95-98, 1997.

Pluta, R.; Barcikowska, M.; Mossakowski, M.J.; Zelman, I. Cerebral accumulation of β-amyloid following ischemic brain injury with long-term survival. *Acta Neurochir.* **[Suppl.] 71:** 206-208, 1998.

Polvikoski, T.; Sulkava, R.; Myllykangas, L.; Notkola, I.L.; Niinisto, L.; Verkkoniemi, A.; Kainulainen, K.; Kontula, K.; Perez-Tur, J.; Hardy, J.; Haltia, M. Prevalence of Alzheimer's disease in a very elderly people: a prospective neuropathological study. *Neurology* **56:** 1690-1696, 2001.

Potkin, S.; Anand, R.; Fleming, K.; Alva, G.; Keator, D.; Carreon, D.; Messina, J.; Wu, J.C.; Hartman, R.; Fallon, J.H. Brain metabolic and clinical effects of rivastigmine in Alzheimer's disease. *Internat. J. Neuropsychopharmacol.* **4:** 223-230, 2001.

Pulsinelli, J.P.; Brierley, J.B. A new model of bilateral hemispheric ischemia in the unanesthetized rat. *Stroke* **10:** 267-272, 1979.

Rapoport, S.I.; Hatanpää, K.; Brady, D.R.; Chandrasekaran, K. Brain energy metabolism, cognitive function and down-regulated oxidative phosphorylation in Alzheimer's disease. *Neurodegeneration* **5:** 473-476, 1996.

Reed, J.C. Cytochrome c: can't live with it — can't live without it. *Cell* **91:** 559-562, 1997.

Reiman, E.M.; Caselli, R.J.; Yun, L.S.; Chen, K.; Bandy, D.; Minoshima, S.; Thibodeau, S.N.; Osborne, D. Preclinical evidence of Alzheimer's disease in persons homozygous for the epsilon 4 allele for apolipoprotein E. *N. Eng. J. Med.* **334:** 752-758, 1996.

Reis, D.J.; Golanov, E.V.; Ruggiero, D.A.; Sun, M.-K. Sympathoexcitatory neurons of the rostral ventrolateral medulla are oxygen sensors and essential elements in the tonic and reflex control of the systemic and cerebral circulations. *J. Hypertens.* **12 (suppl. 10):** S159-S180, 1994.

Rempel-Clower, N.L.; Zola, S.M.; Squire, L.R.; Amaral, D.G. Three cases of enduring memory impairment following bilateral damage limited to the hippocampal formation. *J. Nuerosci.* **16:** 5233-5255, 1996.

Resnick, S.M.; Maki, P.M.; Golski, S.; Kraut, M.; Zonderman, A. Effects of estrogen replacement therapy on PET cerebral blood flow and neuropsychological performance. *Horm. Behav.* **34:** 171-182, 1998.

Rhodin, J.A.; Thoman, T. A vascular connection to Alzheimer's disease. *Microcirculation* **8:** 207-220, 2001.

Rodrigueza, G.; Vitalia, P.; Calvinib, P.; Bordonia, C.; Girtler, N.; Taddeic, G.; Marianic, G.; Nobilia, F. Hippocampal perfusion in mild Alzheimer's disease. *Psychiat. Res. Neuroimag.* **100:** 65-74, 2000.

Rogers, J.; Kirby, L.C.; Hempelman, S.R.; Berry, D.L.; McGeer, P.L.; Kaszniak, A.W.; Zalinski, J.; Cofield, M.; Mansukhani, L.; Willson, P.; et al. Clinical trial of indomethacin in Alzheimer's disease. *Neurology* **43:** 1609-1611, 1993.

Roses, A. From genes to mechanisms to therapies: lessons to be learned for neurological disorders. *Nature Med.* **2:** 267-269, 1996.

Sakamoto, S.; Ishii, K.; Sasaki, M.; Hosaka, K.; Mori, T.; Matsui, M.; Hirono, N.; Mori, E. Differences in cerebral metabolic impairment between early and late onset types of Alzheimer's disease. *J. Neurol. Sci.* **200:** 27– 32, 2002.

Salehi, A.; Swaab, D.F. Diminished neuronal metabolic activity in Alzheimer's disease. *J. Neural Transm.* **106:** 955-986, 1999.

Salehi, A.; Ravid, R.; Gonatas, N.K.; Swaab, D.F. Decreased activity of hippocampal neurons in Alzheimer's disease is not related to the presence of neurofibrillary tangles. *J. Neuropathol. Exp. Neurol.* **54:** 704-709, 1995.

Salehi, A.; Pool, C.W.; Mulder, M.; Ravid, R.; Gonatas, N.K.; Swaab, D.F. Limited effect of neuritic plaques on neuronal density in the hippocampal CA1 area of Alzheimer's patients. *Alzh. Dis. Assoc. Dis.* **12:** 77-82, 1998.

Salmon, E.; Gregoire, M.C.; Delfiore, G.; Lemaire, C.; Degueldre, C.; Franck, G.; Comar, D. Combined study of cerebral glucose metabolism and [11C]methionine accumulation in probable Alzheimer's disease using positron emission tomography. *J. Cereb. Blood Flow Metab.* **16:** 399-408, 1996.

Sano, M.; Ernesto, C.; Thomas, R.G.; Klauber, M.R.; Schafer, K.; Grundman, M.; Woodbury, P.; Growdon, J.; Cotman, C.W.; Pfeiffer, E.; Schneider, L.S.; Thal, L.J. A controlled trial of selegiline, α-tocopherol, or both as treatment for Alzheimer's disease. The Alzheimer's disease cooperative study. *N. Eng. J. Med.* **336:** 1216-1222, 1997.

Scarmeas, N.; Zarahn, E.; Anderson, K.E.; Habeck, C.G.; Hilton, J.; Flynn, J.; Marder, K.S.; Bell, K.L.; Sackeim, H.A.; Van Heertum, R.L.; Moeller, J.R.; Stern, Y. Association of life activities with cerebral blood flow in Alzheimer disease. *Arch Neurol.* **60:** 359-365, 2003.

Schagger, H.; Ohm, T.G. Human diseases with defects in oxidative phosphorylation: 2. F_1F0 ATP-synthase defects in Alzheimer's disease revealed by blue native polycrylamide gel electrophoresis. *Eur. J. Biochem.* **227:** 916-921, 1995.

Scheel, P.; Ruge, C.; Petruch, U.R.; Schoning, M. Color duplex measurement of cerebral blood flow volume in healthy adults. *Stroke* **31:** 147-150, 2000.

Scheff, S.W.; Price, D.A. Synaptic loss in the temporal lobe in Alzheimer's disease. *Ann. Neurol.* **33:** 190-199, 1993.

Scheuner, D.; Eckman, C.; Jensen, M.; Song, X.; Citron, Z.M.; Suzuki, N.; Bird, T.D.; Hardy, J.; Hutton, M.; Kukull, W.; Larson, E.; Levy-Lahad, E.; Viitanen, M.; Peskind, E.; Poorkaj, P.; Schellenberg, G.; Tanzi, R.; Wasco, W.; Lannfelt, L.; Selkoe, D.; Younkin, S. Secreted amyloid β-protein similar to that in the senile plaques of Alzheimer's disease is increased *in vivo* by the presenilin 1 and 2 and APP mutations linked to familial Alzheimer's disease. *Nature Med.* **2:** 864-869, 1996.

Schmidt-Kastner, R.; Freund, T.F. Selective vulnerability of the hippocampus in brain ischemia. *Neuroscience* **40:** 599-636, 1991.

Schott, J.M.; Fox, N.C.; Frost, C.; Scahill, M.A.; Janssen, J.C.; Chan, D.; Jenkins, R.; Rossor, M.N. Assessing the onset of structural changes in familial Alzheimer's disease. *Ann. Neurol.* **53:** 181-188, 2003.

Schwartz, C.; Wishart, T.B.; Ijaz, S.; Shuaib, A. Aging and ischemia in gerbils impair spatial memory performance. *Behav. Neurosci.* **112:** 937-941, 1998.

Scremin, O.U.; Scremin, A.M.; Heuser, D.; Hudgell, R.; Romero, E.; Imbimbo, B.P. Prolonged effects of cholinesterase inhibition with eptastigmine on the cerebral blood flow-metabolism ration of normal rats. *J. Cereb. Blood Flow Metab.* **13:** 702-711, 1993.

Selkoe, D.J. Alzheimer's disease is a synaptic failure. *Science* **298:** 789-791, 2002.

Selkoe, D.J.; Schenk, D. Alzheimer's disease: Molecular understanding predicts amyloid-based therapeutics. *Ann. Rev. Pharmacol. Toxicol.* **43:** 545-584, 2003.

Semenza, G.L. Perspectives on oxygen sensing. *Cell* **98:** 281-284, 1999.

Sheehan, J.P.; Swerdlow, R.H.; Miller, S.W.; Davis, R.E.; Parks, J.K.; Parker, W.D.; Tuttle, J.B. Calcium homeostasis and reactive oxygen species production in cells transformed by mitochondria from individuals with sporadic Alzheimer's disease. *J. Neurosci.* **17:** 4612-4622, 1997.

Sheu, K.F.R.; Kim, Y.T.; Blass, J.P.; Weksler, M.E. An immunochemical study of the pyruvate dehydrogenase deficit in Alzheimer's disease brain. *Ann. Neurol.* **17:** 444-449, 1985.

Shibata, M.; Yamada, S.; Kumar, S.R.; Calero, M.; Bading, J.; Frangione, B.; Holtzman, D.M.; Miller, C.A.; Strickland, D.K.; Ghiso, J.; Zlokovic, B.V. Clearance of Alzheimer's amyloid-β 1-40 peptide from brain by LDL receptor-related protein-1 at the blood-brain barrier. *J. Clin. Invest.* **106:** 1489-1499, 2000.

Siekluca, M.; Heim, C.; Sontag, K.-H.; Osborne, N.N. Transient occlusion of rat carotid arteries increases formation of inositol phosphate: Evidence for specific effect on a-1-receptors. *Neuochemistry International* **18:** 175-189, 1991.

Siesjö, B.K.; Asplund, B. Transmitter release, ion and water fluxes, and ischemic brain damage. In:*Volume Transmission in the Brain: Novel Mechanisms for Neural Transmission*, Fuxe, K. and Agnati, L.F. (ed.) New York, Raven Press, pp. 539-547, 1991.

Siesjö, B.K.; Bengtsson, ?. Calcium fluxes, calcium antagonists, and calcium-related pathology in brain ischemia, hypoglycemia, and spreading depression: a unifying hypothesis. *J. Cereb. Blood Flow Metab.* **9:** 127-140, 1989.

Simon, R.P.; Griffiths, T.; Evans, M.C.; Swan, J.H.; Meldrum, B.S. Calcium overload in selectively vulnerable neurons of the hippocampus during and after ischemia: An electron microscopy study in the rat. *J. Cereb. Blood Flow Metab.* **4:** 850-852, 1984.

Simonian, N.A.; Hyman, B.T. Functional alterations in Alzheimer's disease: diminution of cytochrome oxidase in the hippocampal formation. *J. Neuropathol. Exp. Neurol.* **52:** 580-585, 1993.

Simonian, N.A.; Hyman, B.T. Functional alterations in Alzheimer's disease: selective loss of mitochondrial-encoded cytochrome oxidase mRNA in the hippocampal formation. *J. Neuropathol. Exp. Neurol.* **53:** 508-512, 1994.

Simpson, I.A.; Chundu, K.R.; Davies-Hill, T.; Honer, W.G.; Davies, P. Decreased concentrations of GLUT1 and GLUT3 glucose transporters in the brains of patients with Alzheimer's disease. *Ann. Neurol.* **35:** 546-551, 1994.

Sinden, J.D.; Rashid-Doubell, F.; Kershaw, T.R.; Nelson, A.; Chadwick, A.; Jat, P.S.; Noble, M.D.; Hodges, H.; Gray, J.A. Recovery of spatial learning by grafs of a conditionally immortalized hippocampal neuro-epithelial cell line into the ischaemia-lesioned hippocampus. *Neuroscience* **81:** 599-608, 1997.

Singh, M.; Meyer, E.M.; Simpkins, J.W. The effect of ovariectomy and estradiol replacement on brain-derived neurotrophic factor messenger ribonucleic acid expression in cortical and hippocampal brain regions of female Sprague-Dawley rats. *Endocrinology* **136:** 2320-2324, 1995.

Slee, E.A.; Harte, M.T.; Kluck, R.M.; Wolf, B.B.; Casiano, C.A.; Newmeyer, D.D.; Wang, H.G.; Reed, J.C.; Nicholson, D.W.; Alnemri, E.S.; Green, D.R.; Martin, S.J. Ordering the cytochrome c-initiated caspase cascade: hierarchical activation of caspase-2, -3, -6, -7, -8, and –10 in a caspase-9-dependent manner. *J. Cell Biol.* **144:** 281-292, 1999.

Slooter, A.J.; Houwing-Duistermaat, J.J.; van Harskamp, F.; Cruts, M.; Van Broeckhoven, C.; Breteler, M.M.; Hofman, A.; Stijnen, T.; van Duijn, C.M. Apolipoprotein E genotype and progression of Alzheimer's disease: the Rotterdam Study. *J. Neurol.* **246:** 304-308, 1999.

Small, G.W.; Ercoli, I.M.; Silverman, D.H.; Huang, S.C.; Komo, S.; Bookheimer, S.Y.; Lavretsky, H.; Miller, K.; Siddarth, P.; Pasgon, N.I.; Mazziotta, J.C.; Saxena, S.; Wu, H.M.; Mega, M.S.; Cummings, J.L.; Saunders, A.M.; Pericak-Vance, M.A.; Roses, A.D.; Barrio, J.R.; Phelps, M.E. Cerebral metabolic and cognitive decline in persons at genetic risk for Alzheimer's disease. *Proc. Natl. Acad. Sci. USA* **97:** 6037-6042, 2000.

Smith, W.L.; DeWitt, D.L.; Garavito, R.M. Cyclooxygenases: structural, cellular, and molecular biology. *Annu. Rev. Biochem.* **69:** 145-182, 2000.

Snowdon, D.A. Aging and Alzheimer's disease: lessons from the Nun Study. *Gerontologist* **37:** 150-156, 1997.

Sorbi, S.; Bird, E.D.; Blass, J.P. Decreased pyruvate dehydrogenase activity in Huntington and Alzheimer brain. *Ann. Neurol.* **13:** 72-78, 1983.

Sparks, D.L. Coronary artery disease, hypertension, ApoE, and cholesterol: a link to Alzheimer's disease? *Ann. NY Acad. Sci.* **826:** 128-146, 1997.

Squire, L.R.; Shimanura, A.P.; Amaral, D.G. Memory and the hippocampus. Neural model of plasticity. In: *Experimental and Theoretical Approaches*, Byrne, J.H.; Berry, W.O. (ed.) New York, Academic Press, pp. 208-239, 1989.

Squire, L.R.; Zola, S.M. Ischemic brain damage and memory impairment: a commentary. *Hippocampus* **6:** 546-552, 1996.

Sugawara, T.; Fujimura, M.; Morita-Fujimura, Y.; Kawase, M.; Chan, P.H. Mitochondrial release of cytochrome c corresponds to the selective vulnerability of hippocampal CA1 neurons in rats after transient global cerebral ischemia. *J. Neurosci.* **19**(RC39): 1-6, 1999.

Sun, M.-K. Central neural organization and control of sympathetic nervous system in mammals. *Prog. Neurobiol.* **47:** 157-233, 1995.

Sun, M.-K. Pharmacology of reticulospinal vasomotor neurons in cardiovascular regulation. *Pharmacol. Rev.* **48:** 465-494, 1996.

Sun, M.-K. Hypoxia, ischemic stroke, and memory deficits: prospects for therapy. *IUBMB Life* **48:** 373-378, 1999.

Sun, M.-K.; Alkon, D.L. Pharmacological enhancement of synaptic efficacy, spatial learning, and memory through carbonic anhydrase activation in rats. *J. Pharmacol. Exp. Ther.* **297:** 961-967, 2001.

Sun, M.-K.; Alkon, D.L. Perspectives on the cell biology underlying Alzheimer's disease and the potential for therapy. *LifeXY* **1:** 1075-1086, 2001.

Sun, M.-K.; Alkon, D.L. Carbonic anhydrase gating in cognition: memory therapy and enhancement. *Trends Pharmacol. Sci.* **23:** 83-89, 2002a.

Sun, M.-K.; Alkon, D.L. Depressed or demented: common CNS drug targets? ! *Curr. Drug Targets: CNS Neurol. Disord.***1:** 573-589, 2002b.

Sun, M.-K.; Alkon, D.L. Impairment of hippocampal CA1 heterosynaptic transformation and spatial memory by β-amyloid$_{25\text{-}35}$. *J. Neurophysiol.* **87:** 2441-2449, 2002c.

Sun, M.-K.; Nelson, T.J.; Alkon, D.L. Functional switching of GABAergic synapses by ryanodine receptor activation. *Proc. Natl. Acad. Sci. USA* **97:** 12300-12305, 2000.

Sun, M.-K.; Dahl, D.; Alkon, D.L. Heterosynaptic transformation of GABAergic gating in the hippocampus and effects of carbonic anhydrase inhibition. *J. Pharmacol. Exp. Ther.* **296:** 811-817, 2001a.

Sun, M.-K.; Zhao, W.-Q.; Nelson, T.J.; Alkon, D.L. Theta rhythm of hippocampal CA1 neuron activity: gating by GABAergic synaptic depolarization. *J. Neurophysiol.* **85:** 269-279, 2001b.

Sun, M.-K.; Xu, H.; Alkon, D.L. Protection of synaptic function, spatial learning, and memory from transient hypoxia in rats. *J. Pharmacol. Exp. Ther.* **300:** 408-416, 2002.

Swerdlow, R.; Marcus, D.L.; Landman, J.; Kooby, D.; Frey, W.; Freeman, M.L. Brain glucose metabolism in Alzheimer's disease. *Am. J. Med. Sci.* **308:** 141-144, 1994.

Takagi, N.; Miyake, K.; Taguchi,T.; Sugita, N.; Takagi, K.; Tamada, H.; Takeo, S. Changes in cholinergic neurons and failure in learning function after microsphere embolism-induced cerebral ischemia. *Brain Res. Bull.* **43:** 87-92, 1997.

Takahashi, R.H.; Milner, T.A.; Li, F.; Nam, E.E.; Edgar, M.A.; Yamaguchi, H.; Beal, M.F.; Xu, H.; Greengard, P.; Gouras, G.K. Intraneuronal Alzheimer Aβ42 accumulates in multivesicular bodies and is associated with synaptic pathology. *Am. J. Pathol.* **161:** 1869-1879, 2002.

Tatemichi, T.K.; Desmond, D.W.; Mayeux, R.; Paik, M.; Stern, Y.; Sano, M.; Remien, R.H.; Williams, J.B.; Mohr, J.P.; Hauser, W.A.; et al. Dementia after stroke: Baseline frequency risks, and clinical features in a hospitalized cohort. *Neurology* **42:** 1185-1193, 1992.

Tatemichi, T.K.; Desmond, D.W.; Stern, Y.; Paik, M.; Sano, M.; Bagiella, E. Cognitive impairment after stroke: Frequency, patterns, and relationship to functional abilities. *J. Neurol. Neurosurg. Psychiatry* **57:** 202-207, 1994.

Taylor, S.C.; Batten, T.F.C.; Peers, C. Hypoxic enhancement of quantal catecholamine secretion. *J. Biol. Chem.* **274:** 31217-31222, 1999.

Te Koppele, J.M.; Lucassen, P.J.; Sakkee, A.N.; Van Asten, J.G.; Ravid, D.F.; Van Bezooijen, F.A. 80HdG levels in brain do not indicate oxidative DNA damage in Alzheimer's disease. *Neurol. Aging* **17:** 819-826, 1996.

Terry, R.D.; Masloah, E.; Salmon, D.P.; Bullers, N.; DeTeresa, R.; Hill, R.; Hasen, L.; Katzman, R. Physical basis of cognitive alterations in Alzheimer's disease. Synaptic loss is the major correlate of cognitive impairment. *Ann. Neurol.* **30:** 572-580, 1991.

Thal, L.J.; Thomas, R.G.; Mulnard, R.; Sano, M.; Grundman, M.; Schneider, L. Estrogen levels do not correlate with improvement in cognition. *Arch Neurol.* **60:** 209-212, 2003.

Thomas, T.; Thomas, G.; McLendon, C.; Sutton, T.; Mullan, M. β-Amyloid-mediated vasoactivity and vascular endothelial damage. *Nature* **380:** 168-171, 1996.

Thompson, J.K.; Peterson, M.P.; Freeman, R.D. Single-neuron activity and tissue oxygenation in the cerebral cortex. *Science* **299:** 1070-1072, 2003.

Tienari, P.J.; De Strooper, B.; Ikonen, E.; Simons, M.; Weidemann, A.; Czech, C.; Hartmann, T.; Ida, N.; Multhaup, G.; Masters, C.L.; Van Leuven, F.; Beyreuther, K.; Dotti, C.G. The β-amyloid domain is essential for axonal sorting of amyloid precursor protein. *EMBO J.* **15:** 5218-5229, 1996.

Tiernari, P.J.; Ida, N.; Ikonen, E.; Simons, M.; Weidemann, A.; Multhaup, G.; Masters, C.L.; Dotti, C.G.; Beyreuther, K. Intracellular and secreted Alzheimer β-amyloid species are generated by distinct mechanisms in cultured hippocampal neurons. *Proc. Natl. Acad. Sci. USA* **94:** 4125-4130, 1997.

Tomimoto, H.; Wakita, H.; Akiguchi, I.; Nakamura, S.; Kimura, J. Temporal roles of accumulation of amyloid beta/A4 protein precursor in the gerbil after graded ischemic stress. *J. Cereb. Blood Flow Metab.* **14:** 565–573, 1994.

Tominaga, K.; Uetsuki, T.; Ogura, A.; Yoshikawa, K. Glutamate responsiveness enhanced in neurones expressing amyloid precursor protein. *Neuropharmacol Neurotoxicol.* **8:** 2067-2072, 1997.

Torack, R.M.; Miller, J.W. Denervation induced abnormal phosphorylation in hippocampal neurons. *Brain Res.* **669:** 135-139, 1995.

Valla, J.; Berndt, J.D.; Gonzalez-Lima, F. Energy hypometabolism in posterior cingulated cortex of Alzheimer's patients: superficial laminar cytochrome oxidase associated with disease duration. *J. Neurosci.* **21:** 4923-4930, 2001.

van Kooten, F.; de Kooning, I.; van Swieten, J.C.; van Harskamp, F.; Koudstall, P.J. Prevalence of dementia in the Rotterdam stroke databank. *Cerebrovasc. Dis.* **6 (Suppl. 2):** 67, 1996.

Van Leeuwen, F.W.; de Kleijin, D.P.V.; van den Hurk, H.H.; Neubauer, A.; Sonnemans, M.A.F.; Sluijs, J.A.; Köycü, S.; Ramdjielal, R.D.J.; Salehi, A.; Martens, G.J.M.; Grosveld, F.G.;

Burbach, J.P.H.; Hol, E.M. Frameshift mutants of β amyloid precusor protein and ubiquitin-B in Alzheimer's and down patients. *Science* **279:** 242-247, 1998.

Vaucher, E.; Dauphin, F.; Seylaz, J.; Lacombe, P. Autoradiographic study of the cerebrovascular effects of stimulation of the substantia innominata: convenient stimulation paradigm. *J. Auton. Nerv. Syst.* **49 (Suppl.):** S43-S47, 1994.

Vaucher, E.; Borredon, J.; Seylaz, J.; Lacombe, P. Autoradiographic distribution of cerebral blood flow increases elicited by stimulation of the substantia basalis magnocellularis in the unanesthetized rat. *Brain Res.* **691:** 57-68, 1995.

Volpe, B.T.; Davis, H.P. pyramidal neurons correlates with memory impairment in rats with ischemic or neurotoxin lesions. *Behav. Neurosci.* **106:** 457-464, 1992.

Waldemar, G.; Hogh, P.; Paulson, O.B. Functional brain imaging with single-photon emission computed tomography in the diagnosis of Alzheimer's disease. *Int. Psychogeriatr.* **9 (Suppl. 1):** 223-227, 1997.

Waldvogel, D.; van Gelderen, P.; Muellbacher, W.; Ziemann, U.; Immisch, I.; Hallett, M. The relative metabolic demand of inhibition and excitation. *Nature* **406:** 995-998, 2000.

Wang, H.-Y.; Lee, D.H.S.; D'Andrea, M.R.; Peterson, P.A.; Shank, R.P.; Reitz, A.B. β-Amyloid$_{1\text{-}42}$ binds to α7 nicotinic acetylcholine receptor with high affinity. *J. Biol. Chem.* **275:** 5626-5632, 2000a.

Wang, H.-Y.; Lee, D.H.S.; Davis, C.B.; Shank, R.P. Amyloid peptide A$\beta_{1\text{-}42}$ binds selectively and with picomolar affinity to α7 nicotinic acetylcholine receptors. *J. Neurochem.* **75:** 1155-1161, 2000b.

Wang, P.N.; Liao, S.Q.; Liu, R.S.; Liu, C.Y.; Chao, H.T.; Lu, S.R.; Yu, H.Y.; Wang, S.J.; Liu, H.C. Effects of estrogen on cognition, mood, and cerebral blood flow in AD: a controlled study. *Neurology* **54:** 2061-2066, 2000c.

Wang, Z.-Z.; Wu, D.-F.; Vinters, H.V. Hypoxia and reoxygenation of brain microvascular smooth muscle cells in vitro: cellular responses and expression of cerebral amyloid angiopathy-associated proteins. *APMIS* **110:** 423-434, 2002.

Webster, N.J.; Green, K.M.; Peers, C.; Vaughan, P.F.T. Altered processing of amyloid precursor protein in the human neuroblastoma SH-SY5Y by chronic hypoxia. *J. Neurochem.* **83:** 1262-1271, 2002.

Weggen, S.; Eriksen, J.L.; Das, P.; Sagi, S.A.; Wang, R.; Pietrzik, C.U.; Findlay, K.A.; Smith, T.E.; Murphy, M.P.; Bulter, T.; Kang, D.E.; Marquez-Sterling, N.; Golde, T.E.; Koo, E.H. A subset of NSAIDS lower amyloidogenic Aβ42 independently of cyclooxygenase activity. *Nature* **414:** 212-216, 2001.

West, M.J.; Coleman, P.D.; Flood, D.G.; Troncoso, J.C. Differences in the pattern of hippocampal neuronal loss in normal aging and Alzheimer's disease. *Lancet* **344:** 769-772, 1994.

Whitehouse, P.J. The cholinergic deficits in Alzheimer's disease. *J. Clin. Psychiatry* **59 (Suppl. 13):** 19-22, 1998.

Wild-Bode, C.; Yamazaki, T.; Capell, A.; Leimer, U.; Steiner, H.; Ihara, Y.; Haass, C. Intracellular generation and accumulation of Aβ terminating at amino acid 42. *J. Biol. Chem.* **272:** 16085-16088, 1997.

Williams, J.M.; Thompson, V.L.; Mason-Parker, S.E.; Abraham, W.C.; Tate, W.P. Synaptic activity-dependent modulation of mitochondrial gene expression in the rat hippocampus. *Mol. Brain Res.* **60:** 50-56, 1998.

Winblad, B.; Poritis, N. Memantine in severe dementia: results of the 9M-best study (benefit and efficacy in severely demented patients during treatment with memantine. *Int. J. Geristr. Psychiatry* **14:** 135-146, 1999.

Wisniewski, H.M.; Maslinska, D. Beta-protein immunoreactivity in the human brain after cardiac arrest. *Folia Neuropathol.* **34:** 65-71, 1996.

Wu, J.; Amwyl, R.; Rowan, M.J. β-Amyloid-(1-40) increases long-term potentiation in rat hippocampus in vitro. *Eur. J. Pharmacol.* **284:** R1-R3, 1995.

Xia, W.; Zhang, J.; Kholodenko, D.; Citron, M.; Podlisny, M.B.; Teplow, D.B.; Haass, C.; Seubert, P.; Koo, E.H.; Selkoe, D.J. Enhanced production and oligomerization of the 42-residue amyloid β-protein by Chinese hamster cells stably expressing mutant presenilins. *J. Biol. Chem.* **272:** 7977-7982, 1997.

Xu, H.; Sweeney, D.; Wang, R.; Thinakaran, G.; Lo, A.C.; Sisodia, S.S.; Greengard, P.; Gandy, S. Generation of Alzheimer β-amyloid protein in the *trans*-Golgi network in the apparent absence of vesicle formation. *Proc. Natl. Acad. Sci. USA* **94:** 3748-3752, 1997.

Yamada, K.; Tanaka, T.; Senzaki, K.; Kameyama, T.; Nabeshima, T. Propentofylline improves learning and memory deficits in rats induced by β-amyloid protein-(1-40). *Eur. J. Pharmacol.* **349:** 15-22, 1998.

Yan, S.-D.; Soto, C.; Chen, X.; Zhu, H.; Al-Mohanna, F.; Collison, K.; Zhu, A.; Stern, E.; Saido, T.; Tohyama, M.; Ogawa, S.; Roher, A.; Stern, D. An intracellular protein that binds amyloid-β peptide and mediates neurotoxicity in Alzheimer's disease. *Nature* **389:** 689-695, 1997.

Yan, S.-D.; Chen, X.; Fu, J.; Chen, M.; Zhu, H.; Roher, A.; Slattery, T.; Zhao, L.; Nagashima, M.; Morser, J.; Migheli, A.; Nawroth, P.; Stern, D.; Schmidt, A.M. RAGE in Alzheimer's disease: a receptor mediating amyloid-β peptide-induced oxidant stress and neurotoxicity, and microglial activation. *Nature* **382:** 685-691, 1996.

Yang, J.; Liu, X.; Bhalla, K.; Kim, C.N.; Ibrado, A.M.; Cai, J.; Peng, T.I.; Jones, D.P.; Wang, X. Prevention of apoptosis by Bcl-2: release of cytochrome c from mitochondria blocked. *Science* **275:** 1129-1132, 1997.

Yang, D.-S.; McLaurin, J.; Qin, K.; Westaway, D.; Fraser, P.E. Examining the zinc binding site of the amyloid-β peptide. *Eur. J. Biochem.* **267:** 6692-6698, 2000.

Yankner, B.A.; Dawes, L.R.; Fisher, S.; Villa-Komaroff, L.; Oster-Granite, M.L.; Neve, R.L. Neurotoxicity of a fragment of the amyloid precusor associated with Alzheimer's disease. *Science* **245:** 417-420, 1989.

Yankner, B.A; Duffy, L.; Kirschner, D. Neurotropic and neurotoxic effects of amyloid β protein: reversal by tachykinin neuropeptides. *Science* **250:** 279-282, 1990.

Yasojima, K.; McGeer, E.G.; McGeer, P.L. Relationship between beta-amyloid peptide generating molecules and neprilysin in Alzheimer's disease and normal brain. *Brain Res.* **919:** 115-121, 2001.

Yokota, M.; Saido, T.C.; Tani, E.; Yamaura, I.; Minami, N. Cytotoxic fragment of amyloid precursor protein accumulates in hippocampus after global forebrain ischemia. *J. Cereb. Blood Flow Metab.* **16:** 1219–1223, 1996.

Yonemori, F.; Yamada, H.; Yamaguchi, T.; Uemura, A.; Tamura, A. Spatial memory disturbance after focal cerebral ischemia in rats. *J. Cereb. Blood Flow Metab.* **16:** 973-980, 1996.

Yoshida, H.; Kong, Y.Y.; Yoshida, R.; Elia, A.J.; Hakem, A.; Hakem, R.; Penninger, J.M.; Mak, T.W. Apafl is required for mitochondrial pathways of apoptosis and brain development. *Cell* **94:** 739-750, 1998.

Yoshikawa, K.; Aizawa, T.; Hayashi, Y. Degeneration *in vitro* of post-mitotic neurons overexpressing the Alzheimer amyloid protein precusor. *Nature* **359:** 64-67, 1992.

Zarron, C.; Barron, E.; Chang Chui, H.; Perlmutter, L.S. Vascular basement membrane pathology and Alzheimer's disease. *Ann. NY Acad. Sci.* **826:** 147-160, 1997.

Zhivotovsky, B.; Orrenius, S.; Brustugun, O.T.; Doskeland, S.O. Injected cytochrome c induces apoptosis. *Nature* **391:** 449-450, 1998.

Zivin, J.A.; Choi, D.W. Stroke therapy. *Sci. Am.* **7:** 36-43, 1991.

Zola-Morgan, S.; Squire, L.R.; Amaral, D.G. Human amnesia and the medial temporal region: enduring memory impairment following a bilateral lesion limited to the CA1 field of the hippocampus. *J. Neurosci.***6:** 2950-2967, 1986.

Chapter II

DEMENTIA, ESTROGEN, AND DIET: A POSSIBLE ROLE OF PHYTOESTROGENS (ISOFLAVONES) IN ALZHEIMER'S DISEASE?

Edwin D. Lephart[1, 3*] *and Dawson W. Hedges*[2, 3]

[1]Departments of Physiology and Developmental Biology

[2]and Psychology and [3]The Neuroscience Center

Brigham Young University

Provo, Utah USA 84602

ABSTRACT

Alzheimer's disease (AD) is the most common type of dementia and as humans experience longer life spans AD prevalence is estimated to increase with age. This devastating disease is characterized by memory loss, confusion, and cognitive deficits. The treatment and prevention of AD in women includes hormone replacement therapy (HRT) due to estrogen's hormonal action on cognitive abilities and the physiological benefits in brain via estrogen receptors. However, the known benefits and more importantly the potentially adverse effects of HRT in postmenopausal women have produced concerns about reproductive, endocrine and brain health issues. These concerns have stimulated a sustained surge of 'natural' alternative therapy usage such as dietary or nutritional supplement products. Since soy foods and nutritional supplements are readily available and contain high levels of natural estrogen-like molecules [produced in plants (phytoestrogens)] consumption of these products has increased dramatically. Specifically a particular group of phytoestrogens, namely isoflavones principally derived from soy foods, has gained increased usage. Isoflavones bind to the mammalian estrogen receptor (ER) system (ER-alpha and ER-beta) and initial studies in women show a possible advantage in dealing with age-related diseases that provide an alternative to traditional

* Address Correspondence to: Dr. Edwin Lephart, 633 WIDB, Neuroscience Center, Brigham Young University, Provo, Utah USA 84602, Telephone (801) 422-1218, FAX (801) 422-0601, Email: NeuroscienceCenter@byu.edu

HRT. A few recent animal studies suggest that isoflavones may have neuroprotective effects related to AD. Although, there is a scarcity of data examining whether consumption of phytoestrogens via diet or supplements are neuroprotective and this link remains to be elucidated. Given the recognized importance of estrogen hormone action in brain and its link to dementia such as AD justifies further research to investigate the neurobehavioral aspects of phytoestrogens. The outlined topics/themes above are covered in this brief review.

Introduction

As the population of the United States ages (Gramlich 2002), the prevention and treatment of Alzheimer's Disease (AD) will become ever more important as it prevalence increases (Norbury et al. 2003). AD is the most common type of dementia (Kasckow 2002), estimated to cause 70 percent of all dementia (Small et al. 1997), and there are an estimated 4 million cases of AD in the United States alone (Evans 1990). Because of the aging United States population, this number is expected to increase to 14 million by 2050 (Evans 1990). Although it can occur before age 50, AD is generally considered a disease of later life (Small et al. 1997), affecting approximately 3 percent of the 65- to 74-year-old population (Friedman 2002) and up to one-half of the eighty-five-old and older population (Friedman 2002). Although AD is undoubtedly a complex disease involving numerous brain systems, a substantial literature has developed regarding the role of estrogen physiology in the etiology, prevention, and treatment of AD.

Clinical and Pathological Features

Presenting with memory loss, episodes of mild confusion, and visuospatial limitations, the course of AD is progressive and characterized by worsening cognitive deficits, affective disturbances, and delusions, as well as the onset of motor and sensory problems in its later stages. The average time between diagnosis and death is 10 years (Small et al., 1997), with the immediate cause of death often due to pneumonia or sepsis (Bonner and Peskind 2002). Hallmark neuropathological findings associated with AD are beta-amyloid neuritic plaques in neocortical and hippocampal regions, neurofibrillary tangles, and loss of neurons (Bonner and Peskind 2002, Rogan and Lippa 2002). Abnormal amyloid precursor protein is also present in AD (Rogan and Lippa 2002). Produced from amyloid precursor protein, amyloid beta peptide appears to be a crucial element in the pathophysiology of AD as it is incorporated into neuritic plaques (Dodel 2003). Furthermore, an early loss of acetylcholine-producing neurons in the basal forebrain, particularly in the nucleus basalis of Meynert, occurs early in AD (Whitehouse et al.1982) accompanied by altered concentrations of acetylcholine-synthesizing enzymes (Perry et al.1978). Loss of other neurons also occurs with AD. Magnetic resonance imaging, for instance, in even early AD shows hippocampal and entorhinal atrophy (Petrella et al. 2003), findings that may account for some of the cognitive and memory deficits that characterize AD. This is an important issue in information processing since the entorhinal cortex is a major pathway to the hippocampus and surrounding neuronal areas that affect memory storage (see Figure 1).

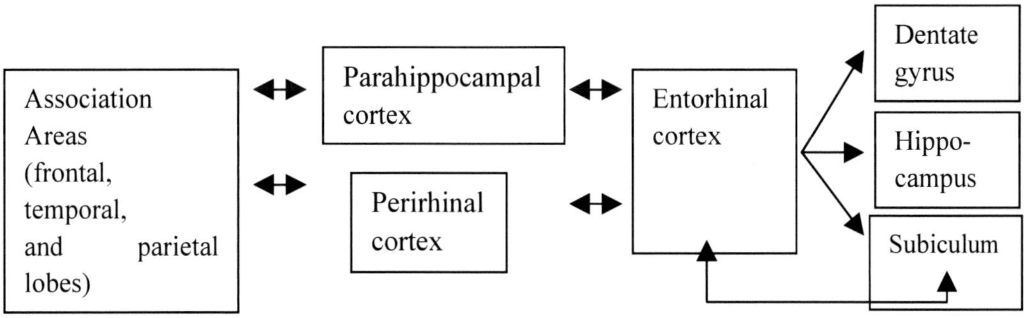

Figure 1. Pathways of information processing via the entorhinal cortex.

Several etiologies and risk factors are proposed for AD, including genetic causes. In some families, AD appears to be inherited in an autosomal dominant fashion (Rogan and Lippa 2002). More common, however, are sporadic patterns of inheritance that may involve more than one gene and possible environmental factors (Mattson et al. 2002). Underscoring the apparent genetic heterogeneity of AD are findings of abnormal genes on chromosome 21 for the amyloid precursor protein, on chromosome 14 for presenilin 1, or for presenilin 2 on chromosome 1 in half the cases of AD presenting before age 60 (Rogan and Lippa, 2002). The epsilon-4 allele on chromosome 19 coding for apolipoprotein E-4 is associated with some cases of AD that present after age 60 (Rogan and Lippa 2002), although greater than half of AD cases do not have this allele.

Despite the intriguing genetic findings associated with AD, certain non-genetic factors increase the risk for AD. For example, repetitive head injuries increase the risk of AD (Uryu et al. 2002). This observation is consistent with the so-called cerebral-reverse hypothesis, which postulates that a larger number of premorbid brain neurons are protective against AD (Chan 2002). Similarly, relatively poor neurocognitive development in early life may increase the likelihood of developing AD in late life (Snowdon et al., 2000), although not all investigations support the neural-reserve hypothesis (Jenkins et al. 2000).

Treatment and Prevention

With the putative complex etiology and pathophysiology of AD, several types of treatments are available and others are under development. The most prominent among these are the acetylcholinesterase inhibitors, which appear to initiate their effects by inhibiting acetylcholinesterase, thereby increasing levels of acetylcholine in critical pathways. Four acetylcholinesterase inhibitors are available in the United States. Sharing the common mechanism of acetylcholinesterase inhibition, these drugs also differ from each other in several ways. Tacrine, for instance, also appears to increase the presynaptic release of acetylcholine (Wagstaff and McTavish 1994). Possibly more selective for acetylcholinesterase inhibition than other acetylcholinesterase inhibitors (Jann et al. 2002), donepezil results in less hepatotoxicity than tacrine (Rogers and Friedhoff 1998). In addition to inhibiting acetylcholinesterase, rivastigmine blocks butyrylcholinesterase (Cutler 1998), an enzyme increased in AD (Nordberg and Svennson 1998). The most recently introduced of the acetylcholinesterase inhibitors, galantamine also interacts directly with nicotinic receptors, a mechanism postulated to contribute to its effects on cognition (Samochocki et al. 2000). However, the acetylcholinesterase inhibitors only slow down the progression of AD and do not fundamentally alter the underlying pathophysiology.

In part due to the significant limitations of the acetylcholinesterase inhibitors, other approaches to the treatment of AD are required. For example, drugs that alter beta and gamma secretase and affect amyloid precursor protein are being investigated (Rochette and Murphy 2002). Vaccines to alter the immune clearance of amyloid are also under investigation (Friedman 2002). Immunization with synthetic amyloid beta peptide, for instance, has been attempted in humans, although an inflammatory meningoencephalitis halted further testing. Other drugs that result in antibodies against amyloid beta peptide are under development (Dodel 2003). Agents that stimulate nerve-growth factors are also being considered for the treatment of AD (Nordberg and Svennson 1998). Possibly due to its ability to scavenge free radicals, vitamin E may slow the progression of AD and is often used as an adjunct in the treatment of AD.

An alternative approach is the investigation of factors that protect against AD. For example, premorbid use of anti-inflammatory agents, such as ibuprofen and acetaminophen, may offer protection against AD (Knopman and Morris 1997). Education also appears to have protective effects against AD (Burns and Murphy 1996), although the mechanism of this association in unknown.

Estrogen and Alzheimer's Disease

Because of estrogen's widespread actions on the brain and differences in cognitive abilities between the sexes (Norbury et al. 2003), estrogen has been considered as a potential treatment for AD, a notion that offers intriguing theoretical and clinical insight into the nature of AD. Furthermore, some evidence suggests that AD may present differently in men and women. AD appears to affect women more frequently than it does men (Jorm et al. 1987). For example, Andersen and colleagues (1999) found a higher incidence of AD in women than in men after age 85. Consistent with this report, a study of the prevalence of dementia in people over age 60 in China found that women had a prevalence of AD of 2.10 percent and men a prevalence of 0.76 percent (Liu et al. 2003), arguing for a role of gender and possibly estrogen in AD.

The course of AD also may differ between genders. In an investigation of nursing-home admissions for men and women with AD, women overall were found to have less physical and cognitive impairment than men (Young 2003), a finding that again may implicate a role of estrogen in the course of AD.

Estrogen has been postulated to slow the deposition of beta amyloid protein and increase cholinergic function in the aging brain (Zandi et al. 2002), as well as modulate brain activation in regions affected by AD (Resnick and Henderson 2002). Moreover, estrogen appears to protect the hippocampus from the amyloid beta peptide in animal models (Behl et al. 1997). These observations suggest a potential role for estrogen in the prevention and treatment of AD.

Epidemiological studies have suggested that women with histories of only limited estrogen deficiency due to hormone replacement therapy (HRT) have a lower prevalence of AD than women not taking HRT (Norbury et al. 2003), although these studies may be confounded by the increased socioeconomic status of HRT users and differences in the HRT preparations (Norbury et al. 2003). Zandi et al (2002) found that women treated with HRT in excess of 10 years had a 2.5-fold reduction in the incidence of AD compared to women who did not use HRT and noted that HRT users had an incidence of AD similar to that in men. Even so, the relationship between estrogen and cognitive performance in late life is far from clear. An investigation of endogenous estrogen in 210 postmenopausal women and 202 men, between 60 and 90 years of age and without a diagnosis of AD, for instance, found higher estradiol levels associated with smaller hippocampal volumes and poorer memory in the women and no relationship between hippocampal volume and estradiol levels in the men. Furthermore, there was a trend for higher estradiol in men to be associated with poorer memory (den Heijer et al. 2003).

Mixed results have been found in women with already present AD who were subsequently treated with estrogen. In an open trial, low-dose estradiol was associated with improvement in measures of attention and orientation in women with AD; these benefits were lost after estradiol discontinuation (Fillit et al. 1986). Estradiol patches in a randomized study were reported to improve cognition in women with AD (Asthana et al. 2001). In contrast, no benefit from estrogen compared to placebo was found in a placebo-controlled, year-long study in women already diagnosed with AD (Mulnard 2000), suggesting that HRT may not alter the course of already present AD. Further investigating this same group of women, Thal et al. (2003) found no relationship between plasma estradiol concentrations and cognitive performance.

Taken as a whole, these findings on the effects of estrogen on the prevention and treatment of AD suggest that while estrogen replacement may protect against the development of AD, it may offer little benefit on cognitive performance when dementia is already present. Because of the differences in the expression and course of AD by gender and the equivocal effects of estrogen in the prevention and treatment of AD, the role of alpha and beta estrogen receptors, through which estrogen exerts its effects, requires consideration.

ESTROGEN AND ESTROGEN RECEPTORS

Estrogen is a potent circulating sex steroid hormone produced by the ovary during the menstrual cycle. As a neuroprotective and neurotrophic factor, estrogen: 1) influences memory and cognition (Shughrue and Merchenthaler 2000, Wise et al. 2001), 2) attenuates the extent of cell death resulting from brain injuries (i.e., from cerebrovascular stroke and neurotrauma) (Roof and Hall 2000, Wise et al. 2001) and, 3) decreases the risk and potentially delays the onset of neurological disorders such as, Alzheimer's disease (Shughrue and Merchenthaler 2000, Wise and Dubal 2000, Wise et al., 2001) (and see above). Numerous studies indicate that estrogen is essential for optimal brain function, as estrogen has been shown to increase cerebral blood flow, act as an anti-inflammatory agent, and enhance activity at neuronal synapses (Halpern 2000, Roof and Hall 2000, Shughrue and Merchenthaler 2000, Wise and Dubal 2000, Wise et al., 2001, Behl 2002).

It is well established that estrogen exerts its effects via estrogen receptors, representing the ligand (estrogen)-estrogen receptor complex. Estrogen receptors (ER) are members of the nuclear receptor superfamily that includes steroid receptors [glucocorticoid receptor (GR), androgen receptor (AR), and mineralocorticoid receptor (MR), thyroid receptor (TR), vitamin D receptor (VDR), retinoic acid receptor (RAR)] and other receptors such as retinoid X receptor (RXR) and peroxisome proliferator-activated receptor (PPAR), all of which control gene expression (Evans 1988, Mangelsdorf and Evans 1995, Muramatsu and Inour 2000, Nilsson et al. 2001). Alpha estrogen receptor (ER-alpha) and beta estrogen receptor (ER-beta) are composed of three independent but interacting functional domains: the NH_2-terminal or A/B domain, the C or DNA-binding domain, and the D/E/F or ligand-binding domain. Binding of estrogen to ER triggers conformational changes in the receptor and this leads, via a number of events, to changes in the rate of transcription of estrogen-regulated genes. These events, and the order in which they occur in the overall process, are not completely understood, but they include receptor dimerization, receptor-DNA interaction, recruitment of and interaction with co-activators and other transcription factors, and formation of a preinitiation complex (Nilsson et al. 2001). In reference to co-activators or co-regulators, it is known that these elements are important in determining whether ligands act as agonists or antagonist at the estrogen receptor complex (Dutertre and Smith 2000). Effectively, estrogen and some estrogen-like molecules can act as selective estrogen receptor modulators (SERMS) in a tissue-specific fashion based upon the presence of certain co-regulators (Dutertre and Smith 2000).

It is known that estrogen hormone action via ER-alpha vs. ER-beta mediate various aspects of neuroendocrine and reproductive behaviors (Lindsay et al. 1997, Pfaff et al. 2000, McEwen 2001). Additionally, the information obtained by ER knockout mice studies has dramatically expanded our understanding of the ER system and the mechanisms of estrogen-mediated signal transduction on neurobehavioral parameters (Rissman et al. 1999, Couse and Korach 2001, Rissman et al. 2002).

The distribution and/or the relative levels of ER-alpha and ER-beta expression in brain have been elucidated mostly in experimental animal models (Shughrue et al. 1997, Kritzer 2002, Zhang et al. 2002). Brain regions that contain exclusively ER-beta receptors are neurons of the olfactory bulb, supraoptic, paraventricular, suprachiasmatic, and tuberal hypothalamic nuclei, zona incerta, ventral tegmental area, cerebellum (Purkinje cells) and pineal gland. Likewise, in the entorhinal cortex, ER-beta immunoreactivity is present in calbindin-containing cells in layers III-VI (Kritzer 2002). In contrast, only ER-alpha receptors were detected in neurons of the ventromedial hypothalamic nucleus and subfornical organ (Shughrue et al. 1997). Several brain areas express both ER-alpha and –beta, such as the bed nucleus of the stria terminalis, amygdala, preoptic area, periaqueductal gray, locus ceruleus and solitary tract (Shughrue et al. 1997, Zhang et al. 2002). Interestingly, the cerebral cortex and hippocampus predominately expressed ER-beta receptors (Shughrue et al. 1997).

There is a scarcity of data examining the human brain; however, a few reports describe the expression of ER-alpha and ER-beta (Osterlund et al. 2000, Osterlund and Hurd 2001).

Both ER subtypes are primarily expressed in limbic-related areas with distinct patterns of distribution (Osterlund and Hurd 2001). For ER-alpha high expression is found in the hypothalamus and amygdala, suggesting that autonomic and reproductive neuroendoendcrine functions, emotional interpretation and processing may be regulated by this ER subtype (Osterlund and Hurd 2001). Conversely, the hippocampus, entorhinal cortex and thalamus express high levels of ER-beta suggesting putative roles in cognition, memory and motor function (Osterlund et al. 2000, Osterlund and Hurd 2001).

Pertaining to AD and ER-alpha/-beta expression, only one study reported a connection between levels of ER-beta in the hippocampus of AD patients compared to controls. This finding described a distinct increase in hippocampal ER-beta immunoreactivity in all AD cases and suggests a potential role for ER-beta mediated estrogen effects in AD-related neuropathology (Savaskan et al. 2001). The significance of these results and the mechanism of action involving ER-beta changes and the expression of AD remain to be elucidated.

Therefore, these findings suggest that estrogen hormone action via ER-alpha and ER-beta can have restricted effects based upon the distribution and abundance of ERs in certain brain regions. Also, it is notable that estrogen can influence particular aspects of neuronal structure and function. Finally, it is important to consider the known benefits and potential adverse effects of hormone replacement therapy in postmenopausal women in reference to reproductive-endocrine health issues and AD.

HRT, The Women's Health Initiative (WHI) and Alternative Therapies

Most women do not elect to take hormone replacement therapy and those that do usually stop or decrease their compliance due to the potential adverse effects of this treatment, especially in reference to cancer issues (White and Schilling 2000). However, there are several data sets attesting to the value of HRT in decreasing such menopausal symptoms such as hot flashes, insomnia, vaginal dryness, osteoporosis and cardiovascular disease and others on the positive effects HRT has on cognition and the prevention of AD (White and Schilling 2000, Nelson et al. 2002, Notman and Nadelson 2002).

The safety of HRT has been challenged recently especially in light of the results from the women's health initiative (WHI) where HRT using estrogen plus progestin was shown to increase the risk of coronary heart disease (CHD), venous thromboembolic disease, stroke and breast cancer while the risk of colorectal cancer and bone fracture was decreased (Rossouw et al. 2002). Due to the confusion of the obtained research findings that suggest that it is a combination of estrogen plus progestin (as opposed to estrogen alone) that increases breast cancer and other studies that imply that estrogen alone may increase endometrial and cervical cancer, many women are turning to 'natural' alternative therapies to treat perimenopausal and postmemopausal symptoms (Messina 2002). Especially during the 1990s there has been a dramatic increase in the use of alternative therapies (Fitzpatrick 2003).

It is estimated that 50% of Americans use some type dietary supplement on a regular basis (Fitzpatrick 2003) and 30 to 50% of women use a 'natural' remedy during the postmenopausal interval to address their physical condition in an attempt to improve reproductive-endocrine function and at the same time avoid the potential adverse effects associated with traditional HRT (Fitzpatrick 2003, Mackey and Eden 1998, Messerer et al. 2001, Messina 2002). In fact, surveys indicate that women and older individuals are more likely to be dietary supplement and/or natural remedy users and the trend of usage is prevalent starting in the adolescent years where expectations are high among users for increased health benefits, the prevention of illness, improved immunity and to rectify poor diet habits (Messerer et al. 2001, O'Dea 2003). Consequently, as more and more older women turn to natural health remedies one of the most common and readily available sources of nutritional consumption is via soy products that contain estrogen-like molecules called phytoestrogens made in plants that have potential health benefits for both men and women (Messina 2002, Fitzpatrick 2003). The growing number of research studies suggesting that phytoestrogens, particularly isoflavones, have protective effects in reference to women's health merits coverage of this topic.

PHYTOESTROGENS (ISOFLAVONES)

Phytoestrogens are non-steroidal, diphenolic structures found in many plants (e.g. fruits, vegetables, legumes, wholegrains, and especially soy food products) that have similar chemical and structural properties to that of estrogens (Adlercreutz 1997, Kurzer and Xu 1997, Barnes 1998, Setchell 1998, Patisaul and Whitten 1998, Vincent and Fitzpatrick 2000). Hundreds of molecules fall under this classification and there are three main groups of phytoestrogens (see Figure 2): 1) isoflavones (derived principally from soybeans), 2) lignans (found in flaxseed), and 3) coumestans (derived from sprouting plants like alfalfa). Of these three main classifications, human consumption of isoflavones has the largest impact due to their availability and variety in food products and the use of nutritional supplements containing soy.

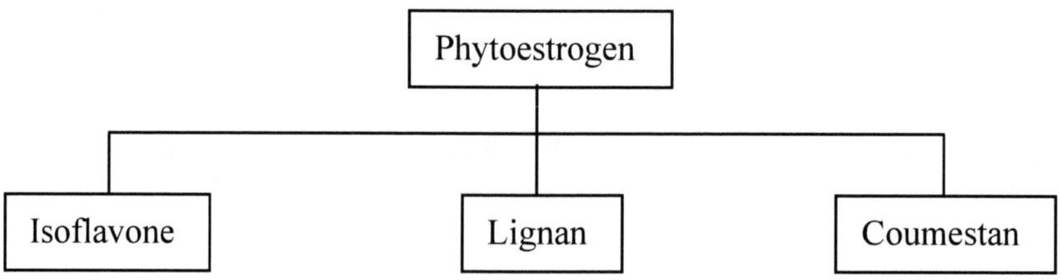

Figure 2. Classification of Phytoestrogens

In October 1999, the United States Food and Drug Administration (FDA) authorized the use of food labels claiming that: "soy protein can reduce the risk of coronary heart disease by lowering blood cholesterol levels (when included in a diet low in saturated fat and cholesterol)" (Vincent and Fitzpatrick 2000, Glazier and Bowman 2001). Due to this approval, there has been a dramatic increase in the interest of potential health benefits by phytoestrogens.

Of the isoflavones, genistein and daidzein are thought to exert the most potent estrogenic *in vivo* hormone activity, and thus most research attention has been directed toward these molecules (Adlercreutz 1997, Kurzer and Xu 1997, Barnes 1998, Setchell 1998, Setchell et al. 2002). (Figure 3, below, shows the chemical structures of genistein and daidzein compared to the steroid hormone, 17-beta estradiol. Also, equol, a metabolite of daidzein is shown.)

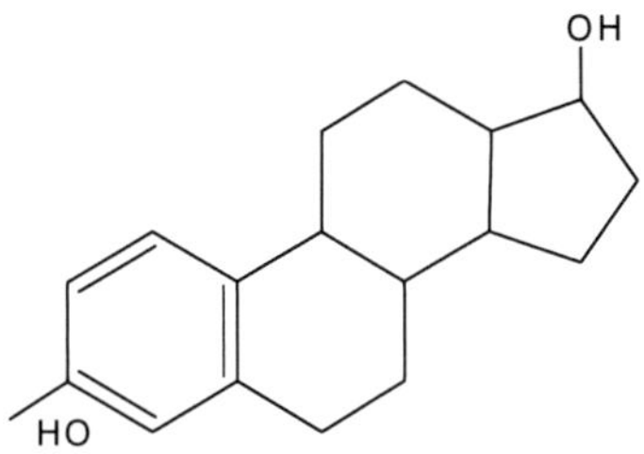

17-β-Estradiol

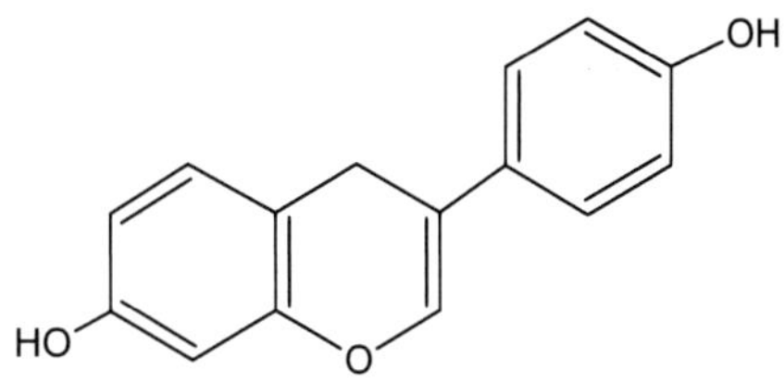

Equol

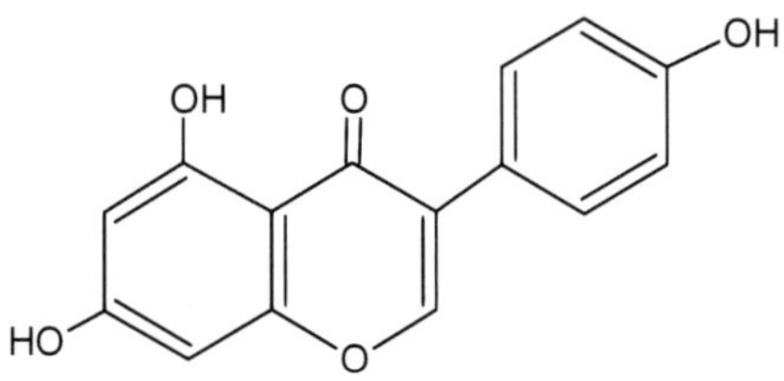

Genistein

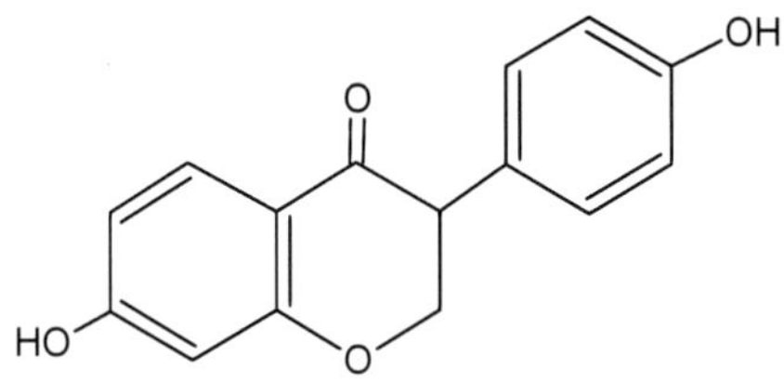

Daidzein

Figure 3.

However, these isoflavone molecules do not exist at high levels in their biologically active form in soy foods, but rather are at high abundance in a precursor form (Setchell 1998). For example, genistin (the precursor of genistein, which is the glycosidic form that contains a carbohydrate portion of the molecule) is metabolized in the gastrointestinal tract by bacteria (that hydrolyze, the carbohydrate moiety) to the biologically active phytoestrogen, genistein (the aglycone form) (Patisaul and Whitten 1998, Setchell 1998). Therefore, phyotestrogens are not biologically active until they are converted from the glycosidic to the aglycone forms. The same metabolic step occurs for daidzein (the aglycone) [being converted from daidzin (the glycosidic form)]. Dadizein is further metabolized to equol, another important and abundant phytoestrogen metabolite with estrogenic-hormonal activity (Setchell et al. 2002). Distributed throughout the body by the circulatory system, genistien, daidzein and equol bind via phenolic ring structures to alpha and beta estrogen receptors (ER-beta > ER-alpha), albeit at a lower affinity than does estradiol (Kuiper et al. 1998, Patisaul and Whitten 1998). Finally, phytoestrogens act like natural selective estrogen receptor modulators (SERMs) at various tissue sites throughout the body (Hol et al. 1997, Kuiper et al. 1997). In some cases, there is evidence that phytoestrogens act as estrogen agonists at tissue-specific targets, whereas, in others they display antagonistic characteristics comparable to that of tamoxifen or especially raloxifene where SERM activity appears to be sex hormone and gender dependent (Halbreich and Kahn 2000).

Neurobehavioral Effects of Phytoestrogens and a Potential Role in Alzheimer's Disease?

While the important link between estrogen and cognitive function is well established throughout the female lifespan (Sherwin 2000), research regarding the effects of soy consumption on reproductive and neuroendocrine function in women has been more recent (Nicholls 2002). Furthermore, recent studies examining over-the-counter nutritional supplements containing soy-derived phytoestrogens (i.e., isoflavones) found that they antagonized brain ER-beta receptors in rats and influenced reproductive behavior but had negligible activity via brain ER-alpha receptors (Patisaul et al. 2001, Patisaul et al. 2002). The altered reproductive behavior was most likely due to the antiestrogenic effects of the isoflavone supplement in brain (Patisaul et al. 2001, Patisaul et al. 2002). Neurobehavioral effects of phytoestrogens have been reviewed (Lephart et al. 2002), however, limited data exists examining the use of soy isoflavones in regards to anxiety, learning, and memory and cognitive function in animal and human studies.

In animal studies, experimental evidence supports the role of ovarian hormones, such as estradiol, in altering indices of anxiety (Imhof et al., 1993, Diaz-Veliz et al., 1997). High levels of estradiol, present during proestrus, or following exogenous hormone replacement in ovariectomized rats, exert an anti-anxiety effect in behavioral paradigms, such as the elevated plus-maze (Imhof et al., 1993, Diaz-Veliz et al., 1997). Consumption of dietary phytoestrogens produced an anxiolytic effect (decreased anxiety) as measured in the elevated plus-maze, of both young adult male and female rats (Lund and Lephart 2001), possibly by interacting with brain $GABA_A$ receptors. Support for this notion may be given by 1) estrogens are known to increase benzodiazepine-binding sites on GABA receptors, 2) genistein has been shown to directly inhibit $GABA_A$ receptors, or 3) some other mechanism is potentially operating independently or in addition to the above mediated interactions (Huang et al., 1999, Lund and Lephart 2001). Hence, anxiety may be influenced by consumption of dietary phytoestrogen in a positive manner.

In examining learning and memory, two animal studies have reported beneficial effects of phytoestrogens as tested in the radial-arm maze. In one study, Pan et al. (2000) found that consumption of a soy diet improved memory in ovariectomzied retired breeder females. The second study by Lund et al. (2001) demonstrated that visual spatial memory was enhanced in young adult females fed dietary soy phytoestrogens and that brain calbindin and cyclooxygense-2 levels in the frontal cortex were not significantly altered. In fact, in this latter study, the concentrations of phytoestrogens were determined in: 1) the diet, 2) the steady-state circulating plasma levels, and 3) brain regions of the diet treatment groups (see Table 1 below). Interestingly, the highest brain content of phytoestrogens occurred in the frontal cortex and cerebellum where high expression of ER-beta receptors is known to exist (Lund et al. 2001) that corresponds with cortical brain function in learning and memory. Finally, both studies suggest that consumption of dietary phytoestrogens improves learning and memory characteristics in females regardless of age.

Table 1. Phytoestrogen Levels in the Diet, Plasma and Brain Regions of Soy-Fed vs. Non-Soy Fed Animals. Brain Phytoestrogen Levels are Compared to the Abundance of Estrogen Receptor Alpha and Beta (In Each Brain Area)

Diet	Non-Soy (10 ppm)	Soy (600 ppm)		
Plasma Levels (isoflavones)	40 ng/ml	1,800 ng/ml		
Brain Levels			ER-alpha	ER-beta
Frontal Cortex	27 ng/g	1,227 ng/g	o	+++
Cerebellum	24 ng/g	219 ng/g	o	++
Hypothalamus	40 ng/g	134 ng/g	++	++
Amygdala	25 ng/g	73 ng/g	++	++

pm = parts per million of isoflavone content in the diets
ng = nanograms, g = grams and ml = milliliters
o = zero or very little expression of ER-alpha receptors
++ = moderate expression of ER-alpha or ER-beta receptors
+++ = high expression of ER beta receptors

To date very limited data is available in humans. One study suggests that eating soya improves memory in young adult men and women; however, this was not a controlled study, which diminishes the significance of these findings (File et al. 2001). Conversely, a recent epidemiological study conducted by White et al. (2000), created concern as deteriorating brain function was found (i.e., decreased brain weight, increased ventricular size and dementia) in Japanese-American men living in Oahu that consumed high levels of tofu (soy) during their lives. While no direct evidence for an effect of phytoestrogens was provided by this study, there was a clear link to tofu consumption in these men and the incidence of dementia. However, there was no evidence of increased dementia in their spouses who presumably consumed similar tofu meals. This suggests that women respond differently compared to men, lending to a clear gender bias in the estrogen-like hormone action of these molecules, particularly in brain where phytoestrogens exhibit positive effects in females (but not in males) (as described in one study above, Lund et al. 2001).

Few studies have examined whether consumption of soy diets are neuroprotective against AD. The available data suggest that individuals in China and Japan have similar rates of AD to those living in the United States (Ogura et al. 1995). However, recent animal data sets suggest that phytoestrogens may have beneficial effects indirectly or directly related to AD. Pan et al. (1999 and 1999a) showed that soy phytoestrogens regulate choline acetyltranserase, nerve growth factor and brain-derived neurotrophic factor in the frontal cortex and hippocampus of female rats. Subsequently, Kim et al. (2000) examined the hyperphosphorylation of the microtubule-associated tau protein that is a hallmark of several human dementias including AD. In this study, they utilized a primate model for menopause and found that dietary isoflavones attenuated tau protein phosphorylations associated with AD, suggesting a neuroprotective effect of phytoestrogens. Finally, Linford and Dorsa (2002) showed evidence that genistein diminished neuronal programmed cell death *in vitro* in primary cortical cultures. Therefore, based upon the incomplete data available to evaluate the influence of dietary phytoestrogens on AD further research will be required to consider and examine the potential favorable effects of isoflavones on brain health during development, adulthood and especially in aging.

Summary

As humans experience longer life spans AD prevalence is estimated to increase as a function of age and time. This devastating disease is characterized by memory loss, confusion, visuospatial limitations and cognitive deficits. The benefits of phytoestrogens [compared to hormone replacement therapy (HRT)] in women have received increased media attention directed mainly at the prevention and treatment of perimenopausal and menopausal symptoms via estrogen hormone receptor actions. It is noteworthy that by the year 2020, it is anticipated that there will be almost 46 million postmenopausal women in the United States alone (Yen et al. 1999, Lu et al. 2000) and that 22 million people worldwide will have AD. While recent animal studies suggest that phytoestrogens may have beneficial effects related to AD, clearly, the scarcity of data regarding the effects of phytoestrogens on the central nervous system (CNS) justifies further research given the recognized importance of estrogen hormone action in the brain and its link to stroke, depression, anxiety, neuronal plasticity, cognition and dementia such as AD.

Acknowledgements

This work was supported, in part, by grants from the USDA 2002-00798 (EDL), BYU research office (EDL), psychology department, research award (to DWH) and The Ira Fulton Foundation (DWH).

References

Adlercreutz H (1997): Evolution, nutrition, intestinal microflora, and prevention of cancer: a hypothesis. *Proceedings of the Society for Experimental Biology and Medicine* 217:241-246

Andersen K, Launer LJ, Dewey ME, Letenneur L, Ott A, Copeland JR, Dartigues JF, Kragh-Sorensen P, Baldereschi M, Brayne C. Lobo A, Martinez-Lage JM, Stijnen T, Hofman A (1999): Gender differences in the incidence of AD and vascular dementia The EURODEM Studies. EURODEM Incidence Research Group. *Neurology* 53:1992-1997

Asthana S, Baker LD, Craft S, Stanczyk FZ, Veith RC, Raskind MA, Plymate SR (2001): High-dose estradiol improves cognition for women with AD: results of a randomized study. *Neurology* 57:605-612

Barnes S (1998): Evolution of the health benefits of soy isoflavones. *Proceedings of the Society for Experimental Biology and Medicine* 217:386-392

Behl C (2002): Oestrogen as a neuroprotective hormone. *Nature Review Neuroscience* 6:433-42

Behl C, Skutella T, Lezoualc'h F, Post A, Widmann M, Newton CJ, Holsboer F (1997): Neuroprotection against oxidative stress by estrogens: structure-activity relationship. *Molecular Pharmacology* 51:535-541

Bonner LT, Peskind ER (2002): Pharmacologic treatments of dementia. *The Medical Clinics of North America* 86:657-674

Burns A, Murphy D (1996): Protection against Alzheimer's disease? *Lancet* 348:420-421

Chan DK (2002): A new hypothesis (concept) of diagnosing Alzheimer's disease. *Journals of Gerontology Series A: Biological Sciences and Medical Sciences* 57:M 645-647.

Couse JF, Korach KS (2001): Contrasting phenotypes in reproductive tissues of female estrogen receptor null mice. *Annals of the New York Academy of Sciences* 948:1-8

Cutler NR, Polinsky RJ, Sramek JJ, Enz A, Jhee SS, Mancione L, Hourani J, Zolnouni P (1998): Dose-dependent CSF acetylcholine inhibition by SDZ ENA 713 in Alzheimer's disease. *Acta Neurologica Scandinavica* 97:244-250

den Heijer T, Geerlings MI, Hofman A, de Jong FH, Launer LJ, Pols HAP, Breteler MMB (2003): Higher estrogen levels are not associated with larger hippocampi and better memory performance. *Archives of Neurology* 60:213-220

Diaz-Veliz G, Alarcon T, Espinoza C, Dussaubat N, Mora S (1997): Ketanserin and anxiety levels: Influence of gender, estrous cycle, ovariectomy and ovarian hormones in female rats. Pharmacology, *Biochemistry, and Behavior* 58:637-642

Dodel RC, Hampel H, Yangsheng Du (2003): Immunotherapy for Alzheimer's disease. *The Lancet Neurology* 2:215-220

Dutertre M, Smith CL (2000): Molecular mechanisms of selective estrogen receptor modulator (SERM) action. *The Journal of Pharmacology and Experimental Therapeutics* 295:431-7

Evans DA (1990): Estimated prevalence of Alzheimer's disease in the United States. *Milbank Quarterly* 68:267-289

Evans RM (1988): The steroid and thyroid hormone receptor superfamily. *Science* 24-:889-95

File SE, Jarrett N, Fluck E, Duffy R, Casey K, Wiseman H (2001): Eating soya improves human memory. *Psychopharmacology* 157:430-6

Fillit H, Weinreb H. Cholst I, Luine V, McEwen B, Amador R, Zabriskie J (1986): Observations in a preliminary open trial of estradiol therapy for senile dementia-Alzheimer's type. *Psychoneuroendocrinology* 11:337-345

Fitzpatrick LA (2003): Soy isoflavones: hope or hype? *Maturitas 44 Suppl* 1:S21-9

Friedman L (2002): New drugs, mechanisms are coming for Alzheimer's disease. *Current Psychiatry* 1:63-69

Glazier MG, Bowman MA (2001): A review of the evidence for the use of phytoestrogens as a replacement for traditional estrogen replacement therapy. *Archives of Internal Medicine* 161:11611-1172.

Gramlich EM (2002): Social security reform in the twenty-first century: the United States. *Journal of Aging and Social Policy* 14:67-80

Halbreich U, Kahn LS (2000): Selective oestrogen receptor modulators--current and future brain and behaviour applications. *Expert Opinion on Pharmacotherapy* 1:1385-98

Halpern DF (2000): *Sex differences in cognitive abilities* 3rd Edition, San Bernadino CA, LEA press

Hol T, Cox MB, Bryant HU, Draper MW (1997): Selective estrogen receptor modulators and postmenopausal women's health. *Journal of Women's Health* 6:523-531

Huang RQ, Fang MJ, Dillon GH (1999): The tyrosine kinase inhibitor genistein directly inhibits GABAA receptors. *Brain Research Molecular Brain Research* 67:177-83

Imhof JT, Coelho ZMI, Schmitt ML, Morato GS, Carobrez AP (1993): Influence of gender and age on performance of rats in the elevated plus maze apparatus. *Behavioural Brain Research* 56:177-180

Jann MW, Shirley KL, Small GW (2002): Clinical pharmacokinetics and pharmacodynamics of cholinesterase inhibitors. *Clinical Pharmacokinetics* 41:719-739

Jenkins R, Fox NC, Rossor AM, Harvey RJ, Rossor MN (2000): Intracranial volume and Alzheimer's disease: evidence against the cerebral reserve hypothesis. *Archives of Neurology* 57:220-224

Jorm AF, Korten AE, Henderson AS (1987): The prevalence of dementia: a quantitative integration of the literature. *Acta Psychiatrica Scandinavica* 76:465-479

Kasckow J (2002): Cognitive enhancers for dementia: do they work? *Current Psychiatry* 1:22-28

Kim H, Xia H, Li L, Gewin J (2000): Attenuation of neurodegeneratioin-relevant modifications of brain proteins by dietary soy. *Biofactors* 12:243-50

Knopman DS, Morris JC (1997): An update on primary drug therapies for Alzheimer's disease. *Archives of Neurology* 54:1406-1409

Kritzer MF (2002): Regional, laminar, and cellular distribution of immunoreactivity of ER alpha and ER beta in the cerebral cortex of hormonally intact, adult male and female rats. *Cerebral Cortex* 12:116-128

Kuiper GG, Lemmen JG, Carlsson B, Corton JC, Safe SH, van der Saag PT, van der Burg B, Gustafsson JA (1998): *Interaction of estrogenic chemicals and phytoestrogens with estrogen receptor beta. Endocrinology* 139:4252-4263

Kuiper GG, Carlsson B, Grandien K, Enmark E, Haggblad J, Nilsson S, Gustafsson JA (1997): Comparison of the ligand binding specificity and transcript tissue distribution of estrogen receptors alpha and beta. *Endocrinology* 138:863-870

Kurzer MS, Xu X (1997): Dietary phytoestrogens. *Annual Review of Nutrition* 17:353-381

Lephart ED, West TW, Weber KS, Rhees RW, Setchell KD, Adlercreutz H, Lund TD (2002): Neurobehavioral effects of dietary soy phytoestrogens. *Neurotoxicology and Teratology* 24:5-16

Lindsay R, Dempster DW, Jordan VC (1997): *Estrogens and Antiestrogens*. Lippincott-Raven 122-123

Linford NJ, Dorsa DM (2002): 17β-Estradiol and the phytoestrogen genistein attenuate neuronal apoptosis induced by the endoplasmic reticulum calcium-ATPase inhibitor thapsigargin. *Steroids* 67:1029-40

Liu L, Guo XE, Zhou YQ, Xia JL (2003): Prevalence of dementia in China. *Dementia and Geriatric Cognitive Disorders* 15:226-230

Lu LJ, Tice JA, Bellino FL (2000): NIH workshop-The role of isoflavones in menopausal Health: Consensus opinion of the North American Menopause Society. *Menopause* 7:215-229

Lund TD, Lephart ED (2001): Dietary soy phytoestrogens produce anxiolytic effects in the elevated plus-maze. *Brain Research* 913:180-184

Lund TD, West TW, Tian LY, Bu LH, Simmons DL, Setchell KD, Adlercreutz H, Lephart ED (2001): Visual spatial memory is enhanced in female rats (but inhibited in males) by dietary soy phytoestrogens. *BMC Neuroscience* 2:20

Mackey R, Eden J (1998): Phytoestrogens and the menopause. *Climacteric* 1:302-8

Mangelsdorf DJ, Evans RM (1995): The RXR heterodimers and orphan receptors. *Cell* 83:841-50

Mattson MP, Duan W, Chan SL, Cheng A, Haughey N, Gary DS, Guo Z, Lee J, Furukawa K (2002): Neuroprotective and neurorestorative signal transduction mechanisms in brain aging: modification by genes, diet, and behavior. *Neurobiology of Aging* 23:695

McEwan BS (2001): Estrogens effects on the brain: multiple sites and molecular mechanisms. *Journal of Applied Physiology* 91:2785-801

Messerer M, Johansson SE, Wolk A (2001): Sociodemographic and health behaviour factors among dietary supplement and natural remedy users. *European journal of clinical nutrition* 55:1104-10

Messina MJ (2002): Soy foods and soybean isoflavones and menopausal health. *Nutrition in Clinical Care* 5:272-82

Mulnard RA, Cotman CW, Kawas C, van Dyck CH, Sano M, Doody R, Koss E, Pfeiffer E, Jin S, Gamst A, Grundman M, Thomas R, Thal LJ (2000): Estrogen replacement therapy for treatment of mild to moderate Alzheimer's disease: a randomized controlled trial. Alzheimer's disease cooperative study. *Journal of the American Medical Association* 283:1007-1015

Muramatsu M, Inour S (2000): Estrogen receptors: how do they control reproductive and nonreproductive functions? *Biochemistry Biophysiology Research Community* 270:1-10

Nelson HD, Humphrey LL, Nygren P, Teutsch SM, Allan JD (2002): Postmenopausal hormone replacement therapy: scientific review. *Journal American Medical Association* 288:872-81

Nicholls J, Lasley BL, Nakajima ST, Setchell KD, Schneeman BO (2002): Effects of soy consumption on gonadotropin secretion and acute pituitary responses to gonadotropin-releasing hormone in women. *Journal of Nutrition* 132:708-14

Nilsson S, Makela S, Treuter E, Tujague M, Thomsen J, Andersson G, Enmark E, Pettersson K, Warner M, Gustafsson JA (2001): Mechanisms of estrogen action. *Physiology Review* 81:1535-1565

Norbury R, Cutter WJ, Compton J, Robertson DM, Craig M, Whitehead M, Murphy DG (2003): The neuroprotective effects of estrogen on the aging brain. *Experimental Gerontology* 38:109-117

Nordberg A, Svennson AL (1998): Cholinesterase inhibitors in the treatment of Alzheimer's disease: a comparison of tolerability and pharmacology. *Drug Safety* 19:465-480

Notman MT, Nadelson C (2002): The hormone replacement therapy controversy. *Archives of Women's Mental Health* 5:33-5

O'Dea JA (2003): Consumption of nutritional supplements among adolescents: usage and perceived benefits. *Health Education Research* 18:98-107

Ogura C, Nakamoto H, Uema T, Yamamoto K, Yonemori T, Yoshimura T (1995): Prevalence of senile dementia in Okinawa, Japan. COSEPO Group. Study Group of Epidemiology for Psychiatry in Okinawa. *International Journal of Epidemiology* 24:373-380

Osterlund MK, Hurd YL (2001): Estrogen receptors in the human forebrain and the relation to neuropsychiatric disorders. *Progress in Neurobiology* 64:251-67

Osterlund MK, Keller E, Hurd YL (2000): The human forebrain has discrete estrogen receptor alpha messenger RNA expression: high levels in the amygdaloid complex. *Neuroscience* 95:333-42

Pan Y, Anthony M, Watson S, Clarkson TB (2000): Soy phytoestrognes improve radial arm maze performance in ovariectomized retired breeder rats and do not attenuate benefits of 17β-estradiol treatment. *Menopause* 7:230-235

Pan Y, Anthony M, Clarkson TB (1999): Effect of estradiol and soy phytoestrogens on choline acetyltransferase and nerve growth factor mRNAs in the frontal cortex and hippocampus of female rats. *Proceedings of the Society for Experimental Biology and Medicine* 221:118-25

Pan Y, Anthony M, Clarkson TB (1999a): Evidence for up-regulation of brain-derived neurotrophic factor mRNA by soy phytoestrogens in the frontal cortex of retired breeder female rats. *Neuroscience Letters* 261:17-20

Patisaul HB, Melby M, Whitten PL, Young LJ (2002): Genistein Affects Erβ- But Not Erα-Dependent Gene Expression in the Hypothalamus. *Endocrinology* 143:2189-2197

Patisaul HB, Dindo M, Whitten PL, Young LJ (2001): Soy isoflavone supplements antagonize reproductive behavior and estrogen receptor alpha- and beta-dependent gene expression in the brain. *Endocrinology* 142:2946-2952

Patisaul HB, Whitten PL (1998): Dietary Phytoestrogens, In: R.K. Naz (ed), *Endocrine Disruptors*, CRC Press, New York, NY, pp. 100-123

Perry E, Perry R, Blessed G, Tomlinson BE (1978): Changes in brain cholinesterases in senile dementia of Alzheimer's type. *Neuropathology & Applied Neurobiology* 4:273-277

Petrella JR, Coleman RE, Doraiswamy PM (2003): Neuroimaging and early diagnosis of Alzheimer disease: a look to the future. *Radiology* 226:315-336

Pfaff DW, Vasudevan N, Kia HK, Zhu YS, Chan J, Garey J, Morgan M, Ogawa S (2000): Estrogens, brain and behavior: studies in fundamental neurobiology and observations related to women's health. *The Journal of Steroid Biochemistry and Molecular Biology* 74:365-73

Resnick SM, Henderson VW (2002): Hormone therapy and risk of Alzheimer disease: a critical time. *Journal of the American Medical Association* 288:2170-2172

Rissman EF, Heck AL, Leonard JE, Shupnik MA, Gustafsson JA (2002): Disruption of estrogen receptor beta gene impairs spatial learning in female mice. *Proceedings of the National Academy of Sciences of the United States of America* 99:3996-4001

Rissman EF, Wersinger SR, Fugger HN, Foster TC (1999): Sex with knockout models: behavioral studies of estrogen receptor alpha. *Brain Research* 835:80-90

Rochette MJ, Murphy MP (2002): Gamma-secretase: substrates and inhibitors. *Molecular Neurobiology* 26:81-95

Rogan S, Lippa CF (2002): Alzheimer's disease and other dementias: a review. *American Journal of Alzheimer's disease and Other Dementias* 17:11-17

Rogers SL, Friedhoff LT (1998): Long-term efficacy and safety of donepezil in the treatment of Alzheimer's disease: an interim analysis of the results of a US multicentre open label extension study. *European Neuropharmacology* 8:67-75

Roof RL, Hall ED (2000): Gender differences in acute CNS trauma and stroke: neuroprotective effects of estrogen and progesterone. *Journal of Neurotrauma* 17:367-388

Rossouw JE, Anderson GL, Prentice RL, LaCroix AZ, Kooperberg C, Stefanick ML, Jackson RD, Beresford SA, Howard BV, Johnson KC, Kotchen JM, Ockene J (2002): Risks and benefits of estrogen plus progestin in healthy postmenopausal women: principal results From the Women's Health Initiative randomized controlled trial. *Journal of the American Medical Association* 288:321-33

Samochocki M, Zerlin M, Jostock R, Groot Kormelink PJ, Luyten WH, Albuquerque EX, Maelicke A (2000): Galantamine is an allosterically potentiating ligand of the human alpha4/beta2 nAChR. *Acta Neurologica Scandinavica* 176 (supplement):68-73

Savaskan E, Olivieri G, Meier F, Ravid R, Muller-Spahn F (2001): Hippocampal estrogen beta-receptor immunoreactivity is increased in Alzheimer's disease. *Brain Research* 908:113-119

Setchell KDR, Brown N, Lyderking-Olsen E (2002): Equol-The clinical importance of the metabolite equol – A clue to the effectiveness of soy and its isoflavones. *Journal of Nutrition* 132:3577-3584

Setchell KDR (1998): Phytoestrogens: biochemistry, physiology and implications for human health of soy isoflavones. *The American Journal of Clinical Nutrition* 129:1333S-1346S

Sherwin BB (2000): Oestrogen and cognitive function throughout the female lifespan. *Novartis Foundation Symposium* 230:188-96

Shughrue PJ, Merchenthaler I (2000): Estrogen is more than just a "sex hormone": novel sites for estrogen action in the hippocampus and cerebral cortex. *Frontiers in Neuroendocrinology* 21:95-101

Shughrue PJ, Lane MV, Merchenthaler I (1997): Comparative Distribution of Estrogen Receptor-α and –β mRNA in the Rat Central Nervous System. *Journal of Comparative Neurology* 388:507-525

Small GW, Rabins PV, Barry PP, Buckholtz NS, DeKosky ST, Ferris SH, Finkel SI, Gwyther LP, Khachaturian ZS, Lebowitz BD, McRae TD, Morris JC, Oakley F, Schneider LS, Streim JE, Sunderland T, Teri LA, Tune LE (1997): Diagnosis and treatment of

Alzheimer's disease and related disorders: Consensus statement of the American Association for geriatric psychiatry, the Alzheimer's Association, and the American Geriatrics Society. *Journal of the American Medical Association* 278:1363-1371

Snowdon DA, Greiner LH, Markesbery WR (2000): Linguistic ability in early life and the pathophysiology of Alzheimer's disease and cerebrovascular disease. Findings from the Nun Study. *Annals of the New York Academy of Sciences* 903:34-38

Thal LJ, Thomas RG, Mulnard R, Sano M, Grundman M, Schneider L (2003): Estrogen levels do not correlate with improvement in cognition. *Archives of Neurology* 60:209-212

Uryu K, Laurer H, McIntosh T, Pratico D, Martinez D, Leight S, Lee VM, Trojanowski JQ (2002): Repetitive mild brain trauma accelerates Abeta deposition, lipid peroxidation, and cognitive impairment in a transgenic mouse model of Alzheimer amyloidosis. *Journal of Neuroscience* 22:446-454

Vincent A, Fitzpatrick LA (2000): Soy Isoflavones: Are they useful in menopause? *Mayo Clinic Proceedings* 75:1174-1184

Wagstaff A, McTavish D (1994): Tacrine: a review of its pharmacological and pharmacokinetic properties and their therapeutic potential in Alzheimer's disease. *Drugs & Aging* 4:1-31

White JP, Schilling JS (2000): Postmenopausal hormone replacement: historical perspectives and current concerns. *Clinical Excellence for Nurse Practitioners* 4:277-85

White L, Petrovitch H, Ross G, Masaki K, Hardman J, Nelson J, Davis D, Markesbery W (2000): Brain aging and midlife tofu consumption. *Journal of American College of Nutrition* 19:242-255

Whitehouse PJ, Price DL, Struble RG, Clark AW, Coyle GT, DeLong MR (1982): Alzheimer's disease and senile dementia: loss of neurons in the basal forebrain. *Science* 215:1237-1239

Wise PM, Dubal DB, Wilson ME, Rau SW, Böttner M (2001): Minireview: neuroprotective effects of estrogen-new insights into mechanisms and action. *Endocrinology* 142:969-973

Wise PM, Dubal DB (2000): Estradiol protects against ischemic brain injury in middle-aged rats. *Biology of Reproduction* 63:982-985

Yen SSC, Jaffe RB, Barbieri RL (1999): *Reproductive Endocrinology*. W.B. Saunders, Philadelphia, PA

Young RF (2003): Nursing home admissions of female Alzheimer's patients: family care aspects. *Womens Health Issues* 13:2-7

Zandi PP, Carlson MC, Plassman BL, Welsh-Bohmer KA, Mayer LS, Steffens DC, Breitner JCS (2002): Hormone replacement therapy and incidence of Alzheimer disease in older women: The Cache County Study. *Journal of the American Medical Association* 288:2123-2129

Chapter III

CLINICAL PERSPECTIVES FOR THE USE OF MELATONIN IN ALZHEIMER'S DISEASE

Daniel P. Cardinali**, *Analía M. Furio*, *Luis I. Brusco* and *Cynthia Liberczuk

Department of Physiology
Faculty of Medicine
University of Buenos Aires
Argentina

ABSTRACT

Melatonin administration synchronizes the sleep-wake cycle in blind people and in individuals suffering from delayed sleep phase syndrome or jet lag. In elderly insomniacs, melatonin treatment decreased sleep latency and increased sleep efficiency. The effect of melatonin on sleep is probably the consequence of increasing sleep propensity (by inducing a fall in body temperature) and of a synchronizing effect on the circadian clock (chronobiotic effect); typically the latter takes several days (or weeks) to occur. Daily melatonin production decreases with age, and in several pathologies, attaining its lowest values in Alzheimer's disease (AD) patients. About 45% of AD patients have disruptions in their sleep and sundowning agitation. Based on this evidence, the supplementary administration of melatonin to treat sleep and behavior disorders in AD patients was a logical therapeutic approach. The sleep-promoting action of melatonin in AD was examined mainly in open studies and for varying times, from a few days to more than 3 years. Generally, melatonin decreased sundowning in AD patients and reduced variability of sleep onset time, with improvement in mood and memory. The effect of melatonin was seen regardless of the concomitant medication employed to treat cognitive or behavioral signs of disease. In a case report study which

* Address Correspondence to: Dr. D.P. Cardinali, Departamento de Fisiología, Facultad de Medicina, UBA, Paraguay 2155, 1121 Buenos Aires. ARGENTINA, Telephone/FAX: 54-11-59509611, E-mail: cardinal@mail.retina.ar

included two identical twins with AD and similar cognitive and neuroimaging findings, the twin receiving 6 mg of melatonin each night at bedtime for 3 years did not have significant progression of the cognitive and behavioral signs while the untreated twin had significant deterioration with sleep disorder, loss of speech abilities, and psychomotor agitation. However, observations in AD patients were not always consistent and the effect of melatonin treatment was absent in a short term (e.g., two weeks) study at least. The mechanisms accounting for the possible therapeutic effect of melatonin in AD patients remain unknown. Melatonin treatment promotes mainly slow sleep in the elderly and could be beneficial in AD by augmenting the restorative phases of sleep, including the augmented secretion of growth hormone. In addition, in vitro and in vivo data indicated that melatonin protects neurons against beta amyloid toxicity, prevents beta amyloid-induced lipid peroxidation and alters the metabolism of the beta amyloid precursor protein. A recent study indicated that melatonin prevented the chronobiological consequences of injecting beta amyloid peptide 25 – 35 in the suprachiasmatic nuclei of hamsters. Although melatonin treatment appears to constitute a selection therapy to ameliorate sundowning and to slow evolution of cognitive impairment in AD patients, the majority of studies are open, and knowledge about side effects and long-term effects of melatonin is still limited.

Key words: melatonin - Alzheimer's disease - sleep disorders - cognitive impairment – aging.

Pineal Melatonin Acts as an "Endocrine Arm" of the Biologic Clock

Melatonin (N-acetyl-5-methoxytryptamine) is synthesized from serotonin through two enzymatic steps. The first step in melatonin synthesis is the N-acetylation by serotonin N-acetyltransferase (SNAT) to yield N-acetylserotonin. The second is the transfer of a methyl group from S-adenosylmethionine to the 5-hydroxy group of N-acetylserotonin to yield melatonin, a reaction catalyzed by the enzyme hydroxyindole-O-methyl transferase (Cardinali & Pevet, 1998). Melatonin synthesis occurs in the pineal gland as well as in many peripheral organs (Reiter, 1995). Yet, circulating levels of melatonin principally at night are mainly, if not exclusively, derived form the pineal gland (Kennaway & Wright, 2002). The physiological regulation of pineal SNAT, with its sharp increase in activity at night, has received considerable attention as a major regulatory step in pineal melatonin synthesis. Melatonin is primarily secreted from the pineal gland during the subjective night, its plasma levels showing in humans a characteristic profile with excretion rising in the early evening to a peak in the early morning and then declining to undetectable levels during daylight (Cagnacci, 1996).

Melatonin lipophilicity contributes to its easy passive diffusion across cell membranes as well as through cell layers. Radioactive melatonin administered intravenously rapidly disappears from the blood with a half-life of about 30 min depending on the species examined. About 60-70% of melatonin in plasma is bound to albumin and none is bound in the cerebrospinal fluid (CSF) (Cardinali et al., 1972). Most of melatonin in the general circulation is converted to 6-hydroxymelatonin in the liver, which clears 92-97% of circulating melatonin on a single pass (Tetsuo et al., 1980). The 6-hydroxymelatonin formed is conjugated and excreted into the urine. The sulfate derivative of 6-hydroxymelatonin amounts for 50-80% and the glucuronide for 5-30% of the excreted melatonin. The remaining melatonin is excreted either unchanged (less than 1%), as 5-methoxyindoleacetic acid (0.5%), or as the non-indolic metabolite N-acetyl-5-methoxykynurenamine (15%). Other melatonin metabolites, like cyclic 3-hydroxymelatonin, are indicators of the endogenous hydroxyl radical scavenging properties of melatonin (Tan et al., 1999).

While melatonin is produced in most organisms from algae to mammals, and its role varies considerably across the phylogenetic spectra (Reiter et al., 2001b), in humans it seems to play a major function in the coordination of circadian rhythmicity, the remarkable sleep-wake cycle (Cardinali & Pevet, 1998; Kennaway & Wright, 2002). The circadian rhythm of melatonin is generated by a central pacemaker located in the suprachiasmatic nuclei (SCN) of the hypothalamus, and like many other circadian rhythms, it is synchronized to a 24-hour period largely by cues from the light–dark cycle received via the retino-hypothalamic pathway to the SCN.

The evening increase in melatonin secretion is associated with an increase in the propensity for sleep. Secretion of melatonin during the day, as occurs in diverse pathologic or occupational health situations, is strongly associated with daytime sleepiness or napping, and the administration of melatonin during the day induces sleepiness (Zhdanova et al., 2001). Melatonin secretion is thus an "arm" of the biologic clock in the sense that it responds to signals from the SCN and in that the timing of the melatonin rhythm indicates the status of the clock, both in terms of phase (i.e., internal clock time relative to external clock time) and amplitude. From another point of view, melatonin is also a chemical code of night: the longer the night, the longer the duration of its secretion. In many species, this pattern of production serves as a time cue for seasonal rhythms (Cardinali & Pevet, 1998).

Daily timed administration of melatonin in rats shifts the phase of the circadian clock, and this phase shifting may explain melatonin effect on sleep in humans. Indirect support for this physiological role came from clinical studies on blind subjects showing free running of their circadian rhythms while more direct support for this hypothesis was provided when the phase response curve for melatonin was demonstrated to be the opposite (i.e. 180 degrees out of phase) to that of light (Kennaway & Wright, 2002).

The human sleep-wake cycle is generated by a circadian process originating from the SCN, in interaction with a separate oscillatory process: the sleep homeostat (Pace-Schott & Hobson, 2002). The sleep-wake cycle is normally timed to occur at a specific phase relative to the external cycle of light-dark exposure. It is also timed at a specific phase relative to internal circadian rhythms, such as the pineal melatonin rhythm, the circadian sleep-wake propensity rhythm, and the rhythm of responsiveness of the circadian pacemaker to light. Variations in these internal and external phase relationships, such as those that occur in blindness, aging, morning and evening, and advanced and delayed sleep-phase syndrome, lead to sleep disruptions and complaints (Dijk & Lockley, 2002).

Melatonin (at a dose of 5 mg daily, timed to advance the phase of the internal clock) can maintain synchronization of the circadian rhythm to a 24-hour cycle in sighted persons who are living in conditions likely to induce a free-running rhythm, and it synchronizes the rhythm in some persons after a short period of free-running. In blind subjects with free-running rhythms, it has been possible to stabilize, or entrain, the sleep–wake cycle to a 24-hour period by giving melatonin, with resulting improvements in sleep and mood (Skene et al., 1999a). The phase shifting effects of melatonin were also sufficient to explain its utility as a treatment for circadian-related sleep disorders such as jet lag or the delayed phase sleep syndrome.

Melatonin Administration Induces Sleep in Healthy Subjects

The promoting effect of exogenous melatonin administration on sleep and sedation has been long known. Shortly after the isolation and characterization of melatonin, Lerner and Case established that the intravenous administration of 80 mg of melatonin increased self-reported sleepiness in two young adults (Lerner & Case, 1960). Initial studies addressing the effect of melatonin on sleep made use of the i.v. or the intranasal route (Anton-Tay, 1974; Cramer et al., 1974; Vollrath et al., 1981) or administered very large doses of methoxyindole via the oral route (Anton-Tay, 1974; Lieberman et al., 1984). From these early studies it was concluded that melatonin reduces sleep latency and induces sleepiness and fatigue. Such an effect of melatonin is probably the consequence of increasing sleep propensity (by inducing a fall in body temperature) and of a synchronizing effect on the circadian clock (chronobiotic effect). A dose of 5 mg of melatonin at 1400 h significantly reduced sleep onset latency and reduced core body temperature, the decline being due to an increase in peripheral heat loss and a reduction in heat production (Holmes et al., 2002). Typically, the thermoregulatory effect of melatonin rises immediately after melatonin administration while the second one requires some days (or weeks) to develop.

More recently, the effect of lower doses of melatonin was examined. These studies included normal young volunteers and patients with insomnia of different origins including Alzheimer's disease (AD) patients exhibiting a sundowning syndrome. In most instances, melatonin significantly improved subjective and/or objective sleep parameters.

Melatonin 0.3 or 1 mg p.o. significantly reduced sleep latency and increased sleep efficiency in normal volunteers (Zhdanova et al., 1995; Zhdanova et al., 1996). In contrast, a 5-mg dose did not modify sleep induction or maintenance (James et al., 1987). In healthy nocturnal young subjects, oral administration of exogenous melatonin before going to bed increased stage 2 sleep significantly, with few hypothermic actions (Shirakawa et al., 2001). The effect of a high melatonin dose (80 mg p.o.), when tested in subjects with insomnia induced by exposure to recorded traffic noise, was a reduction of sleep latency and of the number of awakening episodes and an increase of stage 2 sleep and sleep efficiency (Waldhauser et al., 1990).

Administered during the day to normal volunteers, melatonin (1-40 mg) significantly reduced sleep latency and increased total sleep time (Badia et al., 1996; Nave et al., 1995; Reid et al., 1996). In addition, sleep-onset latency, oral temperature and the number of correct responses to the Wilkinson vigilance task decreased significantly (Dollins et al., 1994). Administration of melatonin prior to a nap in subjects who were partially sleep deprived and allowed a 4-h nap starting at 1300 h, did not significantly modify sleep induction or maintenance (Dijk et al., 1995).

After the administration of a 5 mg dose of melatonin p.o. at either 1300 or 1800 h, sleepiness increased significantly as well as theta/alpha frequencies of waking EEG (Cajochen et al., 1996). Alertness and performance decreased following a morning melatonin administration to healthy young individuals, an effect that lasted for 6 h (Graw et al., 2001). Melatonin (0.1, 0.5 and 5 mg p.o.) decreased wake time after sleep onset and increased feelings of sleepiness and fatigue in the late afternoon (1700-2100 h) in healthy volunteers (Terlo et al., 1997). When melatonin (0.1-10 mg) was administered at 1145 h, all doses increased significantly sleep duration and self-reported sleepiness and fatigue.

Assessment of the hypnotic action of melatonin during daytime administration and its comparison with triazolam indicated that a 6 mg dose of melatonin demonstrated hypnotic effects that were nearly equal to those of triazolam at 0.125 mg. Rectal temperature was significantly decreased by melatonin (Satomura et al., 2001). In another placebo-controlled and double-blind with a cross-over design including temazepam (20 mg), the hypnotic activity of melatonin at early evening (presumably in the absence of endogenous melatonin) was similar to 20 mg temazepam (Gilbert et al., 1999; Stone et al., 2000). These data in humans reproduced previous findings in rodents (Golombek et al., 1993).

It has been contended that high pharmacological doses of melatonin are needed to improve sleep of normal volunteers during nighttime (Lavie, 1997). However, an important question, not yet solved, concerns what "physiological" means in terms of intracerebral melatonin levels (Reiter & Tan, 2003). The levels of a lipophilic substance like melatonin reaching neurons under physiological conditions may differ considerably from circulating hormone concentration. Indeed, in early studies in rats using HPLC (Cardinali et al., 1991) or RIA (Catala et al., 1987; Pang & Brown, 1983) hypothalamic melatonin concentrations were found to be about 50 times greater than in plasma. In sheep, third ventricle CSF melatonin levels were 20-fold higher than nocturnal plasma concentrations (Skinner & Malpaux, 1999; Tricoire et al., 2002; Tricoire et al., 2003).

EXOGENOUS MELATONIN IS USEFUL TO IMPROVE SLEEP IN AGED SUBJECTS SUFFERING INSOMNIA

The effect of melatonin on the polysomnographic sleep of insomniac patients was assessed in several studies. Melatonin (1 or 5 mg, 15 min before bedtime for 1 night) did not modify variables related to sleep induction and maintenance (Ellis et al., 1996; James et al., 1990). It must be noted that in these studies the subject population under placebo showed low sleep efficiency (about 85%); hence any possible effect of melatonin could have been limited by a ceiling effect.

Melatonin levels in the pineal gland decline with age, such that in elderly humans the levels of melatonin available to the organism are a fraction of that of young individuals (Iguchi et al., 1982). Hence a feasible situation in which melatonin may have a beneficial effect is age-related insomnia.

In middle-aged and elderly insomniacs who made use of immediate-release (0.5 mg) and controlled release (0.5 mg) preparations of melatonin 30 min before bedtime, polysomnographic recordings and sleep actigraphy showed that melatonin shortened latencies to persistent sleep (Hughes et al., 1998). There was no correlation between prior melatonin production and responsiveness to melatonin replacement.

Administration of a 3-mg dose of melatonin during 14 nights to elderly patients with chronic primary insomnia brought about a significant reduction in wake time after sleep onset while total sleep time and sleep efficiency increased, with an increase of stage 2 sleep (Monti et al., 1999). No correlation was found between prior 6-sulphatoxymelatonin levels in urine and subsequent sleep improvement after receiving melatonin. Generally, the urinary excretion of aMT6s correlated negatively and significantly with age, but not with intensity of sleep disorder or outcome of treatment. Diminished melatonin secretion in the elderly is associated with insufficient environmental illumination (Mishima et al., 2001).

In studies monitoring sleep quality by wrist actigraphy in elderly insomniacs, controlled-release melatonin (2 mg) taken 2 h before the desired bedtime during 3 weeks reduced sleep latency and wake time after sleep onset and increased total sleep time and sleep efficiency (Garfinkel et al., 1995). Melatonin (3 mg) administered 30 min before the expected bedtime for 21 nights to patients with chronic insomnia significantly improved sleep quality and decreased the number of awakenings from day 2-3 of treatment (Fainstein et al., 1997). A sustained-release preparation of melatonin (2 mg) improved sleep initiation, with further improvement of sleep initiation and sleep maintenance after 2 months (Haimov & Lavie, 1995). Insomniac patients receiving 75 mg melatonin at 2200 h for 7 consecutive nights reported improved subjective sleep time and subjective daytime alertness (MacFarlane et al., 1991). Low amounts of melatonin (0.3 mg) given during 3 nights to middle-aged and elderly patients with chronic insomnia reduced sleep latency, the number of nocturnal awakenings and body movements per night, whereas the core temperature remained unchanged (Zhdanova et al., 2001). In medically ill persons with initial insomnia receiving 5.4 mg melatonin or placebo, double-blind assessments of aspects of sleep indicated that melatonin significantly hastened sleep onset, improved quality and depth of sleep, and increased sleep duration (Andrade et al., 2001).

Administration of melatonin (3 mg p.o.) for up to 6 months in elderly insomniac females did not affect circulating PRL, FSH, TSH or estradiol, nor were any indications of hematological or blood biochemistry alteration found (Siegrist et al., 2001). In a study assessing the acute effect of melatonin (1 mg) on serum PRL, LH, FSH, GH and TSH, only levels of PRL were stimulated (Ninomiya et al., 2001). Melatonin augmented sleep quality and duration, and decreased sleep latency and the number of awakening episodes; estimates of next-day function also improved significantly (Siegrist et al., 2001). The urinary excretion of 6-sulphatoxymelatonin before starting administration of melatonin correlated negatively and significantly with age but not with intensity of sleep disorder or outcome of treatment. In another study, blood parameters were not affected by a dose of 10 mg of melatonin for 28 days (Seabra et al., 2000)

It is interesting to note that melatonin can facilitate discontinuation of benzodiazepine therapy while maintaining good sleep quality. This can be helpful in the elderly in view of the contraindications for a prolonged use of benzodiazepine at this age. In the elderly, sleep disturbance is complex and often difficult to relieve because the physiologic parameters of sleep normally change with age. Since any long-term use of benzodiazepines should be avoided, particularly in the elderly, appropriate strategies to decrease or to halt benzodiazepine use should be welcome. A number of animal studies indicated that several behavioral effects of melatonin can be suppressed by inhibiting central benzodiazepine receptors (Golombek et al., 1992; Golombek et al., 1996; Wang et al., 2003). Indeed melatonin and benzodiazepines share several properties, remarkable anxiolytic effects, and therefore melatonin could be useful to help patients to discontinue benzodiazepine treatment. In one study, 14 out of 18 subjects under benzodiazepine therapy receiving melatonin (2 mg in a controlled-release formulation) discontinued benzodiazepine therapy and after a 6-month follow-up assessment of the 24 patients who discontinued benzodiazepine and received melatonin therapy, 19 maintained good sleep quality (Garfinkel et al., 1999). In another study, 13 of 20 patients taking benzodiazepines together with melatonin, benzodiazepine use could be stopped, and in another four patients, the benzodiazepine dose could be decreased to 25-66% of the initial dose (Siegrist et al., 2001).

Many times, old patients with minor or no sleep disturbance received, on a long-term basis, anxiolytic benzodiazepines in low doses for relief of a disturbance that has numerous, often concurrent etiologies, including medical conditions, medication or poor sleep hygiene. Recently we carried out a study to assess whether melatonin could be useful to reduce low benzodiazepine dosage in this group of patients, as it is in insomniac patients treated with hypnotic benzodiazepines. A double blind-placebo controlled study on the efficacy of a 3 mg-melatonin dose p.o. was undertaken. The possible correlation of urinary excretion of 6-sulphatoxymelatonin (aMT6s) before starting treatment and outcome of treatment was also examined. The results indicated that melatonin failed to affect subjective assessment of wakefulness or sleep in this group of patients with minor sleep disturbance. The only effect that melatonin had in this group of patients was to advance sleep onset and to decrease significantly the variability of sleep onset time as compared to placebo. Indeed, this melatonin efficacy to reduce variability of the sleep onset time was first described in demented patients exhibiting sundowning (Fainstein et al., 1997) and is the basis for an indication of melatonin as an effective therapy of sundowning in AD, discussed below.

Melatonin Is Useful in Other Types of Insomnia

Melatonin was found helpful in sleep disturbance liked to restless leg syndrome (Kunz & Bes, 2001) and Gilles de la Tourette syndrome (Ayalon et al., 2002) as well as in parasomnia like REM sleep behavior disorder (Kunz & Bes, 1999; Takeuchi et al., 2001). Typically, circadian sleep disorders like delayed sleep phase syndrome and non-24 h sleep-wake syndromes can be treated with melatonin (Kamei et al., 2000; Lockley et al., 2000; Nagtegaal et al., 2000; Yang et al., 2001). Melatonin is regarded as the most beneficial therapy to treat sleep disturbances found in mucopolysaccharidosis type III (Sanfilippo syndrome) (Dijk & Lockley, 2002; Fraser et al., 2002) and in the Angelman syndrome (Galvan et al., 2002; Zhdanova et al., 1999), as well as in postoperative delirium (Hanania & Kitain, 2002).

Melatonin improves sleep quality of patients with treatment-resistant depression (Dalton et al., 2000). However, as was observed previously (Fainstein et al., 1997), depression itself is not modified by melatonin treatment. Melatonin can be also useful for sleep disturbances in manic patients with treatment resistant insomnia (Bersani & Garavini, 2000) and in patients with fibromyalgia (Citera et al., 2000). Melatonin improved sleep in intensive care patients (Shilo et al., 2000), a finding that is correlated with data indicating that patients with coronary disease had a low melatonin production rate, with higher decreases in those with a higher risk of cardiac infarction (Girotti et al., 2000a).

Another promising field of application for melatonin is that of sleep disorders in children. There is a high prevalence of chronic sleep-wake cycle disorders in developmentally and neurologically disabled children. Such disorders are often resistant to hypnotic and psychotropic drugs. Administration of exogenous melatonin can have an effect upon the circadian rhythm and establish a normal sleep-wake cycle. Reported results generally indicate that melatonin improves sleep-wake cycle disorders in these children. Observations included patients with childhood sleep onset insomnia (Jan et al., 2001; Smits et al., 2001; Wassmer et al., 2001) as well as children with sleep disorders linked to developmental disabilities (Hayashi, 2000; Jan et al., 2000; Pillar et al., 2000; Ross et al., 2002; Zhdanova et al., 1999). However, the majority of studies were open, and knowledge about side effects and long-term effects is limited.

With few exceptions (Spitzer et al., 1999), published evidence indicates that melatonin is useful for ameliorating "jet-lag" symptoms in air travelers (Arendt et al., 1997; Arendt, 1999; Claustrat et al., 1992; Czeisler, 1997; Edwards et al.,; Lino et al., 1993; Manfredini et al.,; Petrie et al., 1989; Samel, 1999; Skene et al., 1999b). A meta-analysis on the efficacy of melatonin to prevent and treat jet-lag indicated that melatonin, taken close to the target bedtime at the destination, decreased effectively jet-lag from flights crossing five or more time zones (Herxheimer & Petrie, 2001). We recently demonstrated that a combination of melatonin treatment, an appropriate environmental light schedule and timely applied physical exercise was useful to help elite athletes to overcome the consequences of jet-lag after a transmeridian flight of 12 time zones (Cardinali et al., 2002a).

SLEEP DISORDERS ARE COMMON IN DEMENTED PATIENTS

The prevalence of AD is rapidly increasing as a growing number of people are living to old age. Sleep disturbances are common, and highly disruptive, symptoms associated with AD. Approximately 4.5 - 5 million Argentines (13-15% of the national population) are 65 years or more. Approximately 450, 000 Argentines are currently afflicted with AD and this number is expected to increase 3-4-fold over the next 50 years.

Cross-sectional studies report that about 40% of AD patients have disruptions in their sleep (Carpenter et al., 1995; McCurry et al., 2000). Indeed, most older people with dementia at some point in their illness develop behavioral disturbances such as wandering, sleep disturbance and agitation. Collectively, these are termed behavioral symptoms of dementia. When sleep disturbances do occur, they constitute a significant physical and psychological stress for the caregiver and are frequently related to patient institutionalization.

Pathological aging is associated with poor quality of the sleep-waking cycle. Increased duration and frequency of awakenings and daytime napping and decreased non-REM and to a less extent REM sleep, characterize the sleep of AD patients (Vitiello et al., 1990). Shifts in the basic circadian sleep-wake rhythm of dementia patients can be severe, and in extreme cases may lead to complete day/night sleep pattern reversals. Cross-sectional studies have shown that sleep disturbances are associated with increased memory and functional impairment in AD patients, as well as with more rapid cognitive decline (McCurry et al., 2000). For these reasons, optimization in management of sleep disturbances is a treatment priority for AD patients.

After excluding treatable causes such as concurrent infections, non-pharmacological approaches are the recommended first line intervention in AD patients with sleep disturbances. In practice, however, drugs such as neuroleptics and other sedatives are often prescribed in an attempt to control what can be an alarming situation (McCurry et al., 2000). However, the chronic use of benzodiazepines to treat sleep in AD patients is associated with risk, since the use of sedative-hypnotics can result in habituation and drug-induced insomnia, without significant improvements in daytime function (Kripke, 2000). Therefore, new developments in pharmacological strategies to treat sleep disorders in AD are needed.

CIRCADIAN ALTERATIONS UNDERLIE "SUNDOWNING" IN DEMENTIA

Clinical findings strongly argue in favor of disruption of the circadian timing system in AD (Giubilei et al., 2001; Harper et al., 2001; Hoogendijk et al., 1996). Dementia is associated with circadian rhythm disturbances expressed in several dimensions including body temperature, hormonal concentrations and rest-activity cycles. The fragmented sleep/wake patterns observed in the elderly and to a greater extent in patients with Alzheimer's disease have been shown to be partly related to an altered retina-SCN-pineal axis (Skene & Swaab, 2003). Loss or damage of neurons in the hypothalamic SCN and other parts of the circadian-timing system have been implicated in the circadian disturbances of demented patients (Swabb et al., 1985; van Someren, 2000).

In several studies the circadian rhythmicity of core body temperature (one of the most stable indicators of circadian oscillation that influences length and timing of sleep, for ref. see (Mishima et al., 2000)) was found to be disturbed in AD patients. Circadian alterations are detectable at an advanced stage of AD, with large acrophases between rest activity and core body temperature rhythms and reduced rhythm amplitudes and nocturnal rest, indicating a diminished capacity to synchronize body rhythms with behavior (Satlin et al., 1995). At an earlier phase of AD circadian alterations tended to be attenuated (Mishima et al., 2000).

A chronobiological phenomenon in AD related to sleep disturbances is "sundowning". Symptoms of sundowning agitation include a reduced ability to maintain attention to external stimuli, disorganized thinking and speech, a variety of motor disturbances including agitation, wandering and repetitious physical behaviors, and perceptual and emotional disturbances (Taylor et al., 1997). The delirium-like symptoms associated with sundowning are usually more prevalent in the late afternoon to early evening. Medication toxicity, infection, electrolytic disturbance or environmental factors can all be triggers for sundowning. Partial arousals from REM sleep have also been linked in dementia patients to episodes of increased night time confusion and agitation (Feinberg et al., 1965). Management of sundowning behavior is difficult because most drugs have undesirable side effects in AD.

Because of this a chronobiological approach including restriction of daytime sleep, exposure to bright light and social interaction schedules during the day have been proposed for regulating sleep disorders and behavioral problems in the elderly (McGaffigan & Bliwise, 1997; Mishima et al., 2000).

However, there is a very significant risk of retinal damage from repetitious exposure to the high intensities of visible light provided by bright light units in this population since a substantial number of studies have indicated that age related macular degeneration is the result of natural aging processes exacerbated by the cumulative effects of photo-oxidative damage (Barron et al., 2001; Beatty et al., 2000; Boulton & Dayhaw-Barker, 2001; Cai et al., 2000; Hall & Gale, 2002; Roberts, 2001). In the elderly, the capacity of protective mechanisms which naturally protect the retina from light induced oxidative damage is greatly impaired. Additionally elderly people have a very high probability of preexisting retinal damage.

A recent development in this aspect is the demonstration that the spectral sensitivity of the circadian system is very different than the spectral sensitivity of the retina used in visual activities such as reading and used to measure light in illuminating engineering (Brainard et al., 2001). Very short wavelength (blue) light is maximally effective at affecting the circadian system whereas middle wavelengths (yellow-green) are maximally effective for visual performance. By restricting light emission to wavelengths between 480 nm and 515 nm, one can reduce the intensity of light to levels normally used in artificially illuminated environments, thus providing effective stimulation in a comfortable environment and without the risk of retinal damage from high intensity light. In addition, the associate use of an antioxidant substance like melatonin may be useful to reduce potential photooxidative damage in AD patients.

Melatonin can be Effective to Treat Sleep Disorders and Sundowning in Demented Patients

Decreased secretion of melatonin with aging is well documented (Dori et al., 1994; Girotti et al., 2000b; Iguchi et al., 1982; Luboshitzky et al., 2001; Mishima et al., 2000; Mishima et al., 2001; Siegrist et al., 2001) and more profound reductions are reported in populations with dementia (Liu et al., 1999). Moreover a significantly positive correlation between the abnormalities of the rest-activity cycle and a decrease in melatonin secretion occurs (Mishima et al., 2000), although not uniformly (Baskett et al., 2001). An increased melatonin MT1 receptor immunoreactivity signal was recently reported in the hippocampus of AD patients and was attributed to the up-regulation of the receptor as a compensatory response to impaired melatonin levels (Savaskan et al., 2002).

Based on this evidence the supplementary administration of melatonin to treat sleep and behavior disorders in AD patients seemed to be a logical therapeutic approach. Indeed, initial studies of melatonin therapy in AD have had positive results. However, the majority of studies are open, and knowledge about side effects and long-term effects of melatonin is still limited.

In the first examination of the sleep-promoting action of melatonin (3 mg p.o. for 21 days) in a small non-homogenous group of elderly patients with primary insomnia and with insomnia associated with dementia or depression, 7 out of 10 dementia patients having sleep disorders and treated with melatonin (3 mg p.o. at bed time) showed decreased sundowning and reduced variability of sleep onset time (Fainstein et al., 1997). In another study, 10 individuals with mild cognitive impairment were given 6 mg of melatonin before bedtime. Improvement was found in sleep, mood and memory (Jean-Louis et al., 1998a).

Other studies include daily administration of 6-9 mg melatonin for longer periods of time to AD patients with sleep disorders and sundowning agitation. The retrospective account of 14 AD patients after a 2-3-year period of treatment with melatonin indicated that all improved sleep quality (Brusco et al., 1998a). Sundowning, diagnosed clinically in all patients examined, was not longer detectable in 12 of them, and persisted attenuated in the other 2 patients. Another significant observation in this study was the halted evolution of the cognitive and mnesic alterations expected in comparable populations of patients not receiving melatonin. This should be contrasted with the significant deterioration of clinical conditions of the disease expected from patients after 1-3 years of AD evolution.

Further support for the hypothesis that melatonin can be useful in AD patients was given by a case report study which included two 79 years old male monozygotic twins with AD diagnosed 8 years earlier (Brusco et al., 1998b). The onset of the disease differed by about 6 months between the twins. The patients exhibited similar cognitive and neuroimaging alterations at diagnosis. Patients were treated with vitamin E (800 I.U./day) and, starting about 3 years in advance of assessment, they received 50 mg/day of thioridazine because of behavioral and sleep disorders. Patient NN, who is still alive, has been treated with 6 mg /day of melatonin at bed time daily for more than 6 years. Three months after starting melatonin treatment, patient NN discontinued thioridazine. At the time of case report publication (36 months of treatment), a neuropsychological evaluation by the Functional Assessment Tool For Alzheimer's Disease (FAST) indicated a 7b stage for patient ZZ and a 5 stage for patient NN, with Mini-Mental scores of 0/30 and 10/30, respectively. A generalized cortical atrophy in both patients, with a more important bitemporal atrophy and ventricular enlargement in patient ZZ, was seen in NMR (Brusco et al., 1998b). Pacing in patient ZZ was intense and increased at the evening; he was an insomniac and exhibited sundowning episodes. Patient NN showed normal walking and only rudiments of primitive reflexes. Sleep-vigilance rhythm in patient NN was unimpaired. Six months after case report publication, the twin not receiving melatonin died because of a complication from AD while his brother was still alive, showing normal sleep and severe impairment of cognitive function (Mini-Mental has changed from 10/30 to 0/30; FAST: 6b stage).

Other studies also support the efficacy of melatonin treatment in AD patients. Mishima and co-workers administered a 6 mg dose of melatonin for 4 weeks to 7 inpatients with AD who exhibited irregular sleep-waking cycle (Mishima et al., 2000). Melatonin significantly reduced percentage of nighttime activity compared to placebo. Cohen-Mansfield et al. reported the efficacy of melatonin (3 mg/day at bed time) for improving sleep and alleviating sundowning in 11 elderly AD patients (Cohen-Mansfield et al., 2000). An analysis revealed a significant decrease in agitated behavior and a significant decrease in daytime sleepiness. In a case report observation on two AD patients, melatonin administration enhanced and stabilized the circadian rest-activity rhythm in one of them along with reduction of daytime sleepiness and improvement in mood (Jean-Louis et al., 1998b). Likewise, another observation on two AD patients given 6 mg melatonin daily for one year indicated appreciable improvement of the Mini-Mental score (Pappolla et al., 2000).

We recently assessed the capacity of melatonin to improve sleep in 45 AD patients with sleep disturbances following 4 months of treatment with 6-9 mg melatonin/day (Cardinali et al., 2002b). A significant effect of the treatment on global subjective evaluation of sleep was detected in this group. Moreover, sundowning, clinically diagnosed in all patients disappeared after 4 months of treatment with melatonin. The effect of melatonin was seen regardless of any concomitant medication employed to treat cognitive or behavioral signs of disease.

Observations in AD patients, however, are not always consistent. In a double blind randomized placebo controlled trial on the effect of 6 mg/day of melatonin for two weeks in demented patients with sleep disorders, melatonin had no effect on median total time asleep, number of awakenings or sleep efficiency (Serfaty et al., 2002). It must be noted that the doses employed and, particularly, the short term of observation might account for this discrepancy with earlier results. As noted above, melatonin effect in synchronizing the circadian clock sometimes needs weeks to develop.

Melatonin May Act Both as a Chronobiotic and an Antioxidant in AD

The mechanisms accounting for the possible therapeutic effect of melatonin in AD patients remain unknown. Melatonin treatment promotes mainly non-REM sleep in the elderly (Monti et al., 1999), and can be beneficial in AD by augmenting the restorative phases of sleep, including the augmented secretion of growth hormone (van Coevorden et al., 1991). In addition, a compelling amount of evidence now indicates that melatonin is also a potent antioxidant that passes through cell membranes, thus differing from other clinically employed antioxidants like vitamin E which promotes the synthesis of a number of antioxidant enzymes [for ref. see (Reiter et al., 2001a; Reiter et al., 2002)].

Formation of insoluble senile (amyloid) plaques and of neurofibrillary tangles are typical findings in the brain of AD patients (Mesulam, 1999; Vassar et al., 1999). Beta amyloid peptide, the primary component of senile plaques, is formed by proteolytic cleavage of a large transmembrane glycoprotein, the amyloid precursor protein (Haass et al., 1992). Degeneration of neurons is often seen in association with senile plaques (Selkoe, 1991), an effect attributed to beta amyloid-induced generation of free radicals resulting in neuronal dysfunction and loss (Miranda et al., 2000; Reiter et al., 1999; Reiter et al., 2000; Shearman et al., 1994). Toxic effects of beta amyloid peptide also include alteration of Ca^{2+} homeostasis (Weiss et al., 1994) and induction of apoptosis (Loo et al., 1993). The toxic activity of the molecule is localized to amino acid residues 25-35 of the full-length beta amyloid peptide (Mattson et al., 1992).

In vitro data indicated that melatonin protects neurons against beta amyloid toxicity, prevents beta amyloid-induced lipid peroxidation and alters the metabolism of the beta amyloid precursor protein [for ref. see (Pappolla et al., 2000)]. Since there was no published study on the circadian consequences of injecting beta amyloid peptide in experimental animals, we recently assessed whether melatonin had the ability to protect against the circadian changes produced by beta amyloid peptide 25 – 35 microinjection in SCN of golden hamsters (Furio et al., 2002). Melatonin was given in the drinking water (25 μg/ml) starting 15 days in advance to the microinjection of beta amyloid peptide into SCN. Beta amyloid-treated hamsters exhibited a significant phase advance of onset of running activity as compared to saline-injected animals. They also showed a significantly greater variability in onset time of wheel running activity, mainly evident from 6 to 15 days of treatment. Melatonin administration prevented the phase advance of onset time and the increased variability of onset time brought about by the beta amyloid peptide. These results described for the first time the circadian consequences of injecting beta amyloid peptide 25 – 35 in the SCN of hamsters (Furio et al., 2002). The "fixing" effect of melatonin on onset time reported in hamsters administered with beta amyloid peptide in their SCN somewhat resembles the reduction in variability of sleep onset time reported in demented (Fainstein et al., 1997) and non-demented patients (Cardinali et al., 2002c).

Since there is information indicating that supplementation with antioxidants delayed development of AD (Kontush et al., 2001; Sano et al., 1997), melatonin treatment may constitute a selection therapy to slow evolution of cognitive impairment in AD patients because it combines a potent antioxidant activity with the amelioration of sundowning, the latter not observed with the use of regular antioxidants. Moreover, the combined treatment of melatonin together with bright light has the potential advantage of a preventing antioxidant effect of melatonin on harmful photooxidative processes at the retinal level.

A note of caution, however, emerges as far as the associated use of both procedures. In a placebo-controlled study on the efficacy of bright light therapy and melatonin in motor restless behavior in dementia, 6 demented inpatients who completed the trial exhibited positive when bright light was combined with placebo but not with melatonin (Haffmans et al., 2001). To what extent the timing of the melatonin intake could interfere with light deserves to be further examined.

CONCLUSIONS

People with dementia are among the most vulnerable in our society. Symptoms often need to be treated expediently, and commonly employed drugs, although moderately effective, can be hazardous. Melatonin and light treatment seem to be safe and effective and may have an important role in managing sundowning in people with dementia. Indeed, initial studies of melatonin therapy in AD have had positive results. However, these studies are only few in number and are open, and knowledge about side effects and long-term effects of melatonin is still limited.

Acknowledgments

Studies in the authors′ laboratory were supported by the University of Buenos Aires, the Consejo Nacional de Investigaciones Científicas y Técnicas, Argentina, the Agencia Nacional de Promoción Científica y Tecnológica, Argentina (PICT 6153), Fundación Bunge y Born, Buenos Aires and Fundación Antorchas, Buenos Aires.

References

Andrade C, Srihari BS, Reddy KP, Chandramma L (2001): Melatonin in medically ill patients with insomnia: a double-blind, placebo-controlled study. *J Clin Psychiatry 62:* 41-45

Anton-Tay F, (1974): Melatonin: effects on brain function. *Adv Biochem Psychopharmacol 11:* 315-324

Arendt J, (1999): Jet-lag and shift work: (2). Therapeutic use of melatonin. *J R Soc Med 92:* 402-405

Arendt J, Skene DJ, Middleton B, Lockley SW, Deacon S (1997): Efficacy of melatonin treatment in jet lag, shift work, and blindness. *J Biol Rhythms 12:* 604-617

Ayalon L, Hermesh H, Dagan Y (2002): Case study of circadian rhythm sleep disorder following haloperidol treatment: reversal by risperidone and melatonin. *Chronobiol Int 19:* 947-959

Badia P, Hughes R, Murphy BD, Myers BL, Wright K (1996): Effects of exogenous melatonin on memory, sleepiness, and performance after a 4-hr nap. *J Sleep Res 5 (suppl. 1):* 11

Barron MJ, Johnson MA, Andrews RM, Clarke MP, Griffiths PG, Bristow E, He LP, Durham S, Turnbull DM (2001): Mitochondrial abnormalities in ageing macular photoreceptors. *Investigative Ophthalmology and Visual Science 42:* 3016-3022

Baskett JJ, Wood PC, Broad JB, Duncan JR, English J, Arendt J (2001): Melatonin in older people with age-related sleep maintenance problems: a comparison with age matched normal sleepers. *Sleep 24:* 418-424

Beatty S, Koh H, Phil M, Henson D, Boulton M (2000): The role of oxidative stress in the pathogenesis of age-related macular degeneration. *Surv Ophthalmol 45:* 115-134

Bersani G, Garavini A (2000): Melatonin add-on in manic patients with treatment resistant insomnia. *Prog Neuropsychopharmacol Biol Psychiatry 24:* 185-191

Boulton M, Dayhaw-Barker P (2001): The role of the retinal pigment epithelium: topographical variation and ageing changes. *Eye 15:* 384-389

Brainard GC, Hanifin JP, Greeson JM, Byrne B, Glickman G, Gerner E, Rollag MD (2001): Action spectrum for melatonin regulation in humans: evidence for a novel circadian photoreceptor. *J Neurosci 21:* 6405-6412

Brusco LI, Marquez M, Cardinali DP (1998a): Melatonin treatment stabilizes chronobiologic and cognitive symptoms in Alzheimer's disease. *Neuroendocrinology Letters 19:* 111-115

Brusco LI, Marquez M, Cardinali DP (1998b): Monozygotic twins with Alzheimer's disease treated with melatonin: Case report. *J Pineal Res 25:* 260-263

Cagnacci A, (1996): Melatonin in relation to physiology in adult humans. *J Pineal Res 21:* 200-213

Cai J, Nelson KC, Wub M, Sternberg P, Jones DP (2000): Oxidative damage and protection of the RPE. *Progress in Retinal and Eye Research 19:* 205-221

Cajochen C, Krauchi K, von Arx MA, Mori D, Graw P, Wirz-Justice A (1996): Daytime melatonin administration enhances sleepiness and theta/alpha activity in the waking EEG. *Neurosci Lett 207:* 209-213

Cardinali DP, Bortman GP, Liotta G, Perez LS, Albornoz LE, Cutrera RA, Batista J, Ortega GP (2002a): A multifactorial approach employing melatonin to accelerate resynchronization of sleep-wake cycle after a 12 time-zone westerly transmeridian flight in elite soccer athletes. *J Pineal Res 32:* 41-46

Cardinali DP, Brusco LI, Liberczuk C, Furio AM (2002b): The use of melatonin in Alzheimer's disease. *Neuroendocrinology Letters 23 (suppl. 1):* 26-29

Cardinali DP, Gvozdenovich, E., Kaplan MR, Fainstein I, Shifis HA, Pérez Lloret S, Albornoz LE, Negri A (2002c): A double blind-placebo controlled study on melatonin efficacy to reduce anxiolytic benzodiazepine use in the elderly. *Neuroendocrinology Letters 23:* 55-60

Cardinali DP, Lynch HJ, Wurtman RJ (1972): Binding of melatonin to human and rat plasma proteins. *Endocrinology 91:* 1213-1218

Cardinali DP, Pevet P (1998): Basic aspects of melatonin action. *Sleep Med Rev 2:* 175-190

Cardinali DP, Rosenstein RE, Golombek DA, Chuluyan HE, Kanterewicz B, Del Zar MM, Vacas MI (1991): Melatonin binding sites in brain: Single or multiple? *Advances in Pineal Research 5:* 159-165

Carpenter BD, Strauss ME, Patterson MB (1995): Sleep disturbances in community-dwelling patients with Alzheimer's disease. *Clin Gerontologist 16:* 35-49

Catala MD, Quay WB, Vibat PS, Timiras PS (1987): Hypothyroidism and rehabilitation of day and night melatonin levels in pineal, hypothalamus and serum of male rats. *Neuroendocrinol Lett 9:* 378-388

Citera G, Arias MA, Maldonado-Cocco JA, Lazaro MA, Rosemffet MG, Brusco LI, Scheines EJ, Cardinalli DP (2000): The effect of melatonin in patients with fibromyalgia: a pilot study. *Clin Rheumatol 19:* 9-13

Claustrat B, Brun J, David M, Sassolas G, Chazot G (1992): Melatonin and jet lag: confirmatory result using a simplified protocol. *Biol Psychiatry 32:* 705-711

Cohen-Mansfield J, Garfinkel D, Lipson S (2000): Melatonin for treatment of sundowning in elderly persons with dementia. *Arch Gerontol Geriatr 31:* 65-76

Cramer H, Rudolph J, Consbruch U, Kendel K (1974): On the effects of melatonin on sleep and behavior in man. *Adv Biochem Psychopharmacol 11:* 187-191

Czeisler CA, (1997): Commentary: evidence for melatonin as a circadian phase-shifting agent. *J Biol Rhythms 12:* 618-623

Dalton EJ, Rotondi D, Levitan RD, Kennedy SH, Brown GM (2000): Use of slow-release melatonin in treatment-resistant depression. *J Psychiatry Neurosci 25:* 48-52

Dijk DJ, Lockley SW (2002): Integration of human sleep-wake regulation and circadian rhythmicity. *J Appl Physiol 92:* 852-862

Dijk DJ, Roth C, Landolt HP, Werth E, Aeppli M, Achermann P, Borbely AA (1995): Melatonin effect on daytime sleep in men: suppression of EEG low frequency activity and enhancement of spindle frequency activity. *Neurosci Lett 201:* 13-16

Dollins AB, Zhdanova IV, Wurtman RJ, Lynch HJ, Deng MH (1994): Effect of inducing nocturnal serum melatonin concentrations in daytime on sleep, mood, body temperature, and performance. *Proc Natl Acad Sci U S A 91:* 1824-1828

Dori D, Casale G, Solerte SB, Fioravanti M, Migliorati G, Cuzzoni G, Ferrari E (1994): Chrono-neuroendocrinological aspects of physiological aging and senile dementia. *Chronobiologia 21:* 121-126

Edwards BJ, Atkinson G, Waterhouse J, Reilly T, Godfrey R, Budgett R Use of melatonin in recovery from jet-lag following an eastward flight across 10 time-zones. *Ergonomics 2000 Oct;43 (10):1501 -13 43:* 1501-1513

Ellis CM, Lemmens G, Parkes JD (1996): Melatonin and insomnia. *J Sleep Res 5:* 61-65

Fainstein I, Bonetto A, Brusco LI, Cardinali DP (1997): Effects of melatonin in elderly patients with sleep disturbance. A pilot study. *Curr Ther Res 58:* 990-1000

Feinberg I, Koresco RL, Schaffner IR (1965): Sleep electroencephalographic and eye-movement patterns in patients with chronic brain syndrome. *J Psychiatric Res 3:* 11-26

Fraser J, Wraith JE, Delatycki MB (2002): Sleep disturbance in mucopolysaccharidosis type III (Sanfilippo syndrome): a survey of managing clinicians. *Clin Genet 62:* 418-421

Furio AM, Cutrera RA, Castillo Thea V, Pérez Lloret S, Riccio P, Caccuri RL, Brusco LI, Cardinali DP (2002): Effect of melatonin on changes in locomotor activity rhythm of Syrian hamsters injected with beta amyloid peptide 25–35 in the suprachiasmatic nuclei. *Cel Mol Neurobiol 22:* 699-709

Galvan MM, Campistol J, Monros E, Poo P, Vernet AM, Pineda M, Sans A, Colomer J, Conill JJ, Sanmarti FX (2002): Angelman syndrome: physical characteristics and behavioural phenotype in 37 patients with confirmed genetic diagnosis. *Rev Neurol 35:* 425-429

Garfinkel D, Laudon M, Nof D, Zisapel N (1995): Improvement of sleep quality in elderly people by controlled-release melatonin. *Lancet 346:* 541-544

Garfinkel D, Zisapel N, Wainstein J, Laudon M (1999): Facilitation of benzodiazepine discontinuation by melatonin: a new clinical approach. *Arch Intern Med 159:* 2456-2460

Gilbert SS, Van Den Heuvel CJ, Dawson D (1999): Daytime melatonin and temazepam in young adult humans: equivalent effects on sleep latency and body temperatures. *J Physiol (Lond) 514 (Pt 3):* 905-914

Girotti L, Lago M, Ianovsky O, Carbajales J, Elizari MV, Brusco LI, Cardinali DP (2000a): Low urinary 6-sulphatoxymelatonin levels in patients with coronary artery disease. *J Pineal Res 29:* 138-142

Girotti L, Lago M, Yanovsky O, Carbajales J, Elizari M, Brusco LI, Cardinali DP (2000b): Low urinary 6-sulphatoxymelatonin levels in patients with coronary artery disease. *J Pineal Res 29:* 138-142

Giubilei F, Patacchioli FR, Antonini G, Sepe MM, Tisei P, Bastianello S, Monnazzi P, Angelucci L (2001): Altered circadian cortisol secretion in Alzheimer's disease: clinical and neuroradiological aspects. *J Neurosci Res 66:* 262-265

Golombek DA, Escolar E, Burin LJ, De Brito S, Fernandez DD, Cardinali DP (1992): Chronopharmacology of melatonin: inhibition by benzodiazepine antagonism. *Chronobiol Int 9:* 124-131

Golombek DA, Martini M, Cardinali DP (1993): Melatonin as an anxiolytic in rats: Time-dependence and interaction with the central gabaergic system. *Eur J Pharmacol 237:* 231-236

Golombek DA, Pevet P, Cardinali DP (1996): Melatonin effects on behavior: possible mediation by the central GABAergic system. *Neurosci Biobehav Rev 20:* 403-412

Graw P, Werth E, Krauchi K, Gutzwiller F, Cajochen C, Wirz-Justice A (2001): Early morning melatonin administration impairs psychomotor vigilance. *Behav Brain Res 121:* 167-172

Haass C, Schlossmacher MG, Hung AY, Vigo-Pelfrey C, Mellon A, Ostaszewski BL (1992): Amyloid beta-peptide is produced by cultured cells during normal metabolism. *Nature 359:* 322-325

Haffmans PMJ, Sival RC, Lucius SAP, Cats Q, Van Gelder L (2001): Bright light therapy and melatonin in motor restless behaviour in dementia: A placebo-controlled study. *International Journal of Geriatric Psychiatry 16:* 106-110

Haimov I, Lavie P (1995): Potential of melatonin replacement therapy in older patients with sleep disorders. *Drugs Aging 7:* 75-78

Hall NF, Gale CR (2002): Prevention of age related macular degeneration. *BMJ 325:* 1-2

Hanania M, Kitain E (2002): Melatonin for treatment and prevention of postoperative delirium. *Anesth Analg 94:* 338-9, table

Harper DG, Stopa EG, McKee AC, Satlin A, Harlan PC, Goldstein R, Volicer L (2001): Differential circadian rhythm disturbances in men with Alzheimer disease and frontotemporal degeneration. *Arch Gen Psychiatry 58:* 353-360

Hayashi E, (2000): Effect of melatonin on sleep-wake rhythm: the sleep diary of an autistic male. *Psychiatry Clin Neurosci 54:* 383-384

Herxheimer A, Petrie KJ (2001): Melatonin for preventing and treating jet lag (Cochrane Review). *Cochrane Database Syst Rev 1:* CD001520

Holmes AL, Gilbert SS, Dawson D (2002): Melatonin and zopiclone: the relationship between sleep propensity and body temperature. *Sleep 25:* 301-306

Hoogendijk WJ, van Someren EJ, Mirmiran M, Hofman MA, Lucassen PJ, Zhou JN, Swaab DE (1996): Circadian rhythm-related behavioral disturbances and structural hypothalamic changes in Alzheimer's disease. *Int Psychogeriatr 8:* 245-252

Hughes RJ, Sack RL, Lewy AJ (1998): The role of melatonin and circadian phase in age-related sleep- maintenance insomnia: assessment in a clinical trial of melatonin replacement. *Sleep 21:* 52-68

Iguchi H, Kato KI, Ibayashi H (1982): Age-dependent reduction in serum melatonin concentrations in healthy human subjects. *J Clin Endocrinol Metab 55:* 27-29

James SP, Mendelson WB, Sack DA, Rosenthal NE, Wehr TA (1987): The effect of melatonin on normal sleep. *Neuropsychopharmacology 1:* 41-44

James SP, Sack DA, Rosenthal NE, Mendelson WB (1990): Melatonin administration in insomnia. *Neuropsychopharmacology 3:* 19-23

Jan JE, Hamilton D, Seward N, Fast DK, Freeman RD, Laudon M (2000): Clinical trials of controlled-release melatonin in children with sleep-wake cycle disorders. *J Pineal Res 29:* 34-39

Jan JE, Tai J, Hahn G, Rothstein RR (2001): Melatonin replacement therapy in a child with a pineal tumor. *J Child Neurol 16:* 139-140

Jean-Louis G, von Gizycki H, Zizi F (1998a): Melatonin effects on sleep, mood, and cognition in elderly with mild cognitive impairment. *J Pineal Res 25:* 177-183

Jean-Louis G, Zizi F, von Gizycki H, Taub H (1998b): Effects of melatonin in two individuals with Alzheimer's disease. *Percept Mot Skills 87:* 331-339

Kamei Y, Hayakawa T, Urata J, Uchiyama M, Shibui K, Kim K, Kudo Y, Okawa M (2000): Melatonin treatment for circadian rhythm sleep disorders. *Psychiatry Clin Neurosci 54:* 381-382

Kennaway DJ, Wright H (2002): Melatonin and circadian rhythms. *Curr Top Med Chem 2:* 199-209

Kontush A, Mann U, Ant S, Ujeyl A, Lürs C, Müller-Thomsen T, Beisiegel U (2001): Influence of vitamin E and C supplementation on lipoprotein oxidation in patients with Alzheimer's disease. *Free Rad Biol Med 31:* 345-354

Kripke DF, (2000): Chronic hypnotic use: Deadly risks, doubtful benefit. *Sleep Medicine Rev 4:* 5-20

Kunz D, Bes F (1999): Melatonin as a therapy in REM sleep behavior disorder patients: an open- labeled pilot study on the possible influence of melatonin on REM-sleep regulation. *Mov Disord 14:* 507-511

Kunz D, Bes F (2001): Exogenous melatonin in periodic limb movement disorder: an open clinical trial and a hypothesis. *Sleep 24:* 183-187

Lavie P, (1997): Melatonin: role in gating nocturnal rise in sleep propensity. *J Biol Rhythms 12:* 657-665

Lerner AB, Case MD (1960): Melatonin. *Fed Proc 19:* 590-592

Lieberman HR, Waldhauser F, Garfield G, Lynch HJ, Wurtman RJ (1984): Effects of melatonin on human mood and performance. *Brain Res 323:* 201-207

Lino A, Silvy S, Condorelli L, Rusconi AC (1993): Melatonin and jet lag: treatment schedule. *Biol Psychiatry 34:* 587

Liu RY, Zhou JN, van Heerikhuize J, Hofman MA, Swaab DF (1999): Decreased melatonin levels in postmortem cerebrospinal fluid in relation to aging, Alzheimer's disease, and apolipoprotein E-epsilon4/4 genotype. *J Clin Endocrinol Metab 84:* 323-327

Lockley SW, Skene DJ, James K, Thapan K, Wright J, Arendt J (2000): Melatonin administration can entrain the free-running circadian system of blind subjects. *J Endocrinol 164:* R1-R6

Loo DT, Copani A, Pike CJ, Whittemore ER, Walencewicz AJ, Cotman CW (1993): Apoptosis is induced by beta-amyloid in culture central nervous system neurons. *Proc Natl Acad Sci U S A 90:* 7951-7955

Luboshitzky R, Shen-Orr Z, Tzischichinsky O, Maldonado M, Herer P, Lavie P (2001): Actigraphic sleep-wake patterns and urinary 6-sulfatoxymelatonin excretion in patients with Alzheimer's disease. *Chronobiol Int 18:* 513-524

MacFarlane JG, Cleghorn JM, Brown GM, Streiner DL (1991): The effects of exogenous melatonin on the total sleep time and daytime alertness of chronic insomniacs: a preliminary study. *Biol Psychiatry 30:* 371-376

Manfredini R, Manfredini F, Conconi F Standard melatonin intake and circadian rhythms of elite athletes after a transmeridian flight. *J Int Med Res 2000 Jul -Aug; 28 (4):182 -6 28:* 182-186

Mattson MP, Cheng B, Davis D, Bryant K, Lieberburg I, Rydel RE (1992): Beta-Amyloid peptides destabilize calcium homeostasis and render human cortical neurons vulnerable to excitotoxicity. *J Neurosci 12:* 376-389

McCurry SM, Reynolds CF, Ancoli-Israel S, Teri L, Vitiello MV (2000): Treatment of sleep disturbance in Alzheimer's disease. *Sleep Medicine Rev 4:* 603-628

McGaffigan S, Bliwise DL (1997): The treatment of sundowning. A selective review of pharmacological and nonpharmacological studies. *Drugs Aging 10:* 10-17

Mesulam MM, (1999): Neuroplasticity failure in Alzheimer's disease: bridging the gap between plaques and tangles. *Neuron 24:* 521-529

Miranda S, Opaza C, Larrondo LF, Mu±oz FJ, Ruiz F, Leighton F, Inestrosa NC (2000): The role of oxidative stress in the toxicity induced by amyloid beta-peptide in Alzheimer's disease. *Prog Neurobiol 62:* 633-648

Mishima K, Okawa M, Hozumi S, Hishikawa Y (2000): Supplementary administration of artificial bright light and melatonin as potent treatment for disorganized circadian rest-activity and dysfunctional autonomic and neuroendocrine systems in institutionalized demented elderly persons. *Chronobiol Int 17:* 419-432

Mishima K, Okawa M, Shimizu T, Hishikawa Y (2001): Diminished melatonin secretion in the elderly caused by insufficient environmental illumination. *J Clin Endocrinol Metab 86:* 129-134

Monti JM, Alvarino F, Cardinali D, Savio I, Pintos A (1999): Polysomnographic study of the effect of melatonin on sleep in elderly patients with chronic primary insomnia. *Archives of Gerontology and Geriatrics 28:* 85-98

Nagtegaal JE, Laurant MW, Kerkhof GA, Smits MG, van der Meer YG, Coenen AM (2000): Effects of melatonin on the quality of life in patients with delayed sleep phase syndrome. *J Psychosom Res 48:* 45-50

Nave R, Peled R, Lavie P (1995): Melatonin improves evening napping. *Eur J Pharmacol 275:* 213-216

Ninomiya T, Iwatani N, Tomoda A, Miike T (2001): Effects of exogenous melatonin on pituitary hormones in humans. *Clin Physiol 21:* 292-299

Pace-Schott EF, Hobson JA (2002): The neurobiology of sleep: genetics, cellular physiology and subcortical networks. *Nature Neurosci Rev 3:* 591-605

Pang SF, Brown G (1983): Regional concentrations of melatonin in in the rat brain in the light and dark period. *Life Sci 33:* 1199-1204

Pappolla MA, Chyan Y, Poeggeler B, Frangione B, Wilson G, Ghiso J, Reiter RJ (2000): An assessment of the antioxidant and the antiamyloidogenic properties of melatonin: Implications for Alzheimer's disease. *J Neural Transm 107:* 203-231

Petrie K, Conaglen JV, Thompson L, Chamberlain K (1989): Effect of melatonin on jet lag after long haul flights. *BMJ 298:* 705-707

Pillar G, Shahar E, Peled N, Ravid S, Lavie P, Etzioni A (2000): Melatonin improves sleep-wake patterns in psychomotor retarded children. *Pediatr Neurol 23:* 225-228

Reid K, Van den Heuvel C, Dawson D (1996): Day-time melatonin administration: effects on core temperature and sleep onset latency. *J Sleep Res 5:* 150-154

Reiter RJ, (1995): Functional pleiotropy of the neurohormone melatonin: antioxidant protection and neuroendocrine regulation. *Front Neuroendocrinol 16:* 383-415

Reiter RJ, Acuna-Castroviejo D, Tan DX, Burkhardt S (2001a): Free radical-mediated molecular damage. Mechanisms for the protective actions of melatonin in the central nervous system. *Ann N Y Acad Sci 939:* 200-215

Reiter RJ, Cabrera J, Sainz RM, Mayo JC, Manchester LC, Tan DX (1999): Melatonin as a pharmacological agent against neuronal loss in experimental models of Huntington's disease, Alzheimer's disease and Parkinsonism. *Ann N Y Acad Sci 890:* 471-485

Reiter RJ, Tan DX (2003): What constitutes a physiological concentration of melatonin? *J Pineal Res 34:* 79-80

Reiter RJ, Tan DX, Acuna-Castroviejo D, Burkhardt S, Karbownik M (2000): Melatonin: Mechanisms and actions as an antioxidant. *Curr Top Biophys 24:* 171-183

Reiter RJ, Tan DX, Allegra M (2002): Melatonin: Reducing molecular pathology and dysfunction due to free radicals and associated reactants. *Neuroendocrinol Lett 23 Suppl 1:* 3-8

Reiter RJ, Tan DX, Burkhardt S, Manchester LC (2001b): Melatonin in plants. *Nutr Rev 59:* 286-290

Roberts JE, (2001): Ocular phototoxicity. *J Photochem Photobiol B 64:* 136-143

Ross C, Davies P, Whitehouse W (2002): Melatonin treatment for sleep disorders in children with neurodevelopmental disorders: an observational study. *Dev Med Child Neurol 44:* 339-344

Samel A, (1999): Melatonin and jet-lag. *Eur J Med Res 4:* 385-388

Sano M, Ernesto C, Thomas RG, Klauber MR, Schafer K, Grundman M, Woodbury P, Growdon J, Corman CW (1997): A controlled trial of selegiline, alpha-tocopherol, or both as treatment for Alzheimer's disease. *N Engl J Med 336:* 1216-1222

Satlin A, Volicer L, Stopa EG, Harper D (1995): Circadian locomotor activity and core-body temperature rhythms in Alzheimer's disease. *Neurobiol Aging 16:* 765-771

Satomura T, Sakamoto T, Shirakawa S, Tsutsumi Y, Mukai M, Ohyama T, Uchimura N, Maeda H (2001): Hypnotic action of melatonin during daytime administration and its comparison with triazolam. *Psychiatry Clin Neurosci 55:* 303-304

Savaskan E, Olivieri G, Meier F, Brydon L, Jockers R, Ravid R, Wirz-Justice A (2002): Increased melatonin 1a-receptor immunoreactivity in the hippocampus of Alzheimer's disease patients. *J Pineal Res 32:* 59-62

Seabra MLV, Bignotto M, Pinto LR, Tufik S (2000): Randomized, double-blind clinical trial, controlled with placebo, of the toxicology of chronic melatonin treatment. *J Pineal Res 29:* 193-200

Selkoe DJ, (1991): The molecular pathology of Alzheimer's disease. *Nature 6:* 487-498

Serfaty M, Kennell-Webb S, Warner J, Blizard R, Raven P (2002): Double blind randomised placebo controlled trial of low dose melatonin for sleep disorders in dementia. *Int J Geriatr Psychiatry 17:* 1120-1127

Shearman MS, Ragan CI, Iversen LL (1994): Inhibition of PC12 cell redox activity is a specific, early indicator of the mechanism of beta-amyloid-mediated cell death. *Proc Natl Acad Sci U S A 91:* 1470-1474

Shilo L, Dagan Y, Smorjik Y, Weinberg U, Dolev S, Komptel B, Shenkman L (2000): Effect of melatonin on sleep quality of COPD intensive care patients: a pilot study. *Chronobiol Int 17:* 71-76

Shirakawa SI, Sakamoto T, Uchimura N, Tsutsumi Y, Tanaka J, Maeda H (2001): Effect of melatonin on sleep and rectal temperature of young healthy evening types. *Psychiatry Clin Neurosci 55:* 301-302

Siegrist C, Benedetti C, Orlando A, Beltran JM, Tuchscherr L, Noseda CM, Brusco LI, Cardinali DP (2001): Lack of changes in serum prolactin, FSH, TSH, and estradiol after melatonin treatment in doses that improve sleep and reduce benzodiazepine consumption in sleep-disturbed, middle-aged, and elderly patients. *J Pineal Res 30:* 34-42

Skene DJ, Lockley SW, Arendt J (1999a): Melatonin in Circadian Sleep Disorders in the Blind. *Biol Signals Recept 8:* 90-95

Skene DJ, Lockley SW, Arendt J (1999b): Use of melatonin in the treatment of phase shift and sleep disorders. *Adv Exp Med Biol 467:* 79-84

Skene DJ, Swaab DF (2003): Melatonin rhythmicity: effect of age and Alzheimer's disease. *Exp Gerontol 38:* 199-206

Skinner DC, Malpaux B (1999): High melatonin concentrations in third ventricular cerebrospinal fluid are not due to Galen vein blood recirculating through the choroid plexus. *Endocrinology 140:* 4399-4405

Smits MG, Nagtegaal EE, van der HJ, Coenen AM, Kerkhof GA (2001): Melatonin for chronic sleep onset insomnia in children: a randomized placebo-controlled trial. *J Child Neurol 16:* 86-92

Spitzer RL, Terman M, Williams JB, Terman JS, Malt UF, Singer F, Lewy AJ (1999): Jet lag: clinical features, validation of a new syndrome-specific scale, and lack of response to melatonin in a randomized, double-blind trial. *Am J Psychiatry 156:* 1392-1396

Stone BM, Turner C, Mills SL, Nicholson AN (2000): Hypnotic activity of melatonin. *Sleep 23:* 663-669

Swabb DF, Fliers E, Partiman TS (1985): The suprachiasmatic nucleus of the human brain in relation to sex, age and senile dementia. *Brain Res 342:* 37-44

Takeuchi N, Uchimura N, Hashizume Y, Mukai M, Etoh Y, Yamamoto K, Kotorii T, Ohshima H, Ohshima M, Maeda H (2001): Melatonin therapy for REM sleep behavior disorder. *Psychiatry Clin Neurosci 55:* 267-269

Tan D, Manchester LC, Reiter RJ, Plummer BF (1999): Cyclic 3-hydroxymelatonin: A melatonin metabolite generated as a result of hydroxyl radical scavenging. *Biol Signals Recept 8:* 70-74

Taylor JL, Friedman L, Sheikh J, Yesavage JA (1997): Assessment and management of "sundowning" phenomena. *Semin Clin Neuropsychiatry 2:* 113-122

Terlo L, Laudon M, Tarasch R, Schatz T, Caine YG, Zisapel N (1997): Effects of low doses of melatonin on late afternoon napping and mood. *Biol Rhythm Res 28:* 2-15

Tetsuo M, Markey SP, Kopin IJ (1980): Measurement of 6-hydroxymelatonin in human urine and its diurnal variations. *Life Sci 27:* 105-109

Tricoire H, Locatelli A, Chemineau P, Malpaux B (2002): Melatonin enters the cerebrospinal fluid through the pineal recess. *Endocrinology 143:* 84-90

Tricoire H, Malpaux B, Moller M (2003): Cellular lining of the sheep pineal recess studied by light-, transmission-, and scanning electron microscopy: Morphologic indications for a direct secretion of melatonin from the pineal gland to the cerebrospinal fluid. *J Comp Neurol 456:* 39-47

van Coevorden A, Mockel J, Laurent E, Kerkhofs M, L'Hermite-Baleriaux M, Decoster C, Neve P, Van Cauter E (1991): Neuroendocrine rhythms and sleep in aging men. *Am J Physiol 260:* E651-E661

van Someren EJW, (2000): Circadian rhythms and sleep in human aging. *Chronobiology International 17:* 233-243

Vassar R, Bennett BD, Babu-Khan S, Kahn S, Mendiaz EA, Denis P, Teplow DB, Ross S, Amarante P, Loeloff R, Luo Y, Fisher S, Fuller J, Edenson S, Lile J, Jarosinski MA, Biere AL, Curran E, Burgess T, Louis JC, Collins F, Treanor J, Rogers G, Citron M (1999): Secretase cleavage of Alzheimer's amyloid precursor protein by the transmembrane aspartic protease BACE. *Science 286:* 735-741

Vitiello MV, Prinz PN, Williams DE, Frommlet MS, Ries RK (1990): Sleep disturbances in patients with mild-stage Alzheimer's disease. *J Gerontol Med Sci 45:* M131-M138

Vollrath L, Semm P, Gammel G (1981): Sleep induction by intranasal administration of melatonin. *Adv Biosci 29:* 327-329

Waldhauser F, Saletu B, Trinchard-Lugan I (1990): Sleep laboratory investigations on hypnotic properties of melatonin. *Psychopharmacology (Berl) 100:* 222-226

Wang F, Li J, Wu C, Yang J, Xu F, Zhao Q (2003): The GABA(A) receptor mediates the hypnotic activity of melatonin in rats. *Pharmacol Biochem Behav 74:* 573-578

Wassmer E, Quinn E, Whitehouse W, Seri S (2001): Melatonin as a sleep inductor for electroencephalogram recordings in children. *Clin Neurophysiol 112:* 683-685

Weiss JH, Pike CJ, Cotman CW (1994): Ca2+ channel blockers attenuate beta-amloid peptide toxicity to cortical neurons in culture. *J Neurochem 62:* 372-375

Yang CM, Spielman AJ, D'Ambrosio P, Serizawa S, Nunes J, Birnbaum J (2001): A single dose of melatonin prevents the phase delay associated with a delayed weekend sleep pattern. *Sleep 24:* 272-281

Zhdanova IV, Wurtman RJ, Lynch HJ, Ives JR, Dollins AB, Morabito C, Matheson JK, Schomer DL (1995): Sleep-inducing effects of low doses of melatonin ingested in the evening. *Clin Pharmacol Ther 57:* 552-558

Zhdanova IV, Wurtman RJ, Morabito C, Piotrovska VR, Lynch HJ (1996): Effects of low oral doses of melatonin, given 2-4 hours before habitual bedtime, on sleep in normal young humans. *Sleep 19:* 423-431

Zhdanova IV, Wurtman RJ, Regan MM, Taylor JA, Shi JP, Leclair OU (2001): Melatonin treatment for age-related insomnia. *J Clin Endocrinol Metab 86:* 4727-4730

Zhdanova IV, Wurtman RJ, Wagstaff J (1999): Effects of a low dose of melatonin on sleep in children with Angelman syndrome. *J Pediatr Endocrinol Metab 12:* 57-67

Chapter IV

CYTOKINES IN ALZHEIMER'S DISEASE: VIEWS THROUGH A KALEIDOSCOPE

Ning Quan[*]
Department of Oral Biology
Ohio State University
Columbus, OH 43210

ABSTRACT

Increasing evidence has placed cytokines prominently in the landscape of Alzheimer's pathology. What remain elusive are the functional roles of cytokines in the brain of Alzheimer patients. Three types of hypotheses can be formulated regarding the initiation and progression of Alzheimer's disease in relation to the presence of cytokines in the brain: 1) cytokines are part of the driving force for the pathogenesis of Alzheimer's disease, 2) cytokines are produced as an adaptive response to protect against the neural injury of the Alzheimer's disease that is caused primarily by other factors, and 3) cytokine expression in Alzheimer brains is part of the overall deterioration in the aging process of the central nervous system which results, not from any predominant inducing factors, but from the chronic wear and tear of the entire cellular machinery of the brain. Each of these hypotheses argues for a different treatment strategy. The first suggests that blocking the action of cytokines may be beneficial, the second suggests the contrary, and the third implies that manipulating cytokine pathways in Alzheimer's disease may not be productive at all. Viewing through these hypothetical glasses, it is the hope of this review to identify both the promises and deficits of the emerging research on cytokines and Alzheimer's disease.

[*] Address Correspondence to: Ning Quan, 2214 Postle Hall, 305 W. 12th Avenue, Department of Oral Biology, Ohio State University, Columbus, OH 43210, Phone: 614-292-1657, Fax: 614-292-6087, Email: quan.14@osu.edu.

The classical neuropathology for Alzheimer's disease (AD) was described a century ago. The hallmark features of AD neuropathology are the neuritic plaques (NP) and neurofibrillary tangles (NFT) (see Figure 1). These neural lesions are usually associated with the presence of reactive astrocytes and microglia [3]. In addition, there is selective neuronal loss in the cholinergic nucleus basalis, noradrenergic locus coeruleus, and the dopaminergic substantia nigra in the AD brains [58]. This disease causes significant damage to the neural circuits residing in the cortex and hippocampus. The functional outcome of AD is usually an insidious and progressive decline of cognitive abilities, especially those related to memory. This disease debilitates the elderly and brings forth an enormous burden for the family and community.

The etiology of AD remained unknown for much of the past century. Research in the last 20 years, however, has identified several biochemical pathways through which AD might be induced. The most compelling theories today are the amyloid cascade hypothesis [40] and its antithesis the oxidative stress theory [101]. It is in relationship to these major theories that the involvement of cytokines in AD is evaluated. Although contradicting conclusions have been generated, current AD research has already propelled our understanding of AD into a new era wherein effective therapeutic treatments and management for AD may be rationally designed.

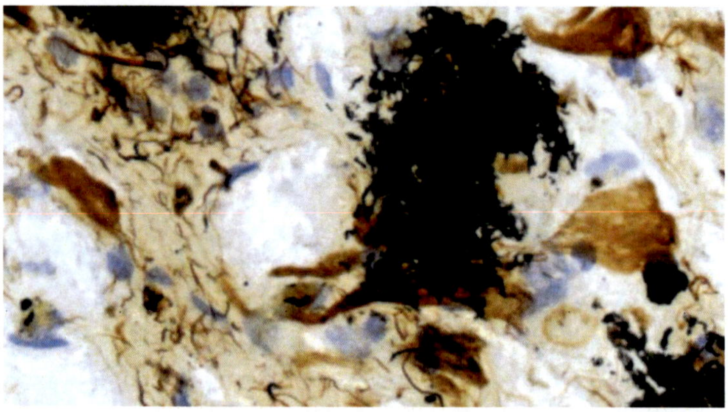

Figure 1. Plaques and tangles in the brain of Alzheimer's disease. Silver staining shows plaques (black) and tangles (brown) from highly affected hippocampus. This figure is generously provided by Dr. Miles Herkenham at the National Institute of Mental Health.

THE AMYLOID CASCADE THEORY

The major advance in AD research started with the biochemical identification of a principal component of the NP, the β-amyloid protein (Aβ) [28]. Subsequently, cDNA of β-amyloid precursor protein (APP) was cloned [49]. β-amyloid protein is derived from enzymatic digestion of APP by the combined activity of β- and γ-secretases [107]. The gene for APP was localized to chromosome 21. This is significant because Down's syndrome is caused by trisomy 21, and aged Down's patients invariably display many of the same neuropathological features as those seen in AD patients [117]. The cloning of the APP naturally led to the postulation that β-amyloid may be a cause rather than a consequence of AD. Soon thereafter, the major component of the neurofibrillary tangles (NFT) was also identified. The protein tau, a microtubule-associated phosphoprotein [37], was shown to form paired helical filaments in the NFT.

The strongest evidence supporting the theory that Aβ is a pathogenic factor for AD came from genetic analysis of inherited forms of AD. A rare form of AD exists in families demonstrating the pattern of autosomal dominant inheritance (Familial AD, FAD). The person carrying the gene mutation invariably developed AD with early onset. Goate et al. were the first to identify a missense mutation of the APP gene that causes FAD [29]. Similar analysis led to the discovery that mutations of two other genes presenilin 1 [97] and presenilin 2 [55] [86] also cause FAD. In addition, the polymorphic allele of apolipoprotein E, ε4, was found to increase the susceptibility in late-onset AD [13]. All of these mutations result in increased production of Aβ, especially Aβ42, which is the earliest and most abundant Aβ species found in the NP of FAD patients [59]. These findings were the basis for the amyloid cascade theory, which states that the deposition of Aβ is the causative agent of AD pathology that initiates the formation of NP and NFT, which in turn, leads to loss of neurons, cerebrovascular damage, and finally the development of dementia [41].

Not surprisingly, studies investigating the role of cytokines in the pathogenesis of AD are tightly linked with the amyloid cascade theory. In fact, the scientific approach for elucidating the role of cytokines in AD is strikingly similar to that used for identifying the importance of Aβ in AD.

THE AMYLOID CASCADE'S CYTOKINE CYCLE COMPONENT

Over-expression of an inflammatory cytokine, interleukin-1α (IL-1) was noted first in the brains of both Down's syndrome and AD patients [35]. IL-1α immunoreactivity was found in activated microglial cells that are located close to the NPs. Specifically, IL-1α immunoreactivity was preferentially localized to activated microglia in NPs without the dense Aβ core (presumably the developing NPs). Less intense IL-1α immunoreactivity was found in the more mature NPs (those with dense Aβ core) and no IL-1α immunoreactivity was found in the so-called burnt-out plaques [33]. Thus, through temporal and spatial association, IL-1 was thought to contribute to the development of NPs in AD [34]. Later, increased levels of IL-6 [119] and tumor necrosis factor–α (TNFα) [18] were also found in the brains of the AD patients. Examination of these cytokines in the cerebrospinal fluid, however, has failed to document increased levels of these inflammatory cytokines in AD patients [23]. Therefore, these inflammatory cytokines may increase and act only locally in the brain regions where NPs are located.

That over-expressed IL-1, TNFα, and IL-6 are biologically active in AD brain may be corroborated by the fact that numerous inflammatory mediators that can be induced by these cytokines are also present in AD brains. These include complement factors C1q, C3b, C3c, C3d, and C4 [22]; chemokines such as the monocyte chemoattractant protein-1 [47] and IP-10[120]; chemokine receptors CXCR2, CCR3 and CCR5 [121]; and key enzymes of inflammation such as nitric oxide synthase (NOS) and cyclooxygenase (COX) [72] [74] [126]

[43]. In addition, inflammatory acute-phase proteins, adhesion molecules, and proteins of the blood coagulation and fibrinolysis systems can all be found near AD Pathology (for an exhaustive review, see Akiyama et al. [1]). Similar molecules and patterns of events are seen in the periphery, where IL-1, IL-6, and TNFα are critical for the induction of the inflammatory machinery that orchestrates a coordinated innate immune response [5,30]. More specifically, the inflammatory mediators found in AD pathology resemble those seen during the inflammatory phase of peripheral wound healing. A cut in the skin, for example, induces the coagulation system to stop bleeding, stimulates the release and synthesis of chemotactic factors in order to recruit phagocytic cells to the wound area to defend against infectious organisms and clear debris, and triggers synthesis of cytokines that induce the production of growth factors important for wound repair [38]. The difference here is that circulating leukocytes do not appear to infiltrate AD brains significantly, and local immune cells, microglia, may function as the major phagocytic cells [105]. These findings were the basis for the suggestion that a chronic inflammatory state exists in AD brains [21].

Further supporting the pathogenic role of inflammatory cytokines in AD is the fact that these cytokines are expressed in conditions that predispose patients to AD-like lesions—head injury [32] [99], aging [67] [9], and epilepsy [96]. Recently, the influence of cytokines on the risk of developing AD has been studied by genetic analyses. For example, IL-1A 2 (-889) is a polymorphism of the IL-1α promoter that confers a four-fold increase in IL-1α levels in vivo [98]. Carriers of this polymorphism have been associated with a three-fold increase in the risk of developing AD [70]. Similarly, polymorphisms of the IL-6 and TNFα genes that lead to increased levels of the respective cytokines were also found to be associated with enhanced risk of AD development [57] [75]. Therefore, inflammatory cytokines are considered by many researchers as significant contributors to the development of AD pathology.

Consistent with this notion are the epidemiological findings that the use of non-steroidal anti-inflammatory drugs (NSAIDs) is associated with significant reduction in the likelihood of developing AD [62]. NSAIDs are known traditionally as the inhibitors of the enzyme COX, which can be induced by inflammatory cytokines. Several studies conducted recently with small sample sizes have showed that the use of NSAIDs may slow down the progression of AD [84,87,90].

Two mechanisms have been proposed regarding how inflammatory cytokines might contribute to the pathogenesis of AD. The first mechanism is that inflammatory cytokines may directly affect the function of the neurons involved in AD. This is supported by one study that showed that IL-1 can enhance the expression of neuronal acetylcholinesterase in vitro and in vivo [56]. Acetylcholinesterase is an enzyme that catalyzes the hydrolysis of the neurotransmitter acetylcholine. Selective depletion of acetylcholine and cholinergic neurons is known to be the most important part of AD neurodegeneration. Therefore, it is possible that IL-1 contributes to the pathogenesis of AD by directly reducing the function of cholinergic neural circuits.

Much more abundant evidence exists supporting the hypothesis that inflammatory cytokines are pathogenic for AD because they induce the production and deposition of Aβ and augment its neurotoxicity. An early study by Donnelly et al. showed that IL-1 can stimulate the promoter for the amyloid precursor protein (APP) gene, suggesting that the production of Aβ may be enhanced by IL-1 [19]. Yang et al., on the other hand, showed that adding IL-1 to cultured glioma cells decreased the expression of APP [124]. Since then, results from most studies favor the conclusion that inflammatory cytokines promote the production of Aβ [6,8,16,36,85,95,125], or indirectly facilitate the production of Aβ by inducing factors such as S100 that stimulate its synthesis [66]. In addition, inflammatory cytokines can stimulate the production of pathological chaperone molecules such as ACT [51] and apo-E to accelerate the assembly of isolated Aβ molecules into Aβ filaments [78]. The formation of the insoluble aggregated Aβ filaments is thought to be a key step that converts the relatively harmless Aβ to the neurotoxic Aβ [65]. Interestingly, Aβ and APP have also been shown to induce the production of various inflammatory cytokines [4,12,16,46,64,108,110,127]. Further, in cultures, it has been shown that high levels of inflammatory cytokines enhance the cytotoxicity of Aβ[25]. Therefore, a vicious cycle can be envisioned whereby Aβ production stimulates cytokine synthesis and cytokines, in turn, stimulate Aβ production and amyloid formation. The end point is the cytokine-enhanced cytotoxicity of Aβ. Figure 2 shows a simplified scheme of the cytokine cycle as championed by Griffin et al. [34].

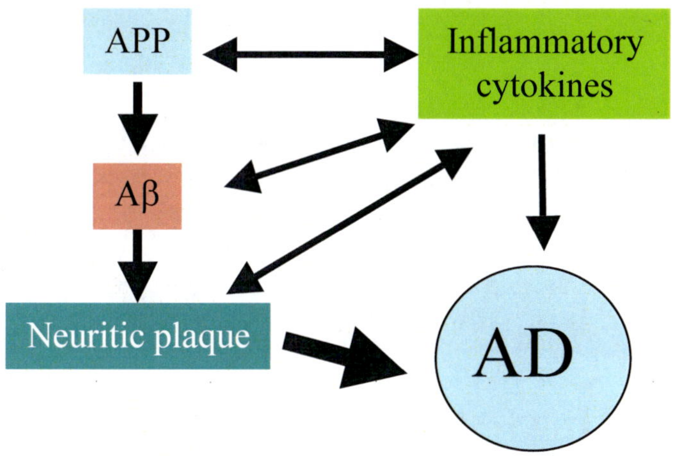

Figure 2. Schematic diagram showing that inflammatory cytokines stimulate the synthesis of APP, enhance the production of Aβ, and contribute to the formation of NP, which may cause AD. In turn, APP, Aβ, and the processes associated with NP trigger the production of inflammatory cytokines. Thus, a cytokine-amyloid cycle may be envisioned as a driving force for the pathogenesis of AD.

Both the amyloid cascade theory and the cytokine cycle theory were generated by a lesion-centric approach. The evidence was gathered in the following manner. First, the AD-specific lesion (the NP) was carefully examined. Second, the presence of molecules associated with the NPs was determined. Third, in vitro and animal experiments were conducted to show that the molecules found at the site of the lesion actually contribute the formation of the lesion. Fourth, genetic analysis was applied to show whether the suspected pathogenic molecules are genetic risk factors. While this approach has undoubtedly made some of the most significant contributions to our understanding of AD, an implicit assumption was that the cause(s) of AD can be found in AD specific lesions. What was obviously ignored was that the cause(s) of AD may exist *before* the formation of the lesions.

The studies conducted by the lesion-centric approach may, therefore, not be able to identify the root cause(s) of AD, but nevertheless pinpoint important mechanisms for the progression of specific types of lesions in AD. Indeed, various lines of transgenic mice mimicking amyloid deposition in AD have failed to demonstrate the complete phenotype of AD pathology [48] [44] [20]. Specifically, none of the AD transgenic mice displayed NFT (although separate taupathy models have been generated), and many of them did not show significant neuronal loss, although varying degrees of cognitive dysfunction have been detected in these animals. What appears definitive is that enhanced production of Aβ (especially Aβ40/42) is necessary and sufficient to drive the development of amyloid plaques. It should be pointed out, however, due to phylogenetic differences, an exact mouse AD model may never be attainable. Therefore, the results obtained from the mouse models should not be used to exclude the possibility that the production of Aβ is sufficient to drive the complete development of AD in humans.

What does deserve further consideration regarding the importance of Aβ in AD is the crucial factor of age. In FAD and in AD transgenic animals, AD-like pathology is only demonstrable after mid-life. In sporadic form of AD (the majority of AD cases in human), AD affects 10% of the individuals older than 65 years and about 40% of people older than 80 [24] [63]. Thus, the role of Aβ in the pathogenesis of AD should be considered in the context of age, meaning that Aβ may only become toxic in the aged cellular environment, and its appearance may indicate presence of pathogenic processes occurring earlier in life.

Intending to find an earlier event in the brain's aging processes that paves the way for the development of AD, Smith et al. have intensely studied the role of oxidative stress. Their hypothesis, the oxidative stress theory, threatens to turn the amyloid cascade theory on its head [101]. These investigators argue that chronic oxidative stress, not the deposition of Aβ and taupathy, is the cause of AD.

The Oxidative Stress Theory

The starting point of the oxidative stress theory is the evidence that molecular damage caused by oxidative stress can be found in AD brains. This includes advanced glycation end products (AGEs) [53] [104] [114] [122], protein nitration [103] [31], lipid peroxidation [89], and carbonyl modification of neurofilaments [100] [102]. These oxidation-mediated modifications of proteins and lipids were found in AD-susceptible neurons before the appearance of lesions such as the NP and NFT suggesting that oxidative stress is an early event in the development of AD. It is proposed that the accumulation of modified proteins and lipids after chronic oxidative attack results in dysfunction of neurons that leads to AD.

To investigate oxidative damage in situ and in real time (the above-mentioned modifications form relatively stable molecules that resist degradation), these investigators also studied the presence of 8-hydroxyguanosine (8OHG), a modification of RNA that results from oxidative attack [71]. 8OHG is a short-lived molecule, so it may be used to trace ongoing oxidative events in vivo. Smith et al. found that while oxidative damage in the brain was restricted to the cytosol of neurons, this damage was actually diminished in areas of Aβ deposition and NFT [101]. This is interesting because it has been demonstrated that neurons respond to oxidative stress by increasing Aβ production [123], and Aβ can act as a potent superoxide dismutase, thus, an antioxidant [14]. In terms of NTF, it has been shown that due to the high content of lysine-serine-proline of tau and other neurofilament proteins, their extensive phosphorylation may produce an oxidative sponge of surface-modifiable lysine residues [116].

Thus the seemingly startling conclusion is that oxidative stress may drive the development of AD and the production of Aβ and phosphorylated tau proteins as part of an antioxidant defense, which is an adaptive response of the nervous system. Here, an apparently un-bridgeable chiasm seems to cut across our understanding of AD pathogenesis: on one side, Aβ is seen as the ultimate foe that unleashes AD, on the other, Aβ and tau are considered as faithful friends that come to the rescue in times of need.

PRO-INFLAMMATORY CYTOKINES AS PART OF THE ADAPTIVE RESPONSES TO AD PATHOLOGY

No one has proposed a counter-theory for the cytokine cycle theory, but the evidence for such a theory already exist if one applies the same analyses as those used in the oxidative stress theory.

As reviewed earlier, evidence exists demonstrating that 1) the expression of pro-inflammatory cytokines is found near NPs, 2) pro-inflammatory cytokines can promote the production and Aβ, and 3) Aβ can induce the production of pro-inflammatory cytokines. Viewing these data through lens of the amyloid cascade theory, one might conclude that the expression pro-inflammatory cytokines help drive the development of AD. Viewing these data through the oxidative stress theory, on the other hand, one might suspect that the production of inflammatory cytokines may help alleviate the oxidative stress in the AD brain.

Searching outside the field of AD research is helpful because one gains the insight that increased production of inflammatory cytokines in the brain does not necessarily lead to AD pathology. Thus, inflammatory cytokines are well known as the key mediators of innate immune responses to infection and tissue injury (including brain tissue) [80]. Any tissue injury invariably triggers the expression of pro-inflammatory cytokines at the wound site [26]. Inflammatory cytokines are also found in the hippocampus of the normal brain [83], where they may participate in the physiological functions of learning [27] and memory [79]. Induced production of pro-inflammatory cytokines in the brain has been found during peripheral infections [68,81,82,112]. Actions of these cytokines under these conditions mainly mediate various CNS-controlled responses to infection including fever, prolonged slow-wave sleep, sickness behavior, and reduced appetite (see Quan et al. for review [80]). These responses are important physiological responses to peripheral infection. Production of inflammatory cytokines under these conditions is not likely to contribute to AD development.

Similar to Aβ, when inflammatory cytokines were added at high levels directly to neural cell cultures in vitro, they were neurotoxic [11,106,109]. However, even though gross neural damage can be induced in transgenic mice that chronically over-express inflammatory cytokines in the brain, such cytokine-induced neuropathology does not resemble the pattern of selective neural damage in AD. In fact, unlike Aβ over-expressing mice, no study has ever shown that over-expression of inflammatory cytokines in the brain produces amyloid plaques [10]. Therefore, inflammatory cytokines do not promote the formation of NPs by themselves in vivo, and the effects of cytokines in amyloidosis must be at best secondary to the initial over-production of Aβ.

Besides inducing Aβ, it has been shown that inflammatory cytokines can stimulate the production of antioxidant enzymes [42,73,93,111,113], neurotrophic factors [2,45,60], and cell-death inhibitors [52,77,115]. These actions suggest the potential beneficial effects of cytokines during neurodegeneration. A dramatic demonstration of this point was produced in transgenic animals lacking the gene for the TNFα receptor. Brain damage in a stroke model in these TNF receptor-knockout mice was greatly exacerbated, illustrating an essential role of this inflammatory cytokine in brain wound repair [7].

In relation to Aβ, it has been shown that microglia is the major cell type that removes extracellular Aβ [94] and Aβ fibril [50]. Inflammatory cytokines have recently been recognized as potent stimulators of microglial cells (see Hanisch et al. for review [39]). Therefore, the presence of inflammatory cytokines in AD brains may reflect their role in controlling the level of Aβ instead of promoting the formation of NP. Supporting the idea that immunological activity against Aβ may be an important means for Aβ clearance, it has been shown that immunization with Aβ in transgenic mice over-expressing Aβ retards the progression of amyloid plaques [91]. (It should be noted that when Elan Pharmaceuticals went to clinical trials with AN-1792, a vaccine against Aβ, 15 patients developed encephalitis and meningitis-like symptoms, causing cancellation of the trial.) Thus, appropriate inflammatory/immunological activity in AD brain may effectively reduce amyloid burden. Another unorthodox idea that deserves consideration here is a mechanism proposed by Wolfgang Streit who postulates that even microglia-mediated neuronal killing may be beneficial because the elimination of neurons that have been compromised beyond viability and functionality may be critical for the overall maintenance of the healthy brain [105].

Taken together, a cytokine regulation theory may be formulated as the following. First, age related oxidative stress induces dysfunction and injury to the neurons. Then, Aβ and phosphorylated tau and other antioxidants are induced to curtail oxidative damage. Cytokines are also produced in this context as an adaptive response to stimulate Aβ production as well as to facilitate the clearance of over-produced Aβ. Activated microglia during the development of AD produce and receive cytokine signals. This cell type plays a key role in the clearance of both Aβ and unsalvageable neurons. This cytokine regulation theory is shown in Figure 3.

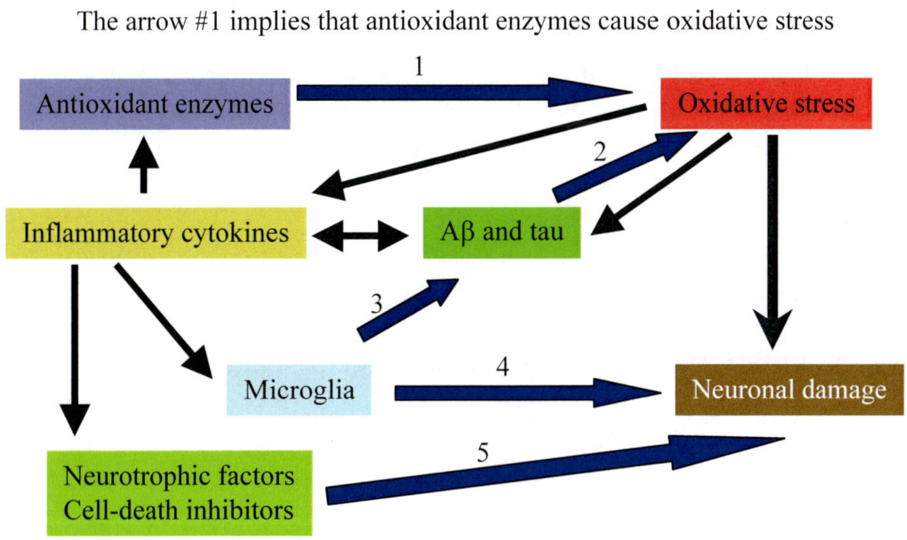

Figure 3. A schematic diagram illustrates the postulated cytokine regulation theory. Inflammatory cytokines are viewed as an adaptive response to AD-related neural damage. Their actions may result in enhanced antioxidant defense (pathways 1 and 2), control of Aβ levels (pathway 3), and enhanced neural repair (pathways 4 and 5).

PARTIAL TRUTH AND THE THIRD POSSIBILITY

Comparing Figures 1 and 2, we are left with diametrically opposed views on the pathogenesis of AD. Scientists on either side tend to continue gathering further evidence to support their side of the story. What has not been discussed is the possibility that both of them are partially correct because they are different sides of the same coin.

A great difficulty in AD research is the lack of a method to experimentally test a hypothesis. This unique human disease develops in an individual over a long period of time, and no animal model has been able to recapitulate the complete phenotype of AD. By necessity, essentially all of the evidence obtained so far regarding AD are the results from the following types of studies: 1) postmortem examination of AD and control brains, 2) analysis of neural cultures, 3) epidemiological analysis of risk factors, 4) animal models that partially reproduce AD pathology. With rapid advances in molecular biology (gene chip, realtime PCR, new antibodies, to name a few), we are now able to identify numerous molecular (cytokines, neurotransmitters, enzymes, adhesion molecules, chemokines, complements, transcription factors, phosphorylated molecules, oxidatively modified molecules, etc.) and cellular (microglial and astrocyte activation, neuronal damage and cell loss, infiltration of peripheral immune cells) changes in the postmortem AD brain. While it is clear that damage to the cholinergic cortex and hippocampus is central to the manifestation of AD, the pathogenic role of many molecules found at the site of AD pathology can only be assumed by "guilt by association." When these molecules are tested in vitro, their neurotoxic and/or neuroprotective effects may or may not reflect in vivo situations because the concentrations, kinetics, and the cellular environment in an in vitro system are unquestionably different from those found in the living brain. In addition, because AD occurs after a certain age (even FAD occurs after mid-life), tissue cultures that do not use cells from aged brains (most of the studies) are not likely to precisely reveal relevant molecular events related to AD. In terms of risk factors obtained from epidemiological analysis, it is important to point out that they are correlative factors, not causative factors. For example, the Apo ε4 allele has been shown as significant risk factor [92], but it is not sufficiently specific or sensitive to be used a diagnostic test for AD [15]. As for animal models, although they are extremely useful for the demonstration that mutation of APP or deposition ofAβ1-42 leads to amyloidosis, no complete human AD pathology has been simulated.

Keeping in mind these shortcomings in methodology, it is perhaps more productive to examine the contradictory theories as partial truths rather than to determine which theory is entirely right and which is entirely wrong. It is irrefutable that mutations of the APP, PS1, or PS2 gene that lead to heightened production of Aβ1–42 is deterministic for the development of early-onset AD in human [65]. It is a leap of faith to conclude that Aβ produced by the normal APP, PS1, and PS2 genes is *the* cause of sporadic form of AD (the common form of AD). In humans, significant Aβ deposits have been found in normal non-demented as well as AD brains, and no clear-cut correlation can been established between the presence of Aβ and cognitive dysfunction [17]. In animal models, direct injection of Aβ into the brain or over-expressing Aβ using transgenes of APP and PS produced variable results. While age-dependent deposition of Aβ and the formation of amyloid plaques can be induced in animal models, no NFT has been induced by these transgenes and there is also poor correlation between the distribution of amyloid depositions in the brain and several parameters of AD pathology, including degree of cognitive and behavior dysfunction, loss of synapses, loss of neurons, and abnormalities of the cytoskeleton [69]. These findings suggest: 1) the presumed toxic effects of Aβ (or APP for that matter) do not depend upon its deposition, 2) the full spectrum of the toxic effects of Aβ in humans may not be reproducible in other species, and 3) the age-dependent alterations in the cellular environment of the brain are critical for the manifestation of the harmful effects of Aβ. An interesting fact here is that the deposition of Aβ is not detectable before mid-life in both humans (including FAD patients) and the transgenic animal models, suggesting that there may be increased production and/or diminished clearance of Aβ with age. This age-related alteration in Aβ processing may not cause the neurodegeneration of AD by itself, but may accelerate normal age-related deterioration of specific neural circuits such that the AD phenotype will result. In this context, inflammatory cytokines may indeed be significant contributors of AD pathogenesis as suggested by the "cytokine cycle theory."

Natural age-related neural deterioration, albeit not enough to significantly affect brain functioning, is most likely to precede the harmful effects of Aβ-related molecules and may indeed be attributable to some extent to oxidation-mediated modifications of neural tissue. It has been demonstrated that in the normal aging brain, although there is no significant loss of cortical neurons, neurons acquire pigment and lose branches and synapses. There are also decreases in the levels of some neurotransmitters and receptors, thickening of the glial limiting membrane, signs of myelin sheath breakdown, and accumulation of phagocytosed material in microglia and astrocytes [76]. Therefore, the aging brain is certainly a site of structural and functional decline. It is possible that oxidative stress contributes to the age-related neural damage that may be the prerequisite for the development of AD. One should also be aware, however, that oxidative stress has been implicated in just about every age-related disease [54] and it is not clear why oxidative stress sometimes selectively induces AD but other times another disease, e.g., Parkinson's disease. Ironically, it is possible that APP and its derivatives may be the key ingredients that direct the general oxidative damage into the specific AD phenotype.

One scenario, that the above-reviewed contradictory theories might co-exist, is postulated in the following. At the first stage, there is age-related increase of oxidative stress in the normal brain that leads to increased oxidative damage and increased demand for antioxidant defense (normal aging). At the second stage, adaptive responses are induced to meet this demand. These responses include the production of antioxidants including Aβ, phosphorylated tau, and cytokine-mediated activation of various glial cells. At this stage, the production of Aβ, tau, and the inflammatory cytokines are protective (oxidative stress and cytokine regulation theories). An effective clearance mechanism may be operative at this stage such that accumulation of the excess Aβ and phosphorylated tau is minimized. At the third stage, accumulation of Aβ and phosphorylated tau contributes to the formation of senile plaques and NFTs. These structures may still exert some antioxidant effects, but no one should argue that these lesions are brain's best choice for antioxidant defense, and these lesions do not interfere with neural functions. At the fourth stage, the new task for the inflammatory cytokines and activated microglia is to clear the ever increasing number of lesions and severely damaged neurons. The lesions are winning the battle in the aging brain, and the metabolically compromised brain at this point allows the manifestation of the neurotoxic effects of Aβ that leads to AD (amyloid cascade theory). Finally, at this stage, the effects of inflammatory cytokines result in further production of Aβ and enhanced toxicity of Aβ, aiding the progression of AD (cytokine cycle theory). Although purely speculative, the merit of the above postulate is the recognition that the function of a given molecule may change in the aging environment and friends may indeed turn into foes with time.

Besides debating whether Aβ or oxidative stress is the cause of AD, there is a third possibility. While the reductionistic approach would like to identify a molecule or a process as the cause of AD, one should not forget the biggest risk factor for AD is age. With age, there may be functional declines of the entire cellular machinery rather than a few selected processes such as Aβ production, inflammation, and oxidation-reduction. In other words, the alterations in Aβ production and inflammatory and oxidative status of the brain are part, not the cause, of the overall brain aging. This is underlined by the fact that clinical trials targeting the clearance of Aβ [118], employing anti-inflammatory drugs [128], and supplementing antioxidants [88] have not provided convincing benefits to AD patients and sometimes produced adverse effects [118]. It is also interesting in this regard that higher levels of education, moderate levels of wine consumption, lower levels of food consumption, and higher levels of fish in the diet have been associated with lower risk for AD [61] [15]. These associations do not suggest beneficial effects of interventions aimed at modifying any single biochemical process, rather perhaps lifestyles and behaviors favoring the overall maintenance of the healthy brain could help delay the development of AD.

Concluding Remarks

It is firmly established that inflammatory cytokines are elevated in the AD brain. Both beneficial and pathological effects have been suggested by different studies. It is possible that at one stage of the AD development these cytokines are neuroprotective but become neurotoxic at another. The AD stage (early vs. late, for example) -dependent cytokine effects have not been investigated. Whether an anti-inflammatory treatment for AD would bear fruit may critically depend upon our thorough understanding of the full spectrum of cytokine actions in the AD brain. Finally, while waiting for an effective magic bullet therapy for the treatment for AD, altering ones behavior and lifestyle (diet and exercise) may go a long way for delaying the onset of AD.

Acknowledgement

My sincere thanks to Dr. Mile Herkenham, Dr. Cheryl Kassed, Dr. Firdaus Dhadhar, and Dr. Phillip Marucha for their careful reading of the manuscript and helpful suggestions.

References

[1] Akiyama, H., Barger, S., Barnum, S., Bradt, B., Bauer, J., Cole, G.M., Cooper, N.R., Eikelenboom, P., Emmerling, M., Fiebich, B.L., Finch, C.E., Frautschy, S., Griffin, W.S., Hampel, H., Hull, M., Landreth, G., Lue, L., Mrak, R., Mackenzie, I.R., McGeer, P.L., O'Banion, M.K., Pachter, J., Pasinetti, G., Plata-Salaman, C., Rogers, J., Rydel, R., Shen, Y., Streit, W., Strohmeyer, R., Tooyoma, I., Van Muiswinkel, F.L., Veerhuis, R., Walker, D., Webster, S., Wegrzyniak, B., Wenk, G. and Wyss-Coray, T., Inflammation and Alzheimer's disease, *Neurobiol Aging*, 21 (2000) 383-421.

[2] Aloe, L., Properzi, F., Probert, L., Akassoglou, K., Kassiotis, G., Micera, A. and Fiore, M., Learning abilities, NGF and BDNF brain levels in two lines of TNF-alpha transgenic mice, one characterized by neurological disorders, the other phenotypically normal, *Brain Res*, 840 (1999) 125-37.

[3] Alzhermer, A., Uber eine eigenartige Erkrankung der Hirnride, *Allg Z Psychiatr Psych-Gerichtl*, 64 (1907) 146-148.

[4] Araujo, D.M. and Cotman, C.W., Beta-amyloid stimulates glial cells in vitro to produce growth factors that accumulate in senile plaques in Alzheimer's disease, *Brain Res*, 569 (1992) 141-5.

[5] Berge, V., Johnson, E. and Berge, K.E., Interleukin-1 alpha, interleukin 6 and tumor necrosis factor alpha increase the synthesis and expression of the functional alternative and terminal complement pathways by human umbilical vein endothelial cells in vitro, *Apmis*, 104 (1996) 213-9.

[6] Blasko, I., Veerhuis, R., Stampfer-Kountchev, M., Saurwein-Teissl, M., Eikelenboom, P. and Grubeck-Loebenstein, B., Costimulatory effects of interferon-gamma and interleukin-1beta or tumor necrosis factor alpha on the synthesis of Abeta1-40 and Abeta1-42 by human astrocytes, *Neurobiol Dis*, 7 (2000) 682-9.

[7] Bruce, A.J., Boling, W., Kindy, M.S., Peschon, J., Kraemer, P.J., Carpenter, M.K., Holtsberg, F.W. and Mattson, M.P., Altered neuronal and microglial responses to excitotoxic and ischemic brain injury in mice lacking TNF receptors, *Nat Med*, 2 (1996) 788-94.

[8] Brugg, B., Dubreuil, Y.L., Huber, G., Wollman, E.E., Delhaye-Bouchaud, N. and Mariani, J., Inflammatory processes induce beta-amyloid precursor protein changes in mouse brain, *Proc Natl Acad Sci U S A*, 92 (1995) 3032-5.

[9] Bruunsgaard, H., Pedersen, M. and Pedersen, B.K., Aging and proinflammatory cytokines, *Curr Opin Hematol*, 8 (2001) 131-6.

[10] Campbell, I.L., Stalder, A.K., Chiang, C.S., Bellinger, R., Heyser, C.J., Steffensen, S., Masliah, E., Powell, H.C., Gold, L.H., Henriksen, S.J. and Siggins, G.R., Transgenic models to assess the pathogenic actions of cytokines in the central nervous system, *Mol. Psychiatry.*, 2 (1997) 125-129.

[11] Chao, C.C., Hu, S., Ehrlich, L. and Peterson, P.K., Interleukin-1 and tumor necrosis factor-α synergistically mediate neurotoxicity: involvement of nitric oxide and of N-methyl-D-aspartate receptors, *Brain Behav. Immun.*, 9 (1995) 355-65.

[12] Chong, Y., Effect of a carboxy-terminal fragment of the Alzheimer's amyloid precursor protein on expression of proinflammatory cytokines in rat glial cells, *Life Sci*, 61 (1997) 2323-33.

[13] Corder, E.H., Saunders, A.M., Strittmatter, W.J., Schmechel, D.E., Gaskell, P.C., Small, G.W., Roses, A.D., Haines, J.L. and Pericak-Vance, M.A., Gene dose of apolipoprotein E type 4 allele and the risk of Alzheimer's disease in late onset families, *Science*, 261 (1993) 921-3.

[14] Cuajungco, M.P., Goldstein, L.E., Nunomura, A., Smith, M.A., Lim, J.T., Atwood, C.S., Huang, X., Farrag, Y.W., Perry, G. and Bush, A.I., Evidence that the beta-amyloid plaques of Alzheimer's disease represent the redox-silencing and entombment of abeta by zinc, *J Biol Chem*, 275 (2000) 19439-42.

[15] Cummings, J.L. and Cole, G., Alzheimer disease, *Jama*, 287 (2002) 2335-8.

[16] Del Bo, R., Angeretti, N., Lucca, E., De Simoni, M.G. and Forloni, G., Reciprocal control of inflammatory cytokines, IL-1 and IL-6, and beta-amyloid production in cultures, *Neurosci Lett*, 188 (1995) 70-4.

[17] Dickson, D.W., Crystal, H.A., Mattiace, L.A., Masur, D.M., Blau, A.D., Davies, P., Yen, S.H. and Aronson, M.K., Identification of normal and pathological aging in prospectively studied nondemented elderly humans, *Neurobiol Aging*, 13 (1992) 179-89.

[18] Dickson, D.W., Lee, S.C., Mattiace, L.A., Yen, S.H. and Brosnan, C., Microglia and cytokines in neurological disease, with special reference to AIDS and Alzheimer's disease, *Glia*, 7 (1993) 75-83.

[19] Donnelly, R.J., Friedhoff, A.J., Beer, B., Blume, A.J. and Vitek, M.P., Interleukin-1 stimulates the beta-amyloid precursor protein promoter, *Cell Mol Neurobiol*, 10 (1990) 485-95.

[20] Duff, K., Transgenic mouse models of Alzheimer's disease: phenotype and mechanisms of pathogenesis, *Biochem Soc Symp* (2001) 195-202.

[21] Eikelenboom, P., Hoogendijk, W.J., Jonker, C. and van Tilburg, W., Immunological mechanisms and the spectrum of psychiatric syndromes in Alzheimer's disease, *J Psychiatr Res*, 36 (2002) 269-80.

[22] Eikelenboom, P. and Stam, F.C., Immunoglobulins and complement factors in senile plaques. An immunoperoxidase study, *Acta Neuropathol (Berl)*, 57 (1982) 239-42.

[23] Engelborghs, S., De Brabander, M., De Cree, J., D'Hooge, R., Geerts, H., Verhaegen, H. and De Deyn, P.P., Unchanged levels of interleukins, neopterin, interferon-gamma and tumor necrosis factor-alpha in cerebrospinal fluid of patients with dementia of the Alzheimer type, *Neurochem Int*, 34 (1999) 523-30.

[24] Evans, D.A., Funkenstein, H.H., Albert, M.S., Scherr, P.A., Cook, N.R., Chown, M.J., Hebert, L.E., Hennekens, C.H. and Taylor, J.O., Prevalence of Alzheimer's disease in a community population of older persons. Higher than previously reported, *Jama*, 262 (1989) 2551-6.

[25] Fagarasan, M.O. and Aisen, P.S., IL-1 and anti-inflammatory drugs modulate A beta cytotoxicity in PC12 cells, *Brain Res*, 723 (1996) 231-4.

[26] Gharaee-Kermani, M. and Phan, S.H., Role of cytokines and cytokine therapy in wound healing and fibrotic diseases, *Curr Pharm Des*, 7 (2001) 1083-103.

[27] Gibertini, M., IL1 beta impairs relational but not procedural rodent learning in a water maze task, *Adv Exp Med Biol*, 402 (1996) 207-17.

[28] Glenner, G.G. and Wong, C.W., Alzheimer's disease: initial report of the purification and characterization of a novel cerebrovascular amyloid protein, *Biochem Biophys Res Commun*, 120 (1984) 885-90.

[29] Goate, A., Chartier-Harlin, M.C., Mullan, M., Brown, J., Crawford, F., Fidani, L., Giuffra, L., Haynes, A., Irving, N., James, L. and et al., Segregation of a missense mutation in the amyloid precursor protein gene with familial Alzheimer's disease, *Nature*, 349 (1991) 704-6.

[30] Goebeler, M., Yoshimura, T., Toksoy, A., Ritter, U., Brocker, E.B. and Gillitzer, R., The chemokine repertoire of human dermal microvascular endothelial cells and its regulation by inflammatory cytokines, *J Invest Dermatol*, 108 (1997) 445-51.

[31] Good, P.F., Werner, P., Hsu, A., Olanow, C.W. and Perl, D.P., Evidence of neuronal oxidative damage in Alzheimer's disease, *Am J Pathol*, 149 (1996) 21-8.

[32] Griffin, W.S., Sheng, J.G., Gentleman, S.M., Graham, D.I., Mrak, R.E. and Roberts, G.W., Microglial interleukin-1 alpha expression in human head injury: correlations with neuronal and neuritic beta-amyloid precursor protein expression, *Neurosci Lett*, 176 (1994) 133-6.

[33] Griffin, W.S., Sheng, J.G., Roberts, G.W. and Mrak, R.E., Interleukin-1 expression in different plaque types in Alzheimer's disease: significance in plaque evolution, *J Neuropathol Exp Neurol*, 54 (1995) 276-81.

[34] Griffin, W.S., Sheng, J.G., Royston, M.C., Gentleman, S.M., McKenzie, J.E., Graham, D.I., Roberts, G.W. and Mrak, R.E., Glial-neuronal interactions in Alzheimer's disease: the potential role of a 'cytokine cycle' in disease progression, *Brain Pathol.*, 8 (1998) 65-72.

[35] Griffin, W.S., Stanley, L.C., Ling, C., White, L., MacLeod, V., Perrot, L.J., White, C.L.d. and Araoz, C., Brain interleukin 1 and S-100 immunoreactivity are elevated in Down syndrome and Alzheimer disease, *Proc Natl Acad Sci U S A*, 86 (1989) 7611-5.

[36] Grilli, M., Goffi, F., Memo, M. and Spano, P., Interleukin-1beta and glutamate activate the NF-kappaB/Rel binding site from the regulatory region of the amyloid precursor protein gene in primary neuronal cultures, *J Biol Chem*, 271 (1996) 15002-7.

[37] Grundke-Iqbal, I., Iqbal, K., Quinlan, M., Tung, Y.C., Zaidi, M.S. and Wisniewski, H.M., Microtubule-associated protein tau. A component of Alzheimer paired helical filaments, *J Biol Chem*, 261 (1986) 6084-9.

[38] Hackam, D.J. and Ford, H.R., Cellular, biochemical, and clinical aspects of wound healing, *Surg Infect (Larchmt)*, 3 Suppl 1 (2002) 23-35.

[39] Hanisch, U.K., Microglia as a source and target of cytokines, *Glia*, 40 (2002) 140-55.

[40] Hardy, J., An 'anatomical cascade hypothesis' for Alzheimer's disease, *Trends Neurosci*, 15 (1992) 200-1.

[41] Hardy, J.A. and Higgins, G.A., Alzheimer's disease: the amyloid cascade hypothesis, *Science*, 256 (1992) 184-5.

[42] Harris, C.A., Derbin, K.S., Hunte-McDonough, B., Krauss, M.R., Chen, K.T., Smith, D.M. and Epstein, L.B., Manganese superoxide dismutase is induced by IFN-gamma in multiple cell types. Synergistic induction by IFN-gamma and tumor necrosis factor or IL-1, *J Immunol*, 147 (1991) 149-54.

[43] Ho, L., Pieroni, C., Winger, D., Purohit, D.P., Aisen, P.S. and Pasinetti, G.M., Regional distribution of cyclooxygenase-2 in the hippocampal formation in Alzheimer's disease, *J Neurosci Res*, 57 (1999) 295-303.

[44] Hock, B.J., Jr. and Lamb, B.T., Transgenic mouse models of Alzheimer's disease, *Trends Genet*, 17 (2001) S7-12.

[45] Horie, H., Sakai, I., Akahori, Y. and Kadoya, T., IL-1 beta enhances neurite regeneration from transected-nerve terminals of adult rat DRG, *Neuroreport*, 8 (1997) 1955-9.

[46] Hu, J., Akama, K.T., Krafft, G.A., Chromy, B.A. and Van Eldik, L.J., Amyloid-beta peptide activates cultured astrocytes: morphological alterations, cytokine induction and nitric oxide release, *Brain Res*, 785 (1998) 195-206.

[47] Ishizuka, K., Kimura, T., Igata-yi, R., Katsuragi, S., Takamatsu, J. and Miyakawa, T., Identification of monocyte chemoattractant protein-1 in senile plaques and reactive microglia of Alzheimer's disease, *Psychiatry Clin Neurosci*, 51 (1997) 135-8.

[48] Janus, C. and Westaway, D., Transgenic mouse models of Alzheimer's disease, *Physiol Behav*, 73 (2001) 873-86.

[49] Kang, J., Lemaire, H.G., Unterbeck, A., Salbaum, J.M., Masters, C.L., Grzeschik, K.H., Multhaup, G., Beyreuther, K. and Muller-Hill, B., The precursor of Alzheimer's disease amyloid A4 protein resembles a cell-surface receptor, *Nature*, 325 (1987) 733-6.

[50] Kopec, K.K. and Carroll, R.T., Alzheimer's beta-amyloid peptide 1-42 induces a phagocytic response in murine microglia, *J Neurochem*, 71 (1998) 2123-31.

[51] Kordula, T., Bugno, M., Rydel, R.E. and Travis, J., Mechanism of interleukin-1- and tumor necrosis factor alpha-dependent regulation of the alpha 1-antichymotrypsin gene in human astrocytes, *J Neurosci*, 20 (2000) 7510-6.

[52] Kuhn, K., Hashimoto, S. and Lotz, M., IL-1 beta protects human chondrocytes from CD95-induced apoptosis, *J Immunol*, 164 (2000) 2233-9.

[53] Ledesma, M.D., Bonay, P., Colaco, C. and Avila, J., Analysis of microtubule-associated protein tau glycation in paired helical filaments, *J Biol Chem*, 269 (1994) 21614-9.

[54] Levine, R.L., Carbonyl modified proteins in cellular regulation, aging, and disease, *Free Radic Biol Med*, 32 (2002) 790-6.

[55] Levy-Lahad, E., Wijsman, E.M., Nemens, E., Anderson, L., Goddard, K.A., Weber, J.L., Bird, T.D. and Schellenberg, G.D., A familial Alzheimer's disease locus on chromosome 1, *Science*, 269 (1995) 970-3.

[56] Li, Y., Liu, L., Kang, J., Sheng, J.G., Barger, S.W., Mrak, R.E. and Griffin, W.S., Neuronal-glial interactions mediated by interleukin-1 enhance neuronal acetylcholinesterase activity and mRNA expression, *J Neurosci*, 20 (2000) 149-55.

[57] Licastro, F., Pegrini, F., Bonafe, M., Grimaldi, L.M., Olivieri, F., Cavallone, L., Giovannetti, S. and Franceschi, C., Polymorphisms of the IL-6 gene increase the risk for late onset Alzheimer's disease and affected IL-6 plasma levels., *Neurobiol Aging*, 21(Suppl. 1) (2002) S38.

[58] Lyness, S.A., Zarow, C. and Chui, H.C., Neuron loss in key cholinergic and aminergic nuclei in Alzheimer disease: a meta-analysis, *Neurobiol Aging*, 24 (2003) 1-23.

[59] Mann, D.M., Iwatsubo, T., Cairns, N.J., Lantos, P.L., Nochlin, D., Sumi, S.M., Bird, T.D., Poorkaj, P., Hardy, J., Hutton, M., Prihar, G., Crook, R., Rossor, M.N. and Haltia, M., Amyloid beta protein (Abeta) deposition in chromosome 14-linked Alzheimer's disease: predominance of Abeta42(43), *Ann Neurol*, 40 (1996) 149-56.

[60] Manni, L. and Aloe, L., Role of IL-1 beta and TNF-alpha in the regulation of NGF in experimentally induced arthritis in mice, *Rheumatol Int*, 18 (1998) 97-102.

[61] Mattson, M.P., Emerging neuroprotective strategies for Alzheimer's disease: dietary restriction, telomerase activation, and stem cell therapy, *Exp Gerontol*, 35 (2000) 489-502.

[62] McGeer, P.L. and McGeer, E.G., Anti-inflammatory drugs in the fight against Alzheimer's disease, *Ann. NY Acad. Sci.*, 777 (1996) 213-220.

[63] McKhann, G., Drachman, D., Folstein, M., Katzman, R., Price, D. and Stadlan, E.M., Clinical diagnosis of Alzheimer's disease: report of the NINCDS-ADRDA Work Group under the auspices of Department of Health and Human Services Task Force on Alzheimer's Disease, *Neurology*, 34 (1984) 939-44.

[64] Meda, L., Baron, P., Prat, E., Scarpini, E., Scarlato, G., Cassatella, M.A. and Rossi, F., Proinflammatory profile of cytokine production by human monocytes and murine microglia stimulated with beta-amyloid [25-35], *J Neuroimmunol*, 93 (1999) 45-52.

[65] Morishima-Kawashima, M. and Ihara, Y., Alzheimer's disease: beta-Amyloid protein and tau, *J Neurosci Res*, 70 (2002) 392-401.

[66] Mrak, R.E. and Griffinbc, W.S., The role of activated astrocytes and of the neurotrophic cytokine S100B in the pathogenesis of Alzheimer's disease, *Neurobiol Aging*, 22 (2001) 915-22.

[67] Mrak, R.E., Sheng, J.G. and Griffin, W.S.T., Activated and phagoocytic IL-1α^+ microglia, but not primary IL-1α^+ microglia, increase with age in normal human brain., *Soc Neurosci Abstr*, 22 (1996) 213.

[68] Nadeau, S. and Rivest, S., Regulation of the gene encoding tumor necrosis factor alpha (TNF-alpha) in the rat brain and pituitary in response in different models of systemic immune challenge, *J Neuropathol Exp Neurol*, 58 (1999) 61-77.

[69] Neve, R.L. and Robakis, N.K., Alzheimer's disease: a re-examination of the amyloid hypothesis, *Trends Neurosci*, 21 (1998) 15-9.

[70] Nicoll, J.A., Mrak, R.E., Graham, D.I., Stewart, J., Wilcock, G., MacGowan, S., Esiri, M.M., Murray, L.S., Dewar, D., Love, S., Moss, T. and Griffin, W.S., Association of interleukin-1 gene polymorphisms with Alzheimer's disease, *Ann Neurol*, 47 (2000) 365-8.

[71] Nunomura, A., Perry, G., Pappolla, M.A., Wade, R., Hirai, K., Chiba, S. and Smith, M.A., RNA oxidation is a prominent feature of vulnerable neurons in Alzheimer's disease, *J Neurosci*, 19 (1999) 1959-64.

[72] Oka, A. and Takashima, S., Induction of cyclo-oxygenase 2 in brains of patients with Down's syndrome and dementia of Alzheimer type: specific localization in affected neurones and axons, *Neuroreport*, 8 (1997) 1161-4.

[73] Ono, M., Kohda, H., Kawaguchi, T., Ohhira, M., Sekiya, C., Namiki, M., Takeyasu, A. and Taniguchi, N., Induction of Mn-superoxide dismutase by tumor necrosis factor, interleukin-1 and interleukin-6 in human hepatoma cells, *Biochem Biophys Res Commun*, 182 (1992) 1100-7.

[74] Pasinetti, G.M. and Aisen, P.S., Cyclooxygenase-2 expression is increased in frontal cortex of Alzheimer's disease brain, *Neuroscience*, 87 (1998) 319-24.

[75] Perry, R.T., Collins, J.S., Wiener, H., Acton, R. and Go, R.C., The role of TNF and its receptors in Alzheimer's disease, *Neurobiol Aging*, 22 (2001) 873-83.

[76] Peters, A., Structural changes that occur during normal aging of primate cerebral hemispheres, *Neurosci Biobehav Rev*, 26 (2002) 733-41.

[77] Pezzano, M., Philp, D., Stephenson, S., Li, Y., Reid, V., Maitta, R. and Guyden, J.C., Positive selection by thymic nurse cells requires IL-1 beta and is associated with an increased Bcl-2 expression, *Cell Immunol*, 169 (1996) 174-84.

[78] Potter, H., Wefes, I.M. and Nilsson, L.N., The inflammation-induced pathological chaperones ACT and apo-E are necessary catalysts of Alzheimer amyloid formation, *Neurobiol Aging*, 22 (2001) 923-30.

[79] Pugh, C.R., Nguyen, K.T., Gonyea, J.L., Fleshner, M., Wakins, L.R., Maier, S.F. and Rudy, J.W., Role of interleukin-1 beta in impairment of contextual fear conditioning caused by social isolation, *Behav Brain Res*, 106 (1999) 109-18.

[80] Quan, N. and Herkenham, M., Connecting cytokines and brain: a review of current issues, *Histol Histopathol*, 17 (2002) 273-88.

[81] Quan, N., Mhlanga, J.D., Whiteside, M.B., McCoy, A.N., Kristensson, K. and Herkenham, M., Chronic overexpression of proinflammatory cytokines and histopathology in the brains of rats infected with Trypanosoma brucei, *J Comp Neurol*, 414 (1999) 114-30.

[82] Quan, N., Stern, E.L., Whiteside, M.B. and Herkenham, M., Induction of pro-inflammatory cytokine mRNAs in the brain after peripheral injection of subseptic doses of lipopolysaccharide in the rat, *J Neuroimmunol*, 93 (1999) 72-80.

[83] Quan, N., Zhang, Z., Emery, M., Bonsall, R. and Weiss, J.M., Detection of interleukin-1 bioactivity in various brain regions of normal healthy rats, *Neuroimmunomodulation*, 3 (1996) 47-55.

[84] Rich, J.B., Rasmusson, D.X., Folstein, M.F., Carson, K.A., Kawas, C. and Brandt, J., Nonsteroidal anti-inflammatory drugs in Alzheimer's disease, *Neurology*, 45 (1995) 51-5.

[85] Ringheim, G.E., Szczepanik, A.M., Petko, W., Burgher, K.L., Zhu, S.Z. and Chao, C.C., Enhancement of beta-amyloid precursor protein transcription and expression by the soluble interleukin-6 receptor/interleukin-6 complex, *Brain Res Mol Brain Res*, 55 (1998) 35-44.

[86] Rogaev, E.I., Sherrington, R., Rogaeva, E.A., Levesque, G., Ikeda, M., Liang, Y., Chi, H., Lin, C., Holman, K., Tsuda, T. and et al., Familial Alzheimer's disease in kindreds with missense mutations in a gene on chromosome 1 related to the Alzheimer's disease type 3 gene, *Nature*, 376 (1995) 775-8.

[87] Rogers, J., Kirby, L.C., Hempelman, S.R., Berry, D.L., McGeer, P.L., Kaszniak, A.W., Zalinski, J., Cofield, M., Mansukhani, L., Willson, P. and et al., Clinical trial of indomethacin in Alzheimer's disease, *Neurology*, 43 (1993) 1609-11.

[88] Rottkamp, C.A., Nunomura, A., Hirai, K., Sayre, L.M., Perry, G. and Smith, M.A., Will antioxidants fulfill their expectations for the treatment of Alzheimer disease?, *Mech Ageing Dev*, 116 (2000) 169-79.

[89] Sayre, L.M., Zelasko, D.A., Harris, P.L., Perry, G., Salomon, R.G. and Smith, M.A., 4-Hydroxynonenal-derived advanced lipid peroxidation end products are increased in Alzheimer's disease, *J Neurochem*, 68 (1997) 2092-7.

[90] Scharf, S., Mander, A., Ugoni, A., Vajda, F. and Christophidis, N., A double-blind, placebo-controlled trial of diclofenac/misoprostol in Alzheimer's disease, *Neurology*, 53 (1999) 197-201.

[91] Schenk, D., Barbour, R., Dunn, W., Gordon, G., Grajeda, H., Guido, T., Hu, K., Huang, J., Johnson-Wood, K., Khan, K., Kholodenko, D., Lee, M., Liao, Z., Lieberburg, I., Motter, R., Mutter, L., Soriano, F., Shopp, G., Vasquez, N., Vandevert, C., Walker, S., Wogulis, M., Yednock, T., Games, D. and Seubert, P., Immunization with amyloid-beta attenuates Alzheimer-disease-like pathology in the PDAPP mouse, *Nature*, 400 (1999) 173-7.

[92] Seshadri, S., Drachman, D.A. and Lippa, C.F., Apolipoprotein E epsilon 4 allele and the lifetime risk of Alzheimer's disease. What physicians know, and what they should know, *Arch Neurol*, 52 (1995) 1074-9.

[93] Shaffer, J.B., Treanor, C.P. and Del Vecchio, P.J., Expression of bovine and mouse endothelial cell antioxidant enzymes following TNF-alpha exposure, *Free Radic Biol Med*, 8 (1990) 497-502.

[94] Shaffer, L.M., Dority, M.D., Gupta-Bansal, R., Frederickson, R.C., Younkin, S.G. and Brunden, K.R., Amyloid beta protein (A beta) removal by neuroglial cells in culture, *Neurobiol Aging*, 16 (1995) 737-45.

[95] Shaw, K.T., Utsuki, T., Rogers, J., Yu, Q.S., Sambamurti, K., Brossi, A., Ge, Y.W., Lahiri, D.K. and Greig, N.H., Phenserine regulates translation of beta -amyloid precursor protein mRNA by a putative interleukin-1 responsive element, a target for drug development, *Proc Natl Acad Sci U S A*, 98 (2001) 7605-10.

[96] Sheng, J.G., Boop, F.A., Mrak, R.E. and Griffin, W.S., Increased neuronal beta-amyloid precursor protein expression in human temporal lobe epilepsy: association with interleukin-1 alpha immunoreactivity, *J Neurochem*, 63 (1994) 1872-9.

[97] Sherrington, R., Rogaev, E.I., Liang, Y., Rogaeva, E.A., Levesque, G., Ikeda, M., Chi, H., Lin, C., Li, G., Holman, K. and et al., Cloning of a gene bearing missense mutations in early-onset familial Alzheimer's disease, *Nature*, 375 (1995) 754-60.

[98] Shirodaria, S., Smith, J., McKay, I.J., Kennett, C.N. and Hughes, F.J., Polymorphisms in the IL-1A gene are correlated with levels of interleukin-1alpha protein in gingival crevicular fluid of teeth with severe periodontal disease, *J Dent Res*, 79 (2000) 1864-9.

[99] Shohami, E., Novikov, M., Bass, R., Yamin, A. and Gallily, R., Closed head injury triggers early production of TNF alpha and IL-6 by brain tissue, *J Cereb Blood Flow Metab*, 14 (1994) 615-9.

[100] Smith, C.D., Carney, J.M., Starke-Reed, P.E., Oliver, C.N., Stadtman, E.R., Floyd, R.A. and Markesbery, W.R., Excess brain protein oxidation and enzyme dysfunction in normal aging and in Alzheimer disease, *Proc Natl Acad Sci U S A*, 88 (1991) 10540-3.

[101] Smith, M.A., Casadesus, G., Joseph, J.A. and Perry, G., Amyloid-beta and tau serve antioxidant functions in the aging and Alzheimer brain, *Free Radic Biol Med*, 33 (2002) 1194-9.

[102] Smith, M.A., Perry, G., Richey, P.L., Sayre, L.M., Anderson, V.E., Beal, M.F. and Kowall, N., Oxidative damage in Alzheimer's, *Nature*, 382 (1996) 120-1.

[103] Smith, M.A., Richey Harris, P.L., Sayre, L.M., Beckman, J.S. and Perry, G., Widespread peroxynitrite-mediated damage in Alzheimer's disease, *J Neurosci*, 17 (1997) 2653-7.

[104] Smith, M.A., Taneda, S., Richey, P.L., Miyata, S., Yan, S.D., Stern, D., Sayre, L.M., Monnier, V.M. and Perry, G., Advanced Maillard reaction end products are associated with Alzheimer disease pathology, *Proc Natl Acad Sci U S A*, 91 (1994) 5710-4.

[105] Streit, W.J., Microglia as neuroprotective, immunocompetent cells of the CNS, *Glia*, 40 (2002) 133-9.

[106] Strijbos, P.J. and Rothwell, N.J., Interleukin-1β attenuates excitatory amino acid-induced neurodegeneration in vitro: involvement of nerve growth factor, *J. Neurosci.*, 15 (1995) 3468-3474.

[107] Suh, Y.H. and Checler, F., Amyloid precursor protein, presenilins, and alpha-synuclein: molecular pathogenesis and pharmacological applications in Alzheimer's disease, *Pharmacol Rev*, 54 (2002) 469-525.

[108] Suo, Z., Tan, J., Placzek, A., Crawford, F., Fang, C. and Mullan, M., Alzheimer's beta-amyloid peptides induce inflammatory cascade in human vascular cells: the roles of cytokines and CD40, *Brain Res*, 807 (1998) 110-7.

[109] Tauber, M.G., Sachdeva, M., Kennedy, S.L., Loetscher, H. and Lesslauer, W., Toxicity in neuronal cells caused by cerebrospinal fluid from pneumococcal and gram-negative meningitis, *J Infect Dis*, 166 (1992) 1045-50.

[110] Toro, V.C., Tehranian, R., Zetterstrom, M., Eriksson, G., Langel, U., Bartfai, T. and Iverfeld, K., Increased gene expression of interleukin-1alpha and interleukin-6 in rat primary glial cells induced by beta-amyloid fragment, *J Mol Neurosci*, 17 (2001) 341-50.

[111] Tsan, M.F., White, J.E., Del Vecchio, P.J. and Shaffer, J.B., IL-6 enhances TNF-alpha- and IL-1-induced increase of Mn superoxide dismutase mRNA and O2 tolerance, *Am J Physiol*, 263 (1992) L22-6.

[112] Vallieres, L. and Rivest, S., Regulation of the genes encoding interleukin-6, its receptor, and gp130 in the rat brain in response to the immune activator lipopolysaccharide and the proinflammatory cytokine interleukin-1beta, *J Neurochem*, 69 (1997) 1668-83.

[113] Visner, G.A., Chesrown, S.E., Monnier, J., Ryan, U.S. and Nick, H.S., Regulation of manganese superoxide dismutase: IL-1 and TNF induction in pulmonary artery and microvascular endothelial cells, *Biochem Biophys Res Commun*, 188 (1992) 453-62.

[114] Vitek, M.P., Bhattacharya, K., Glendening, J.M., Stopa, E., Vlassara, H., Bucala, R., Manogue, K. and Cerami, A., Advanced glycation end products contribute to amyloidosis in Alzheimer disease, *Proc Natl Acad Sci U S A*, 91 (1994) 4766-70.

[115] Ward, N.S., Waxman, A.B., Homer, R.J., Mantell, L.L., Einarsson, O., Du, Y. and Elias, J.A., Interleukin-6-induced protection in hyperoxic acute lung injury, *Am J Respir Cell Mol Biol*, 22 (2000) 535-42.

[116] Wataya, T., Nunomura, A., Smith, M.A., Siedlak, S.L., Harris, P.L., Shimohama, S., Szweda, L.I., Kaminski, M.A., Avila, J., Price, D.L., Cleveland, D.W., Sayre, L.M. and Perry, G., High molecular weight neurofilament proteins are physiological substrates of adduction by the lipid peroxidation product hydroxynonenal, *J Biol Chem*, 277 (2002) 4644-8.

[117] Wisniewski, K.E., Wisniewski, H.M. and Wen, G.Y., Occurrence of neuropathological changes and dementia of Alzheimer's disease in Down's syndrome, *Ann Neurol*, 17 (1985) 278-82.

[118] Wisniewski, T. and Sigurdsson, E.M., Immunization treatment approaches in Alzheimer's and prion diseases, *Curr Neurol Neurosci Rep*, 2 (2002) 400-4.

[119] Wood, J.A., Wood, P.L., Ryan, R., Graff-Radford, N.R., Pilapil, C., Robitaille, Y. and Quirion, R., Cytokine indices in Alzheimer's temporal cortex: no changes in mature IL-1 beta or IL-1RA but increases in the associated acute phase proteins IL-6, alpha 2-macroglobulin and C-reactive protein, *Brain Res*, 629 (1993) 245-52.

[120] Xia, M.Q., Bacskai, B.J., Knowles, R.B., Qin, S.X. and Hyman, B.T., Expression of the chemokine receptor CXCR3 on neurons and the elevated expression of its ligand IP-10 in reactive astrocytes: in vitro ERK1/2 activation and role in Alzheimer's disease, *J Neuroimmunol*, 108 (2000) 227-35.

[121] Xia, M.Q., Qin, S.X., Wu, L.J., Mackay, C.R. and Hyman, B.T., Immunohistochemical study of the beta-chemokine receptors CCR3 and CCR5 and their ligands in normal and Alzheimer's disease brains, *Am J Pathol*, 153 (1998) 31-7.

[122] Yan, S.D., Chen, X., Schmidt, A.M., Brett, J., Godman, G., Zou, Y.S., Scott, C.W., Caputo, C., Frappier, T., Smith, M.A. and et al., Glycated tau protein in Alzheimer

disease: a mechanism for induction of oxidant stress, *Proc Natl Acad Sci U S A*, 91 (1994) 7787-91.

[123] Yan, S.D., Yan, S.F., Chen, X., Fu, J., Chen, M., Kuppusamy, P., Smith, M.A., Perry, G., Godman, G.C., Nawroth, P. and et al., Non-enzymatically glycated tau in Alzheimer's disease induces neuronal oxidant stress resulting in cytokine gene expression and release of amyloid beta-peptide, *Nat Med*, 1 (1995) 693-9.

[124] Yang, F., Jansen, L., Friedrichs, W.E., Buchanan, J.M. and Bowman, B.H., IL-1 beta decreases expression of amyloid precursor protein gene in human glioma cells, *Biochem Biophys Res Commun*, 191 (1993) 1014-9.

[125] Yang, Y., Quitschke, W.W. and Brewer, G.J., Upregulation of amyloid precursor protein gene promoter in rat primary hippocampal neurons by phorbol ester, IL-1 and retinoic acid, but not by reactive oxygen species, *Brain Res Mol Brain Res*, 60 (1998) 40-9.

[126] Yasojima, K., Schwab, C., McGeer, E.G. and McGeer, P.L., Distribution of cyclooxygenase-1 and cyclooxygenase-2 mRNAs and proteins in human brain and peripheral organs, *Brain Res*, 830 (1999) 226-36.

[127] Yates, S.L., Burgess, L.H., Kocsis-Angle, J., Antal, J.M., Dority, M.D., Embury, P.B., Piotrkowski, A.M. and Brunden, K.R., Amyloid beta and amylin fibrils induce increases in proinflammatory cytokine and chemokine production by THP-1 cells and murine microglia, *J Neurochem*, 74 (2000) 1017-25.

[128] Zandi, P.P. and Breitner, J.C., Do NSAIDs prevent Alzheimer's disease? And, if so, why? The epidemiological evidence, *Neurobiol Aging*, 22 (2001) 811-7.

Chapter V

DYSFUNCTION AND ACTIVATION OF THE LYSOSOMAL SYSTEM: IMPLICATIONS FOR AND AGAINST ALZHEIMER'S DISEASE

Ben A. Bahr[*]

Department of Pharmaceutical Sciences and the Neurosciences Program
University of Connecticut
Storrs, Connecticut

ABSTRACT

Lysosomes develop a propensity for free radical formation with age and an associated reduction in their protein processing capability. Gradual decay of lysosomal function likely contributes to the aging risk factor that enhances the susceptibility to neurodegenerative conditions. In fact, lysosomal disturbances are common among age-related protein accumulation disorders including Alzheimer's disease. Many reports have shown that lysosomal dysfunction facilitates protein aggregation, intracellular deposits, and microtubule destabilization. These events are part of a deleterious cascade that leads to transport failure and synaptic decline. While lysosomal disruption promotes neuronal pathogenesis, evidence suggests that activation of the lysosomal system constitutes a compensatory response capable of neuroprotection. Lysosomal activation, as indicated by the up-regulation of catabolic enzymes, is a characteristic feature of Alzheimer brains, perhaps to slow the progressive neurodegeneration and extend the disease's duration. Activated compensatory systems indicate that the brain is not a passive recipient of neurodegenerative disease, but rather fights a long battle before losing the functional capacity of memory encoding and retrieval. In a model system, enhancing the lysosomal activation response restored synaptic integrity by clearing protein deposits and re-establishing microtubule-based transport mechanisms. The need for early clearance of protein accumulations is critical for a variety of age-related diseases. With the elderly

---

[*] Address Correspondence to: Ben A. Bahr, Dept. of Pharmaceutical Sciences, University of Connecticut, Storrs, CT 06269-2092, Tel: (860) 486-6043; Fax: (860) 486-6858, Email: Bahr@uconn.edu

population rapidly growing, it is imperative to find ways to reduce the brain's acute vulnerability to protein deposition. Lysosomal activation represents a compensatory response that can be exploited as a therapeutic avenue against protein accumulation diseases.

Lysosomal organelles are part of a dynamic system that processes cellular waste and recycles the basic components necessary for cell maintenance. Lysosome abnormalities, thus, can contribute to an assortment of diseases. Lysosomal storage disorders (LSDs) account for dozens of pre-adult diseases caused by genetic mutations in specific enzymes (Walkley, 1998). The lysosomal enzyme deficiencies produce intracellular deposits, abnormal brain development, and mental retardation, with an onset of disease starting before birth to 25 years of age. Neurodegeneration and progressive cognitive decline are associated with the accumulation of various protein species, glycosphingolipids, and lipofuscin in LSDs such as Tay-Sach's, Sandhoff's, Fabry's, and Batten disease. Adding to the many examples of the lysosome's role in cellular degeneration, the lysosomal system plays a part in the early pathogenesis of prion encephalopathies (Laszlo et al., 1992) and in apoptotic and necrotic episodes (Nilsson et al., 1997; Antunes et al., 2001; Yuan et al., 2002). In addition, a mutated cholesterol homeostasis gene causes lysosomal accumulation of lipoprotein-derived cholesterol in the neurodegenerative disease Niemann-Pick (Loftus et al., 1997).

Lysosomal dysfunction apparently contributes to protein deposition disorders that exhibit mental deterioration similar to that characteristic of LSDs. In Alzheimer-type pathogenesis, lysosomal disruption has been implicated in the development of amyloidogenic material (Benowitz et al., 1989; Cataldo et al., 1991; Golde et al., 1992; Bahr et al., 1994a; Hajimohammadreza et al., 1994; Nixon et al., 2001) and tau deposits related to neurofibrillary tangles (NFTs) (Ivy, 1992; Bahr, 1995; Takauchi and Miyoshi, 1995; Bi et al., 2001; Bendiske et al., 2002). Lysosomal structures also appear to be involved in the formation of huntingtin protein aggregates in Huntington's disease (DiFiglia et al., 1997; Sapp et al., 1997). Thus, abnormal lysosome functioning is associated with early-onset and late-onset pathologies.

Lysosomal instability and dysfunction occur gradually during an animal's lifespan (see Brunk and Brun, 1972; Nakamura et al., 1989ab; Kikugawa et al., 1994). These lysosomal changes represent a distinct feature of brain aging, and they likely help establish age as a major risk factor for protein accumulation events and their aggregated protein stress responses (see review: Bahr and Bendiske, 2002). Protein misfolding, aggregation, and related stress responses may constitute fundamental problems underlying various protein deposition diseases (see Welihinda et al., 1999; Bucciantini et al., 2002; Lashuel et al., 2002; Ma et al., 2002; Muchowski et al., 2002). Correspondingly, experimentally-induced lysosomal disturbances cause cytoskeletal breakdown, dystrophic neurites, and eventual cell death (Takauchi and Miyoshi, 1989, 1995; Hajimohammadreza et al., 1994; Okada et al., 1994; Bahr, 1995; Bendiske et al., 2002). These are strong indications that functional alterations to the lysosomal system promote early- and late-stage neurodegeneration. Lysosomal dysfunction thereby has broad reaching effects, and early clearance of protein accumulations is required to effectively treat the diverse group of protein deposition disorders.

DYSFUNCTION OF THE LYSOSOMAL SYSTEM

Role in Amyloidogenic Processing and Accumulation

Protein accumulation is a common event among age-related neurodegenerative disorders including Huntington's disease (DiFiglia et al., 1997; Sapp et al., 1997) and α-synuclein disorders such as frontotemporal dementia and Parkinson's disease (Clark and Trojanowski, 2000; Fahn and Przedborski, 2000). Alzheimer's disease and tauopathies (e.g., FTDP-17) are also among those disorders with protein deposition linked, at least in part, to lysosomal perturbation and disruption of protein processing pathways (Cataldo et al., 1996; Kegel et al., 2000; Stefanis et al., 2001; Bahr and Bendiske, 2002). Regarding one of the hallmark deposits of Alzheimer's disease, amyloid plaques, lysosomal dysfunction is thought to contribute to the formation of aggregation-prone fragments of the amyloid precursor protein (APP) (Benowitz et al., 1989; Nixon et al., 1992; Bahr et al., 1994a). While the traditional viewpoint is that the senile plaques are the toxic disease component composed of extracellular deposits of secreted amyloid β-peptide (Aβ), many groups have recently proposed the possibility that intracellular Aβ causes neurotoxicity (Bahr et al., 1998; Skovronsky et al., 1998; Wilson et al., 1999; Gouras et al., 2000; Mochizuki et al., 2000; Puolivali et al., 2002; Takahashi et al., 2002; Walsh et al., 2002).

Interestingly, CA1 hippocampal neurons that are particularly vulnerable to Alzheimer's disease have been shown to internalize Aβ (Bahr et al., 1998; Bahr and Bendiske, 2002). Thus, intraneuronal Aβ and its toxic consequences may be derived from extracellular Aβ. Internalized Aβ may promote abnormal protein processing/accumulation by causing free radical generation within lysosomes and disrupting the lysosomal proton gradient (Yang et al., 1998; Ditaranto et al., 2001). The internalized Aβ peptides become sequestered in lysosomes and they promote the further production of APP fragments (Yang et al., 1995; Bahr et al., 1998; Glabe, 2001), perhaps as part of a vicious cycle of amyloidogenesis (see Bahr and Bendiske, 2002). There are many possible ways in which lysosomal dysfunction could affect APP processing (see Mills and Reiner, 1999), and many ways the amyloidogenic species could foster neuronal deterioration in the CNS (see Small et al., 2001).

Lysosomal disturbances during aging can compromise cellular pathways that process, degrade, and remove damaged and misfolded proteins. Such compromise can potentially cause the accumulation of carboxyterminal fragments of APP (CTFs) and their byproduct of Aβ peptides (see Oster-Granite et al., 1996; McPhie et al., 2001; Selkoe, 2001a). As indicated in cellular models, lysosomal perturbation alters the trafficking and/or metabolism of APP (Caporaso et al., 1992; Bendiske and Bahr, 2003) and promotes the cellular buildup of CTFs (Golde et al., 1992; Bahr et al., 1994a). Altered trafficking may promote APP availability for processing in the trans Golgi network.

Corresponding to the aging effect on lysosomes, intraneuronal Aβ accumulates with age in Alzheimer brains and in transgenic models of the disease (Takahashi et al., 2002). Nixon and colleagues have implicated lysosomal abnormalities as potential contributing factors in the development of Aβ deposits in the form of senile plaques (Cataldo et al., 1991, 1994; Nixon et al., 2001). Changes in the lysosomal system were found to have a marked prevalence in neurons located in brain regions known to be vulnerable to Alzheimer's disease

(Cataldo et al., 1996). These results suggest that age-related lysosomal alterations promote protein accumulation, and that disturbances in the endosomal-lysosomal pathway have a pathogenic role in Alzheimer brains.

In further support of the lysosome's role in amyloidogenic processing, CTFs have been found deposited in compartments consistent with lysosomal organelles (Haass et al., 1992; Bahr et al., 1994a, 1998; Yang et al., 1995; Chen et al., 2000). Altered compartmentation by disturbances in lysosomal function or recycling may promote the action of $A\beta_{1-42}$–specific γ-secretase in order to increase the ratio between $A\beta_{1-42}$ and the less amyloidogenic $A\beta_{1-40}$ peptide. There are in fact recent studies on distinct γ-secretases that are responsible for generating the different Aβ species (Klafki et al., 1996; Skovronsky et al., 2000). Alternatively, compartmentation that prevents γ-secretase activity may actually promote CTF-mediated pathogenesis (see McPhie et al., 2001; Amtul et al., 2002; Dewachter et al., 2002). Modified compartmentation of lysosomal hydrolases also may be a path that accelerates Aβ generation (Mathews et al., 2002).

Experimental evidence from model systems adds to the lysosome case. There is evidence for alternative protein processing pathways involving lysosomes that enhance the production of amyloidogenic species (Cole et al., 1989; Golde et al., 1992; Haass et al., 1992, 1993; Koo and Squazzo, 1994; Evin et al., 1995; D'Andrea et al., 2001). Also, experimentally-induced lysosomal disruption was shown to produce Aβ-containing CTFs *in vivo* (Hajimohammadreza et al., 1994; Mielke et al., 1997) and *in vitro* (Hayashi et al., 1992; Siman et al., 1993; Bahr et al., 1994a). Compromised lysosome function would increase the half-life of CTFs produced from APP internalized to the endosomal-lysosomal system, or those generated in the endoplasmic reticulum and trans Golgi network. Amyloidogenic fragments would then accumulate in neurons due to the reduced digestion/excretion activity of the compromised lysosomes. CTF accumulation would contribute to Aβ oligomeric species, or act indirectly by down-regulating Aβ degradation/clearance pathways (Iwata et al., 2001; Selkoe, 2001b) when CTFs are released from neurons. Intracellular generation of amyloidogenic species is also of interest for it has been shown to cause early neurodegeneration (e.g., see Bahr et al., 1998; Hsia et al., 1999; Mucke et al., 2000; Kim et al., 2001a; Walsh et al., 2002). Exactly how lysosomal dysfunction promotes toxic amyloidogenic changes is not known.

Role in Neurofibrillary Degeneration

Studies continue to mount indicating that lysosomal disturbances evident in Alzheimer brains contribute to the progressive pathogenesis. In fact, many characteristic features of Alzheimer's disease are induced by suppressing lysosomal capacity (Bahr and Bendiske, 2002). In addition to promoting amyloidogenic accumulations, lysosomal dysfunction also leads to changes in microtubule-associated proteins and related neurofibrillary degeneration (Bendiske et al., 2002). This work applied acidotropic agents or protease inhibitors to organotypic hippocampal slice cultures prepared with the interface method (Bahr et al., 1995), resulting in the production of intraneuronal deposits throughout the three hippocampal subfields. Similar to Alzheimer's disease NFTs, the deposited material was labeled by antibodies against human paired helical filaments (PHFs) as well as against ubiquitin.

The microtubule-binding protein tau was found to be phosphorylated and to increase in cellular content following lysosomal perturbation (Ivy et al., 1989; Bahr, 1995; Takauchi and Miyoshi, 1995; Bi et al., 1999; Bendiske et al., 2002). The 55-69-kDa tau isoforms affected were similar to those that selectively increase in the aged mouse brain (Bahr et al., 1994b; Bahr and Vicente, 1998) and in Alzheimer brains (Delacourte et al., 1990; Goedert et al., 1992). Phosphorylated tau isoforms are known to deposit in the form of PHFs, and such deposits facilitate production of NFTs in brain regions vulnerable to Alzheimer-type degeneration (Wisniewski et al., 1976; Kosik et al., 1986; Wood et al., 1986; Lee et al., 1991). In fact, the degree to which brain areas targeted by Alzheimer's disease express neurodegeneration appears to be determined by their relative content of tau species that are capable of transforming into PHFs (Bahr and Vicente, 1998).

Additional studies in rats and primates also found that inhibition of lysosomal proteases generates PHF aggregates in the brain (Ivy, 1992; Cavanagh et al., 1993; Takauchi and Miyoshi, 1995). Abnormal tau accumulation occurred in response to the induced lysosomal disturbance, followed by the formation of intraneuronal deposits that resemble tangles at the light microscope level (Bahr, 1995; Takauchi and Miyoshi, 1995; Bi et al., 2001; Bendiske et al., 2002) as well as the electron microscope level (Takauchi and Miyoshi, 1995; Bi et al., 2001). Genetic mutations in tau cause neurofibrillary degeneration in the absence of Aβ plaques, resulting in frontotemporal dementia (see Hardy et al., 1998; Spittaels et al., 1999). Thus, abnormal tau processing alone is sufficient to initiate neurodegenerative events that lead to cognitive decline.

Tau isoforms are thought to be metabolized in lysosomes (Ikeda et al., 1998, 2000). Since A□ peptide is taken up by neurons and causes negative lysosomotropic effects (Bahr et al., 1998; Yang et al., 1998; Ditaranto et al., 2001), there may be a relationship between intracellular A□ accumulation and tangle formation. A connection between A□ and NFTs indeed has been previously suggested (Busciglio et al., 1995) and further strengthened by recent studies using transgenic animals (Gotz et al., 2001; Lewis et al., 2001). In one of the studies, injection of the more amyloidogenic A□$_{1-42}$ peptide into tau mutant mice caused increased tangles. This occurred away from the hippocampal injection site and in a brain region to which hippocampal neurons project. This finding could be related to data that suggest A□ is taken up by neurons and transported to synaptic terminals where local protein processing is disrupted (Bahr et al., 1998; also see Takahashi et al., 2002). This may occur in select populations of neurons that are especially vulnerable to an A□ positive feedback process (see Bahr and Bendiske, 2002). Interestingly, a lysosomotropic feedback loop also may be in effect during tau processing as well. Such an idea stems from a report indicating that altered tau disrupts lysosomes in neurons of FTDP-17 transgenic mice (Lim et al., 2001).

There are likely many types of amyloidogenic pathways to neurodegeneration (e.g., see Bahr et al., 1998; Small et al., 2001; Walsh et al., 2002) that are distinct from the cascade of events that are associated with neurofibrillary degeneration (Fig. 1). Additional pathogenic circumstances involving lysosomes could influence the separate degenerative pathways as well as the potential convergences between Aβ and NFT chemistries. For instance, pathogenic protein accumulations may be intensified by the activation of non-lysosomal proteases that are associated with apoptotic and excitotoxic episodes (e.g., see Blomgren et al., 2001; Caba et al., 2002). Aberrant proteolytic activity generates protein fragments that add to the workload of the lysosomal system, and such events occur with age and in different age-related disease states (Nixon, 2000; Vanderklish and Bahr, 2000; Blomgren et al., 2001; Kim et al., 2001b; Goffredo et al., 2002). The apoptosis-related protease caspase has been found to be activated as a function of Alzheimer's disease progression and to correlate with NFT formation (Rohn et al., 2001). A protease linked to excitotoxicity, calpain, is abnormally active during normal aging and in Alzheimer brains (see Nixon, 2000; Vanderklish and Bahr, 2000). Interestingly, aberrant calpain responses in the aged brain appear to target regions that are vulnerable to Alzheimer's disease (Bahr et al., 1991; Vicente et al., 2002). Calpain activation also occurs during lysosomal disturbances (Bendiske et al., 2002), which can generate further lysosomal disruption as calpain damages the membrane structure of lysosomes (Yamashima, 2000).

Other germane circumstances can compound lysosomal problems. Under unusual lysosomal stress, disruption of lipid trafficking and homeostasis can occur along with the oxidation of unsaturated fatty acids in phospholipids. Such events can lead to transient lysosomal storage of phospholipids and deposition of autofluorescent pigment. Oligomeric Aβ has been suggested to disrupt neuronal lipid homeostasis (Michikawa et al., 2001) and cholesterol trafficking (Yao and Papadopoulos, 2002), thereby contributing to neuronal dysfunction and death (see Wood et al., 2002 for further ideas on cholesterol and Alzheimer's disease). Cholesterol was the main component of lipids released after the addition of Aβ.

Many LSDs exist that cause different types of glycosphingolipids and cholesterol to accumulate in the brain. Interestingly, alterations to neuronal cholesterol metabolism have been shown to result in pathogenic events resembling neurofibrillary degeneration including tau hyperphosphorylation, microtubule depolymerization, and axonal degeneration (Fan et al., 2001; Sawamura et al., 2001). In another example of cholesterol's involvement in brain disorders, the neurodegenerative disease Niemann-Pick type C is characterized by the buildup of lipoprotein-derived cholesterol in lysosomes due to mutations in the NPC1 protein (Loftus et al., 1997). The lysosomal storage of cholesterol may induce abnormal protein processing/accumulation as evidenced by the appearance of PHF-tau and Aβ deposits in Niemann-Pick type C disease (Auer et al., 1995; Saito et al., 2002). This is consistent with studies suggesting that lysosomes are involved in tau processing and the early development of PHFs (Ikeda et al., 1998, 2000; Oyama et al., 1998; Bendiske et al., 2002) and amyloidogenic species (Benowitz et al., 1989; Golde et al., 1992; Bahr et al., 1994a). The described link between cholesterol and Alzheimer's disease may explain why cholesterol-lowering drugs reduce the incidence of Alzheimer-type dementia as well as reduce intra- and extracellular levels of Aβ (Fassbender et al., 2001).

Role in Microtubule Destabilization and Transport Failure

As described, lysosomal dysfunction can influence a cascade of neuropathogenic events including accumulation of amyloidogenic species, hyperphosphorylation of tau, and ubiquitination of intracellular deposits. Formation of PHFs may play a part in disrupting the equilibrium between tau and phosphorylated tau (Tau-p), thus decreasing the availability of native tau for stabilizing microtubules and their transport mechanisms (see Fig. 1). Indeed, production of hyperphosphorylated tau species has been shown to promote microtubule destabilization (Lindwall and Cole, 1984; Alonso et al., 1996, 1997). Abnormal tau processing may also disrupt tau's ability to promote microtubule assembly independent of PHF formation. Soluble forms of mutant human tau have recently been shown to cause neurodegeneration without forming tangles in fruit flies (Wittmann et al., 2001).

In the hippocampal slice model, destabilization of microtubules occurred following a period of lysosomal disturbance, as indicated by the selective loss of acetylated tubulin (Bendiske et al., 2002). A similar reduction in acetylated tubulin has been identified in PHF-containing neurons of Alzheimer tissue (Hempen and Brion, 1996). The intracellular deposition of NFTs coincided with reduced levels of the microtubule stability marker, thus indicating that tangles negatively impact microtubules and their cellular responsibilities. During treatment with lysosomal inhibitors, CTF and PHF accumulations in hippocampal tissue corresponded with the degree of microtubule compromise (Bahr et al., 1994a; Bendiske et al., 2002). Signs of microtubule destabilization not only included the reduction in acetylated tubulin, but also the production of tubulin breakdown products and diminished transport capability.

Over an extended period of lysosomal dysfunction, a strong correspondence occurred between the gradual formation of PHF deposits and the gradual loss of transport (by monitoring the transport of horseradish peroxidase in hippocampal field CA1). Disruption of axonal and dendritic transport is likely mediated by the loss of microtubule integrity as well as through physical obstruction produced by protein deposits (see Bendiske et al., 2002). Intracellular deposition formed a polar cap within pyramidal neurons and granule cells, likely acting as an obstruction of transport corridors. Alternatively, the accumulation could merely be an indicator of material that failed to be transported in that direction. Such indications of early transport dysfunction have been found associated with different neurodegenerative disease states including Alzheimer's disease (Griffin and Watson, 1988; Hempen and Brion, 1996; Sasaki and Iwata, 1996; Li et al., 2001), thus stressing the necessity of efficient transport capability for cell viability. Recent evidence indicates that amyloidogenic species can also disrupt kinesin-mediated transport mechanisms (see Kamal et al., 2001). These studies support the notion that multiple types of protein accumulation events lead to the failure of important transport systems.

Axonal transport appears to be particularly vulnerable to protein deposition as evidenced by the somatic accumulation of protein aggregates and filamentous inclusions found in studies with the human brain (Hempen and Brion, 1996; Li et al., 2001). As discussed above, the microtubule-binding properties of tau label the molecule as a potential trigger point for axonal transport failure. The translation of tau appears to occur at the proximal axon (Mandelkow et al., 1995), thus abnormal processing/aggregation of newly synthesized tau could promote the characteristic early deposition described. Correspondingly, a defect in fast axonal transport and associated axonopathy has been found to be attributable to the overexpression of the four-repeat tau isoform in transgenic mice (Spittaels et al., 1999; also see Higuchi et al., 2002). Severe axonopathy in the brain and spinal cord were discovered in the mice overexpressing four-repeat human tau protein. In the hippocampal slice model of lysosomal dysfunction, protein deposits also appeared to initiate in the surrounding area of the axon hillock (Bendiske et al., 2002). This initial deposition of aggregate material suggests that axons are affected by transport failure first, before dendrites are influenced. Similar indications were found with regards to early protein accumulations of huntingtin aggregates, Lewy body-like inclusions, and lysosomes (Sasaki and Iwata, 1996; Li et al., 2001).

Early protein accumulation events may serve to disrupt transport processes through axons, or they may simply reflect the result of axonal transport failure. In either case, the localized accumulation of deposits encompassing the axon hillock in the slice model provides an explanation for the reduced axonal excitability and faster presynaptic deterioration (Bahr et al., 1994a). Disturbances in axon integrity and transmitter release mechanisms via the loss of transported components could trigger further neurodegeneration by diminishing cell maintenance signals (see Bambrick et al., 1995; Yao and Coleman, 1998; McKinney et al., 1999; Bahr et al., 2002; Limatola et al., 2002; Munirathinam et al., 2002). Thus, lysosomal dysfunction appears to precipitate a series of pathogenic changes leading to transport failure, thereby causing nerve endings to be cutoff from important transmitted signals and replenishing supplies.

Role in Synaptic Pathology

It is apparent that intraneuronal protein accumulation leads to the breakdown of transport mechanisms. The collapse of microtubule integrity and resultant disruption of somatofugal transport have been implicated in Alzheimer-type synaptopathogenic cascades (Bahr et al., 1994a; Heinonen et al., 1995; Hempen and Brion, 1996; Bendiske et al., 2002). Lysosomal dysfunction's role in promoting amyloidogenic and tangle chemistries may establish the pathogenic step(s) that directly or indirectly breaks down transport pathways that are vital for synaptic function, plasticity, and maintenance (Fig. 1). A similar chain of pathogenesis has been proposed, leading from amyloid neurotoxicity to tau hyperphosphorylation, microtubule destabilization, axonal transport disruption, and synaptic failure, before ending with neurodegeneration (Terwel et al., 2002). Synapses are particularly vulnerable to Aβ. Fibrillar Aβ applied to cortical neurons leads to a marked decline in synaptic staining (Grace et al., 2002). The generation of amyloidogenic species also is thought to disrupt synaptic structure and functionality (e.g., Bahr et al., 1994a, 1998; Hsia et al., 1999; Larson et al., 1999; Mucke et al., 2000; Kim et al., 2001a; Apelt et al., 2002; Dewachter et al., 2002; Dodart et al., 2002; Takahashi et al., 2002; Walsh et al., 2002; Wang et al., 2002; Westerman et al., 2002). In Alzheimer brains, a transgenic mouse model of the disease, and in the hippocampal slice model, amyloidogenic species have a tendency to accumulate intracellularly at synaptic connections, and this was associated with signs of synaptic pathology (Bahr et al., 1998; Takahashi et al., 2002).

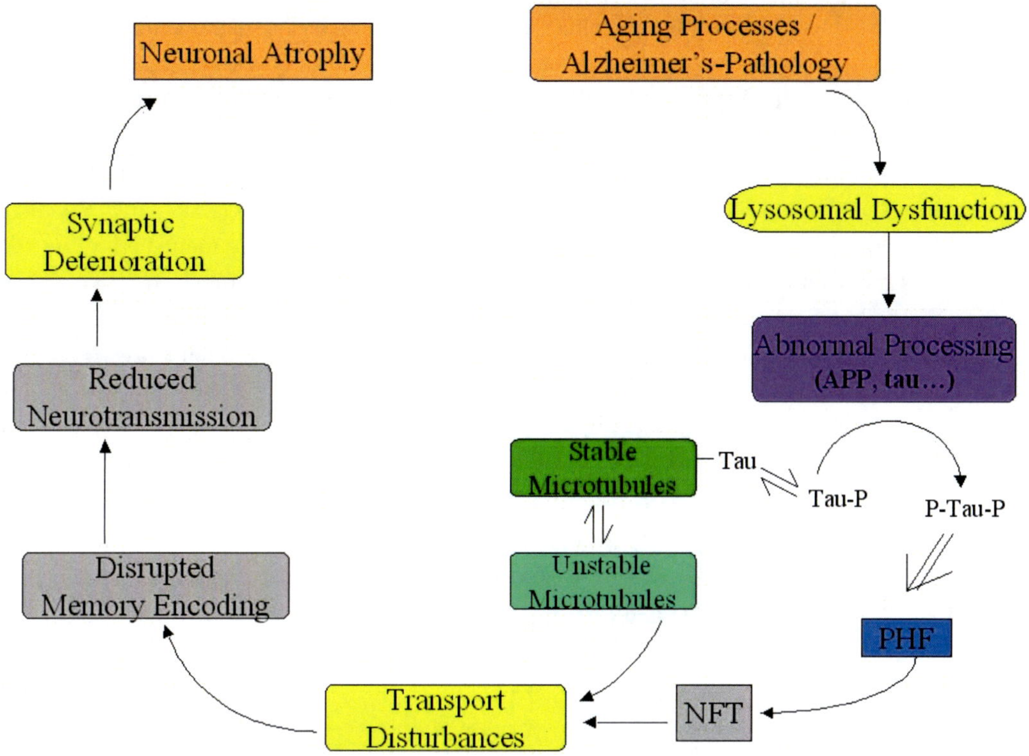

Figure 1. A potential pathogenic cascade involves lysosomal disturbances, leading to early cognitive decline as well as eventual synaptic and cellular deterioration.

Loss of synaptic markers also was discovered to be evident in neurons containing tau deposits (Bahr et al., 1995; Callahan and Coleman, 1995; Callahan et al., 1999; Hall et al., 2000; Bendiske et al., 2002). Interestingly, indications of lysosomal disturbances as well as synaptic decline were found in tangle-bearing neurons but not in neighboring tangle-free neurons of Alzheimer brains (Callahan et al., 1999, 2002). Disturbance of the lysosomal system appears to be especially detrimental to synapses since it increases synaptic vulnerability to other insults that can affect transport systems (Bahr et al., 1994a). Thus, the link between protein accumulation and synaptic pathology in Alzheimer's disease may be the transport failure facilitated by lysosomal perturbation. More specifically, aberrant protein processing/deposition may alter synaptic gene expression by disrupting microtubule integrity and signaling events necessary for efficient transport.

The degree to which lysosomal perturbation induces protein accumulation indeed correlates significantly with the extent of transport failure and synaptic deterioration (Bahr et al., 1994a, 2002; Bendiske et al., 2002). In the hippocampal slice model of lysosomal dysfunction, not only are there clear indications of the breakdown of transport systems and synaptic structure, but synapse function is also affected as evidenced by the gradual reduction in evoked excitatory responses (Bahr et al., 1994a; Bendiske and Bahr, 2003). The loss of synaptic markers in fact occurred over the same time period in which protein deposition, transport failure, and reduced EPSPs were evident. Similar events are thought to be key factors in the progression of Alzheimer's disease. Synaptic loss and reduced cerebral activity are characteristic of Alzheimer patients, thus indicating that the pathogenic targeting of synapses is an early contributor to the disease (Cross et al., 1986; Davies et al., 1987; Terry et al., 1991; Honer et al., 1992; Heinonen et al., 1995; Blennow et al., 1996; Mesulam, 1999; Terry et al., 1999).

Lysosomal dysfunction reproduces many features of Alzheimer-type pathogenesis, especially the protein deposition–synaptopathogenesis relationship (Bahr and Bendiske, 2002). The link between lysosomal dysfunction and synaptic pathology identified in the slice model has received additional supportive evidence from Alzheimers studies (Callahan et al., 1999, 2002; Masliah and Licastro, 2000). In hippocampal slice cultures, reduced synaptic transmission during lysosomal disruption apparently is due to a dramatic decline in the number of synapses per neuron (Bahr et al., 1994a; Bahr and Bendiske, 2002). This corresponds to the findings from transgenic mouse models (Hsia et al., 1999; Moechars et al., 1999), and such a decline in synaptic density is similar to that found in the early stages of clinical Alzheimer's disease (Davies et al., 1987).

Biochemical and morphological parameters in Alzheimer brains also strongly indicate that synapses are the initial target of the disease (see Perdahl et al., 1984; Terry et al., 1991; Honer et al., 1992; Callahan et al., 1999; Selkoe, 2002), especially in the hippocampus (Samuel et al., 1994; Heinonen et al., 1995; Scheff et al., 1996; Sze et al., 1997; Yao et al., 1999; Callahan et al., 2002). In Alzheimer brains and the slice model of lysosomal perturbation, diminished expression of the presynaptic vesicle protein synaptophysin was evident in neurons containing protein deposits (Bahr et al., 1994a; Callahan and Coleman, 1995; Callahan et al., 1999; Bendiske et al., 2002). It is noteworthy that in the slice model, the level of deposition correlated with the degree to which the synaptic marker was reduced. Similarly, protein deposits have been shown to correspond with the severity of Alzheimer's disease, thus explaining the identification of synaptic decay as a major correlate of the pathology (Terry et al., 1991; Samuel et al., 1997; Sze et al., 1997; Brown et al., 1998).

Synaptophysin decline is not only indicative of synaptic deterioration, its loss in hippocampus and other regions correlates with the degree of cognitive decline in Alzheimer's disease (Masliah et al., 1989, 2001; Terry et al., 1991; Sze et al., 1997) and occurs in transgenic models of the disease (Buttini et al., 1999, 2002; Hsia et al., 1999; Mucke et al., 2000; Savage et al., 2002). Many synaptic markers are altered before neuronal loss in Alzheimers brains (Masliah et al., 1989; Pellegrini-Giampietro et al., 1994; Callahan and Coleman, 1995; Yao et al., 1999; Butterfield et al., 2002) as well as in models of amyloidogenesis and lysosomal dysfunction (Bahr et al., 1994a; Mucke et al., 2000; Bendiske et al., 2002; Buttini et al., 2002; Chauhan et al., 2002). Interestingly, presynaptic proteins are lost faster than postsynaptic markers in the slice model. The presynaptic vulnerability is evident at the protein level (Bahr et al., 1994a; Bendiske et al., 2002) as well as at the message level (Bendiske et al., 2002; Bendiske and Bahr, 2003). Reduced expression of synaptic genes likely occurs as a result of either localized depletion of the respective protein species or the somatic buildup of the protein thereby producing a negative feedback response.

As the synaptopathogenesis progresses, the decline in components of presynaptic terminals may be responsible for the reduced expression of postsynaptic neurotransmitter receptors. The hippocampal slice model reproduces the kinds of reductions in AMPA-type and NMDA-type glutamate receptors found in Alzheimer brains, at both the protein and message level (Bahr et al., 1994a, 2002; Bendiske et al., 2002; Bendiske and Bahr, 2003). In Alzheimer's disease, the loss of glutamatergic receptors is especially evident in hippocampus and entorhinal cortex (Garcia-Ladona et al., 1994; Yasuda et al., 1995; Ikonomovic et al., 1997; Thorns et al., 1997; Wakabayashi et al., 1999; Hynd et al., 2001). Suggested by the presynaptic vulnerability, transport failure would lead to the loss of presynaptic proteins with rapid turnover, and this promotes transcriptional regulation that translates into delayed reduction in postsynaptic receptors.

The inter-dependency between presynaptic and postsynaptic elements is a strong indication that the loss of transmitter receptors is a consequence of reduced neurotransmission. In correspondence to this, synaptic vesicle disorders (Lassmann et al., 1992; Yao and Coleman, 1998; Chauhan et al., 2002) and disruption of transmitter re-uptake systems (Apelt et al., 2002; Butterfield et al., 2002) have been implicated in the pathology of synapse loss in Alzheimer brains. Reduced vesicular release of neurotransmitter, glutamate in particular, would indeed have a tendency to disrupt synaptic maintenance signaling (see McKinney et al., 1999). The resultant loss of presynaptic signaling is compounded by the fact that the transmitter receptors lost, including AMPA receptors and nicotinic acetylcholine receptors, are also linked to cell signaling pathways important for synapse maintenance (Wang and Durkin, 1995; Hayashi et al., 1999; Bahr et al., 2002; Limatola et al., 2002; Shaw et al., 2002). Thus, signaling disruption may occur in a cyclic manner to account for the progressive degeneration of presynaptic terminals and dendritic spines.

ACTIVATION OF THE LYSOSOMAL SYSTEM

Role in Enhancing Lysosomal Capacity

While characteristic features of age-related disorders are induced by lysosomal suppression (see review: Bahr and Bendiske, 2002), many studies have revealed evidence that activation of the lysosomal system occurs in diseased brains as indicated by the appearance of numerous lysosomal vacuoles with increased enzyme content (Cross et al., 1986; Cataldo et al., 1991, 1995, 1996; Ii et al., 1993; Lemere et al., 1995; Haas et al., 1996; Callahan et al., 1999; Kegel et al., 2000). Elevated cellular content of lysosomes and their digestive enzymes is generally reflective of lysosomal disturbances. However, the increase in the number of lysosomes could be part of an established repair mechanism in which lysosomes play a vital role in the resealing of damaged cell membranes (McNeil and Terasaki, 2001; McNeil, 2002). The amplification of lysosomal hydrolases is a selective type of cellular regulation and, interestingly, may represent a compensatory enhancement of lysosomal capacity in response to Alzheimer-type pathogenesis (see Cataldo et al., 1995, 1996; Bendiske and Bahr, 2003).

Protein accumulation events may trigger the lysosomal activation response in order to offset the formation of intracellular deposits and slow the progressive neurodegeneration they elicit. This is supported by the fact that enhanced expression of lysosomal enzymes occurs in conjunction with protein accumulation in brain tissue exposed to Aβ. Besides inducing lysosomal decay, amyloidogenic processing, and synaptic degeneration (Burdick et al., 1997;

Bahr et al., 1998; Yang et al., 1998; Ditaranto et al., 2001), the $A\beta_{1-42}$ peptide up-regulated cathepsins in a manner consistent with lysosomal activation (Hoffman et al., 1998; Bendiske and Bahr, 2003).

The correspondence between protein accumulation and lysosomal activation evident during Aβ exposure was also found induced by disruptors of lysosomal function (Bahr, 1995; Bendiske and Bahr, 2003). Treatment of hippocampal tissue with the lysosomal inhibitor chloroquine not only caused amyloidogenic changes and tau accumulation, the acidotropic compound also up-regulated a broad spectrum of lysosomal hydrolases by two- to three-fold. The affected enzymes include cathepsins B, D, and L; cathepsin S was the only enzyme found not to exhibit increased levels. Besides the three members of the cathepsin family, other lysosomal enzymes were up-regulated which included β-glucuronidase and elastase. Together with the Aβ studies, it appears that different stressors that have a negative influence on lysosomal protein processing also induce, in parallel, a positive effect on lysosomal enzyme expression.

As established by the slice model, the lysosomal activation response involves at least cathepsins B, D, and L, β-glucuronidase, and possibly elastase. Elastase is up-regulated in hippocampal tissue that exhibits marked PHF-tau accumulation (Bendiske and Bahr, 2003) and in neurofibrillary tangle-bearing Alzheimer's disease neurons (Smith et al., 1996), thus providing further evidence of a compensatory response. A similar indication that the listed enzymes are involved in compensatory signaling comes from the fact that β-glucuronidase is among the endosomal-lysosomal components highly expressed in Aβ-resistant neurons (Li et al., 1999), thereby implicating the enzyme in neuronal survival during Aβ exposure.

The cysteine proteases cathepsins B and L, and the aspartic acid protease cathepsin D may be key components of the compensatory response for they exhibit pronounced increases during lysosomotropic conditions (Hoffman et al., 1998; Bendiske and Bahr, 2003). The highest expression levels of cathepsins B and L are located in brain regions that are vulnerable to amyloidogenic processing (Petanceska et al., 1994). Cathepsin D is appropriate for a compensatory signaling pathway since it has been suggested to reduce Aβ secretion (Munger et al., 1995) and degrade tau (Kenessey et al., 1997; Ikeda et al., 1998; Bi et al., 2000). In addition, up-regulation of cathepsin D occurs before overt neuronal damage in vulnerable cell populations in Alzheimer brains as well as in animal models of neurodegeneration (Cataldo et al., 1995, 1996; Adamec et al., 2000; Nixon et al., 2001), thus indicative of an early repair process. Interestingly, although a controversial issue in the Alzheimer field, a polymorphism of the cathepsin D gene, perhaps leading to a more active enzyme, is associated with a marked decrease in $A\beta_{1-42}$ in the cerebrospinal fluid of Alzheimer patients (Papassotiropoulos et al., 2002). Be aware, also, that there are alternative views regarding cathepsin D's role in Alzheimer's disease (see Haas and Sparks, 1996).

While chloroquine initiates the enzyme activation response by its disruptive action on the lysosomal proton gradient, specific cathepsin inhibitors also were shown to produce hydrolase up-regulation (Bendiske and Bahr, 2003). N-Cbz-L-phenylalanyl-L-alanyl-diazomethylketone (PADK) selectively inhibits cathepsins B and L, but mild concentrations of the compound were found to cause increases in several lysosomal enzymes. The cathepsin D inhibitor diazoacetyl-DL-2-aminohexanoic acid methyl ester and the cathepsin B inhibitor glycyl-phenylalanyl-glycine-aldehyde semicarbazone also up-regulated cathepsin isoforms.

In contrast to the described acidic lysosomal enzymes, the cysteine protease cathepsin S was reduced in concentration during episodes of lysosomal dysfunction. Since cathepsin S has been shown to be capable of generating Aβ variants under certain conditions (Munger et al., 1995), the reduction in cathepsin S during lysosomal disturbance may be part of the compensatory response represented by up-regulated levels of cathepsins B, D, and L. On the contrary, there are indications of increased cathepsin S in Alzheimer's disease and other neurodegenerative disorders (Lemere et al., 1995).

Regulated expression of lysosome enzymes is not restricted to conditions produced by lysosomal stress and age-related disorders. Normal biological processes are known to induce regulatory signals that affect proteases. For instance, the pituitary surge of luteinizing hormone during ovulation is associated with transcriptional regulation of protease genes including the gene that encodes cathepsin L (Robker et al., 2000). It is also noteworthy that transcriptional activation of cathepsin D expression is mediated by 17β-estradiol (Wang et al., 2001), the same hormone shown to accelerate APP trafficking, reduce the production of Aβ, and decrease the risk for Alzheimer's disease in post-menopausal women (Xu et al., 1998; Petanceska et al., 2000; Turner, 2001; Greenfield et al., 2002; Zheng et al., 2002).

Role in Clearance of Protein Accumulations

With the idea that up-regulation of select lysosomal enzymes is driven by compensatory signaling, it follows that positive modulation of the lysosomal response should act against protein accumulation events. In order to test the concept of compensatory activation, the hippocampal slice model was used since, in this model, the lysosomal enzyme response has been demonstrated to be accessible to modulation (Bendiske and Bahr, 2003). Low concentrations of PADK elicited modulatory action that generated 2-8-fold increases in cathepsin isoforms over the level of activation already produced by chloroquine treatment. PADK modulation markedly increased both the active intermediate form of cathepsin D as well as the cleaved, mature form produced by lysosomal processing. While broad inhibition of pH-dependent enzymes with chloroquine elicited corresponding neurodegeneration and lysosomal activation, the PADK-mediated lysosomal change was not associated with neuronal decay or synaptic decline. Pre- and postsynaptic markers remained at stable concentrations for weeks in the PADK-treated slices while cathepsin levels increased 4-5-fold. The mode of lysosomal activation elicited by PADK is indeed distinct from chloroquine-induced activation by the fact that the effects of the two compounds were additive. Thus, these experiments describe a pharmacological avenue that allows for the controlled, non-pathogenic activation of the lysosomal system.

With an appropriate modulator identified, the lysosomal activation response was tested for its effects against protein accumulation. Chloroquine is known to cause increases in pathogenic tau isoforms of 55-69 kDa (Bendiske et al., 2002), the same isoforms found in the aged brain and Alzheimer's disease. However, in the presence of modulatory concentrations of PADK, chloroquine exposure no longer was associated with increased tau levels (Bendiske and Bahr, 2003). PADK treatment also was shown to promote clearance of pre-existing protein deposits. In this experiment, chloroquine was infused into hippocampal slice cultures for several days, causing intraneuronal deposition of PHF-immunopositive material and carboxyl-terminal fragments of APP as previously reported (Bahr et al., 1994a; Bahr, 1995). When chloroquine was finally removed from the slices after 6 days of treatment, the protein accumulation events continued to be evident, especially in the cell bodies of pyramidal neurons. On the other hand, when chloroquine was instead replaced by modulating levels of PADK, this resulted in the clearance of PHF species and reduced levels of amyloidogenic fragments.

The suspected increase in lysosomal capacity mediated by PADK modulation likely plays a role in the resultant clearance of cellular deposits. As mentioned, many studies suggest that tau degradation and early formation of PHF and amyloidogenic species occurs in lysosomes. Up-regulation of appropriate lysosomal proteases may be part of a feedback system that keeps in check any buildup of modified of misfolded proteins. Cathepsin D stands out in that it is greatly increased by both chloroquine and PADK exposure, and the lysosomal hydrolase has been previously implicated in the processing of APP as well as tau (Munger et al., 1995; Kenessey et al., 1997; Ikeda et al., 1998). An alternative processing mechanism is through the proteasome. Studies have demonstrated proteasomal processing of APP (Skovronsky et al., 2000), tau (David et al., 2002), as well as presenilin 1 (Honda et al., 1999). While the proteasome serves as the major enzymatic system of non-lysosomal protein degradation, no evidence of proteasome up-regulation was found associated with chloroquine-induced protein accumulation or with PADK-mediated clearance of deposits (see Bendiske and Bahr, 2003).

Chloroquine disrupts the pH gradient of the lysosome compartment, thereby reducing the digestive capability of many types of hydrolases and resulting in the accumulation of proteins and their partially digested fragments. With such functional disruption, transcription regulation signals may be produced by a broad range of proteins or glycoconjugates normally processed by lysosomal enzymes. Recent data suggests that specific protease substrates are involved in the activation of gene expression (Bendiske and Bahr, 2003). Activation of the lysosomal system is clearly a global response that affects a number of enzymes. While chloroquine-mediated lysosomal dysfunction indeed affects many enzymes, PADK only targets cathepsins B and L but causes a more robust activation response than chloroquine. PADK modulation not only markedly up-regulates the targeted hydrolases but other lysosomal enzymes as well. Thus, it may be specific cathepsin substrates that are monitored, and their cellular accumulation influences the expression systems of lysosomal enzymes in order to offset further deposition of non-proteolyzed material.

Increasing lysosomal enzymes is an approach for treating the effects of deposited material in neurodegenerative lysosomal storage diseases (Dobrenis et al., 1992; Fallet et al., 1992; Kakkis et al., 1996). It stands to reason that enzymatic up-regulation may also be part of an endogenous compensatory system that is activated during protein accumulation events. The chloroquine-induced up-regulation of lysosomal hydrolases is speculated to be an unsuccessful attempt to restore the normal lysosomal capacity in order to process modified and misfolded proteins. Enhancing the level of lysosomal activation with PADK facilitated the clearance of protein accumulations, thus, providing evidence for the proposed compensatory signaling that can be added to a list of potential therapeutic avenues (see Table 1).

Role in Re-establishing Microtubule Integrity

Besides the clearance effects on tau species and amyloidogenic fragments, PADK modulation also promotes the stable maintenance of microtubules as expected from the link between intracellular deposition and microtubular disruption identified in the slice model. Chloroquine-induced protein accumulation in hippocampal slices was associated with a pronounced decline in an indicator of microtubule integrity, acetylated tubulin. Tubulin acetylation is a specific post-translational modification that provides a valuable marker for stable microtubules (Black et al., 1989). Both the reduction in acetylated tubulin and the increase in tubulin fragmentation events occurred in close correspondence with the steady development of protein deposits (Bendiske et al., 2002). Interestingly, decreases in acetylated tubulin also exhibited a significant correlation with the degree of synaptic decay.

When PADK was administered after several days of chloroquine treatment, the cellular content of acetylated tubulin was gradually restored to levels similar to those expressed by control slices. Of the many enzymes up-regulated by PADK modulation, cathepsin D is a good candidate component of the lysosomal activation response for allowing PADK's influence on APP fragments, tau, as well as the support of microtubule elements. On the contrary, cathepsin D, through its age-related increase, has been suggested to initiate defective microtubule assembly (Matus and Green, 1987). Data from the slice model, however, disagrees with such an idea since positive lysosomal modulation causes both a marked increase in cathepsin D levels and the restoration of microtubule integrity.

PADK's positive influence on microtubule integrity was further indicated by the fact that PADK modulation also restores microtubule-based transport mechanisms that were disrupted by the lysosomal dysfunction protocol (Bendiske and Bahr, 2003). Using the horseradish peroxidase method, gradual loss of transport capability was found to occur during the same time period that protein deposits formed and microtubule breakdown became evident. Transport failure is mediated by direct physical blockage or indirectly through the destabilization of microtubule filaments (Bahr and Bendiske, 2002). Subsequent to the lysosomal perturbation, PADK-treated slice cultures exhibited active transport throughout an elaborate array of dendrites extending from pyramidal neurons. Through the restored transport mechanisms, horseradish peroxidase activity extended into distal dendritic branches, spine structures, and long axons.

Transport failure is thought to be derived from intraneuronal deposits (see Bahr et al., 1994a; Callahan et al., 1999; Bendiske et al., 2002), especially those that disturb the balance of tau species necessary for microtubule assembly and function. Showing that lysosomal modulation promotes microtubule functionality is important since the collapse of microtubule integrity and disruption of somatofugal transport have been implicated in Alzheimer-type pathogenesis (see Hempen and Brion, 1996; Stamer et al., 2002). Further studies with the slice model showed that microtubule stabilization and corresponding transport recuperation are not only consequences of the lysosomal activation response, but also key factors in neuronal repair (see below). These findings illustrate that enhancing lysosomal activity is one why to offset the pathogenic cascade consisting of abnormal protein accumulation, microtubule destabilization, and transport failure.

Role in Synaptic Repair

If lysosomal activation is indeed a result of compensatory signaling, then PADK-mediated deposit clearance, microtubule stabilization, and activated transport should be associated with the repair of those synapses that are damaged by lysosomal dysfunction. As predicted, positive modulation of the lysosomal response restores synaptic integrity by reversing the different pathogenic components that develop through the inability of lysosomes to function properly (see Fig. 2).

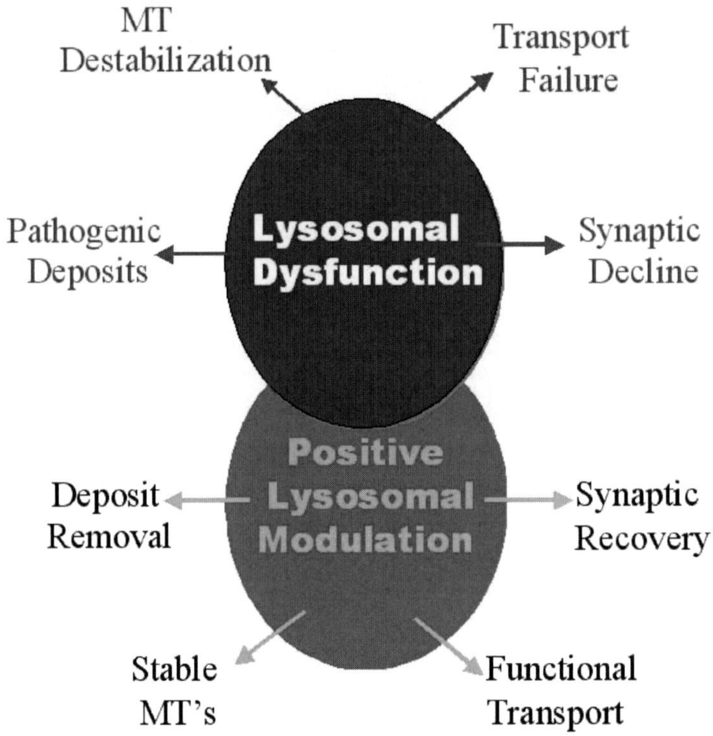

Figure 2. Lysosomal dysfunction leads to pathogenic protein accumulations, destabilization of microtubules (MT), somatofugal transport failure, and synaptic decline, while positive modulation of the lysosomal activation response promotes clearance of protein deposits, restores microtubule integrity, re-establishes transport mechanisms, and supports synaptic repair.

The loss of synaptic proteins represents early Alzheimer-type neurodegeneration and is a useful measure for identifying potential compensatory pathways (Harry et al., 1985; Brock and O'Callaghan, 1987; Bahr et al., 1994a, 1998, 2002). Thus, chloroquine-induced disruption of hippocampal synapses makes the slice model ideal for monitoring synaptic recovery. In a recent study, removal of chloroquine after a lengthy treatment period resulted in only the continuation of neurodegenerative processes. The cellular frequency and intensity of PHF material remained the same or increased, while synaptic decline progressed. This indicates that the chloroquine-induced level of lysosomal activation is too small to offset the pathogenic cascade triggered by intracellular deposition. In striking contrast, replacing chloroquine with the PADK modulator led to clearance of protein deposits and a corresponding recovery of both pre- and postsynaptic markers (Bendiske and Bahr, 2003). Note, this further establishes the link between protein deposition and synaptic decline. Other modulating agents besides PADK elicited neuroprotection, including diazoacetyl-DL-2-aminohexanoic acid methyl ester and glycyl-phenylalanyl-glycine-aldehyde semicarbazone. These data show that by pharmacologically boosting lysosomal activation signals, their effects on altering the balance between damage and repair are uncovered.

Positive modulation of the compensatory signals appears to restore synaptic integrity by promoting a series of protective events including deposit clearance and the re-establishment of microtubule integrity and transport mechanisms (Fig. 2). Compensatory neuroprotection also occurs *in vitro* and *in vivo* when mitogen-activated protein kinase responses to excitotoxicity are similarly modulated (Bahr et al., 2002). Most importantly, synaptic protection via lysosomal activation responses indicates that the deleterious effects of intracellular deposition are not permanent. Under conditions in which removal of the lysosomal disruptive agent allows for reversal of protein deposition, synaptic recovery also occurs (Bahr et al., 1994a). Indeed, clearance of accumulated proteins and disruption of aggregation have been identified as potential treatments for protein accumulation disorders like Huntington's disease (Sânchez et al., 2003) and Alzheimer's and other amyloid diseases (e.g., see Klein et al., 2001; Hammarström et al., 2001, 2003; Selkoe, 2001b). Using transgenic animals possessing brain tissue compromised by protein deposition, reductions of the neuropathology as well as cognitive and behavioral impairment were produced by Aβ-sequestering antibodies raised against Aβ peptides (Schenk et al., 1999; Janus et al., 2000; Morgan et al., 2000; Weiner et al., 2000) or administered passively (Bard et al., 2000; Dodart et al., 2002; Kotilinek et al., 2002). One study showed the loss of a synaptic marker in hippocampal subregions of mice overexpressing mutant APP, and nearly complete recovery of the marker in the CA1 dendritic field one month after administration of anti-Aβ antibody (Chauhan et al., 2002).

In addition to the vaccine-based approaches, reduction in Aβ levels in transgenic mouse brains recently has been achieved with the gelsolin Aβ-binding agent (Matsuoka et al., 2003) and with the noothropic agent Cerebrolysin (Rockenstein et al., 2002). It is noteworthy that the latter study also reported the amelioration of synaptic pathology. The take home message regarding the likelihood of future treatments for Alzheimer's disease is that the resultant deterioration of synaptic integrity by protein deposits is reversible, as shown in a variety of transgenic mouse models and in the slice model. These studies establish yet another strategy to be added to the growing list of avenues for treating Alzheimer's disease (Table 1).

Table 1. Potential Therapeutic Avenues

Inhibition of Synaptic Pathology or Cell Death
- neurotrophins
- caspase inhibitors
- glucocorticoid antagonists
- glutamate receptor antagonists (e.g., memantine)
- microtubule stabilizing agents
- ApoE mimicking drugs
- microglia deactivator agents
- lysosomal modulators

Clearance of Protein Deposits
- amyloid vaccine
- anti-fibrillogenesis compounds
- Aβ-binding agents (e.g., gelsolin)
- noothropic agent (e.g., Cerebrolysin)
- inhibitors of APP synthesis
- inhibitors of β and γ secretases
- α secretase enhancers
- metal chelators (e.g., clioquinol)
- cholesterol lowering agents (e.g., statins)
- inhibitors of protein misfolding energetics
- PHF disruptors
- lysosomal modulators

Promote Synaptic Function
- acetylcholinesterase inhibitors
- AMPA receptor potentiators (e.g., Ampakines)
- M1 muscarinic agonists
- M2 muscarinic antagonists
- cAMP response element-binding protein enhancers
- lysosomal modulators

Reduce Inflammation Processes
- anti-inflammatory compounds (e.g., NSAIDs)

Reduce Free-Radical Production
- anti-oxidants (e.g., vitamin E)
- enhance free-radical scavenger systems

Hormonal Compensation
- estrogen/testosterone replacement
- other hormonal supplements (e.g., melatonin)

Alzheimer brains likely possess endogenous compensatory signaling, although at insufficient levels to ensure synaptic maintenance. Many studies indicate that lysosomal responses are active in the aging brain and in age-related disorders including Alzheimer-type pathogenesis (Cataldo et al., 1995, 1996; Haas and Sparks, 1996; Callahan et al., 1999). Such compensatory signaling may play a role in the early stages of pathology, masking and delaying the onset of clinical symptoms. The gradual buildup of deposits and slow synaptic decline in the slice model (over a 3-9 day period) and the long duration of Alzheimer's disease (about 7 years on average) may be indicative of an extended equilibrium between protein deposition processes and compensatory lysosomal responses. Differential compensatory signaling levels could also explain why the disease's duration has such a wide range (18 years) across Alzheimer patients. Adding to the problem may be non-lysosomal proteases that are activated in response to protein deposition (Bendiske et al., 2002), perhaps as part of apoptotic or oxidative processes.

Lysosomal activation may be among many types of compensatory systems that are activated in response to disease states or toxic protein accumulation (e.g., growth factors, receptor desensitization, glutathione chemistry). With the exception of the lysosomal activation response, there is little previous evidence of endogenous repair systems that act against intracellular deposits and the associated synaptopathogenesis. There are reports of cellular responses that provide functional compensation in protein deposition diseases (Zigmond, 1997; Ho and Blum, 1998). Recently, ApoE (Buttini et al., 2002) and transthyretin (Stein and Johnson, 2002) were implicated in compensatory cell survival pathways that promote synaptic recovery/maintenance and may explain the lack of synaptopathogenesis in some transgenic models of Alzheimer's disease. Alternatively, some repair systems may in fact protect against lysosomal abnormalities through anti-apoptotic pathways (see Zhao et al., 2000). The multitude of endogenous systems should allow cellular repair to occur following even modest intervention of pathogenic events. While the level of lysosomal activation in Alzheimer brains is too small to stop the disease process, the availability of lysosomal modulatory agents may allow the slowing of the progressive neurodegeneration.

ACKNOWLEDGMENTS

Manuscript preparation was assisted by Ms. Alyson Bahr. This work was supported in part by the University of Connecticut Research Foundation and the University of Connecticut Neurosciences Program.

REFERENCES

Adamec E., Mohan P.S., Cataldo A.M., Vonsattel J.P., and Nixon R.A. (2000) Up-regulation of the lysosomal system in experimental models of neuronal injury: Implications for Alzheimer's disease. *Neurosci.* **100**, 663-675.

Alonso A.C., Grundke-Iqbal I., and Iqbal K. (1996) Alzheimer's disease hyperphosphorylated tau sequesters normal tau into tangles of filaments and disassembles microtubules. *Nature Med.* **2**, 783-787.

Alonso A.D., Grundke-Iqbal I., Barra H.S., and Iqbal K. (1997) Abnormal phosphorylation of tau and the mechanism of Alzheimer neurofibrillary degeneration: Sequestration of microtubule-associated proteins 1 and 2 and the disassembly of microtubules by the abnormal tau. *Proc. Natl. Acad. Sci. U.S.A.* **94**, 298-303.

Amtul Z., Lewis P.A., Piper S., Crook R., Baker M., Findlay K., Singleton A., Hogg M., Younkin L., Younkin S.G., Hardy J., Hutton M., Boeve B.F., Tang-Wai D., and Golde T.E. (2002) A presenilin 1 mutation associated with familial frontotemporal dementia inhibits γ-secretase cleavage of APP and notch. *Neurobiol. Dis.* **9**, 269-273.

Antunes F., Cadenas E., and Brunk U.T. (2001) Apoptosis induced by exposure to a low steady-state concentration of H_2O_2 is a consequence of lysosomal rupture. *Biochem. J.* **356**, 549-555.

Apelt J., Kumar A., and Schliebs R. (2002) Impairment of cholinergic neurotransmission in adult and aged transgenic Tg2576 mouse brain expressing the Swedish mutation of human β-amyloid precursor protein. *Brain Res.* **953**, 17-30.

Auer I.A., Schmidt M.L., Lee V.M., Curry B., Suzuki K., Shin R.W., Pentchev P.G., Carstea E.D., and Trojanowski J.Q. (1995) Paired helical filament tau (PHF-tau) in Niemann-Pick type C disease is similar to PHF-tau in Alzheimer's disease. *Acta Neuropathol.* **90**, 547-551.

Bahr B.A. (1995) Long-term hippocampal slices: A model system for investigating synaptic mechanisms and pathologic processes. *J. Neurosci. Res.* **42**, 294-305.

Bahr B.A., and Bendiske J. (2002) The neuropathogenic contributions of lysosomal dysfunction. *J. Neurochem.* **83**, 481-489.

Bahr B.A., and Vicente J.S. (1998) Age-related phosphorylation and fragmentation events influence the distribution profiles of distinct tau isoforms in mouse brain. *J. Neuropathol. Exp. Neurol.* **157**, 111-121.

Bahr B.A., Vanderklish P.W., Ha L.T., Tin M., Kessler M., and Lynch G. (1991) Spectrin breakdown products increase with age in telencephalon of mouse brain. *Neurosci. Lett.* **131**, 237-240.

Bahr B.A., Abai B., Gall C.M., Vanderklish P.W., Hoffman K.B., and Lynch G. (1994a) Induction of β-amyloid-containing polypeptides in hippocampus: Evidence for a concomitant loss of synaptic proteins and interactions with an excitotoxin. *Exp. Neurol.* **129**, 81-94.

Bahr B.A., Lam N., and Lynch G. (1994b) Changes in the concentrations of tau and other structural proteins in the brains of aged mice. *Neurosci. Lett.* **175**, 49-52.

Bahr BA, Kessler M, Rivera S, Vanderklish P.W., Hall R.A., Mutneja M.S., Gall C., and Hoffman K.B. (1995) Stable maintenance of glutamate receptors and other synaptic components in long-term hippocampal slices. *Hippocampus* **5**, 425-439.

Bahr B.A., Hoffman K.B., Yang A.J., Hess U.S., Glabe C.G., and Lynch G. (1998) Amyloid β protein is internalized selectively by hippocampal field CA1 and causes neurons to accumulate amyloidogenic carboxyterminal fragments of the amyloid precursor protein. *J. Comp. Neurol.* **397**, 139-147.

Bahr B.A., Bendiske J., Brown Q.B., Munirathinam S., Caba E., Rudin M., Urwyler S., Sauter A., and Rogers G. (2002) Survival signaling and selective neuroprotection through glutamate transmission. *Exp. Neurol.* **174**, 37-47.

Bambrick L.L., Yarowsky P.J., and Krueger B.K. (1995) Glutamate as a hippocampal neuron survival factor: an inherited defect in the trisomy 16 mouse. *Proc. Natl. Acad. Sci. U.S.A.* **92**, 9692-9696.

Bard F., Cannon C., Barbour R., Burke R.L., Games D., Grajeda H., Guido T., Hu K., Huang J., Johnson-Wood K., Khan K., Kholodenko D., Lee M., Lieberburg I., Motter R., Nguyen M., Soriano F., Vasquez N., Weiss K., and Welch B. (2000) Peripherally administered antibodies against amyloid β-peptide enter the central nervous system and reduce pathology in a mouse model of Alzheimer disease. *Nature Med.* **6**, 916-919.

Bendiske J. and Bahr B.A. (2003) Lysosomal activation is a compensatory response against protein accumulation and associated synaptopathogenesis – An approach for slowing Alzheimer's disease? *J. Neuropathol. Exp. Neurol.*, **62**, 451-463.

Bendiske J., Caba E., Brown Q.B., and Bahr B.A. (2002) Intracellular deposition, microtubule destabilization, and transport failure: An 'early' pathogenic cascade leading to synaptic decline. *J. Neuropathol. Exp. Neurol.* **61**, 640-650.

Benowitz L.I., Rodriguez W., Paskevich P., Mufson E.J., Schenk D., and Neve R.L. (1989) The amyloid precursor protein is concentrated in neuronal lysosomes in normal and Alzheimer disease subjects. *Exp. Neurol.* **106**, 237-250.

Bi X., Zhou J., and Lynch G. (1999) Lysosomal protease inhibitors induce meganeurites and tangle-like structures in entorhinohippocampal regions vulnerable to Alzheimer's disease. *Exp. Neurol.* **158**, 312-327.

Bi X., Haque T.S., Zhou J., Skillman A.G., Lin B., Lee C.E., Kuntz I.D., Ellman J.A., and Lynch G. (2000) Novel cathepsin D inhibitors block the formation of hyperphosphorylated tau fragments in hippocampus. *J. Neurochem.* **74**, 1469-1477.

Bi X., Yong A.P., Zhou J., Ribak C.E., and Lynch G. (2001) Rapid induction of intraneuronal neurofibrillary tangles in apolipoprotein E-deficient mice. *Proc. Natl. Acad. Sci. U.S.A.* **98,** 8832-8837.

Black M.M., Baas P.W., and Humphries S. (1989) Dynamics of α-tubulin deacetylation in intact neurons. *J. Neurosci.* **9**, 358-368.

Blennow K., Bogdanovic N., Alafuzoff I., Ekman R., Davidsson P. (1996) Synaptic pathology in Alzheimer's disease: Relation to severity of dementia, but not to senile plaques, neurofibrillary tangles, or the ApoE4 allele. *J. Neural. Transm.* **103**, 603-618.

Blomgren K., Zhu C., Wang X., Karlsson J.O., Leverin A.L., Bahr B.A., Mallard C., and Hagberg H. (2001) Synergistic activation of caspase-3 by m-calpain after neonatal hypoxia- ischemia: A mechanism of "pathological apoptosis?" *J. Biol. Chem.* **276**, 10191-10198.

Brock T.O., and O'Callaghan J.P. (1987) Quantitative changes in the synaptic vesicle proteins synapsin I and p38 and the astrocyte-specific protein glial fibrillary acidic protein are associated with chemical-induced injury to the rat central nervous system. *J. Neurosci.* **7**, 931-942.

Brown D.F., Risser R.C., Bigio E.H., Tripp P., Stiegler A., Welch E., Eagan K.P., Hladik C.L., and White C.L.I. (1998) Neocortical synapse density and Braak stage in the Lewy body variant of Alzheimer disease: a comparison with classic Alzheimer disease and normal aging. *J. Neuropathol. Exp. Neurol.* **57**, 955-960.

Brunk U. and Brun A. (1972) The effect of aging on lysosomal permeability in nerve cells of the central nervous system. An enzyme histochemical study in rat. *Histochemie* **30,** 315-324.

Bucciantini M., Giannoni E., Chiti F., Baroni F., Formigli L., Zurdo J., Taddei N., Ramponi G., Dobson C.M., and Stefani M. (2002) Inherent toxicity of aggregates implies a common mechanism for protein misfolding diseases. *Nature* **416**, 507-511.

Burdick D., Kosmoski J., Knauer M.F., and Glabe C.G. (1997) Preferential adsorption, internalization and resistance to degradation of the major isoform of the Alzheimer's amyloid peptide, Aβ 1-42, in differentiated PC12 cells. *Brain Res.* **746**, 275-284.

Busciglio J., Lorenzo A., Yeh J., and Yankner B.A. (1995) β-amyloid fibrils induce tau phosphorylation and loss of microtubule binding. *Neuron* **14**, 879-888.

Butterfield D.A., Castegna A., Lauderback C.M., and Drake J. (2002) Evidence that amyloid β-peptide-induced lipid peroxidation and its sequelae in Alzheimer's disease brain contribute to neuronal death. *Neurobiol. Aging* **23**, 655-664.

Buttini M., Orth M., Bellosta S., Akeefe H., Pitas R.E., Wyss-Coray T., Mucke L., and Mahley R.W. (1999) Expression of human apolipoprotein E3 or E4 in the brains of *ApoE* -/- mice: isoform-specific effects on neurodegeneration. *J. Neurosci.* **19**, 4867-4880.

Buttini M., Yu G.Q., Shockley K., Huang Y., Jones B., Masliah E., Mallory M., Yeo T., Longo F.M., and Mucke L. (2002) Modulation of Alzheimer-like synaptic and cholinergic deficits in transgenic mice by human apolipoprotein E depends on isoform, aging, and overexpression of amyloid β peptides but not on plaque formation. *J. Neurosci.* **22**, 10539-10548.

Caba E., Brown Q.B., Kawasaki B., and Bahr B.A. (2002) Peptidyl α-keto amide inhibitors of calpain block excitotoxic damage without affecting signal transduction events. *J. Neurosci. Res.* **67**, 787-794.

Callahan L.M., and Coleman P.D. (1995) Neurons bearing neurofibrillary tangles are responsible for selected synaptic deficits in Alzheimer's disease. *Neurobiol. Aging* **16**, 311-314.

Callahan L.M., Vaules W.A., and Coleman P.D. (1999) Quantitative decrease in synaptophysin message expression and increase in cathepsin D message expression in Alzheimer disease neurons containing neurofibrillary tangles. *J. Neuropathol. Exp. Neurol.* **58**, 275-287.

Callahan L.M., Vaules W.A., and Coleman P.D. (2002) Progressive reduction of synaptophysin message in single neurons in Alzheimer disease. *J. Neuropathol. Exp. Neurol.* **61**, 384-395.

Caporaso G.L., Gandy S.E., Buxbaum J.D., and Greengard P. (1992) Chloroquine inhibits intracellular degradation but not secretion of Alzheimer β/A4 amyloid precursor protein. *Proc. Natl. Acad. Sci. U.S.A.*. **89**, 2252-2256.

Cataldo A.M., Paskevich P.A., Kominami E., and Nixon R.A. (1991) Lysosomal hydrolases of different classes are abnormally distributed in brains of patients with Alzheimer disease. *Proc. Natl. Acad. Sci. U.S.A.* **88**, 10998-11002.

Cataldo A.M., Hamilton D.J., and Nixon R.A. (1994) Lysosomal abnormalities in degenerating neurons link neuronal compromise to senile plaque development in Alzheimer disease. *Brain Res.* **640**, 68-80.

Cataldo A.M., Barnett J.L., Berman S.A., Berman S.A., Li J., Quarless S., and Bursztajn S. (1995) Gene expression and cellular content of cathepsin D in Alzheimer's disease brain: Evidence for early up-regulation of the endosomal-lysosomal system. *Neuron* **14**, 671-680.

Cataldo A.M., Hamilton D.J., Barnett J.L., Paskevich P.A., and Nixon R.A. (1996) Properties of the endosomal-lysosomal system in the human central nervous system: Disturbance mark most neurons in populations at risk to degenerate in Alzheimer's disease. *J. Neurosci.* **16**, 186-199.

Cavanagh J.B., Nolan C.C., Seville M.P., Anderson V.E., and Leigh P.N. (1993) Routes of excretion of neuronal lysosomal dense bodies after ventricular infusion of leupeptin in the rat: A study using ubiquitin and PGP 9.5 immunocytochemistry. *J. Neurocytol.* **22**, 779-791.

Chauhan N.B., and Siegel G.J. (2002) Reversal of amyloid β toxicity in Alzheimer's disease model Tg2576 by intraventricular antiamyloid β antibody. *J. Neurosci. Res.* **69**, 10-23.

Chen F., Yang D.S., Petanceska S., Yang A., Tandon A., Yu G., Rozmabel R., Ghiso J., Nishimura M., Zhang D.M., Kawarai T., Levesque G., Mills J., Levesque L., Song Y.Q., Rogaeva R., Westaway D., Mount H., Gandy S., St George-Hyslop P., and Fraser P.E. (2000) Carboxyl-terminal fragments of Alzheimer β-amyloid precursor protein accumulate in restricted and unpredicted intracellular compartments in presenilin 1-deficient cells. *J. Biol. Chem.* **275**, 36794-36802.

Clark C.M., and Trojanowski J.Q. (2000) Neurodegenerative dementias: Clinical features and pathological mechanisms. New York: McGraw-Hill.

Cole G.M., Huynh T.V., and Saitoh T. (1989) Evidence for lysosomal processing of amyloid β-protein precursor in cultured cells. *Neurochem. Res.* **14**, 933-939.

Cross A.J., Crow T.J., Dawson J.M., Ferrier I.N., Johnson J.A., Peters T.J., and Reynolds G.P. (1986) Subcellular pathology of human neurodegenerative disorders: Alzheimer-type dementia and Huntington's disease. *J. Neurochem.* **47**, 882-889.

D'Andrea, M.R., Nagele R.G., Wang H.Y., Peterson P.A., and Lee D.H. (2001) Evidence that neurones accumulating amyloid can undergo lysis to form amyloid plaques in Alzheimer's disease. *Histopathol.* **38,** 120-134.

David D.C., Layfield R., Serpell L., Narain Y., Goedert M., and Spillantini M.G. (2002) Proteasomal degradation of tau protein. *J. Neurochem.* **83**, 176-185.

Davies C.A., Mann D.M., Sumpter P.Q., and Yates P.O. (1987) A quantitative morphometric analysis of the neuronal and synaptic content of the frontal and temporal cortex in patients with Alzheimer's disease. *J. Neurol. Sci.* **78**, 151-164.

Delacourte A., Flament S., Dibe E.M., Hublau P., Sablonniere B., Hermon B., Sherrer V., and Defossez A. (1990) Pathological proteins Tau 64 and 69 are specifically expressed in the somatodendritic domain of the degenerating cortical neurons during Alzheimer's disease: Demonstration with a panel of antibodies against Tau proteins. *Acta Neuropathol.* **80**, 111-117.

Dewachter I., Reverse D., Caluwaerts N., Ris L., Kuiperi C., Van-den-Haute C., Spittaels K., Umans L., Serneels L., Thiry E., Moechars D., Mercken M., Godaux E., and Van-Leuven F. (2002) Neuronal deficiency of presenilin 1 inhibits amyloid plaque formation and corrects hippocampal long-term potentiation but not a cognitive defect of amyloid precursor protein [V717I] transgenic mice. *J. Neurosci.* **22**, 3445-3453.

DiFiglia M., Sapp E., Chase K.O., Davies S.W., Bates G.P., Vonsattel J.P., and Aronin N. (1997) Aggregation of huntingtin in neuronal intranuclear inclusions and dystrophic neurites in brain. *Science* **277**, 1990-1993.

Ditaranto K., Tekirian T.L., and Yang A.J. (2001) Lysosomal membrane damage in soluble Aβ-mediated cell death in Alzheimer's disease. *Neurobiol. Dis.* **8**, 19-31.

Dobrenis K., Joseph A., and Rattazzi M.C. (1992) Neuronal lysosomal enzyme replacement using fragment C of tetanus toxin. *Proc. Natl. Acad. Sci. U.S.A.* **6**, 2297-2301.

Dodart J.C., Bales K.R., Gannon K.S., Greene S.J., DeMattos R.B., Mathis C., DeLong C.A., Wu S., Wu X., Holtzman D.M., and Paul S.M. (2002) Immunization reverses memory deficits without reducing brain Aβ burden in Alzheimer's disease model. *Nature Neurosci.* **5**, 452-457.

Evin G., Cappai R., Li Q.X., Culvenor J.G., Small D.H., Beyreuther K., and Masters C.L. (1995) Candidate γ-secretases in the generation of the carboxyl terminus of the Alzheimer's disease β A4 amyloid: Possible involvement of cathepsin D. *Biochemistry* **34,** 14185-14192.

Fahn S. and Przedborski S. (2000) Parkinsonism In: Rowland LP, ed. Merritt's Textbook of Neurology. Philadelphia: Williams and Wilkins; 679-693.

Fallet S., Grace M.E., Sibille A., Mendelson D.S., Shapiro R.S., Hermann G., and Grabowski G.A. (1992) Enzyme augmentation in moderate to life-threatening Gaucher disease. *Pediatr. Res.* **31**, 496-502.

Fan Q.W., Yu W., Senda T., Yanagisawa K., and Michikawa M. (2001) Cholesterol-dependent modulation of tau phosphorylation in cultured neurons. *J. Neurochem.* **76**, 391-400.

Fassbender K., Simons M., Bergmann C., Stroick M., Lutjohann D., Keller P., Runz H., Kuhl S., Bertsch T., von Bergmann K., Hennerici M., Beyreuther K., and Hartmann T. (2001) Simvastatin strongly reduces levels of Alzheimer's disease β-amyloid peptides Aβ 42 and Aβ 40 *in vitro* and *in vivo*. *Proc. Natl. Acad. Sci. U.S.A.* **98**, 5856-5861.

Garcia-Ladona F.J., Palacios J.M., Probst A., Wieser H.G., and Mengod G.A. (1994) Excitatory amino acid AMPA receptor mRNA localization in several regions of normal and neurological disease affected human brain. An in situ hybridization histochemistry study. *Brain Res. Mol. Brain Res.* **21**, 75-84.

Glabe C. (2001) Intracellular mechanisms of amyloid accumulation and pathogenesis in Alzheimer's disease. *J. Mol. Neurosci.* **17**, 137-145.

Goedert M., Spillantini M.G., Cairns N.J., and Crowther R.A. (1992) Tau proteins of Alzheimer paired helical filaments: Abnormal phosphorylation of all six brain isoforms. *Neuron* **8**, 159-168.

Goffredo D., Rigamonti D., Tartari M., De-Micheli A., Verderio C., Matteoli M., Zuccato C., and Cattaneo E. (2002) Calcium-dependent cleavage of endogenous wild-type huntingtin in primary cortical neurons. *J. Biol. Chem.* **277**, 39594-39598.

Golde T.E., Estus S., Younkin L.H., Selkoe D.J., and Younkin S.G. (1992) Processing of the amyloid protein precursor to potentially amyloidogenic derivatives. *Science* **255**, 728-730.

Gotz J., Chen F., van Dorpe J., and Nitsch R.M. (2001) Formation of neurofibrillary tangles in P301l tau transgenic mice induced by Aβ 42 fibrils. *Science* **293**, 1491-1495.

Gouras G.K., Xu H., Gross R.S., Greenfield J.P., Hai B., Wang R., and Greengard P. (2000) Testosterone reduces neuronal secretion of Alzheimer's β-amyloid peptides. *Proc. Natl. Acad. Sci. U.S.A.* **97**, 1202-1205.

Grace E., Rabiner A.C., and Busciglio J. (2002) Characterization of neuronal dystrophy induced by fibrillar amyloid β: implications for Alzheimer's disease. *Neurosci.* **11**, 265-273.

Greenfield J.P., Leung L.W., Cai D., Kaasik K., Gross R.S., Rodriguez-Boulan E., Greengrad P., and Xu H. (2002) Estrogen lowers Alzheimer β-amyloid generation by stimulating trans-Golgi network vesicle biogenesis. *J. Biol. Chem.* **277**, 12128-12136.

Griffin J.W., and Watson D.F. (1988) Axonal transport in neurological disease. *Ann. Neurol.* **23**, 3-13.

Haas U., and Sparks D.L. (1996) Cortical cathepsin D activity and immunolocalization in Alzheimer disease, critical coronary artery disease, and aging. *Mol. Chem. Neuropathol.* **29**, 1-14.

Haass C., Koo E.H., Mellon A., Hung A.Y., and Selkoe D.J. (1992) Targeting of cell-surface β-amyloid precursor protein to lysosomes: Alternative processing into amyloid-bearing fragments. *Nature* **357**, 500-503.

Haass C., Hung A.V., Schlossmacher M.G., Teplow D.B., and Selkoe D.J. (1993) β-amyloid peptide and a 3-kDa fragment are derived by distinct cellular mechanisms. *J. Biol. Chem.* **268**, 3021-3024.

Hajimohammadreza I., Anderson V.E.R., Cavanagh J.B., Seville M.P., Nolan C.C., Anderton B.H., and Leigh P.N. (1994) β-Amyloid precursor protein fragments and lysosomal dense bodies are found in rat brain neurons after ventricular infusion of leupeptin. *Brain Res.* **640**, 25-32.

Hall G.F., Chu B., Lee G., and Yao J. (2000) Human tau filaments induce microtubule and synapse loss in an *in vivo* model of neurofibrillary degenerative disease. *J. Cell Sci.* **113,** 1373-1387.

Hammarström P., Schneider F., and Kelly J.W. (2001) Trans-suppression of misfolding in an amyloid disease. *Science* **293**, 2459-2462.

Hammarström P., Wiseman R.L., Powers E.T., and Kelly J.W. (2003) Prevention of transthyretin amyloid disease by changing protein misfolding energetics. *Science* **299**, 713-716.

Hardy J., Duff K., Hardy K.G., Perez-Tur J., and Hutton M. (1998) Genetic dissection of Alzheimer's disease and related dementias: Amyloid and its relationship to tau. *Nature Neurosci.* **1**, 355-358.

Harry G.J., Goodrum J.F., Krigman M.R., and Morell P. (1985) The use of synapsin I as a biochemical marker for neuronal damage by trimethyltin. *Brain Res.* **326**, 9-18.

Hayashi Y., Kashiwagi K., and Yoshikawa K. (1992) Protease inhibitors generate cytotoxic fragments from Alzheimer amyloid protein precursor in cDNA-transfected glioma cells. *Biochem. Biophys. Res. Comm.* **187**, 1249-1255.

Hayashi T., Umemori H., Mishina M., and Yamamoto T. (1999) The AMPA receptor interacts with and signals through the protein tyrosine kinase Lyn. *Nature* **397**, 72-76.

Heinonen O., Soininen H., Sorvari H., Kosunen O., Paljarvi L., Koivisto E., and Riekkinen P.J. Sr. (1995) Loss of synaptophysin-like immunoreactivity in the hippocampal formation is an early phenomenon in Alzheimer's disease. *Neurosci.* **54**, 375-384.

Hempen B., and Brion J.P. (1996) Reduction of acetylated α–tubulin immunoreactivity in neurofibrillary tangle-bearing neurons in Alzheimer's disease. *J. Neuropathol. Exp. Neurol.* **55**, 964-972.

Higuchi M., Lee V.M., and Trojanowski J.Q. (2002) Tau and axonopathy in neurodegenerative disorders. *Neuromol. Med.* **2**, 131-150.

Ho A. and Blum M. (1998) Induction of interleukin-1 associated with compensatory dopaminergic sprouting in the denervated striatum of young mice: Model of aging and neurodegenerative disease. *J. Neurosci.* **18**, 5614-5629.

Hoffman K.B., Bi X., Pham J.T., and Lynch G. (1998) β-Amyloid increases cathepsin D levels in hippocampus. *Neurosci. Lett.* **250**, 75-78.

Honda T., Yasutake K., Nihonmatsu N., Mercken M., Takahashi H., Murayama O., Murayama M., Sato K., Omori A., Tsubuki S., Saido T.C., and Takashima A. (1999) Dual roles of proteasome in the metabolism of presenilin 1. *J. Neurochem.* **72**, 255-261.

Honer W.G., Dickson D.W., Gleeson J., and Davies P. (1992) Regional synaptic pathology in Alzheimer's disease. *Neurobiol. Aging* **13**, 375-382.

Hsia A.Y., Masliah E., McConlogue L., Yu G.Q., Tatsuno G., Hu K., Kholodenko D., Malenka R.C., Nicoll R.A., and Mucke L. (1999) Plaque-independent disruption of neural circuits in Alzheimer's disease mouse models. *Proc. Natl. Acad. Sci. U.S.A.* **96**, 3228-3233.

Hynd M.R., Scott H.L., Dodd P.R. (2001) Glutamate (NMDA) receptor NR1 subunit mRNA expression in Alzheimer's disease. *J. Neurochem.* **78**,175-182.

Ii K., Ito H, Kominami E., and Hirano A. (1993) Abnormal distribution of cathepsin proteinases and endogenous inhibitors (cystatins) in the hippocampus of patients with Alzheimer's disease, Parkinsonism-dementia complex on Guam, and senile dementia and in the aged. *Virchows Arch. A., Path. Anat. Histopath.* **423**, 185-194.

Ikeda K., Akiyama H., Arai T., Kondo H., Haga C., Iritani S., and Tsuchiya K. (1998) Alz-50/Gallyas-positive lysosome-like intraneuronal granules in Alzheimer's disease and control brains. *Neurosci. Lett.* **258**, 113-116.

Ikeda K., Akiyama H., Arai T., Kondo H., Haga C., Tsuchiya K., Yamada S., and Murayama S. (2000) Neurons containing Alz-50-immunoreactive granules around the cerebral infarction: Evidence for the lysosomal degradation of altered tau in human brain? *Neurosci. Lett.* **284**, 187-189.

Ikonomovic M.D., Mizukami K., Davies P., Hamilton R., Sheffield R., and Armstrong D.M. (1997) The loss of GluR2(3) immunoreactivity precedes neurofibrillary tangle formation in the entorhinal cortex and hippocampus of Alzheimer brains. *J. Neuropathol. Exp. Neurol.* **56**, 1018-1027.

Ivy G.O. (1992) Protease inhibition causes some manifestations of aging and Alzheimer's disease in rodent and primate brain. *Ann. N.Y. Acad. Sci.* **674**, 89-102.

Ivy G.O., Kitani K., and Ihara Y. (1989) Anomalous accumulation of tau and ubiquitin immunoreactivities in rat brain caused by protease inhibition and by normal aging: A clue to PHF pathogenesis? *Brain Res.* **498**, 360-365.

Iwata N., Tsubuki S., Takaki Y., Shirotani K., Lu B., Gerard N.P., Gerard C., Hama E., Lee H.J., and Saido T.C. (2001) Metabolic regulation of brain Aβ by neprilysin. *Science* **292**, 1550-1552.

Janus C., Pearson J., McLaurin J., Mathews P.M., Jiang Y., Schmidt S.D., Chishti M.A., Horne P., Heslin D., French J., Mount H.T., Nixon R.A., Mercken M., Bergeron C., Fraser P.E., George-Hyslop P., and Westaway D. (2000) Aβ peptide immunization reduces behavioral impairment and plaques in a model of Alzheimer's disease. *Nature* **408**, 979-982.

Kakkis E.D., McEntee M.F., Schmidtchen A., Neufeld E.F., Ward D.A., Gompf R.E., Kania S., Bedolla C., Chien S.L., and Shull R.M. (1996) Long-term and high-dose trials of enzyme replacement therapy in the canine model of mucopolysaccharidosis I. *Biochem. Mol. Med.* **58**, 156-167.

Kamal A., Almenar-Queralt A., LeBlanc J.F., Roberts E.A., and Goldstein L.S. (2001) Kinesin-mediated axonal transport of a membrane compartment containing β-secretase and presenilin-1 requires APP. *Nature* **414**, 643-648.

Kegel K.B., Kim M., Sapp E., McIntyre C., Castano J.G., Aronin N., and DiFiglia M. (2000) Huntingtin expression stimulates endosomal-lysosomal activity, endosome tubulation, and autophagy. *J. Neurosci.* **20**, 7268-7278.

Kenessey A., Nacharaju P., Ko L.W., and Yen S.H. (1997) Degradation of tau by lysosomal enzyme cathepsin D: Implication for Alzheimer neurofibrillary degeneration. *J. Neurochem.* **69**, 2026-2038.

Kikugawa K., Beppu M., Kato T., Yamaki S., and Kasai H. (1994) Accumulation of autofluorescent yellow lipofuscin in rat tissues estimated by sodium dodecylsulfate extraction. *Mech. Ageing Dev.* **74**, 135-148.

Kim J.H., Anwyl R., Suh Y.H., Djamgoz M.B.A., and Rowan M.J. (2001a) Use-dependent effects of amyloidogenic fragments of β-amyloid precursor protein on synaptic plasticity in rat hippocampus *in vivo*. *J. Neurosci.* **21**, 1327-1333.

Kim Y.J., Yi Y., Sapp E., Wang Y., Cuiffo B., Kegel K.B., Qin Z.H., Aronin N., and DiFiglia M. (2001b) Caspase 3-cleaved N-terminal fragments of wild-type and mutant huntingtin are present in normal and Huntington's disease brains, associate with membranes, and undergo calpain-dependent proteolysis. *Proc. Natl. Acad. Sci. U.S.A.* **98**, 12784-12789.

Klafki H.W., Abramowski D., Swoboda R., Paganetti P.A., and Staufenbiel M. (1996) The carboxyl termini of β amyloid peptides 1-40 and 1-42 are generated by distinct γ-secretase activities. *J. Biol. Chem.* **271**, 28655-28659.

Klein W.L., Krafft G.A., and Finch C.E. (2001) Targeting small Aβ oligomers: The solution to an Alzheimer's disease conundrum? *Trends-Neurosci.* **24**, 219-224.

Koo E.H. and Squazzo S. (1994) Evidence that production and release of amyloid β-protein involves the endocytic pathway. *J. Biol. Chem.* **269,** 17386-17389.

Kosik K.S., Joachim C.L., and Selkoe D.J. (1986) Microtubule-associated protein tau (tau) is a major antigenic component of paired helical filaments in Alzheimer disease. *Proc. Natl. Acad. Sci. U. S. A.* **83**, 4044-4048.

Kotilinek L.A., Bacskai B., Westerman M., Kawarabayashi T., Younkin L., Hyman B.T., Younkin S., and Ashe K.H. (2002) Reversible memory loss in a mouse transgenic model of Alzheimer's disease. *J. Neurosci.* **22**, 6331-6335.

Larson J., Lynch G., Games D., and Seubert P. (1999) Alterations in synaptic transmission and long-term potentiation in hippocampal slices from young and aged PDAPP mice. *Brain Res.* **840**, 23-35.

Lashuel H.A., Hartley D., Petre B.M., Walz T., and Lansbury P.T. Jr. (2002) Neurodegenerative disease: Amyloid pores from pathogenic mutations. *Nature* **418**, 291.

Lassmann H., Weiler P., Fischer P., Bancher C., Jellinger K., Floor E., Danielczyk W., Seitelberger F, and Winkler H. (1992) Synaptic pathology in Alzheimer's disease: Immunological data for markers of synaptic and large dense-core vesicles. *Neurosci.* **46**, 1-8.

Laszlo L., Lowe J., Self T., Kenward N., Landon M., McBride T., Farquhar C., McConnell I., Brown J., and Hope J. (1992) Lysosomes as key organelles in the pathogenesis of prion encephalopathies. *J. Pathol.* **166**, 333-341.

Lee V.M., Balin B.J., Otvos L. Jr., Trojanowski J.Q. (1991) A major subunit of paired helical filaments and derivatized forms of normal tau. *Science* **251**, 675-678.

Lemere C.A., Munger J.S., Shi G.P., Natkin L., Haass C., Chapman H.A., and Selkoe D.J. (1995) The lysosomal cysteine protease, cathepsin S, is increased in Alzheimer's disease and Down syndrome brain. An immunocytochemical study. *Am. J. Path.* **146**, 848-860.

Lewis J., Dickson D.W., Lin W.L., Chisholm L., Corral A., Jones G., Yen S.H., Sahara N., Skipper L., Yager D., Eckman C., Hardy J., Hutton M., and McGowan E. (2001) Enhanced neurofibrillary degeneration in transgenic mice expressing mutant tau and APP. *Science* **293**, 1487-1491.

Li Y., Xu C., and Schubert D. (1999) The up-regulation of endosomal-lysosomal components in amyloid β-resistant cells. *J. Neurochem.* **73**, 1477-1482.

Li H., Li S.H., Yu Z.X., Shelbourne P., and Li X.J. (2001) Huntington aggregate-associated axonal degeneration is an early pathological event in Huntington's disease mice. *J. Neurosci.* **21**, 8473-8481.

Lim F., Hernandez F., Lucas J.J., Gomez-Ramos P., Moran M.A., and Avila J. (2001) FTDP-17 mutations in tau transgenic mice provoke lysosomal abnormalities and tau filaments in forebrain. *Mol. Cell. Neurosci.* **18**, 702-714.

Limatola C., Ciotti M.T., Mercanti D., Santoni A., and Eusebi, F. (2002) Signaling pathways activated by chemokine receptor CXCR2 and AMPA-type glutamate receptors and involvement in granule cells survival. *J. Neuroimmunol.* **123**, 9-17.

Lindwall G. and Cole R.D. (1984) Phosphorylation affects the ability of tau protein to promote microtubule assembly. *J. Biol. Chem.* **259**, 5301-5305.

Loftus S.K., Morris J.A., Carstea E.D., Gu J.Z., Cummings C., Brown A., Ellison J., Ohno K., Rosenfeld M.A., Tagle D.A., Pentchev P.G., and Pavan W.J. (1997) Murine model of Niemann-Pick C disease: Mutation in a cholesterol homeostasis gene. *Science* **277**, 232-235.

Ma J., Wollmann R., and Lindquist S. (2002) Neurotoxicity and neurodegeneration when PrP accumulates in the cytosol. *Science* **298**, 1781-1785.

Mandelkow E.M., Biernat J., Drewes G., Gustke N., Trinczek B., and Mandelkow E. (1995) Tau domains, phosphorylation, and interactions with microtubules. *Neurobiol. Aging* **16**, 355-362.

Masliah E. and Licastro F. (2000) Neuronal and synaptic loss, reactive gliosis, microglial response, and induction of the complement cascade in Alzheimer's disease, in Neurodegenerative Dementias (Clark C. M. and Trojanowski J. Q., eds), pp. 131-146. McGraw-Hill, New York.

Masliah E., Terry R.D., DeTeresa R.M., and Hansen L.A. (1989) Immunohistochemical quantification of the synapse-related protein synaptophysin in Alzheimer disease. *Neurosci. Lett.* **103**, 234-239.

Masliah E., Mallory M., Alford M., DeTersesa T., Hansen L.A., McKeel D.W. Jr., and Morris J.C. (2001) Altered expression of synaptic proteins occurs early during progression of Alzheimer's disease. *Neurology* **56**, 127-129.

Mathews P.M., Guerra C.B., Jiang Y., Grbovic O.M., Kao B.H., Schmidt S.D., Dinakar R., Mercken M., Hille-Rehfeld A., Rohrer J., Mehta P., Cataldo A.M., and Nixon R.A. (2002) Alzheimer's disease-related overexpression of the cation-dependent mannose 6-phosphate receptor increases Aβ secretion: Role for altered lysosomal hydrolase distribution in β-amyloidogenesis. *J. Biol. Chem.* **277**, 5299-5307.

Matsuoka Y., Saito M., LaFrancois J., Saito M., Gaynor K., Olm V., Wang L., Casey E., Lu Y., Shiratori C., Lemere C., and Duff K. (2003) Novel therapeutic approach for the treatment of Alzheimer's disease by peripheral administration of agents with an affinity to β-Amyloid *J. Neurosci.* **23**, 29-33.

Matus A. and Green G.D. (1987) Age-related increase in a cathepsin D like protease that degrades brain microtubule-associated proteins. *Biochemistry* **26**, 8083-8086.

McKinney R.A., Capogna M., Durr R., Gahwiler B.H., and Thompson S.M. (1999) Miniature synaptic events maintain dendritic spines via AMPA receptor activation. *Nature Neurosci.* **2**, 44-49.

McNeil P.L. (2002) Repairing a torn cell surface: make way, lysosomes to the rescue. *J. Cell Sci.* **115**, 873-879.

McNeil P.L., and Terasaki M. (2001) Coping with the inevitable: how cells repair a torn surface membrane. *Nature Cell Biol.* **3**, 124-129.

McPhie D.L., Golde T., Eckman C.B., Yager D., Brant J.B., and Neve R.L (2001) β-Secretase cleavage of the amyloid precursor protein mediates neuronal apoptosis caused by familial Alzheimer's disease mutations. *Mol. Brain Res.* **97**, 103-113.

Mesulam M.M. (1999) Neuroplasticity failure in Alzheimer's disease: Bridging the gap between plaques and tangles. *Neuron* **24,** 521-529.

Michikawa M., Gong J.S., Fan Q.W., Sawamura N., and Yanagisawa K. (2001) A novel action of alzheimer's amyloid β-protein (Aβ): oligomeric Aβ promotes lipid release. *J. Neurosci.* **21**, 7226-7235.

Mielke J.G., Murphy M.P., Maritz J., Bengualid K.M., and Ivy G.O. (1997) Chloroquine administration in mice increases β-amyloid immunoreactivity and attenuates kainate-induced blood-brain barrier dysfunction. *Neurosci. Lett.* **227,** 169-172.

Mills J. and Reiner P.B. (1999) Regulation of amyloid precursor protein cleavage. *J. Neurochem.* **72**, 443-460.

Mochizuki A., Tamaoka A., Shimohata A., Komatsuzaki Y., and Shoji S. (2000) Aβ 42-positive non-pyramidal neurons around amyloid plaques in Alzheimer's disease. *Lancet* **355**, 42-43.

Moechars D., Dewachter I., Lorent K., Reverse D., Baekelandt V., Naidu A., Tesseur I., Spittaels K., Haute C.V., Checler F., Godaux E., Cordell B., and Van-Leuven F. (1999) Early phenotypic changes in transgenic mice that overexpress different mutants of amyloid precursor protein in brain. *J. Biol. Chem.* **274**, 6483-6492.

Morgan D., Diamond D.M., Gottschall P.E., Ugen K.E., Dickey C., Hardy J., Duff K., Jantzen P., DiCarlo G., Wilcock D., Connor K., Hatcher J., Hope C., Gordon M., and Arendash G.W. (2000) Aβ peptide vaccination prevents memory loss in an animal model of Alzheimer's disease. *Nature* **408**, 982-985.

Muchowski P.J. (2002) Protein misfolding, amyloid formation, and neurodegeneration: a critical role for molecular chaperones? *Neuron* **35**, 9-12.

Mucke L., Masliah E., Yu G.O., Mallory M., Rockenstein E.M., Tatsuno G., Hu K., Kholodenko D., Johnson-Wood K., and McConlogue L. (2000) High-level neuronal Expression of Aβ1-42 in wild-type human amyloid protein precursor transgenic mice: Synaptotoxicity without plaque formation. *J. Neurosci.* **20,** 4050-4058.

Munger J.S., Haass C., Lemere C.A., Shi G.P., Wong W.S., Teplow D.B., Selkoe D.J., and Chapman H.A. (1995) Lysosomal processing of the amyloid precursor protein to Aβ peptides: A distinct role for cathepsin S. *Biochem. J.* **311**, 299-305.

Munirathinam S., Rogers G., and Bahr B.A. (2002) Positive modulation of α-amino-3-hydroxy-5-methyl-4-isoxazolepropionic acid-type glutamate receptors elicits neuroprotection after trimethyltin exposure in hippocampus. *Toxicol. Appl. Pharmacol.* **185**, 111-118.

Nakamura Y., Takeda M., Suzuki H., Morita H., Tada K., Hariguchi S., and Nishimura T. (1989a) Age-dependent change in activities of lysosomal enzymes in rat brain. *Mech. Ageing Dev.* **50**, 215-225.

Nakamura Y., Takeda M., Suzuki H., Morita H., Tada K., Hariguchi S., and Nishimura T. (1989b) Lysosome instability in aged rat brain. *Neurosci. Lett.* **97**, 215-220.

Nilsson E., Ghassemifar R., Brunk U.T. (1997) Lysosomal heterogeneity between and within cells with respect to resistance against oxidative stress. *Histochem. J.* **29**, 857-865.

Nixon R.A. (2000) A "protease activation cascade" in the pathogenesis of Alzheimer's disease. *Ann. N.Y. Acad. Sci.* **924,** 117-131.

Nixon R.A., Cataldo A.M., Paskevich P.A., Hamilton D.J., Wheelock T.R., and Kanaley-Andrews L. (1992) The lysosomal system in neurons. Involvement at multiple stages of Alzheimer's disease pathogenesis. *Ann. N.Y. Acad. Sci.* **674**, 65-88.

Nixon R.A., Mathews P.M., and Cataldo A.M. (2001) The neuronal endosomal-lysosomal system in Alzheimer's disease. *J. Alzheimer's Disease* **3**, 97–107.

Okada M., Miyake T., Kitamura T., Kawasaki K., and Mizushima Y. (1994) Anti-ubiquitin immunoreactivity associates with pyramidal cell death induced by intraventricular infusion of leupeptin in rat hippocampus. *Neurosci. Res.* **19**, 59-66.

Oster-Granite M.L., McPhie D.L., Greenan J., and Neve R.L. (1996) Age-dependent neuronal and synaptic degeneration in mice transgenic for the C terminus of the amyloid precursor protein. *J. Neurosci.* **16**, 6732-6741.

Oyama F., Murakami N., and Ihara Y. (1998) Chloroquine myopathy suggests that tau is degraded in lysosomes: Implication for the formation of paired helical filaments in Alzheimer's disease. *Neurosci. Res.* **31**, 1-8.

Papassotiropoulos A., Lewis H.D., Bagli M., Jessen F., Ptok U., Schulte A., Shearman M.S., and Heun R. (2002) Cerebrospinal fluid levels of β-amyloid(42) in patients with Alzheimer's disease are related to the exon 2 polymorphism of the cathepsin D gene. *NeuroReport* **13**, 1291-1294.

Pellegrini-Giampietro D.E., Bennett M.V., and Zukin R.S. (1994) AMPA/kainate receptor gene expression in normal and Alzheimer's disease hippocampus. *Neurosci.* **61**, 41-49.

Perdahl E., Adolfsson R., Alafuzoff I., Albert K.A., Nestler E.J., Greengard P., and Winblad B. (1984) Synapsin I (Protein I) in different brain regions in senile dementia of Alzheimer type and in multiinfarct dementia. *J. Neural. Transm.* **60**, 133-141.

Petanceska S., Burke S., Watson S.J., and Devi L. (1994) Differential distribution of messenger RNAs for cathepsins B, L and S in adult rat brain: An *in situ* hybridization study. *Neurosci.* **59**, 729-738.

Petanceska S.S., Nagy V., Frail D., and Gandy S. (2000) Ovariectomy and 17β-estradiol modulate the levels of Alzheimer's amyloid β peptides in brain. *Neurology* **54**, 2212-2217.

Puolivali J., Wang J., Heikkinen T., Heikkila M., Tapiola T., van-Groen T., and Tanila H. (2002) Hippocampal Aβ 42 levels correlate with spatial memory deficit in APP and PS1 double transgenic mice. *Neurobiol. Dis.* **9**, 339-347.

Robker R.L., Russell D.L., Espey L.L., Lydon J.P., O'Malley B.W., and Richards J.S. (2000) Progesterone-regulated genes in the ovulation process: ADAMTS-1 and cathepsin L proteases. *Proc. Natl. Acad. Sci. U.S.A.* **97**, 4689-4694.

Rockenstein E., Mallory M., Mante M., Alford M., Windisch M., Moessler H., Masliah E. (2002) Effects of Cerebrolysin on amyloid-β deposition in a transgenic model of Alzheimer's disease. *J. Neural.Transm. Suppl.* **62**, 327-336.

Rohn T.T., Head E., Su J.H., Anderson A.J., Bahr B.A., Cotman C.W., and Cribbs D.H. (2001) Correlation between caspase activation and neurofibrillary tangle formation in Alzheimer's disease. *Am. J. Pathol.* **158**, 189-198.

Saito Y., Suzuki K., Nanba E., Yamamoto T., Ohno K., and Murayama S. (2002) Niemann-Pick type C disease: accelerated neurofibrillary tangle formation and amyloid β deposition associated with apolipoprotein E epsilon 4 homozygosity. *Ann. Neurol.* **52**, 351-355.

Samuel W, Masliah E, Hill LR, Butters N, and Terry R. (1994) Hippocampal connectivity and Alzheimer's dementia: Effects of synapse loss and tangle frequency in a two-component model. *Neurology* **44**, 2081-2088.

Samuel W., Alford M., Hofstetter C.R., and Hansen L. (1997) Dementia with Lewy bodies versus pure Alzheimer disease: differences in cognition, neuropathology, cholinergic dysfunction, and synapse density. *J. Neuropathol. Exp. Neurol.* **56**, 499-508.

Sânchez I., Mahlke C., and Yuan J. (2003) Pivotal role of oligomerization in expanded polyglutamine neurodegenerative disorders. *Nature* **421**, 373 –379.

Sapp E., Schwarz C., Chase K., Bhide P.G., Young A.B., Penney J., Vonsattel J.P., Aronin N., and DiFiglia M. (1997) Huntingtin localization in brains of normal and Huntington's disease patients. *Ann. Neurol.* **42**, 604-612.

Sasaki S. and Iwata M. (1996) Impairment of fast axonal transport in the proximal axons of anterior horn neurons in amyotrophic lateral sclerosis. *Neurology* **47**, 535-540.

Savage M.J., Lin Y.G., Ciallella J.R., Flood D.G., and Scott R.W. (2002) Activation of c-Jun N-Terminal kinase and p38 in an Alzheimer's disease model is associated with amyloid deposition. *J. Neurosci.* **22**, 3376-3385.

Sawamura N., Gong J.S., Garver W.S., Heidenreich R.A., Ninomiya H., Ohno K., Yanagisawa K., and Michikawa M. (2001) Site-specific phosphorylation of tau accompanied by activation of mitogen-activated protein kinase (MAPK) in brains of Niemann-Pick type C mice. *J. Biol. Chem.* **276**, 10314-10319.

Scheff S.W., Sparks D.L., and Price D.A. (1996) Quantitative assessment of synaptic density in the outer molecular layer of the hippocampal dentate gyrus in Alzhemer's disease. *Dementia* **7**, 226-232.

Schenk D., Barbour R., Dunn W., Gordon G., Grajeda H., Guido T., Hu K., Huang J., Johnson-Wood K., Khan K., Kholodenko D., Lee M., Liao Z., Lieberburg I., Motter R., Mutter L., Soriano F., Shopp G., Vasquez N., and Vandevert C. (1999) Immunization with amyloid-β attenuates Alzheimer-disease-like pathology in the PDAPP mouse. *Nature* **400**, 173-177.

Selkoe D.J. (2001a). Alzheimer's disease: Genes, proteins and therapies. *Physiol. Rev.* **81**, 742-761.

Selkoe D.J. (2001b) Clearing the brain's amyloid cobwebs. *Neuron* **32**, 177-180.

Selkoe D.J. (2002) Alzheimer's disease is a synaptic failure. *Science* **298**, 789-791.

Shaw S., Bencherif M., and Marrero M.B. (2002) Janus kinase 2, an early target of alpha 7 nicotinic acetylcholine receptor-mediated neuroprotection against Aβ-(1-42) amyloid. *J. Biol. Chem.* 277, 44920-44924.

Siman R., Mistretta S., Durkin J.T., Savage M.J., Loh T., Trusko S., and Scott R.W. (1993) Processing of the β-amyloid precursor. Multiple proteases generate and degrade potentially amyloidogenic fragments. *J. Biol. Chem.* **268**, 16602-16609.

Skovronsky D.M., Doms R.W., and Lee V.M. (1998) Detection of a novel intraneuronal pool of insoluble amyloid β protein that accumulates with time in culture. *J. Cell Biol.* **141**, 1031-1039.

Skovronsky D.M., Pijak D.S., Doms R.W., and Lee V.M. (2000) A distinct ER/IC γ-secretase competes with the proteasome for cleavage of APP. *Biochemistry* **39**, 810-817.

Small D.H., Mok S.S., and Bornstein J.C. (2001) Alzheimer's disease and Aβ toxicity: From top to bottom. *Nature Rev. Neurosci.* **2**, 595-598.

Smith M.A., Richey P.L., Kalaria R.N., and Perry G. (1996) Elastase is associated with the neurofibrillary pathology of Alzheimer disease: A putative link between proteolytic imbalance and oxidative stress. *Restorative Neurol. Neurosci.* **9**, 213-217

Spittaels K., Van den Haute C., Van Dorpe J., Bruynseels K., Vandezande K., Laenen I., Geerts H., Mercken M., Sciot R., Van Lommel A., Loos R., and Van Leuven F. (1999) Prominent axonopathy in the brain and spinal cord of transgenic mice overexpressing four-repeat human tau protein. *Am. J. Pathol.* **155**, 2153-2165.

Stamer K.,Vogel R., Thies E., Mandelkow E., and Mandelkow E.M. (2002) Tau blocks traffic of organelles, neurofilaments, and APP vesicles in neurons and enhances oxidative stress. *J. Cell Biol.* **15**, 1051-1063.

Stefanis L., Larsen K.E., Rideout H.J., Sulzer D., and Greene L.A. (2001) Expression of A53T mutant but not wild-type α-synuclein in PC12 cells induces alteration of the ubiquitin-dependent degradation system, loss of dopamine release and autophagic cell death. *J. Neurosci.* **21**, 9549-9560.

Stein T. D. and Johnson J.A. (2002) Lack of neurodegeneration in transgenic mice overexpressing mutant amyloid precursor protein is associated with increased levels of transthyretin and the activation of cell survival pathways. *J. Neurosci.* **22**, 7380-7388.

Sze C.I., Troncoso J.C., Kawas C., Mouton P., Price D.L., and Martin L.J. (1997) Loss of the presynaptic vesicle protein synaptophysin in hippocampus correlates with cognitive decline in Alzheimer disease. *J. Neuropathol. Exp. Neurol.* **56**, 933-944.

Takahashi R.H., Milner T.A., Li F., Nam E.E., Edgar M.A., Yamaguchi H., Beal M.F., Xu H.X., Greengard P., and Gouras G.K. (2002). Intraneuronal Alzheimer Aβ 42 accumulates in multivesicular bodies and is associated with synaptic pathology. *Am. J. Pathol.* **161**, 1869-1879.

Takauchi S. and Miyoshi K. (1989) Degeneration of neuronal processes in rats induced by a protease inhibitor, leupeptin. *Acta Neuropathol.* **78**, 380-387.

Takauchi S. and Miyoshi K. (1995) Cytoskeletal changes in rat cortical neurons induced by long-term intraventricular infusion of leupeptin. *Acta Neuropathol.* **89**, 8-16.

Terry R.D., Masliah E., Salmon D.P., Butters N., Deteresa R., Hill R., Hansen L.A., and Katzman R. (1991) Physical basis of cognitive alterations in Alzheimer's disease: Synapse loss is the major correlate of cognitive impairment. *Ann. Neurol.* **30,** 572-580.

Terry R.D., Masliah E., and Hansen L.A. (1999) The neuropathology of Alzheimer disease and the structural basis of its cognitive alterations. In: Alzheimer disease, Ed 2 (Terry RD, Katzman R, Bick KL, Sisodia SS, eds), pp 187-206. Philadelphia: Lippincott Williams and Wilkins.

Terwel D., Dewachter L., and Van-Leuven F. (2002) Axonal transport, tau protein, and neurodegeneration in Alzheimer's disease. *Neruomolecular Med.* **2**, 151-165.

Thorns V., Mallory M., Hansen L., and Masliah E. (1997) Alterations in glutamate receptor 2/3 subunits and amyloid precursor protein expression during the course of Alzheimer's disease and Lewy body variant. *Acta Neuropathol.* **94**, 539-548.

Turner R.S. (2001) Alzheimer's disease in man and transgenic mice: Females at higher risk. *Am. J. Pathol.* 158, 797-801.

Vanderklish P.W. and Bahr B.A. (2000) The pathogenic activation of calpain: A marker and mediator of cellular toxicity and disease states. *Int. J. Exp. Pathol.* **81**, 323-339.

Vicente J.S., Munirathinam S., and Bahr B.A. (2002) Calpain-mediated spectrin breakdown identifies vulnerable brain regions at middle age. *J. Mol. Biol. Biotech.* **3,** 1-10.

Wakabayashi K., Narisawa-Saito M., Iwakura Y., Arai T., Ikeda K., Takahashi H., and Nawa H., (1999) Phenotypic down-regulation of glutamate receptor subunit GluR1 in Alzheimer's disease. *Neurobiol. Aging* **20**, 287-295.

Walkley S.U. (1998) Cellular pathology of lysosomal storage disorders. *Brain Pathol.* **8**, 175-193.

Walsh D.M., Klyubin I., Fadeeva J.V., Cullen W.K., Anwyl R., Wolfe M.S., Rowan M.J., and Selkoe D.J. (2002) Naturally secreted oligomers of amyloid β protein potently inhibit hippocampal long-term potentiation *in vivo*. *Nature* **416**, 535-539.

Wang Y., and Durkin J.P. (1995) α-Amino-3-hydroxy-5-methyl-4isoxazolepropionic acid, but not N-methyl-D-aspartate, activates mitogen-activated protein kinase through G-protein subunits in rat cortical neurons. *J. Biol. Chem.* **270**, 22783-22787.

Wang F., Samudio I., and Safe S. (2001) Transcriptional activation of cathepsin D gene expression by 17β-estradiol: Mechanism of aryl hydrocarbon receptor-mediated inhibition. *Mol. Cell Endocrinol.* **172**, 91-103.

Wang H.W., Pasternak J.F., Kuo H., Ristic H., Lambert M.P., Chromy B., Viola K.L., Klein W.L., Stine W.B., Krafft G.A., and Trommer B.L. (2002) Soluble oligomers of β amyloid (1-42) inhibit long-term potentiation but not long-term depression in rat dentate gyrus. *Brain Res.* **924**, 133-140.

Weiner H.L., Lemere C.A., Maron R., Spooner E.T., Grenfell T.J., Mori C., Issazadeh S., Hancock W.W., and Selkoe D.J. (2000) Nasal administration of amyloid-β peptide decreases cerebral amyloid burden in a mouse model of Alzheimer's disease. *Ann. Neurol.* **48**, 567-579.

Welihinda A.A., Tirasophon W., and Kaufman R. (1999) The cellular response to protein misfolding in the endoplasmic reticulum. *Gene Expr.* **7**, 293-300.

Westerman M.A., Cooper-Blacketer D., Mariash A., Kotilinek L., Kawarabayashi T., Younkin L.H., Carlson G.A., Younkin S.G., and Ashe K.H. (2002) The relationship between Aβ and memory in the Tg2576 mouse model of Alzheimer's disease. *J. Neurosci.* **22**, 1858-67.

Wilson C.A., Doms R.W., and Lee V.M.Y. (1999) Intracellular APP processing and Aβ production in Alzheimer's disease. *J. Neurol. and Exp. Neurol.* **58**, 787-794.

Wisniewski H.M., Narang H.K., and Terry R.D. (1976) Neurofibrillary tangles of paired helical filaments. *J. Neurol. Sci.* **27**, 173-181.

Wittmann C.W., Wszolek M.F., Shulman J.M., Salvaterra P.M., Lewis J., Hutton M., and Feany M.B. (2001) Tauopathy in Drosophila: Neurodegeneration without neurofibrillary tangles. *Science* **293**, 711-714.

Wood J.G., Mirra S.S., Pollock N.J., Binder L.I. (1986) Neurofibrillary tangles of Alzheimer's disease share antigenic determinants with the axonal microtubule-associated protein tau. *Proc. Natl. Acad. Sci. U.S A.* **83**, 4040-4043.

Wood W.G., Schroeder F., Igbavboa U., Avdulov N.A., and Chochina S.V. (2002) Brain membrane cholesterol domains, aging and amyloid β-peptides. *Neurobiol. Aging* **23**, 685-694.

Xu H., Gouras G.K., Greenfield J.P., Vincent B., Naslund J., Mazzarelli L., Fried G., Jovanovic J.N., Seeger M., Relkin N.R., Liao F., Checler F., Buxbaum J.D., Chait B.T., Thinakaran G., Sisodia S.S., Wang R., Greengard P., and Gandy S. (1998) Estrogen reduces neuronal generation of Alzheimer β-amyloid peptides. *Nature Med.* **4**, 447-451.

Yamashima T. (2000) Implication of cysteine proteases calpain, cathepsin and caspase in ischemic neuronal death of primates. *Prog. Neurobiol.* **62**, 273-295.

Yang A.J., Knauer M., Burdick D.A., and Glabe C. (1995) Intracellular Aβ 1-42 aggregates stimulate the accumulation of stable, insoluble amyloidogenic fragments of the amyloid precursor protein in transfected cells. *J. Biol. Chem.* **270**, 14786-14792.

Yang A.J., Chandswangbhuvana D., Margol L., and Glabe C.G. (1998) Loss of endosomal/lysosomal membrane impermeability is an early event in amyloid Aβ1-42 pathogenesis. *J. Neurosci. Res.* **52**, 691-698.

Yao P.J. and Coleman P.D. (1998) Reduced O-glycosylated clathrin assembly protein AP180: implication for synaptic vesicle recycling dysfunction in Alzheimer's disease. *Neurosci. Lett.* **252**, 33-36.

Yao Z.X. and Papadopoulos V. (2002) Function of β-amyloid in cholesterol transport: a lead to neurotoxicity. *FASEB J* **16**, 1677-1679.

Yao P.J., Morsch R., Callahan L.M., and Coleman P.D. (1999) Changes in synaptic expression of clathrin assembly protein AP180 in Alzheimer's disease analysed by immunohistochemistry. *Neurosci.* **94**, 389-394.

Yasuda R.P., Ikonomovic M.D., Sheffield R., Rubin R.T., Wolfe B.B., and Armstrong D.M. (1995) Reduction of AMPA-selective glutamate receptor subunits in the entorhinal cortex of patients with Alzheimer's disease pathology: A biochemical study. *Brain Res.* **678**,161-167.

Yuan X.M., Li W., Dalen H., Lotem J., Kama R., Sachs L., and Brunk U.T. (2002) Lysosomal destabilization in p53-induced apoptosis. *Proc. Natl. Acad. Sci. U.S.A.* **99**, 6286-6291.

Zhao M., Eaton J.W., and Brunk U.T. (2000) Protection against oxidant-mediated lysosomal rupture: a new anti-apoptotic activity of Bcl-2? *FEBS Lett.* **485**, 104-108.

Zheng H., Xu H., Uljon S.N., Gross R., Hardy K., Gaynor J., Lafrancois J., Simpkins J., Refolo L.M., Petanceska S., Wang R., and Duff K. (2002) Modulation of Aβ peptides by estrogen in mouse models. *J. Neurochem.* **80**, 191-196.

Zigmond M.J. (1997) Do compensatory processes underlie the preclinical phase of neurodegenerative disease? Insights from an animal model of parkinsonism. *Neurobiol. Dis.* **4**, 247-253.

Chapter VI

LIPID RAFT AS A NIDUS FOR THE CONFORMATIONAL ALTERNATION AND THE AGGREGATION OF ALZHEIMER'S AMYLOID β-PROTEIN

Katsumi Matsuzaki

Graduate School of Pharmaceutical Sciences
Kyoto University
46-29 Yoshida-Shimoadachi-cho
Sakyo-ku, Kyoto 606-8304, Japan
E-mail: katsumim@pharm.kyoto-u.ac.jp

ABSTRACT

The conversion of soluble, nontoxic amyloid β-protein (Aβ) to aggregated, toxic Aβ rich in β-sheet structures by seeded polymerization is considered to be the key step in the development of Alzheimer's disease. Accumulating evidence suggests that lipid rafts (microdomains) in membranes mainly composed of sphingolipids (gangliosides and sphingomyelin) and cholesterol play a pivotal role in this process. Soluble Aβ with unordered structures specifically binds to raft-like membranes containing a ganglioside cluster, the formation of which is facilitated by cholesterol. The membrane-bound Aβ forms an α-helix-rich structure at lower densities. At higher densities, Aβ undergoes a conformational transition to the β-sheet-rich structure that can serve as a seed for toxic amyloid fibril formation. Furthermore, after Aβ binds to the raft-like membranes, the protein can translocate to the phosphatidylcholine membranes to which soluble Aβ does not bind, suggesting that the lipid raft containing a ganglioside cluster serves as a conformational catalyst generating a membrane-active form of Aβ with seeding ability.

1. INTRODUCTION

It is widely accepted that the β-amyloid protein (Aβ) is central to the development of Alzheimer's disease (AD). For a recent review, refer to [1,2]. Aβ composed of 39–42 amino acids (Fig. 1) is generated from the proteolytic cleavage of amyloid precursor protein (APP) by β- and γ-secretases. APP is a type I membrane protein (695–770 residues depending on isoforms) occurring as a normal constituent of the human brain, although its physiological role is not yet clear. The N-terminal part (1–28) contains several charged residues (as highlighted in Fig. 1) whereas the C-terminal portion (29–42) is completely hydrophobic and a part of the transmembrane region of APP. A pathological hallmark of AD is the formation of fibrillar deposits of Aβ in the brain. According to the so-called Aβ hypothesis [3], the conversion of soluble, nontoxic Aβ to aggregated toxic Aβ rich in β-sheet structures ignites the neurotoxic cascade(s) of Aβ, although this theory is still the subject of controversy [4,5].

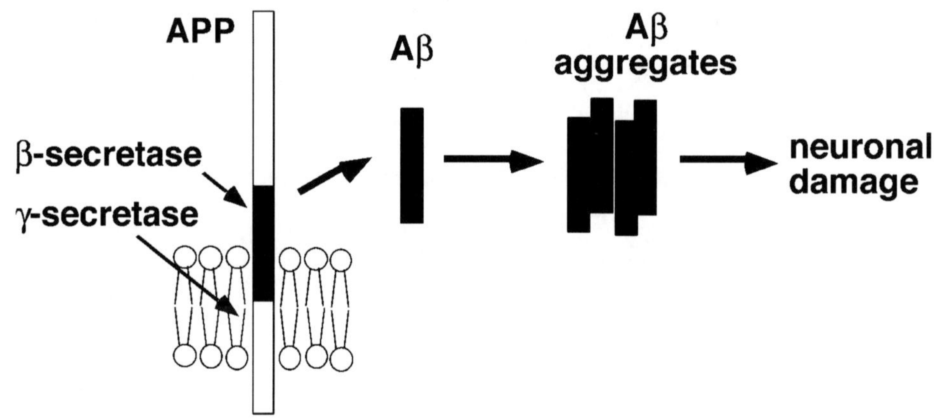

DAEFRHDSGYEVHHQKLVFFAEDVGSNK^{28}GAIIGLMVGGVVIA^{42}

Fig. 1: Schematic illustration of the Aβ hypothesis (upper) and the amino acid sequence of Aβ-(1–42) (lower). Charged amino acids are underlined.

Aβ has been shown to spontaneously form amyloid fibrils upon incubation of Aβ solution at 37 °C, but the concentration required for this (> 10^{-4}–10^{-5} M) [6-8] is much higher than the physiological concentration of Aβ in biological fluids (< 10^{-8} M) [9].

Therefore, there should be alternative mechanisms that promote Aβ aggregation in vivo even at a very low concentration. Seeded (or nucleation-dependent) polymerization has been hypothesized for such a mechanism [10]. The rate-limiting step of Aβ polymerization is the formation of an aggregation seed with a conformation that is characteristic of the aggregate and is different from that of soluble Aβ. Once the seed is formed, soluble Aβ changes its conformation by using the seed as a template (Fig. 2).

In 1995, Yanagisawa and colleagues discovered a specific form of Aβ bound to GM1 ganglioside (Fig. 3) in brains exhibiting early pathological changes of AD and suggested that the GM1-bound form of Aβ (GM1-Aβ) may serve as a seed for the formation of toxic amyloid aggregates / fibrils [11]. In this chapter, the formation mechanisms and the properties of GM1-Aβ are reviewed, and the possibility of the lipid raft (lipid microdomain containing gangliosides) as a nidus for the aggregation of Aβ is discussed.

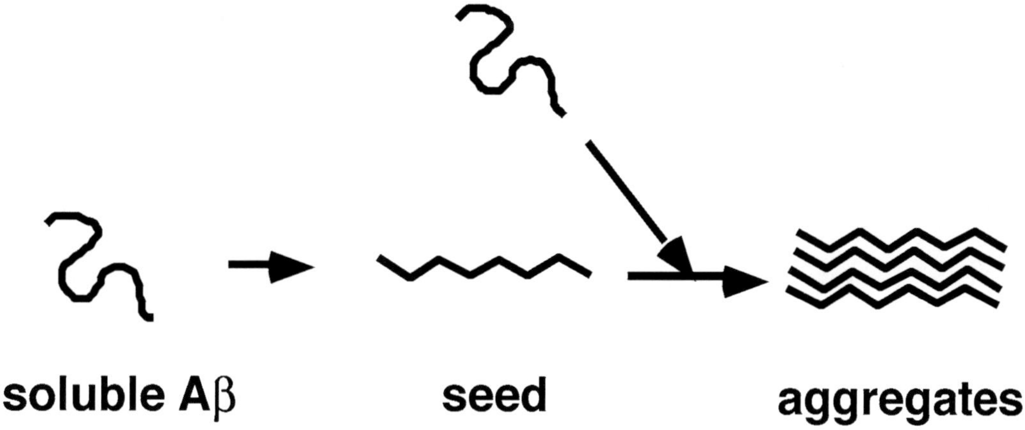

Fig. 2: Schematic illustration of seeded polymerization.

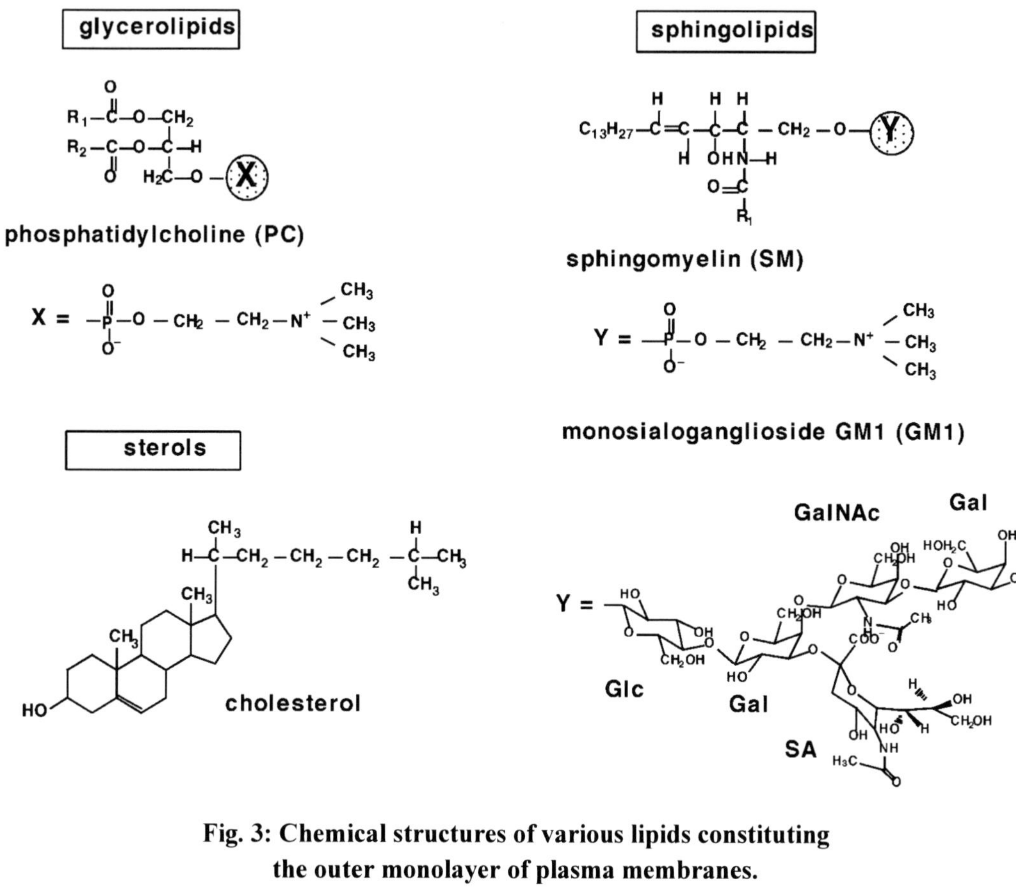

Fig. 3: Chemical structures of various lipids constituting the outer monolayer of plasma membranes.

2. Lipid Raft

The basic structure of a biomembrane is a lipid bilayer in which various functional proteins are embedded [12]. The transversal lipid distribution of the bilayer is completely asymmetric: the outer monolayer (extracellular side) is composed of glycosphingolipids (GSL) and zwitterionic phospholipids, i.e., phosphatidylcholine (PC) and sphingomyelin (SM) (Fig. 3). In contrast, the inner monolayer contains phosphatidylethanolamine (PE) and negatively charged anionic phospholipids, e.g., phosphatidylserine (PS) and phosphatidylinositol. Cholesterol, another important lipid component, distributes in both monolayers.

Physicochemical studies using model membranes suggest that the lateral distribution of lipids is also heterogeneous [13]. In the outer monolayer, GSL, SM and cholesterol (and PC with saturated acyl chains) form a lipid microdomain in the liquid-ordered phase, in which the acyl chains are highly ordered as in the solid state whereas the lipids are laterally mobile as in the fluid state. Proteins important for signal transduction are proposed to localize in this microdomain, which is dubbed 'lipid raft' [14, 15]. It should be noted here that the compositions of the lipid rafts reported are those of the detergent-insoluble fractions of biomembranes, which may differ considerably from the compositions of the true 'putative' rafts in intact membranes.

3. Interactions of Aβ with Phospholipid Membranes

A number of studies have been published on Aβ–membrane interactions. There are sometimes discrepancies between results obtained by different research groups. One reason for this may be different solution states of Aβ. Aβ, especially Aβ-(1–42), tends to easily self-aggregate, forming oligomers in solution. This tendency is dependent on the lot number [16] as well as the salt form (trifluoroacetic acid or HCl) [17] of the synthetic protein. Commercially available Aβ may contain nontrivial amounts of impurities [18]. Furthermore, the method of solution preparation significantly affects the solution state of Aβ. One of the most reliable protocols, which we follow, is that Aβ is dissolved in 0.02% ammonia on ice and any large aggregates are removed by ultracentrifugation at 100000g, 4°C for 3h [8]. Aβ solution prepared by this method does not spontaneously form fibrils upon incubation at 37°C for a few days. Dimethylsulfoxide (DMSO) and hexafluoroisopropanol (HFIP) are the only organic solvents preventing aggregation [19]. However, some researches use other solvents, such as trifluoroethanol, to make stock solution of Aβ Even if DMSO or HFIP is used, the ultracentrifugation procedure is highly recommended. The use of organic solvents may result in another complication. Aβ takes a random coil in aqueous solution whereas it assumes secondary structures in organic solvent-containing media [20,21]. The initial conformation of Aβ in stock solution may affect subsequent protein–lipid interactions. Furthermore, contamination of trace amounts of metals such as zinc, copper, or iron promotes self-aggregation of Aβ [22].

Early work mainly dealt with Aβ–phospholipid interactions. Seelig's group found that Aβ-(1–40) binds to negatively charged 1-palmitoyl-2-oleoyl-L-α-phosphatidylglycerol

(POPG)-containing liposomes only at a low ionic strength and the addition of 0.1 M NaCl inhibits the binding [23,24] The group of Arispe reported that Aβ-(1–40) interacted with planar bilayers composed of PS/PE to form giant ion channels in the presence of ca. 40 mM salts [25,26]. Rhee et al. also observed that the cosonication of PS/PE liposomes with Aβ-(1–42) in a 10 mM Hepes buffer resulted in the formation of a Ca^{2+} permeable channel [27]. Ion channel formation by Aβ-(1–40) was also observed in GT1–7 cell membranes [28]. Several theoretical models have been proposed for the ion channel structure [29].

The protein takes a random coil in solution whereas it assumes both an α-helix and a β-sheet at lower and higher protein-to-lipid ratios, respectively [23,24]. Fibril formation was accelerated in the presence of anionic phospholipids at a low ionic strength [30]. No interaction was observed with zwitterionic PC liposomes [23,31,32], although some studies have reported that Aβ-(1–40) and Aβ-(1–42) interacted with PC liposomes [33,34]. On the other hand, Aβ-(1–40) inserts into various PC monolayers at a surface pressure of 20 mN/m [24,34,35], which is distinctly lower (the lipid packing is looser) than the pressure corresponding to lipid bilayers (32 mN/m) [36]. We have confirmed that Aβ-(1–40) interacts with anionic phospholipids only at a low ionic strength, i.e., the protein does not bind to any phospholipids under physiological conditions [31]. However, at a lower pH of 6, Aβ-(1–40) binds to PG and PI, and more hydrophobic Aβ-(1–42) interacts with these anionic lipids even at pH 7 [21,37]. Metal ions also modulate Aβ–phospholipid interactions [38]. Aβ-(1–40) and Aβ-(1–42) interact with POPG/POPC membranes in the presence of Cu^{2+} or Zn^{2+} at pH 7.5, forming α-helical structures.

The aggregational state of the protein also influences protein–membrane interactions. Aggregated but not freshly solubilized Aβ was found to interact with and decrease the fluidity of PC bilayers [39]. Selective affinity of cholesterol, fatty acids and PC for aggregated Aβ-(1–40) has also been reported [40]. Soluble Aβ-(1–40) increases the electron density of the hydrocarbon core of brain PC membranes whereas aggregated Aβ-(1–40) shows an opposite effect [33].

4. Interactions of Aβ with Gangliosides

After the discovery of GM1-Aβ [11], Aβ–ganglioside interactions were studied by several research groups. McLaurin and Chakrabartty reported that Aβ-(1–40) and Aβ-(1–42) bind to GM1 micelles, forming mixed α-helix/β-sheet structures [21]. The sialic acid is essential for this interaction because asialo-GM1 does not show this property. The group of Surewicz reported that Aβ-(1–40) but not Aβ-(1–28) binds to GM1 micelles as well as the pentasaccharide moiety of GM1 [41]. The affinities of F10W-Aβ-(1–40) for various ganglioside micelles were determined using TRP fluorescence [42]. The dissociation constants (K_d) for the monosialogangliosides GM1 and GM2 were 1.4 and 3.7 X 10^{-6} M, respectively, and were several-fold smaller than the value for the pentasaccharide moiety of GM1. The K_d values were an order of magnitude smaller for the polysialogangliosides GD1a and GT1b compared to the monosialogangliosides.

Conflicting results were reported for the binding of Aβ-(1–40) to GM1 embedded in the matrix of phospholipids. McLaurin et al. [43] and ourselves [31] observed that Aβ-(1–40) did not associate with GM1 in egg PC vesicles until the GM1 content exceeded 30%. On the other hand, Choo-Smith et al. reported that F10W-Aβ-(1–40) was bound to 3mol% GM1 in POPC vesicles [42]. They externally added GM1 to preformed POPC vesicles. A fraction of GM1 molecules may not have been incorporated into the liposomes and existed as micelles. Gangliosides incorporated into PC bilayers facilitate fibril formation of Aβ [42,43].

Early studies did not pay attention to the 'environments' surrounding gangliosides. Recent accumulating evidence suggests that gangliosides form with other sphingolipids and cholesterol lipid rafts rather than being homogeneously distributed in cell membranes [14,15]. We noticed that the Aβ–GM1 interaction was facilitated in a SM/cholesterol mixture compared to a PC matrix [31] and therefore started more systematic studies. For this purpose, we designed the fluorescent DAC-Aβ, in which the N-terminus of Aβ-(1–40) was labeled by the diethylaminocoumarin dye (Fig. 4) [32]. This fluorescent protein was confirmed to behave very similarly to the native Aβ-(1–40). Fluorescence of DAC-Aβ is very sensitive to the polarity of its environment. DAC-Aβ is almost nonfluorescent in aqueous solution whereas strong blue-shifted fluorescence is observed in a less polar medium such as membranes (Fig. 4). This unique property can be used to monitor DAC-Aβ–membrane interaction. DAC-Aβ solution was titrated with liposomes of various lipid compositions. Fig. 5 shows relative fluorescence enhancement as a measure of membrane binding as a function of the lipid-to-protein ratio [32, 44]· DAC-Aβ did not show an affinity for PC or phosphatidylserine (PS) under physiological conditions, consistent with previous observations (see the above section). In contrast, the protein effectively bound to raft-like membranes composed of GM1/cholesterol/SM. Neither cholesterol nor SM constituted a binding site for DAC-Aβ, because the protein did not bind to PC/cholesterol or SM bilayers. The fact that DAC-Aβ showed the most efficient binding to GM1 micelles clearly indicates the importance of GM1. Interestingly, however, GM1/PC membranes did not accept the protein. Thus, DAC-Aβ shows an affinity for GM1 molecules only in a special state.

To obtain information on this state, we measured the binding isotherms of DAC-Aβ to raft-like membranes having various GM1/cholesterol/SM ratios. The obtained parameters are listed in Table 1. The binding constant was independent of lipid composition (2–3 X 10^6 M^{-1}) whereas the binding capacity (maximal number of binding sites) was highly dependent on lipid composition. An increase in GM1 content from 20% to 40% cooperatively increased the binding capacity. This parameter was also sensitive to cholesterol content. Cholesterol facilitated the formation of the binding site. We hypothesized that a cluster of GM1, which is formed in a cholesterol-dependent manner, constituted the binding site. This idea explains well the most effective binding to GM1 micelles, a large cluster of GM1. To prove this hypothesis, we estimated GM1 clustering using BODIPY-labeled GM1 (Fig. 6). The BODIPY dye is known to form an excimer (a complex between a dye molecule in the excited state and one in the ground state) when locally concentrated. The excimer emits broad fluorescence at a wavelength ~100 nm longer compared to the monomer. The excimer-to-monomer ratio is proportional to the local dye concentration, therefore a measure of clustering [45]. One fourth of GM1 contents in the systems listed in Table 1 were replaced by fluorescent GM1. The order of excimer formation (Table 2) was in keeping with the order of the binding capacity (Table 1).

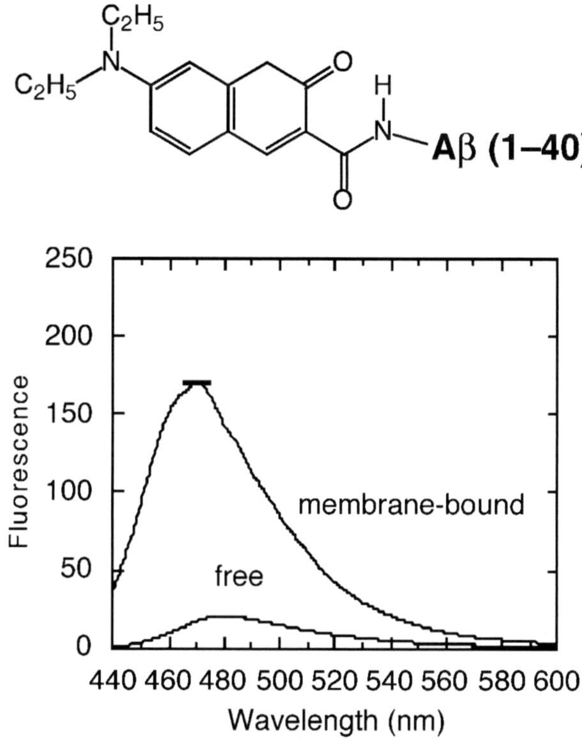

Fig. 4: Chemical structure and fluorescence spectra of DAC-Aβ.

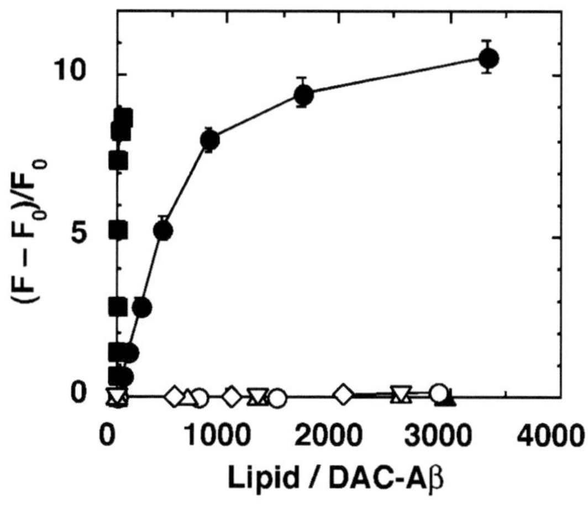

Fig. 5: Lipid specificity of membrane binding of DAC-Aβ. DAC-Aβ solution was titrated with LUVs of various lipid compositions. Relative fluorescence enhancement at 466 nm is plotted as a function of the lipid-to-DAC-Aβ ratio. F_0 and F denote fluorescence intensities in the absence and the presence of lipids, respectively. Lipid composition: closed squares, GM1 micelle; closed circles, GM1/cholesterol/SM (20/40/40); closed triangles, GM1/PC (20/80); open circles, SM; open triangles, PC; inverse triangles, PC/cholesterol (2/1); diamonds, PS.

Table 1: Parameters for Binding of DAC-Aβ to Various Raft-Like Membranes at 30 °C.

Lipid composition	Binding constant	Binding capacity
(GM1/cholesterol/SM)	(10^6 X M^{-1})	ich(DAC-Aβ/exofacial GM1)
40/30/30	2.4 ± 0.1	ch0.057 ± 0.001
20/40/40	2.9 ± 0.4	0.019 ± 0.001
20/16/64	3.0 ± 2.9	0.001 ± h (?)

Table 2: Detection of GM1 Cluster by the Excimer Formation of BODIPY-GM1

Lipid composition	Excimer/monomer ratio
BODIPY-GM1/GM1/cholesterol/SM (10/30/30/30)	0.76
BODIPY-GM1/GM1/cholesterol/SM (5/15/40/40)	0.43
BODIPY-GM1/GM1/cholesterol/SM (5/15/16/64)	0.34
BODIPY-GM1/PC (10/90)	0.24

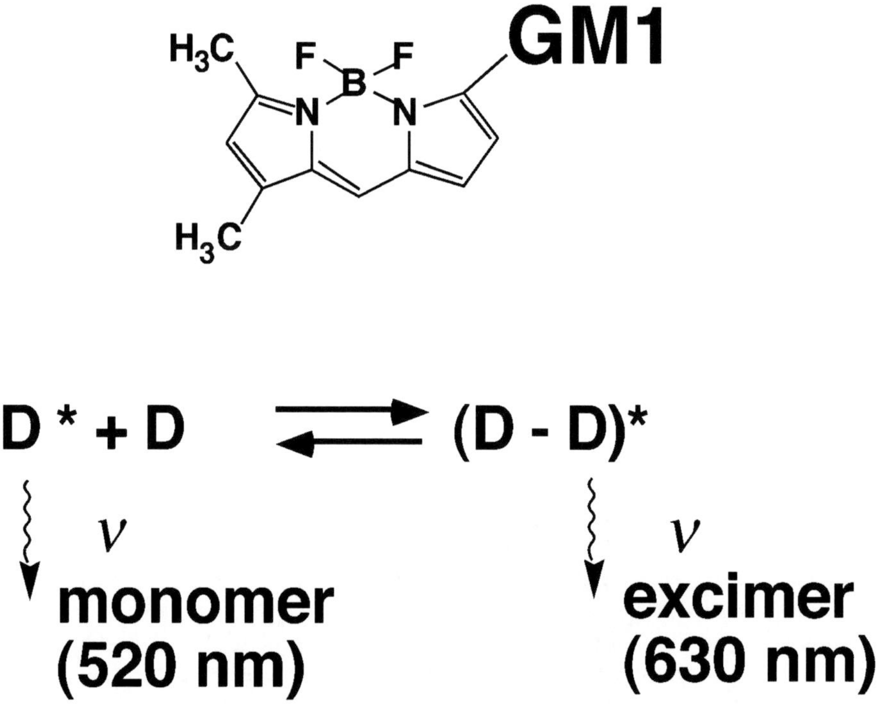

Fig. 6: Excimer formation of BODIPY-GM1. The BODIPY dye is attached to the alkyl chain of GM1.

The binding of DAC-Aβ to various gangliosides was also investigated using raft-like membranes composed of ganglioside/cholesterol/SM (20/40/40) [44]. The binding affinity was again almost independent of ganglioside species whereas the number of binding sites was approximately proportional to the number of sialic acid residues in the gangliosides.

The conformation of Aβ-(1–40) in raft-like membranes was determined by circular dichroism (CD) spectra. In buffer, the soluble protein took an unordered structure. However, upon binding to raft-like membranes, drastic conformational changes were observed depending on the protein-to-ganglioside ratio (Fig. 7). At lower ratios (<= 0.025), the CD spectra of Aβ-(1–40) were characterized by double minima at 208 and 222 nm, typical of an α-helix. However, at higher protein-to-ganglioside ratios, the protein changed its conformation to a β-sheet, as suggested by a minima around 218 nm. An NMR study revealed that both Aβ-(1–40) and Aβ-(1–42) form helix-loop-helix structures in SDS micelles that may serve as precursors of monomeric β-sheets and subsequently formed amyloid fibrils [46, 47].

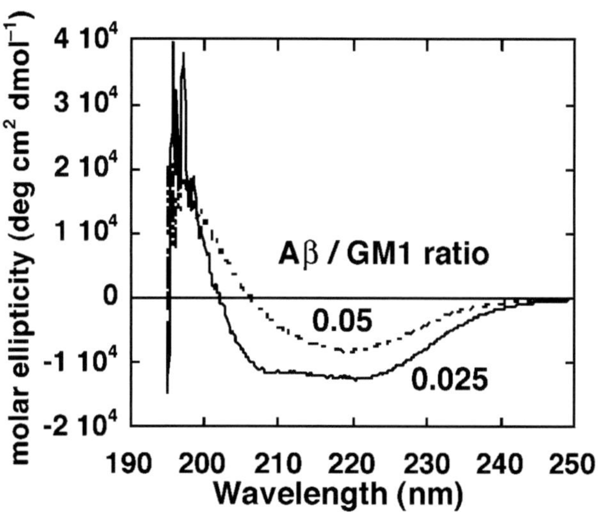

Fig. 7: CD spectra of native Aβ-(1–40) in the presence of raft-like liposomes composed of GM1/cholesterol/SM (40/20/20) at different Aβ-to-GM1 ratios.

Aβ-(1–40) bound to a ganglioside cluster was indeed found to act as a seed for fibril formation [44]. The seeding activity was examined by the thioflavin T assay [48] in the presence of various gangliosides in raft-like membranes at various protein-to-ganglioside ratios. The most effective fibril formation was observed with GM1 under β-sheet-forming conditions.

5. Formation of a Membrane-Active Form of Aβ in a Ganglioside Cluster

Recently, we discovered that after Aβ binds to raft membranes, the protein can be translocated to PC membranes to which soluble Aβ does not bind [49]. The formation of the membrane-active species of Aβ was detected by use of fluorescent resonance energy transfer (FRET) from DAC-Aβ (emission maximum in the membranes around 470 nm) to BODIPY-PC (strong absorption between 460–520 nm). The fluorescence of 0.5 μM DAC-Aβ in buffer was weak and showed the maximum around 480 nm (Fig. 8, trace 1). The addition of 50 μM raft-like LUVs composed of GM1/cholesterol/SM (1/1/1) induced a blue shift and a concomitant intensity increase (trace 2). The simultaneous addition of the raft liposomes (50 μM) and PC liposomes containing 1 mol % BODIPY-PC (500 μM) to 0.5 μM DAC-Aβ solution caused a significant decrease in the DAC fluorescence concomitant with the appearance of the sensitized fluorescence of BODIPY-PC at 520 nm, indicating the occurrence of FRET from DAC-Aβ to BODIPY-PC (trace 3). The contribution from directly excited fluorescence in the absence of the protein was subtracted from the original spectrum. A control experiment showed that the addition of BODIPY-PC-doped egg PC LUVs did not change the fluorescence spectrum of the DAC-Aβ solution (data not shown), in keeping with the previous finding that DAC-Aβ does not bind to PC [32]. The occurrence of FRET (Fig. 8) indicates two possibilities: DAC-Aβ bound to the PC liposomes or the protein induced lipid exchange between the vesicles, e.g. by inducing membrane fusion. We confirmed the absence of lipid exchange using the standard lipid mixing assay.

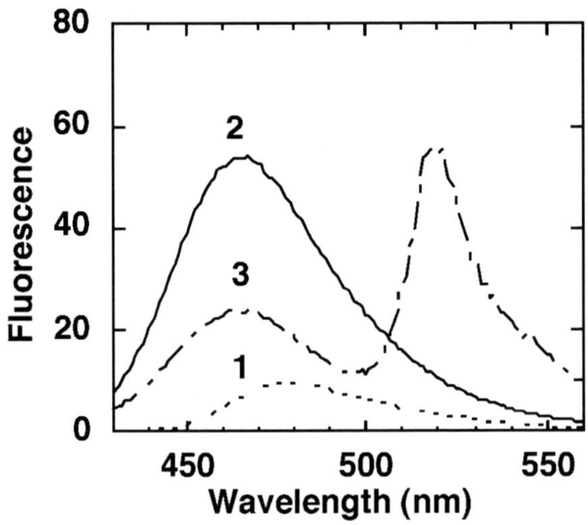

Fig. 8: Formation of a membrane-active Aβ in raft-like membranes. Fluorescence emission spectra of 0.5 μM DAC-Aβ were measured at 37 °C in 10 mM Tris/ 150 mM NaCl/ 2 mM $CaCl_2$, pH 7.4 buffer (trace 1) and after a 5-min incubation with 50 μM raft-like LUVs composed of GM1/cholesterol/SM (1/1/1) (trace 2), and 50 μM raft-like LUVs + 500 μM PC LUVs doped with 1 mol % BODIPY-PC (trace 3).

The fact that formation of the membrane-active Aβ occurred reveals a novel picture regarding the roles of ganglioside clusters: Different from the previous concept, the clusters do not provide a specific high affinity site for soluble Aβ. If this were the case, the protein would stay in the raft-like environment even in the presence of PC membranes. Rather, the cluster serves as a conformational catalyst or a chaperon that lowers the activation energy for the conformational change from unordered structures to the thermodynamically more stable membrane-active form(s). This hypothesis is in keeping with the observation that the binding of Aβ to the raft-like membrane is much slower (~1 min) than that of other peptides (< 1 s). A ganglioside cluster may provide a cocktail of chemical groups that stabilize intermediates of Aβ folding, i.e., hydrogen-bonding groups (OH, COO^-, and CONH), a charged group (COO^-), and hydrophobic CH moieties of the sugar backbone. The membrane-chaperon hypothesis is also supported by the finding that Aβ can bind to acidic phospholipids at a low ionic strength [23,24,31]. However, there remains the possibility that an Aβ–GM1 complex is the translocating species.

6. Concluding Remarks

Based on the above observations, we propose a novel model for Aβ–membrane interactions (Fig. 9). Aβ specifically binds to a ganglioside cluster, the formation of which is facilitated by cholesterol, because the cluster acts as a chaperon, converting the soluble form to membrane-active conformations. Aβ undergoes a conformational transition from an α-helix-rich structure to a β-sheet-rich one with increasing protein density on the membrane [32]. The membrane-bound Aβ with acquired secondary structures, especially the β-sheet form, serves as a seed for amyloid fibril formation [44]· In competition with this process, the membrane-bound Aβ, translocates to other membranes for which soluble Aβ does not show affinity.

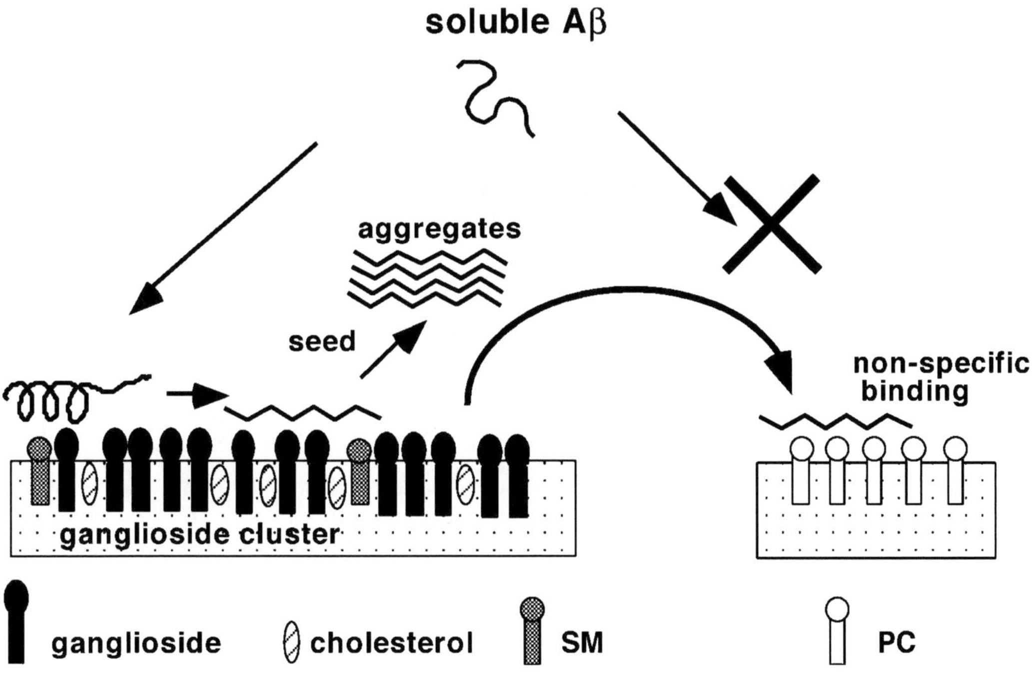

Fig. 9: Schematic illustration of Aβ–raft-like membrane interactions. Aβ specifically recognizes a ganglioside cluster, the formation of which is facilitated by cholesterol. Aβ undergoes a conformational transition from an α-helix-rich structure to a β-sheet-rich one with increasing protein density on the membrane. The membrane-bound Aβ with acquired secondary structures serves both as a seed for amyloid fibril formation and as a membrane-active species, translocating to other membranes for which soluble Aβ does not show affinity.

This model is in keeping with various previous observations: (i) GM1-Aβ was discovered in the brains of patients with AD [11,50]; (ii) Lipid rafts contain soluble [51,52] and insoluble [53] Aβ under physiological and pathological conditions, respectively; (iii) A link between cholesterol, Aβ, and AD have been reported [54, 55], and therefore cholesterol modulation appears to be an emerging strategy for the treatment of AD [56]; (iv) The cholesterol content in the exofacial leaflets of the synaptic plasma membrane increases in aged [57] as well as apolipoprotein E4-knock-in [58] mice. Both the aging and the apolipoprotein E4 allele are strong risk factors for developing AD [59]; (v) Reduction in cholesterol and sialic acid content protects cells from the toxic effects of Aβ [60]. Further characterization of the membrane-active Aβ, including toxicity and detailed conformation, is a subject of future study.

ACKNOWLEDGEMENTS

This work was supported by Grant-in-Aids for Scientific Research on Priority Areas (13024244, 14017048, 15016058 and 12140202) from the Ministry of Education, Science, Sports and Culture, Japan and a Research Grant for Longevity Sciences (14-1) from the Ministry of Health and Welfare.

REFERENCES

[1] Selkoe DJ. Alzheimer's disease: Genes, proteins, and therapy. *Physiol. Rev.* 2001; 81:741–766.

[2] Citron M. Alzheimer's disease: treatments in discovery and development. *Nat. Neurosci.* 2002; 5:1055–1057.

[3] Hardy JA, Higgins GA. Alzheimer's disease: the amyloid cascade hypothesis. *Science* 1992; 256:184–185.

[4] Rottkamp CA, Atwood CS, Joseph JA, Nunomura A, Perry G, Smith MA. The state versus amyloid-β: the trial of the most wanted criminal in Alzheimer disease. *Peptides* 2002; 23:1333–1341.

[5] Robinson SR, Bishop GM. Aβ as a bioflocculant: implications for the amyloid hypothesis of Alzheimer's disease. *Neurobiol. Aging* 2002; 23:1051–1072.

[6] Fraser PE, Nguyen JT, Inoue H, Surewicz WK, Selkoe DJ, Podlinski MB, Kirschner DA. Fibril formation by primate, rodent, and Dutch-hemorrhagic analogues of Alzheimer amyloid β-protein. *Biochemistry* 1992; 31:10716–10723.

[7] Walsh DM, Lomakin A, Benedek GB, Condron MM, Teplow DB. Amyloid β-protein fibrillogenesis. Detection of a protofibrillar intermediate. *J. Biol. Chem.* 1997; 272:22364–22372.

[8] Naiki H, Gejyo F. Kinetic analysis of amyloid fibril formation. *Methods Enzymol.* 1999; 309:305–318.

[9] Seubert P, Vigo-Pelfrey C, Esch F, Lee M, Dovey H, Davis D, Sinha S, Schlossmacher M, Whaley J, Swindlehurst C, McCormack R, Wolfert R, Selkoe J, Lieberburg I, Schenk D. Isolation and quantification of soluble Alzheimer's β-peptide from biological fluids. *Nature* 1992; 359:325–327.

[10] Jarrett JT, Lansbury Jr. PT. Seeding "one-dimensional crystallization" of amyloid: a pathogenic mechanism in Alzheimer's disease and scrapie? *Cell* 1993; 73:1055–1058.

[11] Yanagisawa K, Odaka A, Suzuki N, Ihara Y. GM1 ganglioside-bound amyloid β-protein (Aβ): a possible form of preamyloid in Alzheimer's disease. *Nat. Med.* 1995; 1:1062–1066.

[12] Alberts B, Bray D, Lewis J, Raff M, Roberts K, Watson JD. *Molecular Biology of the Cell*. New York: Garland Publishing, 1994. Chapter 10.

[13] Brown DA. Seeing is believing: visualization of rafts in model membranes. *Proc. Natl. Acad. Sci.*, U.S.A. 2001; 98:10517–10518.

[14] Simons K, Ikonen E. Functional rafts in cell membranes. *Nature* 1997; 385:569–572.

[15] Brown RE. Sphingolipid organization in biomembranes: What physical studies of model membranes reveal. *J. Cell Sci.* 1998; 111:1–9.

[16] May PC, Gitter BD, Waters DC, Simmons LK, Becker GW, Small JS, Robison PM. β-Amyloid peptide in vitro toxicity: lot-to-lot variability. *Neurobiol. Aging* 1992; 13:605–607.

[17] Kaneko I, Tutumi S. Replies to the editor. *J. Neurochem.* 1997; 68:438–439.

[18] Fukuda H, Shimizu T, Nakajima M, Mori H, Shirasawa T. Synthesis, aggregation, and neurotoxicity of the Alzheimer's Aβ 1–42 amyloid peptide and its isoaspartyl isomers. *Bioorg. Med. Chem. Lett.* 1999; 9:953–956.

[19] Snyder SW, Ladror US, Wade WS, Wang GT, Barrett LW, Matayoshi ED, Huffaker HJ, Krafft GA, Holzman TF. Amyloid-β aggregation: selective inhibition of aggregation in mixtures of amyloid with different chain lengths. *Biophys. J.* 1994; 67:1216–1228.

[20] Barrow CJ, Yasuda A, Kenny PTM, Zagorski MG. Solution conformation and aggregational properties of synthetic amyloid β-peptides of Alzheimer's disease. *J. Mol. Biol.* 1992; 225:1075–1093.

[21] McLaurin J, Charkrabartty A. Membrane disruption by Alzheimer β-amyloid peptides mediated through specific binding to either phospholipids or gangliosides. *J. Biol. Chem.* 1996; 271:26482–26489.

[22] Bush AI, Pettingell WH, Multhaup G, d Paradis M, Vonsattel JP, Gusella JF, Beyreuther K, Masters CL, Tanzi RE. Rapid induction of Alzheimer A beta amyloid formation by zinc. *Science* 1994; 265:1464–1467.

[23] Terzi E, Hölzmann G, Seelig J. Self-association of β-amyloid peptide (1–40) in solution and binding to lipid membranes. *J. Mol. Biol.* 1995; 252:633–642.

[24] Terzi E, Hölzemann G, Seelig J. Interaction of Alzheimer β-amyloid peptide(1–40) with lipid membranes. *Biochemistry* 1997; 36:14845–14852.

[25] Arispe N, Rojas E, Pollard HB. Alzheimer disease amyloid β protein forms calcium channels in bilayer membranes: Blockade by tromethamine and aluminum. *Proc. Natl. Acad. Sci.*, U.S.A. 1993; 90:567–571.

[26] Arispe N, Pollard HB, Rojas E. Giant multilevel cation channels formed by Alzheimer disease amyloid β-protein [AβP-(1–40)] in bilayer membranes. *Proc. Natl. Acad. Sci.*, U.S.A. 1993; 90:10573–10577.

[27] Rhee SK, Quist AP, Lal R. Amyloid β protein-(1–42) forms calcium-permeable, Zn^{2+}-sensitive channel. *J. Biol. Chem.* 1998; 273:13379–13382.

[28] Kawahara M, Arispe N, Kuroda Y, Rojas E. Alzheimer's disease amyloid β-protein forms Zn^{2+}-sensitive, cation selective channels across excised membrane patches from hypothalamic neurons. *Biophys. J.* 1997; 73:67–75.

[29] Durell SR, Guy HR, Arispe N, Rojas E, Pollard HB. Theoretical models of the ion channel structure of amyloid β-protein. *Biophys.* J. 1994; 67:2137–2145.

[30] Chauhan A, Ray I, Chauhan VPS. Interaction of amyloid beta-protein with anionic phospholipids: Possible involvement of Lys^{28} and C-terminus aliphatic amino acids. *Neurochem. Res.* 2000; 25:426–429.

[31] Matsuzaki K, Horikiri C. Interactions of amyloid β-peptide (1–40) with ganglioside-containing membranes. *Biochemistry* 1999; 38:4137–4142.

[32] Kakio A, Nishimoto S, Yanagisawa K, Kozutsumi Y, Matsuzaki K. Cholesterol-dependent formation of GM1 ganglioside-bound amyloid β-protein, an endogenous seed for Alzheimer amyloid. *J. Biol. Chem.* 2001; 276:24985–24990.

[33] Mason RP, Jacob RF, Walter MF, Mason PE, Avdulov NA, Chochina SV, Igbavboa U, Wood WG. Distribution and fluidizing action of soluble and aggregated amyloid β-peptide in rat synaptic plasma membranes. *J. Biol. Chem.* 1999; 274:18801–18807.

[34] Ji S-R, Wu Y, Sui S-f. Cholesterol is an important factor affecting the membrane insertion of β-amyloid peptide (Aβ1–40), which may potentially inhibit the fibril formation. *J. Biol. Chem.* 2002; 277:6273–6279.

[35] Koppaka V, Axelsen PH. Accelerated accumulation of amyloid β proteins on oxidatively damaged lipid membranes. *Biochemistry* 2000; 39:10011–10016.

[36] Seelig A. Local anesthetics and pressure: a comparison of dibucaine binding to lipid monolayers and bilayers. *Biochim. Biophys. Acta* 1987; 899:196–204.

[37] McLaurin J, Franklin T, Chakrabartty A, Fraser PE. Phosphatidylinositol involvement in Alzheimer amyloid-β fibril growth and arrest. *J. Mol. Biol.* 1998; 278:183–194.

[38] Curtain CC, Ali FE, Smith DG, Bush AI, Masters CL, Barnham KJ. Metal ions, pH, and cholesterol regulate the interacyions of Alzheimer's disease amyloid peptide with membrane lipid. *J. Biol. Chem.* 2003; 278:2977–2982.

[39] Kremer JJ, Pallitto MM, Sklansky DJ, Murphy RM. Correlation of β-amyloid aggregate size and hydrophobicity with decreased bilayer fluidity of model membranes. *Biochemistry* 2000; 39:10309–10318.

[40] Avdulov NA, Chochina SV, Igbavboa U, Warden CS, Vassiliev AV, Wood WG. Lipid binding to amyloid β-peptide aggregates: Preferential binding of cholesterol as compared with phosohatidylcholine and fatty acids. *J. Neurochem.* 1997; 69:1746–1752.

[41] Choo-Smith LP, Surewicz WK. The interaction between Alzheimer amyloid β(1-40) peptide and ganglioside GM1-containing membranes. *FEBS Lett.* 1997; 402:95–98.

[42] Choo-Smith L-P, Garzon-Rodriguez W, Glabe CG, Surewicz WK. Acceleration of amyloid fibril formation by specific binding of Aβ-(1–40) peptide to ganglioside-containing membrane vesicles. *J. Biol. Chem.* 1997; 272:22987–22990.

[43] McLaurin J, Franklin T, Fraser PE, Chakrabartty A. Structural transitions associated with the interaction of Alzheimer β-amyloid peptides with gangliosides. *J. Biol. Chem.* 1998; 273:4506–4515.

[44] Kakio A, Nishimoto S, Yanagisawa K, Kozutsumi Y, Matsuzaki K. Interactions of amyloid β-protein with various gangliosides in raft-like membranes: Importance of GM1 ganglioside-bound form as an endogenous seed for Alzheimer amyloid. *Biochemistry* 2002; 41:7385–7390.

[45] Förster T. Excimers. Angew. Chem., Int. Ed. Engl. 1969; 8:333–343.

[46] Coles M, Bicknell W, Watson AA, Fairlie DP, Craik DJ. Solution structure of amyloid β-peptide(1–40) in a water–micelle environment. Is the membrane-spanning domain where we think it is? *Biochemistry* 1998; 37:11064–11077.

[47] Shao H, Jao S-c, Ma K, Zagorski G. Solution structure of micelle-bound amyloid β-(1–40) and β-(1–42) peptides of Alzheimer's disease. *J. Mol. Biol.* 1999; 285:755–773.

[48] LeVine III H. Thioflavin T interaction with synthetic Alzheimer's disease β-amyloid peptides: Detection of amyloid aggregation in solution. *Protein Sci.* 1993; 2:404–410.

[49] Kakio A, Nishimoto S, Kozutsumi Y, Matsuzaki K. Formation of a membrane-active form of amyloid β-protein in raft-like membranes. *Biochem. Biophys. Res. Commun.* 2003; 303:514–518.

[50] Yanagisawa K, Ihara Y. GM1 ganglioside-bound amyloid β-protein in Alzheimer's disease brain. *Neurobiol Aging* 1998; 19:S65–S67.

[51] Lee S-J, Liyanage U, Bickel PE, Xia W, Lansbury J, P. T., Kosik KS. A Detergent-insoluble membrane compartment contains Aβ in vivo. *Nat. Med.* 1998; 4:730–734.

[52] Morishima-Kawashima M, Ihara Y. The presence of amyloid β-protein in the detergent-insoluble membrane compartment of neuroblastoma cells. *Biochemistry* 1998; 37:15247–15235.

[53] Sawamura N, Morishima-Kawashima M, Waki H, Kobayashi K, Kuramochi T, Frosch MP, Ding K, Ito M, Kim TW, Tanzi RE, Oyama F, Tabira T, Ando S, Ihara Y. Mutant presenilin 2 transgenic mice. A large increase in the levels of Aβ 42 is presumably associated with the low density membrane domain that contains decreased levels of glycerophospholipids and sphingomyelin. *J. Biol. Chem.* 2000; 275:27901–27908.

[54] Wolozin B. A fluid connection: Cholesterol and Aβ. *Proc. Natl. Acad. Sci.*, U. S. A. 2001; 98:5371–5373.

[55] Marx J. Bad for the heart, bad for the mind? *Science* 2001; 294:508–509.

[56] Golde TE, Eckman CB. Cholesterol modulation as an emerging strategy for the treatment of Alzheimer's disease. *Drug Discovery Today* 2001; 6:1049–1055.

[57] Igbavboa U, Avdulov NA, Schroeder F, Wood WG. Increasing age alters transbilayer fluidity and cholesterol asymmetry in synaptic plasma membranes in mice. *J. Neurochem.* 1996; 66:1717–1725.

[58] Hayashi H, Igbavboa U, Hamanaka H, Kobayashi M, Fujita SC, Wood WG, Yanagisawa K. Cholesterol is increased in the exofacial leaflet of synaptic plasma membranes of human apolipoprotein E4 knock-in mice. *NeuroReport* 2002; 13:383–386.

[59] Law A, Gauthier S, Quirion R. Say NO to Alzheimer's disease: the putative links between nitric oxide and dementia of the Alzheimer's type. *Brain Res. Rev.* 2001; 35:73–96.

[60] Wang SS-S, Rymer DL, Good TA. Reduction in cholesterol and sialic acid content protects cells from the toxic effects of β-amyloid peptides. *J. Biol. Chem.* 2001; 276:42027–42034.

Chapter VII

THE PRESENILINS AND THEIR ROLE IN AMYLOID-β GENERATION

Giuseppe Verdile,[1] *Samuel E. Gandy,*[2] *Paul Fraser,*[3, 4] *Craig S. Atwood*[5] *and Ralph N. Martins*[1*]

[1] Sir James McCusker Alzheimer's Disease Research Unit,
University of Western Australia,
Department of Psychiatry,
Hollywood Private Hospital
Monash Avenue, Nedlands, WA, Australia 6009.

[2] Farber Institute for Neurosciences at Thomas Jefferson University
1015 Walnut Street
Philadelphia PA 19107

[3] Centre for Research in Neurodegenerative Diseases, and,
[4] Departments of Medical Biophysics and Medicine (Neurology)
University of Toronto, 6 Queen's Park Crescent West
Toronto, Ontario, Canada M5S 3H2

[5] Institute of Pathology
Case Western Reserve University
2085 Adelbert Rd, Cleveland, OH 44106

ABSTRACT

Mutations in the presenilin genes (PS1 and PS2) account for the majority of all autosomal dominant early onset familial Alzheimer's disease (AD) cases. The presenilin genes encode for an evolutionary conserved group of transmembrane proteins, which are

---

* Corresponding Author: Associate Professor Ralph N. Martins, University Department of Psychiatry and Neurogenetics, Hollywood Private Hospital, The University of Western Australia, Nedlands, Perth, WA6009, Australia, Tel. 618 9346 6703, Fax 618 9346 6666, Email: rmartins@cyllene.uwa.edu.au

processed into N- and C-terminal fragments that form functionally active heterodimeric complexes. These proteins are involved in cell signalling pathways including those of the unfolded protein response and apoptosis. Most attention however has focussed on their role in the proteolytic processing of the Alzheimer's amyloid-ß precursor protein (AβPP) in the pathogenesis of AD. The presenilins play a pivotal role in the production of the amyloid–β-protein (Aβ), the major component of amyloid deposits that characterize the disease. Indeed, PS1 mutations lead to the increased generation of a particularly malignant species of Aβ that accumulates in the brain. It has been shown that the multifunctional presenilin proteins regulate the intramembranous proteolysis of the C-terminal fragment of AβPP at the "γ-secretase" cleavage site, leading to the release of Aβ. Initial studies provided evidence that the presenilins were the catalytic enzymes that cleave AβPP at the γ-secretase site. However, more recent evidence indicates that γ-secretase is a multisubunit complex of which presenilins is but one key component. Recent studies have identified novel protein components of this complex, which include nicastrin, APH-1, APH-2 and PEN-2 that regulate Aβ production. Reconstitution experiments with these components should provide insight into the molecular mechanism (s) by which PS1 mediates intramembranous γ-secretase cleavage of AβPP.

Keywords: Alzheimer's disease; Amyloid precursor protein; Beta-amyloid, Presenilin, proteolytic processing; γ-Secretase, nicastrin

INTRODUCTION

Alzheimer's disease (AD) is the most common form of dementia worldwide and is neuropathologically characterised by the presence of neurofibrillary tangles and senile plaques in the brain tissue of affected individuals. While the majority of AD cases are sporadic, approximately 5% of AD cases are familial with autosomal dominant inheritance (Lendon et al. 1997). This subgroup of AD is termed Familial Alzheimer's Disease (FAD). The first pathogenic mutations were found on the amyloid precursor protein (AβPP) gene (Goate et al. 1991; Murrell et al. 1991). However, these mutations were rare as they were found only in a handful of families. Subsequently, mutations were found in two genes known as presenilin 1 and presenilin 2 (PS1 and PS2; Sherrington et al. 1995; Rogaev et al. 1995) which accounted for 50% of all early onset familial AD (EOFAD) cases. These genes encode for polytopic transmembrane proteins that are involved in a variety of cellular mechanisms including cell signaling and apoptosis.

Most attention, however, has been directed towards the role of presenilins in AD pathology. Mutations in PS1 and PS2 are associated with increased production of $A\beta_{42}$, the longer and more aggregatable form of the 4 kDa beta amyloid peptide, a key component of amyloid plaques. Subsequent research has shown that the presenilins mediate the intramembranous proteolytic cleavage of the amyloid precursor protein (AβPP), resulting in the release of the Aβ protein. An aspartyl protease termed γ-secretase catalyses this process. It was initially hypothesized that the presenilins were the catalytic components of γ-secretase, but recent findings suggest that γ-secretase is a multisubunit complex of which the presenilins are but one component. Other components of the complex, including the recently identified nicastrin, APH-1 and PEN-2 proteins, have also been shown to regulate Aβ production and γ-secretase activity. However, the mechanisms of γ-secretase cleavage mediated by these proteins are still poorly understood.

THE PRESENILINS

A Candidate Gene for EOFAD

There are at least four genetic loci, which confer inherited susceptibility to AD. Mutations in the AβPP gene on chromosome 21 have been found in a small number of families (<3% of cases) with early onset AD (Tanzi et al. 1991). Genetic linkage studies of the AD3 locus mapped to chromosome 14q24.3 (Schellenberg et al. 1992; St George-Hyslop et al. 1992). Sherrington and colleagues (1995) located the PS1 gene in two clusters of the AD3 locus. The majority of EOAD cases (50%) are caused by mutations in PS1. Another gene, located on chromosome 1q31.42, termed presenilin 2 (PS2) has been associated with AD in the Volga German kindred (Levylahad et al. 1995) and shares 67% identity with PS1. Exon trapping performed by Clark and colleagues (Clark et al. 1995), indicated that the presenilin genes are encoded by multiple exons, with intron/exon boundaries. These studies indicated that PS1 and PS2 consisted of 12 exons, of which 10 comprise the coding sequence (Sherrington et al. 1995; Prihar et al. 1996). The remaining exons, encode a 5'- untranslated region (Lendon et al. 1997). The coding sequence gives rise to two mRNA transcripts, of approximately 2.7 and 7.5 kb in size (Sherrington et al. 1995; Rogaev et al. 1995). Clark and colleagues (1995), also noticed from their exon trapping experiments that a VRSQ amino acid sequence at position 26-29, identified by Sherrington and colleagues (1995), was absent and corresponded to a gap between two exons. This led to the conclusion, that there was alternative splicing of the PS1 gene, resulting in some cDNAs containing and others lacking, the sequence coding for VRSQ. Alternative splicing of the PS2 gene resulting in the omissions of exon 3,4 and 8 has also been reported in a variety of normal tissues (Prihar et al. 1996). The functional significance of this alternative splicing is unknown. Alternate splicing of the presenilin genes can lead to detrimental effects on the protein. For example, the destruction of the splice acceptor site for exon 9 of PS1 results in the loss of this exon. This mutation (referred to as PS1Δ9) results in the removal of the protease cleavage site. Consequently, the Δ9 mutation cannot be proteolytically cleaved into its constitutive N-and C-terminal fragments (discussed below; Thinakaran et al. 1996).

Protein Structure

The PS1 holoprotein is a 467 amino acid protein (PS2 is 448), with an approximate molecular weight of 45 kDa (50 kDa for PS1). The presenilin proteins are thought to contain 6-10 helical, hydrophobic, putative, transmembrane domains linked by hydrophobic sequences, suggesting that it is a multipass integral membrane protein (Fig. 1; Sherrington et al. 1995; Doan et al. 1996; Lehmann et al. 1997; Nakai et al. 1999). Transmembrane domains (TM) 7 and 8 are linked by a long acidic loop, of relatively low conservation and variable length (Levy-Lahad et al. 1995). It has been suggested, that the acidic N- terminus (1-81), C-terminus and the acidic loop (262-408) are located towards the cytoplasm (Fig. 1a; Doan et al. 1996; Lehmann et al. 1997). However, evidence has been presented for the C-terminal end facing the lumen (Fig. 1b; Nakai et al. 1999). Furthermore, in another model, the eighth and ninth transmembrane domains may not span the membrane; with the ninth domain tightly bound to the lipid membrane (Fig. 1b; Nakai et al. 1999). Nakai and colleagues (1999) suggested, that subpopulations of molecules having C-terminus facing the lumen could co-exist physiologically. This raises the possibility, that these different models may have distinct functions. The C-terminal region of PS1 and PS2 has been shown to interact with many proteins (Tesco et al. 1998a; Passer et al. 1999). Thus, it is possible that the C-terminal region may interact with distinct cellular factors that are located in the cytosol or lumenal space of the ER (Nakai et al. 1999). Interaction of the PS1 and PS2 C-terminal region with these cellular factors may determine the ratio of the two postulated presenilin models within the cell (Nakai et al. 1999). If this is the case, interactions with other factors may influence conversion of one form into another. This sort of alternative topology has been reported for SecA, a component of the *E.coli* translocase complex (Nishiyama et al. 1996). It is important to note that all of these topology studies have used cells over-expressing presenilins. It will therefore be important to determine if under physiological conditions these models reflect the native structure of PS1.

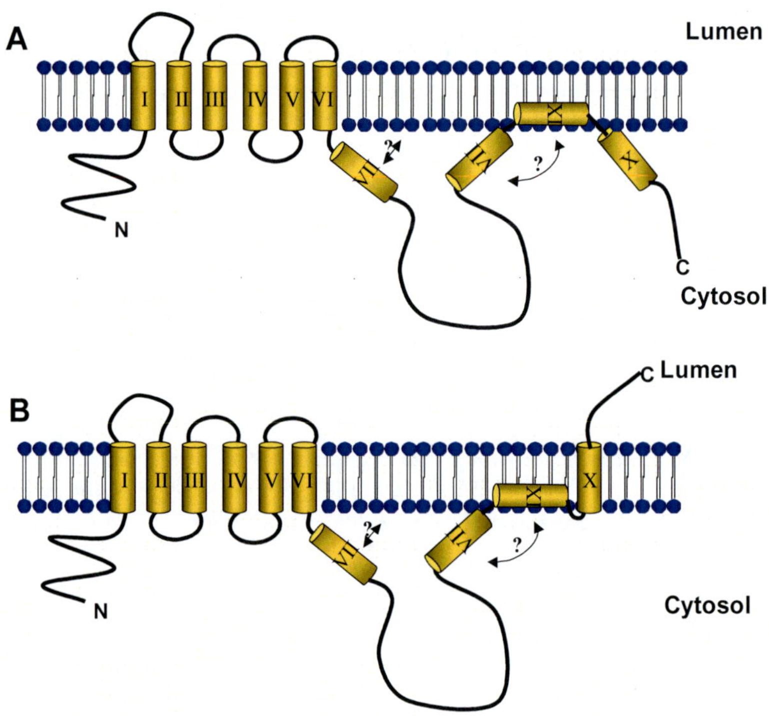

Figure 1: A schematic of the putative structures of PS1. (A) Proposed PS1 structure (Doan et al. 1996); (Lehmann et al. 1997) showing the acidic N-terminus, the C-terminus and the acidic loop (262-408), located towards the cytoplasm. (B) Alternative PS1 structure proposal (Nakai et al. 1999), showing C-terminal end facing the lumenal side of the membrane. In both models the seventh, eighth and ninth transmembrane domains do not span the membrane, although the ninth domain is tightly bound to the lipid membrane.

The presenilin proteins share an overall homology of 67% with the highest similarities in the predicted transmembrane domains. Fewer similarities are found at the N-terminus and in the central region of the hydrophilic loop where PS2 is 24 amino acid residues shorter (Levylahad et al. 1995; Rogaev et al. 1995). The high sequence homology between PS1 and PS2 does however suggest that these proteins may have similar biological functions.

The topology of the presenilin proteins suggests that they are either an integral membrane protein (such as a receptor), a channel protein or a structural membrane protein. The PS1 protein has homology with *Caenerhabiditis elegans* sperm integral membrane proteins SPE-4 (approximately 26% identity) and SEL-12 (approximately 50% identity; (Levitan et al. 1995). The SPE-4 protein plays a role in the membrane trafficking of specialised Golgi-derived organelles, found within spermatocytes of *C.elegans* (L'Hernault & Arduengo 1992). The similarity between SPE-4 and PS1 would suggest that PS1 might play a role in membrane trafficking. The SEL-12 protein facilitates the signaling of lin-12, which is known to be a member of the Notch family of receptors and is involved in signal transmission from the cell surface to the nucleus (L'Hernault & Arduengo 1992). The SEL-12 protein has a higher sequence homology to PS1, and appears to be the *C. elegans* PS1 homologue (Levitan & Greenwald, 1995). Interestingly, most of the mutations in PS1 occur at positions that are conserved in the sel-12 gene. This high degree of homology between PS1 and SEL-12 suggests that these proteins may have similar functions. For example, PS1 may function to modulate receptors at the cell surface in order to regulate signal transduction to the nucleus (Haass, 1996). The PS1 protein also has similarities to portions of several other membrane spanning proteins, including mammalian chromogranin A and the α-subunit of mammalian voltage-dependent calcium channel (Sherrington et al. 1995). These similarities raise the possibility that PS1 may also be involved in Ca^{+2} homeostasis.

Expression and Localisation

The expression profiles of PS1 and PS2 in human tissues are dissimilar. The expression of PS1 is ubiquitous, with mRNA transcripts detected in the brain and most peripheral tissues. In contrast, the expression of PS2 transcripts in the brain is low, except in the corpus callosum where it is high. PS2 is highly expressed in some peripheral tissues including the pancreas, heart and skeletal muscle (Rogaev et al. 1997). The low levels of PS2 and the compensatory activity provided by PS1 in the brain may account for the infrequency and incomplete penetrance of PS2 mutations compared to highly penetrant PS1 mutations, in which to date number over 100 FAD cases.

In the brain, expression of presenilins is primarily neuronal. In particular, PS1 expression has been reported in neuronal populations most susceptible to AD pathology, such as regions of the cerebral cortex and the hippocampus (Mattson et al. 1998). Other areas of neuronal PS1 expression include the thalamus, locus coeruleus and the olfactory bulb (Mattson et al. 1998). The presenilins have been reported to be predominantly expressed within the somatodentric compartments of neurons, with low levels found in axons, though more PS2 is expressed in the axons compared to PS1 (Capell et al. 1997). Immunohistochemical analysis confirmed neuronal localisation of the presenilins (Kovacs et al. 1996). Kovacs and colleagues (1996) showed that FAD associated mutations in PS1 or PS2 do not significantly modify either the migration pattern on SDS-PAGE or the subcellular localisation of this protein. Uchihara and colleagues (1996) demonstrated that PS1 and PS2 immunoreactivity was decreased in NFT bearing neurons and in neuritic plaques compared with undamaged neurons, indicating that the levels of the presenilins might be altered as a response to AD pathology.

Immunocytochemical analysis of cultured neuronal and non-neuronal cells showed that the presenilins are localised to subcellular compartments, with high levels found in the ER (Cook et al. 1996; Guo et al. 1996; Kovacs et al. 1996; Lah et al., 1997). There was also immunochemical staining within the Golgi complex (Kovacs et al. 1996). Culvenor and colleagues (Culvenor et al. 1997) showed that PS1 and PS2 are resident proteins of the ER-Golgi intermediate compartment (ERGIC). Evidence has been provided to show that Golgi-type vesicles contain principally the endoproteolytic fragments of PS1 and PS2, which are thought to be the biologically active forms (Xia et al. 1998; Zhang et al. 1998a). These findings suggest that the presenilins may be involved in vesicular trafficking, between the ER and the Golgi apparatus.

Processing

Constitutive Processing

Thinakaran and colleagues (1996a) initially reported that the 45 kDa PS1 holoprotein was endoproteolytically processed into 27-28 kDa N-terminal fragments and 16-17 kDa C-terminal fragments. Subsequent studies reported that PS2 is processed into larger 34 kDa N-terminal fragments and 20 kDa C-terminal fragments (Kim et al. 1997b; Podlisny et al. 1997). These fragments are the predominant fragments in the brains of rodents, primates, and humans. Proteolytic cleavage of PS1 into its N- and C-terminal fragments was found in all human tissue examined including the cerebral cortices, lungs, spleen, pancreas, and testes (Lee et al. 1996; Okochi et al. 1998). In transgenic mice expressing human PS1, the PS1 fragments accumulated to saturable levels at 1:1 stoichiometry, independent of the level of transgene mRNA (Thinakaran et al. 1996a). These findings indicated that full-length PS1 levels were increased upon over-expression of PS1, while the amount of PS1 fragments remained stable. This suggests that the proteolytic processing of the presenilins is highly regulated, allowing only a small amount of the holoprotein to be utlilised for the generation of N- and C- terminal fragments. The proteolytic processing of PS1 and PS2, into N- and C-terminal fragments, occurs in the proximal portion of the large hydrophilic loop between residues Thr291 and Ala 299 (Podlisny et al. 1997). The N-and C- terminal fragments oligomerize, either before or after cleavage to form a heterodimeric complex (Capell et al. 1998).

The PS1 C-terminal fragment has been reported to be phosphorylated at its serine residues by protein kinase C (PKC; Seeger et al. 1997; Walter et al. 1997b), 1998). This, in turn, resulted in a shift in the electromobility of the C-terminal fragment, from 18 kDa to 20-23 kDa. While PKC activation resulted in the phosphorylation of the C-terminal fragment of PS1, it had no effect on PS1 that lacked the region coded for by exon 9 (Walter et al. 1997b). One explanation for this finding is that the phosphorylation site is located in this cleaved region (Walter et al. 1996, 1997b, 1998). The PS2 C-terminal fragment is also phosphorylated. However, unlike the PKC mediated phosphorylation of PS1, PS2 is constitutively phosphorylated by the serine/threonine protein kinase Casein kinase 1 and 2 (CK-1 and CK-2; Walter et al. 1998). The physiological significance of the selective phosphorylation of the C-terminal fragment is unknown. However, it should be noted that AβPP is phosphorylated, within its ectodomain, by CK 1 and 2 like ectoprotein kinases (Walter et al. 2000). In addition, PKC stimulates the non-amyloidogenic pathway of AβPP processing (Caporaso et al. 1992), increasing the amount of αAβPPs and decreasing Aβ production (Buxbaum et al. 1993; Hung et al. 1993). It could be speculated that the phosphorylation of the PS1 or PS2-CTF may directly influence the processing of AβPP by the non-amyloidogenic pathway. However, since Aβ generation is reduced by PKC activation even in rodent cells where PS1 cannot be phosphorylated (Seeger et al., 1997), there is no obvious important phosphorylation role for PS1 in regulating the effect of PKC.

Proteolytic Cleavage of the Presenilins by Caspases

The constitutive cleavage of the presenilins is thought to be by a putative protease, termed "presenilinase". Although, this protease has not been identified, caspases have been shown to cleave PS1, albeit at alternative sites to the constitutive cleavage sites (Loetscher et al. 1997; Kim et al. 1997b; van de Craen et al. 1999; Grunberg et al. 1998). Kim and colleagues (1997b) found that during apoptosis, PS1 and PS2 were cleaved at sites distal to their normal cleavage sites, by the caspase-3 family protease. This cleavage gave rise to alternative fragments, comprising of a 24 kDa (34 kDa PS2) N- and 14 kDa (20 kDa PS2) C-terminal fragments. Loetscher and colleagues (1997) isolated and sequenced these alternative C-terminal fragments from PS1 and PS2 transfected 293 cells and thus identified the alternative processing sites in PS1 and PS2 at Asp 345/Ser346 and Asp 329/330, respectively. It has been reported that a number of caspases can proteolytically cleave the presenilins. Van de Craen and colleagues (1999) demonstrated that PS1 and PS2 are substrates for different members of the caspase family, which are subdivided into two groups. One group, containing caspase 8, 6 and 11, cleaved PS1 after residue 329 (corresponding to the ENDD motif) and, to a lesser extent, after residue 341 (corresponding to the AQRD motif). A second group, consisting of caspase 3, 7 and 1, only cleaved PS1 after residue 341. Caspase 8, 3, 6 and 7 cleaved PS2 at the recognition site D326SYD329. However, caspases 8 and 3 exhibited the highest proteolytic activity on PS2, which were also the caspases with the highest potency for PS1. Of all the caspases tested, caspase 2 had no effect on either PS1 or PS2. Overall, these studies indicate caspases can proteolytically cleave PS1 and PS2 distal to the constitutive cleavage sites.

This activity of caspases appears to be regulated by the phosphorylation state of presenilins. Walter and colleagues (1999) demonstrated that phosphorylation of the PS2 C-terminal fragment adjacent to the cleavage sites of caspases (Asp 326/329) inhibits PS2 cleavage by caspase 3 (Walter et al. 1999). Furthermore, calsenilin, a novel neuronal calcium binding protein that interacts with PS1 and PS2, regulates the proteolytic processing of PS2 by caspases (Buxbaum et al. 1998) and preferentially binds the ~ 20 kDa PS2 caspase derived C-terminal fragment (Choi et al. 2001). Although the significance of cleavage of PS2 by caspases remains unknown, it does suggest that this process is a regulated biological event that occurs physiologically. The presenilin C-terminal fragments themselves have also been shown to be substrates for caspases, producing a smaller 10 kDa fragment (Grunberg et al. 1998; Steiner et al. 1998). Collectively, these studies indicate that both PS1 and PS2 are cleaved by caspases, and their products could be functionally relevant during apoptosis.

Caspases are an integral part of the apoptotic pathway, involved in the activation of many proteins during apoptosis. Apoptosis is a form of cell death, in which the cells shrink and exhibit nuclear chromatin condensation and DNA fragmentation (for recent review see Annunziato et al. 2003). Aβ has been shown to induce apoptosis in cell culture experiments (Loo et al. 1993; Mattson et al. 1997; Chan et al., 1999). Using similar cell culture models, further studies have shown that mutations in PS1 and PS2 enhance the apoptotic activity induced by Aβ, compared to wild-type PS1 and PS2 (Guo et al. 1996; Wolozin et al. 1996; Guo et al. 1997). Given that Aβ induced apoptosis is increased in cells with PS1 and PS2 mutations, it is conceivable that this enhanced effect is mediated by an interaction between the presenilins and caspases.

Kim and colleagues (1997b) reported that the ratio of alternative to normal PS2 C-terminal fragments was increased in the PS2 mutant (N141I) cells, relative to wild-type cells. Kovacs and colleagues (1996) showed caspase activation led to the increased generation of alternative PS1 C-terminal fragments, in neuroglioma cells expressing PS1 mutants (A246V, L286V, and Δ9) compared to cells expressing wild-type PS1. Furthermore, staurosporine-induced activation of caspase-3 was increased 10-fold in cells expressing the PS1 mutations, compared to those expressing wild-type PS1 (Kovacs et al. 1996). This report provides strong evidence for the notion that PS1 mutations enhance caspase activity.

In contrast to the aforementioned reports, van de Craen and colleagues (1999) assessed the relative sensitivities of wild-type and mutant PS1 to caspase cleavage, using a specific caspase cleavage assay that involved the addition of radiolabelled human PS1 to murine active caspase. The results showed that none of the 5 missense mutations (Y115C, I143F, I143T, E318G, G384A), affected the sensitivity of PS1 to caspase-mediated cleavage, compared to wild-type PS1. In this report, purified caspase was used to cleave PS1, whilst Kovacs and colleagues (1996) activated caspases by inducing apoptosis with staurosporine. Thus, the increased ratio of alternative C-terminal fragments associated with PS1 mutations in the Kovacs study may be in response to another factor induced by staurosporine, which may selectively influence mutant PS1. Whether this process is linked to caspase action remains to be determined.

Caspases have also been shown to cleave AβPP within the intracytoplasmic tail, at a site C-terminal from the constitutive cleavage sites (after Asp^{664} using $A\beta PP_{695}$ numbering; (Pellegrini et al. 1999; Weidemann et al. 1999; Gervais et al. 1999; LeBlanc et al. 1999; Lu et al. 2000; Soriano et al. 2001; Bertrand et al. 2001). The caspase mediated processing of AβPP results in the formation of a cytotoxic C-terminal fragment (C31) and increases the rate of Aβ peptide formation in apoptotic neuronal cells (Gervais et al. 1999; Lu et al. 2000). These studies suggest that the production of cytotoxic fragments and enhanced Aβ formation as a result of caspase cleavage exacerbates apoptosis within the cell. However in contrast to the above reports, a recent study has shown that masking the caspase cleavage by site directed mutagenesis did not affect Aβ levels (Soriano et al. 2001). This study indicates that caspase cleavage at the Asp^{664} site directly does not result in Aβ formation during apoptosis. However, this report does not rule out the possibility that the production of the cytotoxic fragments can exacerbate apoptosis, which in turn enhances the production of Aβ (LeBlanc et al. 1999; Galli et al. 1998). This process could be exacerbated by PS1 or PS2 mutations. The finding that products generated from caspase cleavage were augmented in cells over-expressing PS2 mutations compared to wild-type PS2, provided evidence for this notion (Weidemann et al. 1999). Collectively, these studies suggest that PS2 (or PS1) mutations could enhance caspase activity during apoptosis, which in turn increases the formation of cytotoxic AβPP fragments. The production of these fragments may exacerbate apoptosis resulting in increased Aβ production. Further work is required to determine the role of PS1/PS2 mutations in the production of cytotoxic AβPP fragments and the generation of Aβ during apoptosis.

Degradation of the Presenilins by the Proteasome

It is now well established that the presenilin holoproteins have a short half-life, indicating that they are rapidly processed (Ratovitski et al. 1997; Podlisny et al. 1997). This rapid processing of PS1 and PS2 is known to involve the 26S proteasome (Kim et al. 1997a; Fraser et al. 1998; Steiner et al. 1998). The 26S proteasome is a multicatalytic enzyme, involved in the degradation of homeostatic enzymes, misfolded proteins and other cellular proteins. The proteasome consists of the catalytic 20S core and a 19S cap and is an integral part of the ubiquitin mediated degradation pathway. Although it has been established that full-length PS1 or PS2 is degraded by the proteasome, the degradation of the N-and C-terminal fragments of the presenilins via this pathway remains controversial. Honda and colleagues (1999) reported an increase in N- terminal fragments (with no change in C-terminal fragments), upon inhibiting proteasome activity in SHY5Y and 293 cells, stably transfected with wild type or mutant PS1. In contrast, da Costa and colleagues (1999) reported an increase in C-terminal fragments with protease inhibitor treatment of HEK-293 cells stably transfected with PS1 or PS2. However, these authors did not present data on the effects of inhibiting proteasome activity on N-terminal fragment generation. In complete contrast to the previous reports, Steiner and colleagues (1998) reported that both the N- and C-terminal fragments remained stable upon inhibiting proteasome activity in HEK-293 cells over-expressing wild-type PS1. However, Steiner and colleagues (1998) did observe that those N-terminal fragments not incorporated into the PS1 heterodimeric complex are rapidly degraded by the proteasome. It is possible that the changes seen by Honda et al. (1999) and da Costa et al. (1999) could represent excess fragments not incorporated into the heterodimeric complex but their assays did not distinguish between non-incorporated N-terminal fragments and those present in the heterodimeric complex. Van Gassen and colleagues (1999) have proposed a mechanism by which the proteasome could degrade the presenilins. These authors used interaction trap screening and co-immunoprecipitation to show that PS1 interacts with HC5 and ZETA subunits of the 20S proteasome, the catalytic unit of the 26S proteasome

Consistent with the above reports excess full-length PS1 (that is not processed into N- and C- terminal fragments) is rapidly degraded into small peptides by the proteasome. This suggests that there are two pathways that constitutively process PS1, the "presenilinase" pathway, resulting in the generation of N- and C- terminal fragments, and the proteasome pathway, resulting in the degradation of PS1. Within the cell, a tight balance could exist, between "presenilinase" processing and incorporation into the stable complex, and the proteolytic degradation of excess PS1. Mutations in PS1 could alter how PS1 is distributed between the 2 alternative pathways especially if mutations result in improper folding of the protein or accumulation of the holoprotein.

It has been proposed in the literature that PS1 mutations can interfere with protein folding, in particular the unfolded protein response (UPR; Katayama et al. 1999). The UPR is an intracellular signaling pathway, connecting the ER with the nucleus (for recent review see Kaufman 2002). It has been proposed that cells respond to the accumulation of unfolded proteins in the lumen of the ER, by activating transcription of genes involved in protein folding such as the molecular chaperone 78 kDa glucose-regulated protein precursor/immunoglobulin heavy chain binding protein (GRP78/BiP; reviewed in Kaufman 2002). In a series of *in vitro* experiments involving cells expressing mutant PS1, Katayama and colleagues (1999), found that inducing ER stress with the protein glycosylation inhibitor tunicamycin, failed to induce GRP78/BiP. Furthermore, the authors reported a 75% decrease of GRP78/BiP levels in brain homogenates from FAD patients harboring PS1 mutations. This failure of GRP78 induction was suggested to be due to mutant PS1 interfering with the autophosphorylation of the sensor molecule, interferon response element 1 (IRE1). IRE1 is a transmembrane protein with both serine kinase activity and endoribonuclease activity and is responsible for initiating the UPR (Tirasophon et al. 1998; Wang et al. 1998; reviewed in Kaufman 2002). The failure of UPR induction and thus activation of the molecular chaperones to facilitate protein folding, may lead to the accumulation of misfolded or unfolded protein. These proteins become multi-ubiquitinated and are then targeted for proteasome degradation. However, the amount of multi-ubiquitinated protein may exceed the capacity of the proteasome and, therefore, may aggregate in an ultrastructural complex, called the aggresome (Johnston et al. 1998) resulting in cellular stress.

A second role for the UPR pathway is to suppress protein translation during ER stress (Harding et al. 1999; Harding et al. 2000). It has been suggested that during ER stress, reduced protein synthesis can serve to reduce the load of substrates presented to the folding machinery in the ER (Yasuda et al. 2002). RNA-dependent protein kinase (PKR) -like ER kinase (PERK) is an ER stress transducer that may play a role in the UPR mediated inhibition of translation. PERK is a protein serine /theronine kinase that is activated through transphosphorylation in response to ER stress. Once activated, PERK phosphorylates the α-subunit of translation initiation factor 2 (eIF2α), which results in the inhibition of translation initiation (Harding et al. 1999, Harding et al. 2000; Bertolotti et al. 2000).

Impaired phosphorylation (and thus reduced activity) of PERK and subsequent reduction in levels of phosphorylated eIF2α, has been observed in both neuroblastoma cells overexpressing PS1 mutations and in skin fibroblasts from PS1 mutant knock in mice treated with thapsigargin to induce ER stress (Katayama et al. 1999; Yasuda et al. 2002). Inactivation of PERK results in impaired phosphorylation (and reduced activity) of eIF2α leading to disruption of protein synthesis, ultimately impeding cell survival. It remains unclear how mutant PS1 impairs the activation of PERK, however a clue is provided from a study proposing that PERK could be triggered by its dissociation from the molecular chaperone that facilitates protein folding GRP/Bip (Bertolotti et al. 2000). If mutations in PS1 result in misfolding of the protein, GRP/Bip may bind to mutant PS1 molecules in an attempt to promote their proper folding. The formation of a complex between misfolded PS1 mutant molecules, GRP/Bip and PERK may prevent the dissociation of PERK from GRP/Bip and subsequent inactivation of the PERK signaling pathway. However, it is conceivable that wild type PS1 may bind to the GRP/Bip-PERK complex. Thus, the binding specificities of wild-type and mutant PS1 molecules to the GRP/Bip-PERK complex will be required to, elucidate mechanisms for perturbed PERK function by PS1 mutations.

One report has contradicted the above findings. Sato and colleagues (2000), reported no changes in steady state protein, or mRNA levels, for GRP78/BiP and the UPR transcription factor, CCAAT/enhancer core binding protein-homologous protein (CHOP), from PS1-/+ and PS1 -/- skin fibroblasts. Similar results were observed under UPR induction with the N-glycosylation inhibitor, tunicamycin. Comparable results were also observed with immortalized blastocyst-derived cells, from PS1/PS2 double knockouts and wild-type mice embryos, ruling out the possibility of a compensatory effect from PS2. The authors also found no changes in levels of the IRE1 mammalian homologues (IRE1α and IRE1β), in the PS1-/+, PS1 -/- and double knockout cells, following induction of the UPR with the protein glycosylation inhibitor, tunicamycin or the calcium ATPase inhibitor, thapsigargin. Similar results were observed when levels of PERK were measured, following UPR induction. Interestingly, no changes in UPR marker proteins were observed in N2a, HEK-293 cells, stably transfected with PS1 mutations, or in transgenic mouse and human brain homogenates, harboring PS1 mutations (Sato et al. 2000).

Differences between these two reports might have arisen from variation in experimental design between the studies. For example, Niwa and colleagues (1999) derived conclusions from a single analysis of BiP mRNA induction in PS1-/- and PS1-/+ skin fibroblasts. In contrast, Sato and colleagues (2000) used primary PS1-/- and PS1-/+ fibroblasts, at second or third passage and performed several analyses of independent markers of UPR. In addition, Sato and colleagues (2000) also used double knockouts, ruling out the possibility of a compensatory effect of PS2 in PS1 knockout cells. Although the report by Sato and colleagues (2000) provides strong evidence that markers of the UPR are not altered by the lack of PS1 or PS1 mutations, it does not rule out the possibility that alterations in ER stress signaling by PS1 mutations may be driven by mechanisms distinct from the classical UPR pathway.

Recently, Mah and colleagues (2000) have described an interaction between a novel protein, termed ubiquilin, and PS1. Ubiquilin contains multiple ubiquitin-related domains and hence is thought to be involved in targeting proteins for proteasomal degradation (Mah et al. 2000). However the authors noticed that ubiquilin increased presenilin protein maturation without increasing protein turnover, resulting in an increase in the intracellular pool of PS1. This suggests that ubiquilin could increase presenilin synthesis by increasing transcription, translation or facilitating correct protein folding and maturation of presenilin proteins.

Presenilins - The Multifunctional Proteins

The presenilins are multifunctional proteins and have been shown to bind numerous proteins, including molecules involved in intracellular signaling (ie, UPR pathway described above), suggesting that it is an integral part of the intracellular signaling pathways. The ultimate result of some of these pathways is the activation of gene transcription. One such pathway is the Wnt-signaling pathway. A key mediator of this pathway is β-catenin. Upon activation of the pathway, β-catenin translocates to the nucleus, activating transcription (for recent review see Hendriks et al. 2002). Yu and colleagues (Yu et al. 1998) have shown that PS1 and β-catenin are components of a 250 kDa membrane-bound complex, mostly found in the ER and Golgi. Subsequently, the C-terminus of PS1 has been shown, by co-immunoprecipitation, to interact with β-catenin (Murayama et al. 1998; Tesco et al. 1998b). Interestingly, over-expression of PS1 reduced the levels of cytoplasmic β-catenin and inhibited β-catenin T cell factor regulated transcription (Murayama et al. 1998). Furthermore, the inducible over-expression of PS1 led to increased association of β-catenin with GSK-3β, which initiates the degradation of β-catenin, resulting in the accelerated turnover of β-catenin (Kang et al. 1999). In addition, the turnover rate of β-catenin in skin fibroblasts from PS1-/- mice was lower than that observed for fibroblasts from PS1wt mice. The turnover rate of β-catenin was returned to normal upon transfection of PS1, confirming that β-catenin degradation is mediated by PS1. These studies indicate a role for PS1 as an inhibitor of β-catenin signaling.

Nishimura and colleagues (1999) used immunofluorescence studies to show that upon activating the Wnt-signaling pathway with lithium ions, β-catenin translocated to the nucleus in skin fibroblasts from normal individuals. However β-catenin did not translocate to the nucleus upon activation of skin fibroblasts from FAD patients harboring the PS1 mutations M146L, H163R, A260V, and L286V. This study indicates that PS1 mutations alter the normal trafficking of β-catenin. A subsequent study showed that in cells overexpressing mutant PS1, GSK-3β was not incorporated into the PS1-β-catenin complex, resulting in increased steady state levels of β-catenin (Kang et al. 1999). These studies provided strong evidence that PS1 modulates β-catenin signals, although the finding that β-catenin translocation still occurs in skin fibroblasts from PS1-/- cells indicates that PS1 is not an absolute requirement for β-catenin translocation. This, in turn, could lead to the notion that the increased Aβ production characteristic of PS1 mutations could be due to activation of transcription, through β-catenin, of those molecules involved in AβPP metabolism, perhaps γ-secretase. However, a recent report has shown that γ-secretase inhibitors did not effect the β-catenin/PS1 interaction (Meredith et al. 2002). This report confirms that the presenilins are multifunctional proteins and suggest that PS1 and PS2 have distinct functions that are separate from that of Aβ production. PS1 and PS2 also interact with other proteins that share homology with β-catenin, including δ-catenin (Tanahashi et al. 1999) and the neural- specific plakophilin-related protein (NPRAP; Tanahashi & Tabira 1999; Levesque et al. 1999). Interactions with these proteins could lead to transcriptional activation of genes in a similar manner to β-catenin activated transcription.

β-Catenin also plays an important role in cell-cell adhesion. β-Catenin has been shown to mediate cell-cell adhesion through interactions with cadherins (Aberle et al. 1994; Jou et al. 1995). Cadherins, of which E and N-cadherins have been well studied, are a family of type 1 membrane proteins that mediate Ca^{+2}-dependent cell-cell adhesions and recognition, and control of critical events in neurogenesis, tissue development and tissue homeostasis (Gumbiner 2000; Yagi et al. 2000).

PS1 has been reported to concentrate at synaptic and epithelial cell-cell contacts (Georgakopoulos et al. 1999) where it forms complexes with the cadherin/catenin adhesion system (Georgakopoulos et al. 1999; Baki et al. 2001). Furthermore, PS1 interacts with actin binding filaments (Zhang et al. 1998b; Schwarzman et al. 1999), which are known to link cell surface receptors with the cytoskeleton (reviewed in Carpenter 2000). In a recent report, Baki and colleagues (2001) have shown PS1 to regulate the molecular composition and function of the cadherin-catenin complex through several mechanisms. Firstly, PS1 was shown to displace p120, a cytosolic protein shown to regulate cadherin mediated cell-cell adhesion (for review see Anastasiadis et al. 2001), from E-cadherin. Furthermore, PS1 has been shown to stabilise the binding of β-catenin and γ-catenin to E-cadherins. This, in turn, increases the linkage of the cadherin/catenin complex to the cytoskeleton, simulating Ca^{+2} and cadherin-dependent cell- cell aggregation.

Other intracellular pathways that may be involved in the AD pathology associated with PS1 mutations include those involved in cell fate. Imafuku and colleagues (1999) used the yeast two-hybrid system to show that the QM/Jun interacting factor (Jif)-1 interacted with PS1. This interacting factor is a negative regulator of c-Jun, which mediates transcriptional regulation for a variety of stimulants (Imafuku et al. 1999). This suggests that the PS1-Jif 1 interaction results in a cascade of events leading to cell survival or death (i.e. apoptosis), depending on the final effect of c-Jun. In support of this report, PS1 has been shown, by co-immunoprecipitation and cross-linking studies, to directly interact with a key factor in the regulation of apoptosis, Bcl-2, (Alberici et al. 1999). Interestingly, Passer and colleagues (1999) showed that the C-terminus of both PS1 and PS2 interacts with Bcl-X-L, an anti-apoptotic member of the Bcl-2 family. These studies suggest that the presenilins are an integral member of intracellular signaling pathways involved in cell fate. Mutations in PS1 or PS2 could interact inappropriately with apoptotic molecules, thereby enhancing cell death by apoptosis. Conversely, wild-type PS1or PS2 could interact with anti-apoptotic molecules to promote cell survival. Further studies are required to determine if these molecules have differing affinities for wild type or mutant presenilins.

PS1 interacts with the highly conserved adaptor molecules X11 and X11L, (Lau et al. 2000). The X11 family of proteins contains one phosphotyrosine-interacting domain and two PDZ [(**P**ostsynaptic densityprotein-95, the Drosophila septate junction protein **D**isks-large and epithelial tight junction protein **ZO**-1) domains, reviewed in McLoughlin et al. 1998]. This domain has been shown to interact with AβPP (Lau et al. 2000), as well as with other proteins including the synaptic cell surface protein neurexin (Biederer et al. 2000). The significance of the interaction with PS1 is yet to be elucidated. However, since these molecules have been shown to regulate AβPP processing and to alter Aβ generation (Sastre et al. 1998; Tomita et al. 1999; Lee et al. 2000; Ho et al. 2002), it is conceivable that X11 or X11L may play a role in the AβPP processing. The X11 family of proteins are but only one group of molecules that have been shown to interact with the presenilins and regulate Aβ generation. Others include the XB51 protein which has been shown to regulate the interaction between X11L and APP and enhance the generation of Aβ (Lee et al., 2000). An ER resident membrane protein; referred to as HERP that has been shown to enhance presenilin mediated Aβ generation (Sai et al., 2002). A protein referred to as XB51 been shown to regulate the interaction between X11L and AβPP and enhancing the generation of Aβ (Lee et al., 2000).

Most focus, however, has been on the components of the γ-secretase complex (nicastrin, APH-1 and PEN-2) that interact with the presenilins and are necessary for presenilin-mediated generation of Aβ. Presenilin mediated generation of Aβ and the role of nicastrin, APH-1 and PEN-2 are discussed below.

THE PRESENILINS AND BETA-AMYLOID PRODUCTION

Beta Amyloid (Aβ)

The major protein component found in amyloid deposits is a 4 kDa amyloid-β-protein (Glenner et al. 1984; Masters et al. 1985). The term β reflects its partial β-pleated sheet structure. The 4 kDa Aβ peptide is a proteolytic product of a much larger ~100-130 kDa protein, called the amyloid precursor protein (AβPP). Complete sequencing of Aβ shows that it consists of 40 to 43 amino acid residues, of which 28 residues at the N-terminus of Aβ are extracellular and the remaining 15 residues are located within the transmembrane domain (Fig. 2A; Esch et al. 1990). Twelve amino acid residues at the C-terminus of the Aβ protein are hydrophobic (Fig. 2A) and confer on this protein the ability to self-aggregate and polymerise into amyloid fibrils (Masters et al. 1985; Martins et al. 1991).

Two main forms of Aβ can be distinguished by electrophoresis (Klafki et al. 1996b), the shorter, forty amino acid $A\beta_{40}$ species, and the longer, forty-two amino acid $A\beta_{42}$ species. The $A\beta_{40}$ form accounts for ~ 90% of all Aβ normally released from cells and it appears to contribute only to later phases of the disease pathology (Dovey et al. 1993; Asami-Odaka et al. 1995). The $A\beta_{42}$ form only accounts for ~10% of secreted Aβ, however it is the predominant form found in the amyloid plaques of AD (Iwatsubo et al. 1994; Lippa et al. 1998). Its pathogenecity relates to its readiness to aggregate and ability to polymerise into amyloid fibrils (Burdick et al. 1992; Hensley et al. 1994). The mechanisms by which the proteolytic cleavage of AβPP generates Aβ, including whether this process is mediated by two different enzymes or a single enzyme remains to be determined.

Proteolytic Processing of Amyloid Precursor Protein

The immature form of AβPP undergoes N-glycosylation and is localised within the endoplasmic reticulum and *cis*-Golgi. The subsequent phosphorylation of serine (655) and threonine (654,668) residues, sulfation of tyrosine and the addition of further sugar groups (O-glycosylation), including sialic acid, gives rise to the mature form of AβPP (Weidemann et al. 1989; Schubert et al. 1989; Oltersdorf et al. 1990; Pahlsson et al. 1992; Knops et al. 1993; Graebert et al. 1995; Pahlsson et al. 1996; Oishi et al. 1997; Walter et al. 1997a; Tomita et al. 1998). To date it is not known whether these additional modifications occur in the ER or on route to post Golgi compartments, including the *trans* Golgi network, plasma membrane, or endosomes/lysosomes where AβPP is rapidly proteolytically cleaved (Sambamurti et al. 1992; De Strooper et al. 1993; Kuentzel et al. 1993; Refolo et al. 1995; Thinakaran et al. 1996b; Tomita et al. 1998).

The majority of mature AβPP is proteolytically cleaved by two competing pathways, the non-amyloidogenic and amyloidogenic pathways (reviewed in Nunan et al. 2000; Selkoe 2001). The non-amyloidogenic pathway can be regulated through phosphorylation processes, mediated by protein kinase C [PKC] (Buxbaum et al. 1993; Gillespie et al. 1992; Demaerschalck et al. 1993; Slack et al. 1993; Loffler et al. 1993; Caporaso et al. 1992). However, AβPP can also be proteolytically cleaved via a 'constitutive' non- amyloidogenic pathway, which is not modulated by PKC (Esch et al. 1990). How the non-amyloidogenic and amyloidogenic pathways are regulated is not fully understood. The relative utilisation of the two pathways maybe determined by neurotransmitter and hormone status (Jaffe et al., 1994; Nitsch and Growdon, 1994 Gandy and Petanceska, 2001). However, the levels and activation states of the enzymes involved in the proteolytic cleavage of AβPP, termed 'secretases' may also influence processing via either pathway. There are postulated to be 3 major secretases (or secretase classes) that cleave AβPP. These include α-secretase (TACE/ADAM 17 and ADAM 10 have been shown to be candidates), beta-site AβPP cleaving enzyme [BACE] (formerly known as β-secretase) and γ-secretase (Fig. 2 C and D). The α-secretase cleaves within the Aβ domain of AβPP, to release soluble carboxyl-truncated forms of AβPP (α-AβPPs), which include the first 16 amino acid residues of Aβ. The remnant C-terminal proteolytic products are further cleaved by γ-secretase to yield non-amyloidogenic fragments (Fig. 2 A). In an alternative pathway, BACE cleaves near the N-terminus of Aβ and produces another soluble form of AβPP (βAβPPs) and a potentially amyloidogenic, C-terminal fragment containing the whole Aβ domain. Cleavage of this C-terminal fragment by γ-secretase is the final step in Aβ production (Fig. 2 B). This processing of the AβPP C-terminal fragment by γ-secretase is mediated by the presenilins.

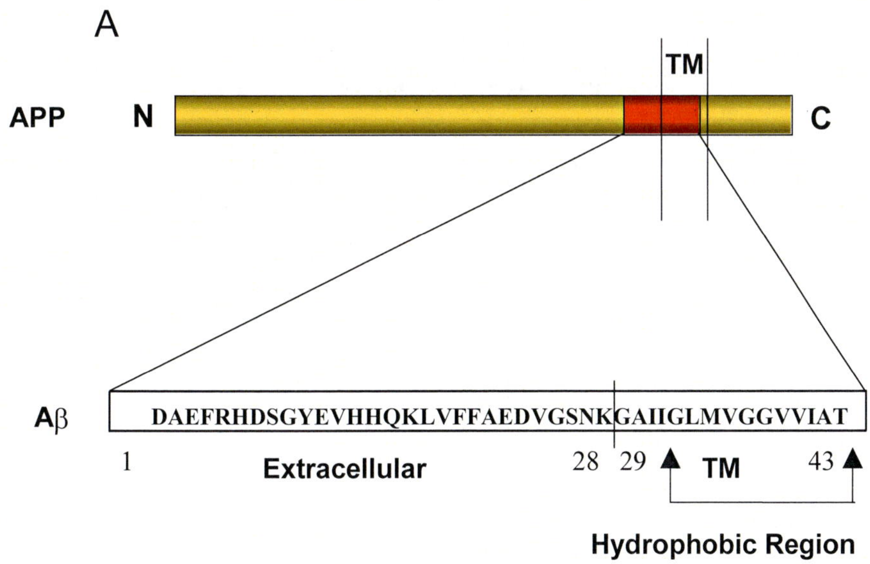

Figure 2A: The amino acid sequence of Aβ and its location within APP. The Aβ peptide is composed of 40-43 amino acids (enclosed sequence), 28 of which are extracellular and the remainder are within the transmembrane (TM) domain. Twelve amino acids are hydrophobic (arrows), and confer on this molecule the ability to self-aggregate and polymerise. (Modified from Martins et al. (1991); Fig. 1).

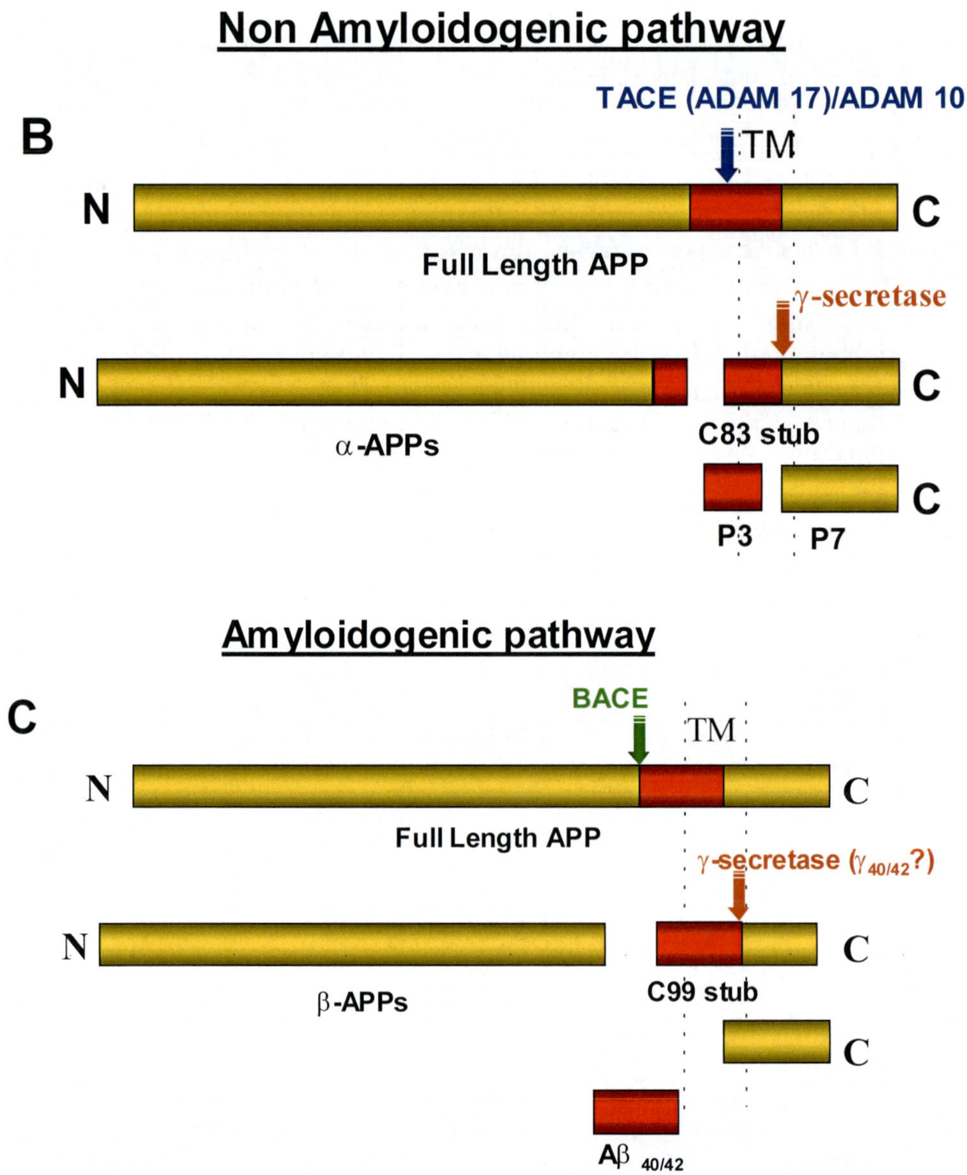

Figure 2 B and C: Putative intracellular pathways of APP processing. Two competing pathways proteolytically cleave the majority of APP (C) In the non-amyloidogenic pathway, α-secretase (now thought to be the metalloprotease TACE [ADAM 17] or ADAM 10) cleaves within the Aβ domain (red) of APP (yellow) to release APPs, thus precluding the formation of Aβ. The C-terminal proteolytic products are further cleaved by γ-secretase to yield non-amyloidogenic fragments (p3 and p7). (D) Alternatively, in the amyloidogenic pathway, BACE cleaves near the N-terminus of the Aβ domain to generated βAPPs. The C-terminal fragment containing the whole Aβ domain is cleaved by γ-secretase to liberate the Aβ peptide, ending at residue 40 or 42.

The Role of the Presenilins in γ-Secretase Cleavage of AβPP

γ-Secretase Cleavage of AβPP

Following cleavage by BACE, the final step in the amyloidogenic pathway is the cleavage of the β-CTF, to liberate Aβ. This cleavage is performed by a protease termed γ-secretase. γ-Secretase cleaves at the C-terminal end of the Aβ region (Fig. 2 B), liberating $A\beta_{40}$ or $A\beta_{42}$ and a recently described C-terminal fragment of AβPP termed γ-CTF (Nunan & Small 2000; Pinnix et al. 2001; Selkoe 2001; Wolfe 2001). AβPP undergoes regulated intramembrane proteolysis, a mechanism that is thought to be active in four other proteins, namely sterol regulatory element-binding protein (SREBP), Notch, interferon response element 1(IRE1), and activated transcription factor 6 (ATF6; recently reviewed in Urban & Freeman 2002). In each case, intramembrane proteolysis of the cytoplasmic domain can only occur prior to removal of the bulk of the protein located on the extracytosolic (lumenal or extracellular) face by a primary cleavage. Subsequent cleavage within the membrane releases a portion of the cytoplasmic (or lumenal) domain. Whilst γ-secretase activity has been proposed to be facilitated by the presenilins (see section 3.3.3 for further discussion), and is involved in the regulated intramembrane proteolysis of AβPP, Notch and Ire-1 (reviewed in Urban & Freeman 2002), cleavage of SREBP requires a membrane-embedded zinc metalloprotease, Site-2 protease (S2P; Rawson et al. 1997; Zelenski et al. 1999). Cleavage of membrane spanning segments poses an unresolved problem since these segments are generally thought to form α-helices. The peptide bonds within the α-helix are stabilised by hydrogen bonds, which preclude attack by proteases (Paetzel et al. 1998), and the lipid environment includes water required for catalysis. Thus for proteolytic cleavage, to occur γ-secretase will need to have the ability to unfold the α-helix, thus forming random coils or extended β-strand-like conformation which are more susceptible to proteolysis (Mathews 1990; Hubbard et al. 1994; Iwata et al. 1998). However, no evidence has been provided to date that this process occurs in γ-secretase cleavage of AβPP.

Based on the putative α-helix model for membrane spanning domains, the cleavage of AβPP to form $A\beta_{42}$ and $A\beta_{40}$ is difficult to explain since the proteolytic sites lie on opposite sides of AβPP (Lichtenthaler et al. 1999). Different theories have been put forward. Some recent reports have proposed there are two different γ-secretases, dubbed γ_{40}-secretase and γ_{42}- secretase, on AβPP to generate $A\beta_{40}$ and $A\beta_{42}$ (Klafki et al. 1996a; Citron et al. 1996; Murphy et al. 1999). These reports used inhibitors of γ-secretase activity (Klafki et al. 1996a; Citron et al. 1996), or mutagenesis of residues within or adjacent to the AβPP transmembrane domain (Murphy et al. 1999; Lichtenthaler et al. 1999), to show differing effects on $A\beta_{40}$ and $A\beta_{42}$ production. Murphy and colleagues (1999) varied the length of AβPP by inserting or deleting residues within the transmembrane domain at the proposed γ-secretase cleavage sites, thereby altering the residues that contact the active site. Together with the FAD associated AβPP mutations, altering the cleavage site, increased total, $A\beta_{40}$, and $A\beta_{42}$ levels relative to wild-type AβPP. Furthermore, the production of other Aβ species ($A\beta_{33}$, $A\beta_{36}$, $A\beta_{37}$, $A\beta_{38}$ and $A\beta_{39}$) was increased in some of the AβPP mutants. These reports provide evidence for proteolytic activity at different sites of the AβPP transmembrane domain and that this activity has a broad range of specificity.

Whilst it is known that γ-secretase cleavage occurs within the transmembrane domain of AβPP-CTF it is not certain whether cleavage occurs while the AβPP-CTF is inserted in the membrane, or after its release from the membrane. Thus understanding the substrate specificity is important. Lichtenthaler and colleagues (Lichtenthaler et al. 1999) replaced all residues in the transmembrane domain of βCTF that are outside the Aβ domain with Phe and measured the $A\beta_{42\backslash40}$ ratio. These investigators found that all mutants were still processed to $A\beta_{40}$ and $A\beta_{42}$, with minimal variation in the secreted amounts. However, compared with wild-type βCTF, some mutations (residues 44, 47 and 50 of β-CTF) led to a decrease in the $A\beta_{42/40}$ ratio. Other residues of βCTF (residues 43, 45, 46, 49 and 51) resulted in an increased $A\beta_{42/40}$ ratio. These results indicate that the cleavage site depends on the amino acid sequence (cleavage specificity) and agrees with previous reports of a broad range of specificity (Murphy et al. 1999) and also suggests that γ-secretase may recognise residues lumenal to the cleavage site within the transmembrane, which may influence cleavage at the fixed proteolytic site.

From their results, Lichtenthaler and colleagues (1999) proposed a α-helix model of AβPP, instead of a linear model. The α-helix model provided the notion that γ-secretase binds one side of the α-helix leading to $A\beta_{40}$ production, whilst binding on the other side leads to $A\beta_{42}$ production. This could possibly be achieved by two different secretases (γ_{40} and γ_{42}) binding to opposite sides of the α-helix. Alternatively, this model does not rule out the possibility that only a single γ-secretase exists, that is able to cleave either side. Proteins that may bind to either side of the helix could alter the precise site of γ-secretase activity, which in turn could result in favoring either $A\beta_{40}$ or $A\beta_{42}$ production. Such proteins could include the presenilins, nicastrin, APH-1 or PEN-2, which have been shown to facilitate γ-secretase activity (see Section 3.3.3 and 3.3.4 for further discussion).

Presenilin Mutations are Associated with Increased Aβ42 Levels

It is now generally accepted that PS1 and PS2 mutations result in elevated levels of $A\beta_{42}$ in AD. Conditioned media from fibroblasts or plasma from affected pedigrees with PS1 and PS2 mutations have been reported to have an increased ratio of $A\beta_{42/40}$, relative to unaffected family members (Scheuner et al. 1996). Subsequent reports, using *in vitro* (Borchelt et al. 1996; Citron et al. 1997; Xia et al. 1997b; Murayama et al. 1999) and *in vivo* studies with human brain tissue (Lemere et al. 1996; Ishii et al. 1997; Nochlin et al. 1998) and brains from transgenic mice (Borchelt et al. 1996; Duff et al. 1996; Oyama et al. 1998; Sawamura et al. 2000), have shown an increased ratio of $A\beta_{42/40}$. Furthermore, the oligomerisation of $A\beta_{42}$ (Xia et al. 1997b) and $A\beta_{42}$ plaque deposition in human brain (Ishii et al. 1997), was reported to be elevated.

The mechanism(s) behind altered $A\beta_{42}$ production associated with PS1 mutations remain unknown. However, the observation of reduced Aβ production in neuronal cultures from PS1 knockout mice (Destrooper et al. 1998) provided overwhelming evidence that PS1 facilitates γ-secretase activity. Subsequent studies have provided further insight into how γ-secretase activity may be altered with PS1 mutations. These studies are described below.

Presenilin Facilitates γ-secretase Activity

De Strooper and colleagues (1998) provided overwhelming evidence for a direct role for PS1 in AβPP metabolism. Using homologous recombination methods, the authors generated a PS1 knockout mice (PS1-/-) model to study the metabolism of AβPP. The PS1-/- mice presented with skeletal abnormalities and died shortly after birth, indicating a role for PS1 in early development (Shen et al. 1997). Results by De Strooper and colleagues (1998), showed that there was no significant difference in secreted AβPP levels (α-AβPPs and β-AβPPs), between PS1-/- and PS1+/+ neuronal cultures. However a two- to five fold accumulation of α- and β-AβPP C-terminal fragments, accompanied by a reduction in Aβ levels, was observed with PS-/- neuronal cultures. A subsequent study reported the complete inhibition of Aβ secretion from PS1 and PS2 knockout mice neuronal cultures (Herreman et al. 2000). This study provided strong evidence that PS1 (and to a lesser extent PS2), is required for γ-secretase activity and, moreover, for a direct involvement of PS1 in AβPP processing.

A study by Wolfe and colleagues (1999), used site directed mutagenesis, to substitute aspartate residues for alanine residues, at residue number 257 and 385 (located on TM6 and 7 respectively). The results from this study, were similar to those observed with PS1-/- neuronal cultures (Destrooper et al. 1998). Similar results were achieved when aspartate residues of PS2 were substituted for alanine, at residue number 366 (Steiner et al. 1999a). These studies suggest that PS1 or PS2 or both may either facilitate γ-secretase activity, or actually be the elusive γ-secretase (s). In an attempt to characterize γ-secretase, Li and colleagues (2000a), incubated membrane extracts from HeLa, HEK-293 and CHO cells with an AβPP C-terminal-FLAG recombinant substrate (AβPP C-terminal fragments) and detected $A\beta_{40}$ and $A\beta_{42}$ production by electrochemiluminescence, using specific antibodies. The authors recovered detergent soluble γ-secretase activity, however this recovery was dependent on the type of detergent used during incubation of isolated membranes with the AβPP C-terminal-FLAG recombinant substrate. Optimum γ-secretase activity was shown with the addition of 0.25% of the non-ionic detergents CHAPS (3-[3-cholamidopropyl dimethylammonio]-1-propanesulfonate) or CHAPSO (3-[3-cholamidopropyl dimethylammonio]-2-hydroxy-1-propanesulfonate). In addition, this activity was suppressed by γ-secretase inhibitors. Li and colleagues (2000a) further characterised the isolated γ-secretase activity and found the optimum concentration of substrate (Km) to be 1μM, at an optimum pH of 7.0 and the time dependence of product formation was linear over 3 hrs. Furthermore, upon gel exclusion chromatography, the solubilised γ-secretase activity co-eluted and co-immunoprecipitated with PS1. This report was the first to characterise γ-secretase activity and provided evidence that PS1 is a critical component of the γ-secretase complex. The high molecular mass of this complex ($Mr \sim 2 \times 10^6$) indicates that the presenilin heterodimers ($Mr \sim 50{,}000$) is one component of this macrocomplex and may play a vital regulatory role. Subsequent reports have shown that the presenilins and the γ-secretase substrate (AβPP-C99) interact with each other within the high molecular weight complex (Verdile et al. 2000; Xia et al. 2000a; Annaert et al. 2001).

Other biochemical evidence has been provided to show that presenilins are the catalytic components of γ-secretase, by identifying γ-secretase inhibitors that affinity label and bind presenilins. Such studies used photolabelled transition state analogue inhibitors to label soluble γ-secretase isolated from HeLa cells (Li et al. 2000a, Li et al. 2000b). The photoreactive groups were incorporated at the N-terminus of one inhibitor (L-852, 505) and the C-terminus of the other (L-852, 646) so that the photoaffinty probes labeled distinct domains of the γ-secretase catalytic site. These inhibitors were shown to label the N and C-terminus of PS1 and PS2 (Li et al. 2000b). Moreover, PS1 wild-type holoprotein was not labeled, although the PS1 Δ9 FAD mutation was labeled, providing further evidence that though the mutation is not processed into a heterodimer, it is still active. The conversion of other transition state analogue compounds, containing a difluoro alcohol group, to a reactive bromoacetamide, provided an affinity reagent that specifically bound to PS1 N-terminal and C-terminal heterodimers in cell lysates, and isolated microsomes (Esler et al. 2000). Likewise, presenilins bind to other non-transition state small molecule γ-secretase inhibitors (Seiffert et al. 2000). However these inhibitors do not resemble known transition state analogues, therefore it is not yet clear whether they bind the catalytic site of γ-secretase (Wolfe 2001). Nonetheless, collectively, these studies indicate that the N and C-terminal heterodimers of presenilins contain the catalytic component of γ-secretase.

Additional evidence that PS1 is a critical catalytic component in the γ-secretase complex is provided by Xia and colleagues (2000b). In cells expressing mutations in AβPP or PS1, Xia and colleagues (2000b) found a significant increase in the IC_{50} of the peptidomimetic inhibitor, reported previously to inhibit γ-secretase cleavage of AβPP (Wolfe et al. 1998). This indicates that FAD associated mutations can decrease the efficacy of γ-secretase inhibitors and that PS1 is a critical catalytic component, of the γ-secretase complex. It could be speculated that PS1 activity may be inhibited/reduced *in vivo*, possibly through interaction with other proteins, resulting in the reduction in Aβ levels or inhibiting $A\beta_{42}$ production. This would occur particularly if the interacting protein binds to the catalytic site on PS1 responsible for $A\beta_{42}$ production (assuming PS1 is γ-secretase). If this scenario occurs, mutations in PS1 may prevent or reduce the capacity for the inhibitory protein to bind to PS1 resulting in increased $A\beta_{42}$ production.

The facilitation of γ-secretase activity extends to Notch signaling. Notch1 is a signaling receptor crucial for cell fate determination, during embryogenesis (Artavanis-Tsakonas et al. 1999). Notch1 is a type I integral membrane protein, that is cleaved by a furin-like protease in the Golgi, during transport to the cell surface. The two fragments remain associated, to form a heterodimeric receptor (Blaumueller et al. 1997; Logeat et al. 1998). Following ligand binding, the ectodomain of Notch1 is shed by the catalytic action of a metalloprotease with similar properties to TACE (Brou et al. 2000). Following ectodomain cleavage, the membrane associated C-terminus of Notch1, undergoes further cleavage close to or within its transmembrane domain, releasing the Notch intracellular domain (NICD). Following nuclear translocation, NICD modifies transcription of target genes, through its association with the CSL (CBF1, Su (H), Lag1) family of transcription factors (Schroeter et al. 1998; Struhl et al. 1998; Lecourtois et al. 1998). The formation and translocation of Notch is required for signaling, as knockout of the entire Notch1 protein or the knock-in of a single point mutation, near the transmembrane cleavage site of Notch1, results in an embryonic lethal phenotype in mice (Huppert et al. 2000), similar to those observed in PS1 knockout mice.

The striking similarities between Notch1 cleavage and AβPP cleavage indicate that similar "secretases" are involved. Indeed, De Strooper and colleagues (1999) reported that the γ-secretase, like cleavage of the C-terminus of Notch1 (releasing NICD), was a PS1 dependent action. Furthermore, γ-secretase inhibitors, which suppress Aβ formation, have been shown to inhibit the release (De Strooper et al. 1999) and reduced nuclear translocation (Berezovska et al. 2000) of NICD. Furthermore, the ablation of PS1 dramatically reduces NICD formation (De Strooper et al. 1999). In addition, expression of the presenilin aspartate mutations D257A and D385A reduces NCID formation, translocation and signaling (De Strooper et al. 1999; Ray et al. 1999; Steiner et al. 1999b; Capell et al. 2000). Moreover, Song and colleagues (1999) reported the pathogenic PS1 mutations (Y115H, G209V and C410Y) reduced the formation of NICD. These studies provide strong evidence that NCID is generated from the C-terminus of Notch1, by PS1 facilitated γ-secretase cleavage. The formation of NICD by presenilin mediated γ-secretase activity is not exclusive to Notch1. Saxena and colleagues (2001) reported that the expression of the murine Notch proteins (Notch 1-4) in NIH 3t3 cells resulted in the formation of NICD and nuclear signaling. Furthermore all of the Notch1 homologues co-precipitated with PS1 and PS2 and inhibiting the presenilins precluded NICD formation. This study indicates that the presenilin mediated γ-secretase cleavage of Notch is universal amongst all Notch protein family members and that this process to generate NICD is conserved amongst species.

Ray and colleagues (1999) reported that Notch1 co-immunoprecipitated with PS1, in transiently transfected HEK-293 cells and in cultured *Drosophila* cells expressing endogenous Notch1, providing further evidence for a physical interaction. Furthermore, this interaction predominantly occurred in the secretory pathway, prior to Notch cleavage in the Golgi (Ray et al. 1999). This report provides a mechanism by which γ-secretase cleavage occurs by binding directly to its substrate. However, PS1 interacted with Notch, prior to cleavage in the Golgi and immunoprecipitation preferentially recovered full-length Notch (Ray et al. 1999). Thus, if PS1 is the γ-secretase, its action is not likely to be through a direct interaction with the γ-secretase cleavage site. A more likely notion is that PS1 facilitates γ-secretase activity, possibly through forming complexes with other proteins.

The proteolytic processing of Notch within its intracellular domain is highly specific and is dependent on PS1 expression (Yu et al. 2001; Armogida et al. 2001). In contrast, PS1-mediated γ-secretase activity has been shown to be non-specific and occurring at multiple sites on AβPP (Yu et al. 2001). Furthermore, Armogida and colleagues (2001) showed that endogenous $A\beta_{40}$ and $A\beta_{42}$ production was not altered in skin fibroblasts from mice lacking both PS1 and PS2. In contrast, presenilin ablation fully abolished NICD formation indicating that Notch processing is fully dependent on presenilin expression whilst Aβ production is not. This study is not in accordance with those studies that use neuronal cultures from PS1 and PS2 knockout mice (Destrooper et al. 1998; Herreman et al. 2000). In these studies, the authors report a reduction or a total inhibition of Aβ production. These conflicting results may suggest that distinct mechanisms of presenilin-mediated γ-secretase cleavage of Notch and AβPP occur in neuronal and non-neuronal cells. A direct comparison of AβPP and Notch cleavage in neuronal and non-neuronal cell cultures from PS1 and PS2 knockout mice would be required to determine if dissimilar γ-secretase activities occur in different cell types.

The Presenilins Interact with other Proteins to Form a γ-Secretase Complex

Nicastrin

As discussed above, γ-secretase is thought to be a macromolecular complex with the heterodimeric presenilin fragments shown to be important components. The next protein identified as part of the complex was termed nicastrin. As with the presenilins, mutations in or deletion of the postulated active domain of nicastrin has drastic effects on Aβ production (Yu et al. 2000). Together with the presenilin fragments, nicastrin was isolated from purified γ-secretase where it interacts with the presenilin fragments and the Aβ precursor, AβPP-C99 (Yu et al. 2000; Esler et al. 2002) providing evidence that nicastrin is a component of γ-secretase. Further evidence that nicastrin is critical for γ-secretase activity, is provided by several studies that report nicastrin to be essential for Notch cleavage in a variety of species including *C.elegans*, and *Drosophila* (Yu et al. 2000; Chung et al. 2001; Levitan et al. 2001; Lopez-Schier et al. 2002; Hu et al. 2002).

The 709 amino acid nicastrin protein contains a putative amino-terminal signal peptide, a long N-terminal hydrophilic domain, containing glycosylation, N-myristoylation and phosphorylation motifs, a short putative hydrophobic transmembrane domain and a hydrophilic C-terminus. Furthermore, homology to other functionally characterised proteins, including the aminopeptidase/transferrin receptor superfamily (Yu et al. 2000; Fagan et al. 2001) indicates that it maybe a receptor or channel protein. Nicastrin is constitutively expressed in both neuronal and non-neuronal cell lines and tissues including skin fibroblasts and skeletal muscle (Satoh et al. 2001). The protein is localised within the perinuclear region, including the ER and Golgi with its distribution overlapping with PS1 to a large extent (Yu et al. 2000; Yang et al. 2002). Within neurons, nicastrin has a perinuclear distribution with expression extending out to the processes (Yang et al. 2002). Glycosidase and subcellular fractionation analysis revealed that both wild type and mutant nicastrin contain a mixture of ER derived high mannose residues and Golgi-derived complex oligosaccharides (Yang et al. 2002). Recently it was shown that nicastrin is modified further by sialylation in the trans-Golgi network (Siman et al. 2003; Herreman et al. 2003).

The maturation process has been shown to be important in nicastrins function. Co-immunoprecipitation studies revealed that PS1 interacts with nicastrin in both HEK-293 cells transfected with nicastrin and in brain homogenates (Yu et al. 2000). In subsequent *in vitro* studies it has been shown that the fully glycosylated mature form of nicastrin interacts with PS1 and PS2 (Yang et al. 2002; Tomita et al. 2002); Edbauer et al. 2002). Kinetic labelling studies of fibroblasts from PS1/PS2 knockout mice revealed that in the absence of the presenilins, nicastrin is incompletely glycosylated (Leem et al. 2002; Edbauer et al. 2002). The incomplete maturation of nicastrin has been shown to be a result of the inability of nicastrin to reach the Golgi apparatus to complete the glycosylation process (Edbauer et al. 2002). Down regulation of nicastrin also results in reduced levels of PS1 and PS2 fragments, as a consequence, destabilisation of the PS-γ-secretase complex occurs (Edbauer et al. 2002). Overall, these studies indicate that PS1 and nicastrin regulate the expression of each other and suggest that a balance of PS1, nicastrin expression and possibly other components of the complex, is required for γ-secretase activity.

APH-1 and PEN-2

Recently identified components of the complex are APH-1 and PEN-2. The Aph -1 gene is involved in Notch signalling in the *C. elegans* embryo. Closely related genes exist in Drosophila, mice and humans (Goutte et al. 2002). Mutations in the Aph-1 gene cause an anterior pharynx defective (Aph) phenotype in *C. elegans* resulting in the absence of the anterior pharynx (Goutte et al. 2002). This phenotype is characteristic of defective Notch signalling in *C. elegans*, and occurs with sel-12 (a presenilin homologue) and aph-2 (a nicastrin homologue) mutants. The aph-1 gene encodes for a 308 amino acid multipass transmembrane protein (APH-1) in *C.elegans* and contains seven hydrophobic regions. This predicted structure is not related to that of any known proteins. However, database searches identify the DNA sequences in humans, mice and Drosophila encoding proteins closely related to APH-1 including presenilins (Goutte et al. 2002). The absence of glycosylation sites on the protein suggests that the majority of APH-1 is embedded in the membrane. A characteristic of the *C.elegans* APH-1 protein is the unique hydrophilic 40 amino acid tail at the C-terminus, which is thought to be important in its function.

The exact function of APH-1 is unknown. However, in *C.elegans,* human aph-1 and another recently identified gene, pen-2 which appears to be homologous to aph-1 (Francis et al. 2002), partially rescues the notch phenotype seen with sel 12, aph-2, aph-1 and pen-2 mutants indicating conserved function in the Notch signalling pathway. Both human aph-1 and pen-2 together are required for the rescue, which is improved by the addition of presenilin, suggesting a close interaction between these molecules. Indeed, APH-1 and PEN-2 have been shown to interact with the presenilins and nicastrin (both immature and mature forms) within the γ-secretase complex (Steiner et al. 2002; Lee et al. 2002; Gu et al. 2003; Luo et al. 2003). Further evidence for an interaction with presenilins and nicastrin is provided by *in vitro* data using small inhibitory RNAs in cultured Drosophila cells (Francis et al. 2002). The inactivation of APH-1, PEN-2 or nicastrin results in the reduction of γ-secretase cleavage of AβPP and Notch indicating that these proteins are required for γ-secretase activity (Francis et al. 2002). Furthermore, the processing of presenilins in these cells is reduced, indicating a possible role for APH-1, PEN-2 and nicastrin in the constitutive "presenilinase" proteolytic processing pathway. A recent study has reported that the down-regulation of PEN-2 inhibits the proteolytic processing of PS1, whilst over-expression of PEN-2 promotes the formation of PS1 N- and C-terminal fragments (Luo et al. 2003). The co-expression of APH-1 with PEN-2 results in a further increase in PS1 fragment levels, indicating that APH-1 facilitates the PEN-2 mediated proteolysis (Luo et al. 2003). Overall, the γ-secretase complex appears to contain at least four components, presenilins, nicastrin, APH-1 and PEN-2, which are tightly regulated such that the loss of one component results in the destabilisation of the complex and loss of activity.

Although it is clear that complex formation with other proteins is needed for γ-secretase activity, it is not clear whether γ-secretase is a single identity or if there are distinct separate activities (i.e. $\gamma_{-40/42}$ secretases). The case for a single γ-secretase could be argued, in which mutations in the presenilins, nicastrin, APH-1 or PEN-2 could alter γ-secretase cleavage to produce $A\beta_{40/42}$, by altering γ-secretase binding to AβPP. However, it is also conceivable that different γ-secretase activities exist and are regulated by presenilins or other components of the complex. Using an aldehyde inhibitor (Boc-glycine-valine-valinal; GVV), directed at the γ-$A\beta_{40}$ site, Murphy and colleagues (2000), further established the existence of pharmacologically distinct γ-secretase sites. In addition to the transmembrane aspartate mutations (D257A and D385A; (Wolfe et al. 1999), Murphy and colleagues (2000) created PS1 mutants that inhibited γ-secretase activity. In the first mutant, termed PS1 out (PS1 ins254-6+ins386-8); the aspartates at residues 257 and 385 are shifted by two 3 amino acid insertions within the transmembrane domain, moving them toward the cytoplasm and out of phase with the putative catalytic site. In the second mutation, referred to as ΔTM1-2, the first two transmembrane domains of PS1 are deleted, theoretically preserving the topology of the remaining protein. These mutations were shown to be as effective at inhibiting Aβ production as the aspartate mutations (Murphy et al. 2000). Furthermore, it was shown that the aspartate mutants equally inhibited γ_{40} and γ_{42} secretase activities. Moreover, it was also shown that the PS1 mutants decreased both GVV sensitive ($A\beta_{37}$) and insensitive ($A\beta_{43}$) cleavage equally (Murphy et al. 2000). These results are difficult to reconcile with the hypothesis that presenilin is the γ-secretase and suggest that PS1 may regulate both γ_{40} and γ_{42} secretase activities. If PS1 is γ-secretase, it must have either multiple active sites or multiple active conformations and represent an unprecedented class of proteolytic enzyme. However, it is possible that the presenilins or the other components of the γ-secretase complex could play a role in positioning AβPP, especially the C-terminal fragment, for γ-secretase cleavage. Another possibility is that the presenilins or other components of the γ-secretase complex play a role in the normal trafficking of the AβPP CTF, following BACE/TACE cleavage of AβPP.

Intracellular Pathways for Aβ Generation

The proposed intracellular pathways of non-amyloidogenic and amyloidogenic processing of AβPP are shown in Figure 3 A. AβPP is located in the ER could be cleaved by BACE/BACE2 and γ-secretase(s) to liberate N–terminally truncated Aβ peptides ($A\beta_{x-42}$) which remains in an insoluble state in the ER. Uncleaved AβPP molecules are packaged into transport vesicles (i.e. clathrin coated vesicles) and are transported through the Golgi apparatus to the trans-Golgi network (TGN). Here soluble and insoluble $A\beta_{42/40}$ are generated through the action of BACE/BACE2 and γ-secretase(s). Soluble $A\beta_{40}$ and $A\beta_{42}$ are packaged into transport vesicles and transported to the plasma membrane where they are secreted. Insoluble Aβ peptides ($A\beta_{x-42/x-40}$) remain in the TGN.

Alternatively, uncleaved AβPP is packaged into transport vesicles and transported to the plasma membrane, where the action of α-secretase (TACE or ADAM10) liberates the ectodomain of AβPP (αAβPPs), which is secreted. A proportion of uncleaved AβPP and its C-terminal fragments at the plasma membrane can be internalised by transport vesicles and travel to the endosomes or lysosomes where, through the action of BACE/BACE2 and γ-secretase, soluble $A\beta_{40}$ and $A\beta_{42}$ are generated and transported to the plasma membrane for secretion. The non-amyloidogenic fragments p3 and p7 (generated through α-secretase and γ-secretase activity in the endosomes/lysosomes) can be transported to the plasma membrane and secreted. Alternatively, a proportion of uncleaved AβPP can be internalised and can be transported to the TGN for an additional round of Aβ generation.

A

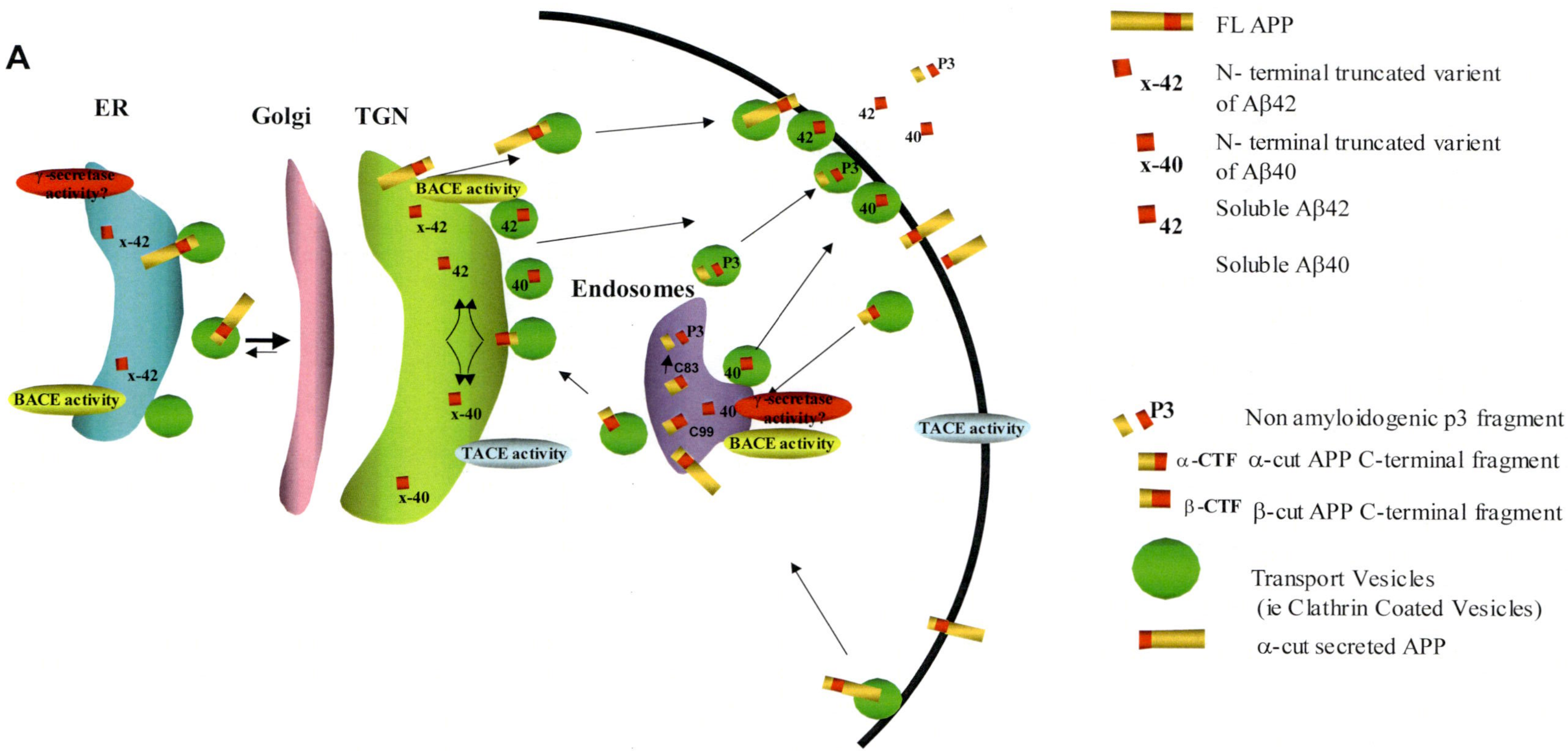

ER
Golgi
TGN
Endosomes
γ-secretase activity?
BACE activity
TACE activity
x-42
x-40
42
40
P3
C83
C99
FL APP
N- terminal truncated varient of Aβ42
N- terminal truncated varient of Aβ40
Soluble Aβ42
Soluble Aβ40
Non amyloidogenic p3 fragment
α-CTF α-cut APP C-terminal fragment
β-CTF β-cut APP C-terminal fragment
Transport Vesicles (ie Clathrin Coated Vesicles)
α-cut secreted APP

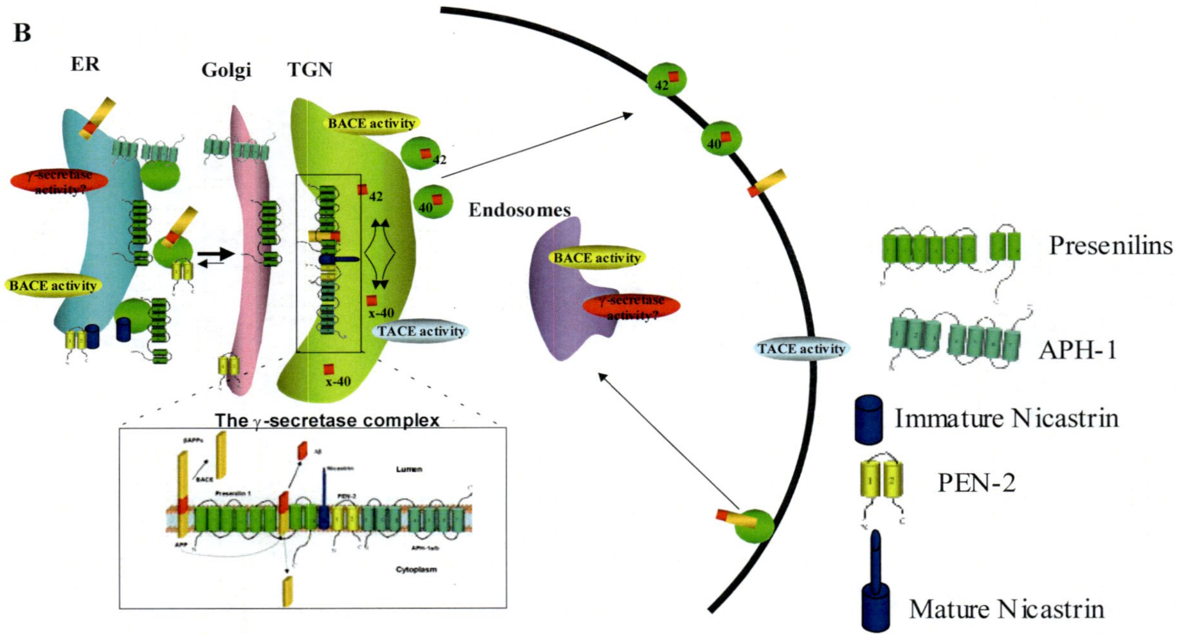

Figure 3: Proposed Intracellular pathways for Aβ generation. (A) The non-amyloidogenic and amyloidogenic intrace llular pathways are described in the text (section 3.3.5). (B) The direct involvement of the γ-secretase complex in Aβ generation with the TGN remains to be determined. However, in this putative model shown in the schematic diagram, the components of the complex are synthesized and undergo posttranslational modifications within the ER and Golgi apparatus. The complex is then assembled with in the TGN where the active γ-secretase cleaves the APP C-terminal stubs, delivered from the endosomes/lysosomes or cell surface, to generate Aβ. The γ-secretase complex (insert – open rectangle) would contain PS1, mature nicastrin, APH-1 and PEN-2 that may act synergistically to stabilize the complex. The collaboration of all the components of the complex results in Aβ generation. Together with BACE, γ-secretase activity would be present in the endosomes/lysosomes to generate $A\beta_{40}$ or the non-amyloidogenic fragments p3 and p7 (A). However, this activity would be separate from that seen with the presenilin containing γ-secretase complex, since none of the components of the complex have been localised to the endosomes/ lysosomes (B). If this is the case it would indicate the presence of another γ-secretase. BACE and γ-secretase would also be active in the ER to generate N-terminal truncated $A\beta_{42}$ (x $A\beta_{42}$). However, the complex could not be assembled in the ER since only fully glycosylated mature nicastrin is contained in the complex (B; Tomita et al. 2002; Edbauer et al. 2002; Siman & Velji 2003). Again this may indicate the presence of another γ-secretase separate from the presenilin-containing complex.

The Presenilins Alter AβPP Trafficking to Generate Aβ

The homology between the presenilins and proteins involved in protein trafficking (i.e.: SPE-4) suggests that PS1 and PS2 could be involved in AβPP trafficking. Using immunocytochemistry, Walter and colleagues (1996), reported small amounts of presenilin proteins in the Golgi apparatus of transfected CHO, COS7 and HEK-293 cells, where they co-localised with AβPP. Subsequently, Weidemann and colleagues (1997) reported an interaction between PS1 and PS2 and immature forms of AβPP. This study suggested an interaction during the transit of AβPP through the ER. This notion was confirmed by a report by Xia and colleagues (1997a) in which a small portion of N-glycosylated AβPP formed complexes with PS1, in both ER and Golgi-rich fractions from discontinuous iodixanol gradients. These reports suggest that PS1 may be involved in the trafficking of AβPP from the ER to the Golgi apparatus.

Evidence has been provided for regulation of γ-secretase processing of AβPP by the presenilins, in the ER and pre-Golgi apparatus. Sudoh and colleagues (1998) reported the intracellular and extracellular generation of $A\beta_{42}$ in mouse neuroblastoma cell lines expressing human wild type or mutated PS1 (M146L or Δexon 9), was blocked by brefelden A (BFA). BFA blocks protein transport from the ER, to the Golgi apparatus (Lippincott-Schwartz et al. 1989). Thus, this report suggests that intracellular $A\beta_{42}$ production does not occur within the ER. In contrast, accumulation of intracellular $A\beta_{42}$ increased with BFA treatment of HEK-293 cells over-expressing wild-type AβPP or FAD associated AβPP mutations (Wild-Bode et al. 1997). These reports indicate that $A\beta_{42}$ generation occurs in distal or post Golgi compartments and is mediated by PS1. However, $A\beta_{42}$ generation can also occur within the ER (Hartmann et al. 1997; Greenfield et al. 1999). Though, the majority of $A\beta_{42}$ generated in the ER is the insoluble N-terminally truncated variant, which remains in the ER (Greenfield et al. 1999).

To determine if there is an association between presenilin localisation and AβPP processing, Annaert and colleagues (Annaert et al. 1999) performed cell fractionation and confocal microscopy, using subcellular marker proteins in brain tissue from transgenic mice, over-expressing PS1 and AβPP and primary cultures of hippocampal neurons. The expression of PS1 was shown to be restricted to the ER, intermediate compartments and early cis- Golgi compartments. Distribution analysis of endogenous AβPP and AβPP C-terminal fragments revealed that the distribution was bimodal, similar to PS1. The authors also reported an enrichment of AβPP C-terminal fragments in the same fractions of the sucrose gradient where PS1 fragments were recovered, confirming the close interaction of PS1 with AβPP. However, virtually no overlap was observed for PS1 and transferrin receptor, a marker for post-Golgi compartments. This suggests that PS1 is not present in endosomes/lysosomes and, therefore, is not associated with AβPP C-terminal fragments located there. These studies indicate, that the presenilins may mediate AβPP processing maybe more indirect through trafficking of AβPP perhaps via molecular chaperones or interactions with transport vesicle proteins. These proteins may include (ie receptor-associated protein, RAP reviewed in Bu et al. 1998), a molecular chaperone shown to assist proteins in their passage between the ER and Golgi apparatus (Williams et al. 1992) or COP II coat complex (reviewed in Gorelick et al. 2001) shown to coat budding transport vesicles (Barlowe et al. 1994), all of which have been shown to be co-localise with PS1 (Annaert et al. 1999).

A number of reports have shown the presenilins to be expressed at the plasma membrane (Takashima et al. 1996; Dewji et al. 1997; Georgakopoulous et al. 1999; Schwarzman et al. 1999; Chung and Struhl et al. 2001). Furthermore, PS1 has been shown to interact with mature nicastrin at the plasma membrane (Chung and Struhl et al. 2001; Kaether et al. 2002). It has been suggested that nicastrin maybe involved in the transport of PS1 to the plasma membrane where it interacts with APP and other γ-secretase substrates (Kaether et al., 2002). Indeed it has been shown that inactivation of PS1 by γ-secretase inhibitors or mutagenesis (aspartate PS1 mutants) affects internalisation of AβPP from the plasma membrane (Kaether et al., 2002). This study suggests that not only is involved in the proteolytic cleavage of AβPP but is also necessary for AβPP trafficking. These studies also suggest that other components of the γ-secretase complex assist in the presenilin mediated trafficking of APP.

Further evidence that the trafficking of AβPP to Aβ generating compartments may involve an interaction between all of the identified components of the γ-secretase complex was has been provided by recent studies. Herreman and colleagues (2003) showed that Aβ production and NICD formation is still present following the inhibition of glycosylation of nicastrin, indicating that γ-secretase activity is not dependent on nicastrin maturation. Instead, γ-secretase was dependent on passage of nicastrin and probably other components of the γ-secretase complex to compartments where the glycosylation occurs (Herreman et al. 2003).

Nicastrin undergoes N-linked sialylation in the TGN (Siman & Velji 2003; Herreman et al. 2003). In PS1 and PS2 deficient cells this does not occur, instead nicastrin accumulates in the ER where it is degraded (Siman & Velji 2003; Herreman et al. 2003). This result indicates that the presenilins are required to transport nicastrin to the trans-Golgi network for maturation. As mentioned above and shown in Figure 3 the majority of Aβ generation occurs in the late secretory compartments including the TGN. Although presenilin expression is mostly restricted to the early biosynthetic compartments (Kovacs et al. 1996; Thinakaran et al. 1996a; Destrooper et al. 1997; Culvenor et al. 1997; Cupers et al. 2001), the distribution of the γ-secretase substrate (AβPP-C83, AβPP-C99), nicastrin and presenilin fragments has been shown to overlap in the TGN (Siman & Velji 2003). In addition complexes of PS1 and sialyated mature nicastrin have been isolated in TGN fractions (Siman & Velji 2003). These studies suggest that the γ-secretase complex assembles in the TGN where the active enzyme cleaves AβPP-C83/C99 to generate Aβ (Figure 3 B). However, a direct involvement of all of the γ-secretase components in Aβ generation within the late secretory compartments remains to be determined. These studies suggest that, apart from being critical in γ-secretase activity, presenilins are critical regulators of the components within the complex which is essential for γ-secretase activity.

THE γ-SECRETASE COMPLEX IDENTIFIED-WHERE TO GO FROM HERE?

It appears likely that all of the candidate proteins involved in Aβ generation have been identified. It is now necessary to demonstrate that γ–secretase activity can be restored when these proteins are reconstituted in different combinations with the presenilins. This may be difficult since activity of these proteins may depend on reconstructing their correct conformations. For example, if AβPP proteolysis is an intramembranous process, it might be necessary to use purified proteins and lipid membrane preparations to reconstruct γ-secretase activity.

An additional question is "how does the hydrolytic γ-secretase cleavage mechanism occur within the highly hydrophobic environment of the lipid bilayer?" If presenilins are the catalytic components of γ-secretase, their transmembrane domains may act as a channel to allow the entry and interaction of catalytic water. This mechanism has already been proposed by some researchers (Annaert et al. 2001; Wolfe 2002). In this model, the substrate (ie AβPP-C99/C83) would probably have to bind the outer surface of the proteolytic enzyme, with subsequent conformational change presenting the substrate to the active (catalytic) site within the membrane. Furthermore, if the substrate (AβPP-C99/C83) is an α-helix, as proposed by Lichtenthaler and colleagues (1999), the proteolytic enzyme (ie PS1/PS2) or one or more accessory proteins (ie nicastrin/APH1/PEN-2) would need to "unwind" the substrate near the site of cleavage before proteolysis could occur.

Although the precise molecular details of γ-secretase activity still remains elusive, the efforts of researchers over the past decade has resulted in a plethora of information that will provide a stepping stone for future research into mechanisms of AβPP proteolysis. Understanding the mechanism by which Aβ is generated will be essential in order to fully elucidate the physiological and pathological functions of this ubiquitously expressed protein.

REFERENCES

Aberle H, Butz S, Stappert J, Weissig H, Kemler R, Hoschuetzky H (1994) Assembly of the cadherin-catenin complex in vitro with recombinant proteins *J Cell Sci* 107, 3655-63.

Alberici A, Moratto D, Benussi L et al. (1999) Presenilin 1 protein directly interacts with Bcl-2 *J Biol Chem* 274, 30764-9.

Anastasiadis PZ, Reynolds AB (2001) Regulation of Rho GTPases by p120-catenin *Curr Opin Cell Biol* 13, 604-10.

Annaert WG, Esselens C, Baert V et al. (2001) Interaction with telencephalin and the amyloid precursor protein predicts a ring structure for presenilins *Neuron* 32, 579-89.

Annaert WG, Levesque L, Craessaerts K et al. (1999) Presenilin 1 controls gamma-secretase processing of amyloid precursor protein in pre-Golgi compartments of hippocampal neurons *Journal of Cell Biology.* 147, 277-94.

Annunziato L, Amoroso S, Pannaccione A et al. (2003) Apoptosis induced in neuronal cells by oxidative stress: role played by caspases and intracellular calcium ions *Toxicol Lett* 139, 125-33.

Armogida M, Petit A, Vincent B, Scarzello S, da Costa CA, Checler F (2001) Endogenous beta-amyloid production in presenilin-deficient embryonic mouse fibroblasts *Nat Cell Biol* 3, 1030-3.

Artavanis-Tsakonas S, Rand MD, Lake RJ (1999) Notch signaling: cell fate control and signal integration in development *Science* 284, 770-6.

Asami-Odaka A, Ishibashi Y, Kikuchi T, Kitada C, Suzuki N (1995) Long amyloid beta-protein secreted from wild-type human neuroblastoma IMR-32 cells *Biochemistry* 34, 10272-8.

Baki L, Marambaud P, Efthimiopoulos S et al. (2001) Presenilin-1 binds cytoplasmic epithelial cadherin, inhibits cadherin/p120 association, and regulates stability and function of the cadherin/catenin adhesion complex *Proc Natl Acad Sci U S A* 98, 2381-6.

Barlowe C, Orci L, Yeung T et al. (1994) COPII: a membrane coat formed by Sec proteins that drive vesicle budding from the endoplasmic reticulum *Cell* 77, 895-907.

Berezovska O, Jack C, McLean P et al. (2000) Rapid Notch1 nuclear translocation after ligand binding depends on presenilin-associated gamma-secretase activity *Ann N Y Acad Sci* 920, 223-6.

Bertolotti A, Zhang Y, Hendershot LM, Harding HP, Ron D (2000) Dynamic interaction of BiP and ER stress transducers in the unfolded-protein response *Nat Cell Biol* 2, 326-32.

Bertrand E, Brouillet E, Caille I et al. (2001) A short cytoplasmic domain of the amyloid precursor protein induces apoptosis in vitro and in vivo *Mol Cell Neurosci* 18, 503-11.

Biederer T, Sudhof TC (2000) Mints as adaptors - Direct binding to neurexins and recruitment of Munc18 *Journal of Biological Chemistry* 275, 39803-6.

Blaumueller CM, Qi H, Zagouras P, Artavanis-Tsakonas S (1997) Intracellular cleavage of Notch leads to a heterodimeric receptor on the plasma membrane *Cell* 90, 281-91.

Borchelt DR, Thinakaran G, Eckman CB et al. (1996) Familial Alzheimer's disease-linked presenilin 1 variants elevate Abeta1-42/1-40 ratio in vitro and in vivo *Neuron* 17, 1005-13.

Brou C, Logeat F, Gupta N et al. (2000) A novel proteolytic cleavage involved in Notch signaling: the role of the disintegrin-metalloprotease TACE *Mol Cell* 5, 207-16.

Bu G, Schwartz AL (1998) RAP, a novel type of ER chaperone *Trends Cell Biol* 8, 272-6.

Burdick D, Soreghan B, Kwon M et al. (1992) Assembly and aggregation properties of synthetic Alzheimer's A4/beta amyloid peptide analogs *J Biol Chem* 267, 546-54.

Buxbaum JD, Choi EK, Luo YX et al. (1998) Calsenilin - a Calcium-Binding Protein That Interacts With the Presenilins and Regulates the Levels of a Presenilin Fragment *Nature Medicine* 4, 1177-81.

Buxbaum JD, Koo EH, Greengard P (1993) Protein phosphorylation inhibits production of Alzheimer amyloid beta/A4 peptide *Proc Natl Acad Sci U S A* 90, 9195-8.

Capell A, Grunberg J, Pesold B et al. (1998) The proteolytic fragments of the Alzheimer's disease-associated presenilin-1 form heterodimers and occur as a 100-150-kDa molecular mass complex *Journal of Biological Chemistry* 273, 3205-11.

Capell A, Saffrich R, Olivo JC et al. (1997) Cellular Expression and Proteolytic Processing of Presenilin Proteins Is Developmentally Regulated During Neuronal Differentiation *Journal of Neurochemistry* 69, 2432-40.

Capell A, Steiner H, Romig H et al. (2000) Presenilin-1 differentially facilitates endoproteolysis of the beta-amyloid precursor protein and Notch *Nature Cell Biology* 2, 205-11.

Caporaso GL, Gandy SE, Buxbaum JD, Ramabhadran TV, Greengard P (1992) Protein phosphorylation regulates secretion of Alzheimer beta/A4 amyloid precursor protein *Proc Natl Acad Sci U S A* 89, 3055-9.

Carpenter CL (2000) Actin cytoskeleton and cell signaling *Crit Care Med* 28, N94-9.

Chan C, Dharmarajan, A., Atwood, C.S., Huang, X., Tanzi, R.E., Bush, A.I. and Martins, R.N (1999) Anti-apoptotic action of Alzheimer Ab *Alzheimer's Reports* 2, 113-9.

Choi EK, Zaidi NF, Miller JS et al. (2001) Calsenilin is a substrate for caspase-3 that preferentially interacts with the familial Alzheimer's disease-associated C-terminal fragment of presenilin 2 *J Biol Chem* 276, 19197-204.

Chung HM, Struhl G (2001) Nicastrin is required for Presenilin-mediated transmembrane cleavage in Drosophila *Nat Cell Biol* 3, 1129-32.

Citron M, Diehl TS, Gordon G, Biere AL, Seubert P, Selkoe DJ (1996) Evidence that the 42- and 40-amino acid forms of amyloid beta protein are generated from the beta-amyloid precursor protein by different protease activities *Proc Natl Acad Sci U S A* 93, 13170-5.

Citron M, Westaway D, Xia W et al. (1997) Mutant presenilins of Alzheimer's disease increase production of 42-residue amyloid beta-protein in both transfected cells and transgenic mice [see comments] *Nature Medicine* 3, 67-72.

Clark RF, Hutton M, Fuldner RA et al. (1995) The Structure of the Presenilin 1 (S182) Gene and Identification of Six Novel Mutations in Early Onset Ad Families *Nature Genetics* 11, 219-22.

Cook DG, Sung JC, Golde TE et al. (1996) Expression and Analysis of Presenilin 1 in a Human Neuronal System - Localization in Cell Bodies and Dendrites *Proceedings of the National Academy of Sciences of the United States of America* 93, 9223-8.

Culvenor JG, Maher F, Evin G et al. (1997) Alzheimer's disease-associated presenilin 1 in neuronal cells: evidence for localization to the endoplasmic reticulum-Golgi intermediate compartment *Journal of Neuroscience Research* 49, 719-31.

Cupers P, Bentahir M, Craessaerts K et al. (2001) The discrepancy between presenilin subcellular localization and gamma-secretase processing of amyloid precursor protein *J Cell Biol* 154, 731-40.

da Costa CA, Ancolio K, Checler F (1999) C-terminal maturation fragments of presenilin 1 and 2 control secretion of APP alpha and A beta by human cells and are degraded by proteasome *Molecular Medicine.* 5, 160-8.

Demaerschalck I, Delvaux A, Octave JN (1993) Activation of protein kinase C increases the extracellular release of the transmembrane amyloid protein precursor of Alzheimer's disease *Biochimica et Biophysica Acta* 1181, 214-8.

Destrooper B, Umans L, Van Leuven F, Van Den Berghe H (1993) Study of the synthesis and secretion of normal and artificial mutants of murine amyloid precursor protein (APP): cleavage of APP occurs in a late compartment of the default secretion pathway *J Cell Biol* 121, 295-304.

Destrooper B, Beullens M, Contreras B et al. (1997) Phosphorylation, Subcellular Localization, and Membrane Orientation of the Alzheimers Disease-Associated Presenilins *Journal of Biological Chemistry* 272, 3590-8.

Destrooper B, Saftig P, Craessaerts K et al. (1998) Deficiency of Presenilin-1 Inhibits the Normal Cleavage of Amyloid Precursor Protein *Nature* 391, 387-90.De Strooper B, Annaert W, Cupers P et al. (1999) A presenilin-1-dependent gamma-secretase-like protease mediates release of Notch intracellular domain *Nature* 398, 518-22.

Dewji NN, Singer SJ. (1997) Cell surface expression of the Alzheimer disease-related presenilin proteins. *Proc Natl Acad Sci U S A* 94, 9926-31

Doan A, Thinakaran G, Borchelt DR et al. (1996) Protein Topology of Presenilin 1 *Neuron* 17, 1023-30.

Dovey HF, Suomensaari-Chrysler S, Lieberburg I, Sinha S, Keim PS (1993) Cells with a familial Alzheimer's disease mutation produce authentic beta-peptide *Neuroreport* 4, 1039-42.

Duff K, Eckman C, Zehr C et al. (1996) Increased Amyloid-Beta-42(43) in Brains of Mice Expressing Mutant Presenilin 1 *Nature* 383, 710-3.

Edbauer D, Winkler E, Haass C, Steiner H (2002) Presenilin and nicastrin regulate each other and determine amyloid beta-peptide production via complex formation *Proc Natl Acad Sci U S A* 99, 8666-71.

Esch FS, Keim PS, Beattie EC et al. (1990) Cleavage of amyloid beta peptide during constitutive processing of its precursor *Science* 248, 1122-4.

Esler WP, Kimberly WT, Ostaszewski BL et al. (2000) Transition-state analogue inhibitors of gamma-secretase bind directly to presenilin-1 *Nat Cell Biol* 2, 428-34.

Esler WP, Kimberly WT, Ostaszewski BL et al. (2002) Activity-dependent isolation of the presenilin- gamma -secretase complex reveals nicastrin and a gamma substrate *Proc Natl Acad Sci U S A* 99, 2720-5.

Fagan R, Swindells M, Overington J, Weir M (2001) Nicastrin, a presenilin-interacting protein, contains an aminopeptidase/transferrin receptor superfamily domain *Trends Biochem Sci* 26, 213-4.

Francis R, McGrath G, Zhang J et al. (2002) aph-1 and pen-2 are required for Notch pathway signaling, gamma-secretase cleavage of betaAPP, and presenilin protein accumulation *Dev Cell* 3, 85-97.

Fraser PE, Levesque G, Yu G et al. (1998) Presenilin 1 Is Actively Degraded By the 26s Proteasome *Neurobiology of Aging* 19, S 19-S 21.

Galli C, Piccini A, Ciotti MT et al. (1998) Increased amyloidogenic secretion in cerebellar granule cells undergoing apoptosis *Proc Natl Acad Sci U S A* 95, 1247-52.

Gandy S, Petanceska S (2001) Regulation of alzheimer beta-amyloid precursor trafficking and metabolism. *Advances in experimental medicine and biology* 487, 85-100.

Georgakopoulos A, Marambaud P, Efthimiopoulos S et al. (1999) Presenilin-1 forms complexes with the cadherin/catenin cell-cell adhesion system and is recruited to intercellular and synaptic contacts *Molecular Cell.* 4, 893-902.

Gervais FG, Xu D, Robertson GS et al. (1999) Involvement of caspases in proteolytic cleavage of Alzheimer's amyloid-beta precursor protein and amyloidogenic A beta peptide formation *Cell* 97, 395-406.

Gillespie SL, Golde TE, Younkin SG (1992) Secretory processing of the Alzheimer amyloid beta/A4 protein precursor is increased by protein phosphorylation *Biochem Biophys Res Commun* 187, 1285-90.

Glenner GG, Wong CW (1984) Alzheimer's disease: initial report of the purification and characterization of a novel cerebrovascular amyloid protein *Biochemical & Biophysical Research Communications* 120, 885-90.

Goate A, Chartier-Harlin MC, Mullan M et al. (1991) Segregation of a missense mutation in the amyloid precursor protein gene with familial Alzheimer's disease [see comments] *Nature* 349, 704-6.

Gorelick FS, Shugrue C (2001) Exiting the endoplasmic reticulum *Mol Cell Endocrinol* 177, 13-8.

Goutte C, Tsunozaki M, Hale VA, Priess JR (2002) APH-1 is a multipass membrane protein essential for the Notch signaling pathway in Caenorhabditis elegans embryos *Proc Natl Acad Sci U S A* 99, 775-9.

Graebert KS, Popp GM, Kehle T, Herzog V (1995) Regulated O-glycosylation of the Alzheimer beta-A4 amyloid precursor protein in thyrocytes *Eur J Cell Biol* 66, 39-46.

Greenfield JP, Tsai J, Gouras GK et al. (1999) Endoplasmic reticulum and trans-Golgi network generate distinct populations of Alzheimer beta-amyloid peptides *Proceedings of the National Academy of Sciences of the United States of America* 96, 742-7.

Grunberg J, Walter J, Loetscher H, Deuschle U, Jacobsen H, Haass C (1998) Alzheimer's disease associated presenilin-1 holoprotein and its 18-20 kDa C-terminal fragment are death substrates for proteases of the caspase family *Biochemistry* 37, 2263-70.

Gu Y, Chen F, Sanjo N et al. (2003) APH-1 interacts with mature and immature forms of presenilins and nicastrin and may play a role in maturation of presenilin.nicastrin complexes *J Biol Chem* 278, 7374-80.

Gumbiner BM (2000) Regulation of cadherin adhesive activity *J Cell Biol* 148, 399-404.

Guo Q, Furukawa K, Sopher BL et al. (1996) Alzheimer's PS-1 mutation perturbs calcium homeostasis and sensitizes PC12 cells to death induced by amyloid beta-peptide *Neuroreport* 8, 379-83.

Guo Q, Sopher BL, Furukawa K et al. (1997) Alzheimer's presenilin mutation sensitizes neural cells to apoptosis induced by trophic factor withdrawal and amyloid beta-peptide: involvement of calcium and oxyradicals *Journal of Neuroscience* 17, 4212-22.

Haass C (1996) Presenile because of presenilin: the presenilin genes and early onset Alzheimer's disease *Current Opinion in Neurology* 9, 254-9.

Harding HP, Zhang Y, Bertolotti A, Zeng H, Ron D (2000) Perk is essential for translational regulation and cell survival during the unfolded protein response *Mol Cell* 5, 897-904.

Harding HP, Zhang Y, Ron D (1999) Protein translation and folding are coupled by an endoplasmic-reticulum-resident kinase *Nature* 397, 271-4.

Hartmann T, Bieger SC, Bruhl B et al. (1997) Distinct sites of intracellular production for Alzheimer's disease A beta40/42 amyloid peptides *Nature Medicine* 3, 1016-20.

Hendriks B, Reichmann E (2002) Wnt signaling: a complex issue *Biol Res* 35, 277-86.

Hensley K, Carney JM, Mattson MP et al. (1994) A model for beta-amyloid aggregation and neurotoxicity based on free radical generation by the peptide: relevance to Alzheimer disease *Proc Natl Acad Sci U S A* 91, 3270-4.

Herreman A, Serneels L, Annaert W, Collen D, Schoonjans L, De Strooper B (2000) Total inactivation of gamma-secretase activity in presenilin-deficient embryonic stem cells *Nature Cell Biology* 2, 461-2.

Herreman A, Van Gassen G, Bentahir M et al. (2003) gamma-Secretase activity requires the presenilin-dependent trafficking of nicastrin through the Golgi apparatus but not its complex glycosylation *J Cell Sci* 116, 1127-36.

Ho CS, Marinescu V, Steinhilb ML, Gaut JR, Turner RS, Stuenkel EL (2002) Synergistic effects of Munc18a and X11 proteins on amyloid precursor protein metabolism *J Biol Chem* 277, 27021-8.

Honda T, Yasutake K, Nihonmatsu N et al. (1999) Dual roles of proteasome in the metabolism of presenilin 1 *Journal of Neurochemistry* 72, 255-61.

Hu Y, Ye Y, Fortini ME (2002) Nicastrin is required for gamma-secretase cleavage of the Drosophila Notch receptor *Dev Cell* 2, 69-78.

Hubbard SJ, Eisenmenger F, Thornton JM (1994) Modeling studies of the change in conformation required for cleavage of limited proteolytic sites *Protein Sci* 3, 757-68.

Hung AY, Haass C, Nitsch RM et al. (1993) Activation of protein kinase C inhibits cellular production of the amyloid beta-protein *J Biol Chem* 268, 22959-62.

Huppert SS, Le A, Schroeter EH et al. (2000) Embryonic lethality in mice homozygous for a processing-deficient allele of Notch1 *Nature* 405, 966-70.

Imafuku I, Masaki T, Waragai M et al. (1999) Presenilin 1 suppresses the function of c-jun homodimers via interaction with QM/Jif-1 *Journal of Cell Biology.* 147, 121-33.

Ishii K, Ii K, Hasegawa T, Shoji S, Doi A, Mori H (1997) Increased a-Beta 42(43)-Plaque Deposition in Early-Onset Familial Alzheimers-Disease Brains With the Deletion of Exon 9 and the Missense Point Mutation (H163r) in the Ps-1 Gene *Neuroscience Letters* 228, 17-20.

Iwata S, Lee JW, Okada K et al. (1998) Complete structure of the 11-subunit bovine mitochondrial cytochrome bc1 complex *Science* 281, 64-71.

Iwatsubo T, Odaka A, Suzuki N, Mizusawa H, Nukina N, Ihara Y (1994) Visualization of A beta 42(43) and A beta 40 in senile plaques with end-specific A beta monoclonals: evidence that an initially deposited species is A beta 42(43) *Neuron* 13, 45-53.

Jaffe AB, Toran-Allerand CD, Greengard P, Gandy SE (1994) Estrogen regulates metabolism of Alzheimer amyloid beta precursor protein. *Journal of Biological Chemistry* 269, 13065-8.

Johnston JA, Ward CL, Kopito RR (1998) Aggresomes: A cellular response to misfolded proteins *Journal of Cell Biology* 143, 1883-98.

Jou TS, Stewart DB, Stappert J, Nelson WJ, Marrs JA (1995) Genetic and biochemical dissection of protein linkages in the cadherin-catenin complex *Proc Natl Acad Sci U S A* 92, 5067-71.

Kaether C, Lammich S, Edbauer D, Ertl M, Rietdorf J, Capell A, Steiner H, Haass C. (2002) Presenilin-1 affects trafficking and processing of betaAPP and is targeted in a complex with nicastrin to the plasma membrane. *Journal of Cell Biology* 158, 551-61

Kang DE, Soriano S, Frosch MP et al. (1999) Presenilin 1 facilitates the constitutive turnover of beta-catenin: differential activity of Alzheimer's disease-linked PS1 mutants in the beta-catenin-signaling pathway *Journal of Neuroscience* 19, 4229-37.

Katayama T, Imaizumi K, Sato N et al. (1999) Presenilin-1 mutations downregulate the signalling pathway of the unfolded-protein response *Nature Cell Biology.* 1, 479-85.

Kaufman RJ (2002) Orchestrating the unfolded protein response in health and disease *J Clin Invest* 110, 1389-98.

Kim TW, Pettingell WH, Hallmark OG, Moir RD, Wasco W, Tanzi RE (1997a) Endoproteolytic cleavage and proteasomal degradation of presenilin 2 in transfected cells *Journal of Biological Chemistry* 272, 11006-10.

Kim TW, Pettingell WH, Jung YK, Kovacs DM, Tanzi RE (1997b) Alternative cleavage of Alzheimer-associated presenilins during apoptosis by a caspase-3 family protease *Science* 277, 373-6.

Klafki H, Abramowski D, Swoboda R, Paganetti PA, Staufenbiel M (1996a) The carboxyl termini of beta-amyloid peptides 1-40 and 1-42 are generated by distinct gamma-secretase activities *J Biol Chem* 271, 28655-9.

Klafki HW, Wiltfang J, Staufenbiel M (1996b) Electrophoretic separation of betaA4 peptides (1-40) and (1-42) *Anal Biochem* 237, 24-9.

Knops J, Gandy S, Greengard P, Lieberburg I, Sinha S (1993) Serine phosphorylation of the secreted extracellular domain of APP *Biochem Biophys Res Commun* 197, 380-5.

Kovacs DM, Fausett HJ, Page KJ et al. (1996) Alzheimer-associated presenilins 1 and 2: neuronal expression in brain and localization to intracellular membranes in mammalian cells *Nature Medicine* 2, 224-9.

Kuentzel SL, Ali SM, Altman RA, Greenberg BD, Raub TJ (1993) The Alzheimer Beta-Amyloid Protein Precursor Protease Nexin-Ii Is Cleaved By Secretase in a Trans-Golgi Secretory Compartment in Human Neuroglioma Cells *Biochemical Journal* 295, 367-78.

Lah JJ, Heilman CJ, Nash NR et al. (1997) Light and Electron Microscopic Localization of Presenilin-1 in Primate Brain *Journal of Neuroscience* 17, 1971-80.

Lau KF, McLoughlin DM, Standen C, Miller CCJ (2000) X11 alpha and x11 beta interact with presenilin-1 via their PDZ domains *Molecular & Cellular Neuroscience* 16, 557-65.

LeBlanc A, Liu H, Goodyer C, Bergeron C, Hammond J (1999) Caspase-6 role in apoptosis of human neurons, amyloidogenesis, and Alzheimer's disease *J Biol Chem* 274, 23426-36.

Lecourtois M, Schweisguth F (1998) Indirect evidence for Delta-dependent intracellular processing of notch in Drosophila embryos *Curr Biol* 8, 771-4.

Lee DS, Tomita S, Kirino Y, Suzuki T (2000) Regulation of X11L-dependent amyloid precursor protein metabolism by XB51, a novel X11L-binding protein *J Biol Chem* 275, 23134-8.

Lee MK, Slunt HH, Martin LJ et al. (1996) Expression of Presenilin 1 and 2 (Ps1 and Ps2) in Human and Murine Tissues *Journal of Neuroscience* 16, 7513-25.

Lee SF, Shah S, Li H, Yu C, Han W, Yu G (2002) Mammalian APH-1 interacts with presenilin and nicastrin and is required for intramembrane proteolysis of amyloid-beta precursor protein and Notch *J Biol Chem* 277, 45013-9.

Leem JY, Vijayan S, Han P et al. (2002) Presenilin 1 is required for maturation and cell surface accumulation of nicastrin *J Biol Chem* 277, 19236-40.

Lehmann S, Chiesa R, Harris DA (1997) Evidence for a six-transmembrane domain structure of presenilin 1 *Journal of Biological Chemistry* 272, 12047-51.

Lemere CA, Lopera F, Kosik KS et al. (1996) The E280a Presenilin 1 Alzheimer Mutation Produces Increased a-Beta-42 Deposition and Severe Cerebellar Pathology *Nature Medicine* 2, 1146-50.

Lendon CL, Ashall F, Goate AM (1997) Exploring the etiology of Alzheimer disease using molecular genetics *Jama* 277, 825-31.

Levesque G, Yu G, Nishimura M et al. (1999) Presenilins interact with armadillo proteins including neural-specific plakophilin-related protein and beta-catenin *Journal of Neurochemistry* 72, 999-1008.

Levitan D, Greenwald I (1995) Facilitation of lin-12-mediated signalling by sel-12, a Caenorhabditis elegans S182 Alzheimer's disease gene *Nature* 377, 351-4.

Levitan D, Yu G, St George Hyslop P, Goutte C (2001) APH-2/nicastrin functions in LIN-12/Notch signaling in the Caenorhabditis elegans somatic gonad *Dev Biol* 240, 654-61.

Levylahad E, Wasco W, Poorkaj P et al. (1995) Candidate Gene For the Chromosome 1 Familial Alzheimers Disease Locus *Science* 269, 973-7.

L'Hernault SW, Arduengo PM (1992) Mutation of a putative sperm membrane protein in Caenorhabditis elegans prevents sperm differentiation but not its associated meiotic divisions *J Cell Biol* 119, 55-68.

Li YM, Lai MT, Xu M et al. (2000a) Presenilin 1 is linked with gamma-secretase activity in the detergent solubilized state *Proceedings of the National Academy of Sciences of the United States of America* 97, 6138-43.

Li YM, Xu M, Lai MT et al. (2000b) Photoactivated gamma-secretase inhibitors directed to the active site covalently label presenilin 1 *Nature* 405, 689-94.

Lichtenthaler SF, Wang R, Grimm H, Uljon SN, Masters CL, Beyreuther K (1999) Mechanism of the cleavage specificity of Alzheimer's disease gamma-secretase identified by phenylalanine-scanning mutagenesis of the transmembrane domain of the amyloid precursor protein *Proceedings of the National Academy of Sciences of the United States of America* 96, 3053-8.

Lippa CF, Nee LE, Mori H, St George-Hyslop P (1998) Abeta-42 deposition precedes other changes in PS-1 Alzheimer's disease [letter] *Lancet* 352, 1117-8.

Lippincott-Schwartz J, Yuan LC, Bonifacino JS, Klausner RD (1989) Rapid redistribution of Golgi proteins into the ER in cells treated with brefeldin A: evidence for membrane cycling from Golgi to ER *Cell* 56, 801-13.

Loetscher H, Deuschle U, Brockhaus M et al. (1997) Presenilins Are Processed By Caspase-Type Proteases *Journal of Biological Chemistry* 272, 20655-9.

Loffler J, Huber G (1993) Modulation of beta-amyloid precursor protein secretion in differentiated and nondifferentiated cells *Biochem Biophys Res Commun* 195, 97-103.

Logeat F, Bessia C, Brou C et al. (1998) The Notch1 receptor is cleaved constitutively by a furin-like convertase *Proc Natl Acad Sci U S A* 95, 8108-12.

Loo DT, Copani A, Pike CJ, Whittemore ER, Walencewicz AJ, Cotman CW (1993) Apoptosis is induced by beta-amyloid in cultured central nervous system neurons *Proc Natl Acad Sci U S A* 90, 7951-5.

Lopez-Schier H, St Johnston D (2002) Drosophila nicastrin is essential for the intramembranous cleavage of notch *Dev Cell* 2, 79-89.

Lu DC, Rabizadeh S, Chandra S et al. (2000) A second cytotoxic proteolytic peptide derived from amyloid beta-protein precursor *Nature Medicine* 6, 397-404.

Luo WJ, Wang H, Li H et al. (2003) PEN-2 and APH-1 coordinately regulate proteolytic processing of presenilin 1 *J Biol Chem* 278, 7850-4.

Mah AL, Perry G, Smith MA, Monteiro MJ (2000) Identification of ubiquilin, a novel presenilin interactor that increases presenilin protein accumulation *Journal of Cell Biology* 151, 847-62.

Martins RN, Robinson PJ, Chleboun JO, Beyreuther K, Masters CL (1991) The molecular pathology of amyloid deposition in Alzheimer's disease *Molecular Neurobiology* 5, 389-98.

Masters CL, Simms G, Weinman NA, Multhaup G, McDonald BL, Beyreuther K (1985) Amyloid plaque core protein in Alzheimer disease and Down syndrome *Proceedings of the National Academy of Sciences of the United States of America* 82, 4245-9.

Mathews CKavH, K.E (1990) *Biochemistry* California: Benjamin/Cummings Publishing Company.

Mattson MP, Guo Q (1997) Cell and molecular neurobiology of presenilins: a role for the endoplasmic reticulum in the pathogenesis of Alzheimer's disease? *Journal of Neuroscience Research* 50, 505-13.

Mattson MP, Guo Q, Furukawa K, Pedersen WA (1998) Presenilins, the endoplasmic reticulum, and neuronal apoptosis in Alzheimers-disease [Review] *Journal of Neurochemistry* 70, 1-14.

McLoughlin DM, Irving NG, Miller CC (1998) The Fe65 and X11 families of proteins: proteins that interact with the Alzheimer's disease amyloid precursor protein *Biochem Soc Trans* 26, 497-500.

Meredith JE, Jr., Wang Q, Mitchell TJ et al. (2002) Gamma-secretase activity is not involved in presenilin-mediated regulation of beta-catenin *Biochem Biophys Res Commun* 299, 744-50.

Murayama M, Tanaka S, Palacino J et al. (1998) Direct Association of Presenilin-1 With Beta-Catenin *FEBS Letters* 433, 73-7.

Murayama O, Tomita T, Nihonmatsu N et al. (1999) Enhancement of amyloid beta 42 secretion by 28 different presenilin 1 mutations of familial Alzheimer's disease *Neuroscience Letters* 265, 61-3.

Murphy MP, Hickman LJ, Eckman CB, Uljon SN, Wang R, Golde TE (1999) gamma-Secretase, evidence for multiple proteolytic activities and influence of membrane positioning of substrate on generation of amyloid beta peptides of varying length *J Biol Chem* 274, 11914-23.

Murphy MP, Uljon SN, Fraser PE et al. (2000) Presenilin 1 regulates pharmacologically distinct gamma-secretase activities - Implications for the role of presenilin in gamma-secretase cleavage *Journal of Biological Chemistry* 275, 26277-84.

Murrell J, Farlow M, Ghetti B, Benson MD (1991) A mutation in the amyloid precursor protein associated with hereditary Alzheimer's disease *Science* 254, 97-9.

Nakai T, Yamasaki A, Sakaguchi M et al. (1999) Membrane topology of Alzheimer's disease-related presenilin 1. Evidence for the existence of a molecular species with a seven membrane-spanning and one membrane-embedded structure *J Biol Chem* 274, 23647-58.

Nishimura M, Yu G, Levesque G et al. (1999) Presenilin mutations associated with Alzheimer disease cause defective intracellular trafficking of beta-catenin, a component of the presenilin protein complex [see comments] *Nature Medicine* 5, 164-9.

Nishiyama K, Suzuki T, Tokuda H (1996) Inversion of the membrane topology of SecG coupled with SecA-dependent preprotein translocation *Cell* 85, 71-81.

Nitsch RM, Growdon JH (1994) Role of neurotransmission in the regulation of amyloid beta-protein precursor processing. *Biochemical pharmacology* 47, 1275-84.

Niwa M, Sidrauski C, Kaufman RJ, Walter P (1999) A role for presenilin-1 in nuclear accumulation of Ire1 fragments and induction of the mammalian unfolded protein response *Cell.* 99, 691-702.

Nochlin D, Bird TD, Nemens EJ, Ball MJ, Sumi SM (1998) Amyloid angiopathy in a Volga German family with Alzheimer's disease and a presenilin-2 mutation (N141I) *Annals of Neurology* 43, 131-5.

Nunan J, Small DH (2000) Regulation of APP cleavage by alpha-, beta- and gamma-secretases [Review] *FEBS Letters* 483, 6-10.

Oishi M, Nairn AC, Czernik AJ et al. (1997) The cytoplasmic domain of Alzheimer's amyloid precursor protein is phosphorylated at Thr654, Ser655, and Thr668 in adult rat brain and cultured cells *Molecular Medicine* 3, 111-23.

Okochi M, Sahara N, Kametani F et al. (1998) Presenilin 1 cleavage is a universal event in human organs *Neurobiology of Aging* 19, S3-10.

Oltersdorf T, Ward PJ, Henriksson T et al. (1990) The Alzheimer amyloid precursor protein. Identification of a stable intermediate in the biosynthetic/degradative pathway *Journal of Biological Chemistry* 265, 4492-7.

Oyama F, Sawamura N, Kobayashi K et al. (1998) Mutant presenilin 2 transgenic mouse: effect on an age-dependent increase of amyloid beta-protein 42 in the brain *Journal of Neurochemistry* 71, 313-22.

Paetzel M, Dalbey RE, Strynadka NC (1998) Crystal structure of a bacterial signal peptidase in complex with a beta-lactam inhibitor *Nature* 396, 186-90.

Pahlsson P, Shakin-Eshleman SH, Spitalnik SL (1992) N-linked glycosylation of beta-amyloid precursor protein *Biochem Biophys Res Commun* 189, 1667-73.

Pahlsson P, Spitalnik SL (1996) The role of glycosylation in synthesis and secretion of beta-amyloid precursor protein by Chinese hamster ovary cells *Arch Biochem Biophys* 331, 177-86.

Passer BJ, Pellegrini L, Vito P, Ganjei JK, L DA (1999) Interaction of Alzheimer's presenilin-1 and presenilin-2 with Bcl-X-L - A potential role in modulating the threshold of cell death *Journal of Biological Chemistry.* 274, 24007-13.

Pellegrini L, Passer BJ, Tabaton M, Ganjei JK, L DA (1999) Alternative, non-secretase processing of Alzheimer's beta-amyloid precursor protein during apoptosis by caspase-6 and -8 *Journal of Biological Chemistry* 274, 21011-6.

Pinnix I, Musunuru U, Tun H et al. (2001) A novel gamma-secretase assay based on detection of the putative C-terminal fragment-gamma of amyloid beta protein precursor *Journal of Biological Chemistry* 276, 481-7.

Podlisny MB, Citron M, Amarante P et al. (1997) Presenilin Proteins Undergo Heterogeneous Endoproteolysis Between Thr(291) and Ala(299) and Occur As Stable N- and C-Terminal Fragments in Normal and Alzheimer Brain Tissue *Neurobiology of Disease* 3, 325-37.

Prihar G, Fuldner RA, Perez-Tur J et al. (1996) Structure and alternative splicing of the presenilin-2 gene *Neuroreport* 7, 1680-4.

Ratovitski T, Slunt HH, Thinakaran G, Price DL, Sisodia SS, Borchelt DR (1997) Endoproteolytic Processing and Stabilization of Wild-Type and Mutant Presenilin *Journal of Biological Chemistry* 272, 24536-41.

Rawson RB, Zelenski NG, Nijhawan D et al. (1997) Complementation cloning of S2P, a gene encoding a putative metalloprotease required for intramembrane cleavage of SREBPs *Mol Cell* 1, 47-57.

Ray WJ, Yao M, Nowotny P et al. (1999) Evidence for a physical interaction between presenilin and Notch *Proceedings of the National Academy of Sciences of the United States of America* 96, 3263-8.

Refolo LM, Sambamurti K, Efthimiopoulos S, Pappolla MA, Robakis NK (1995) Evidence that secretase cleavage of cell surface Alzheimer amyloid precursor occurs after normal endocytic internalization *Journal of Neuroscience Research* 40, 694-706.

Rogaev EI, Sherrington R, Rogaeva EA et al. (1995) Familial Alzheimer's disease in kindreds with missense mutations in a gene on chromosome 1 related to the Alzheimer's disease type 3 gene *Nature* 376, 775-8.

Rogaev EI, Sherrington R, Wu C et al. (1997) Analysis of the 5' Sequence, Genomic Structure, and Alternative Splicing of the Presenilin-1 Gene (Psen1) Associated With Early Onset Alzheimer Disease *Genomics* 40, 415-24.

Sai X, Kawamura Y, Kokame K, Yamaguchi H, Shiraishi H, Suzuki R, Suzuki T, Kawaichi M, Miyata T, Kitamura T, De Strooper B, Yanagisawa K, Komano H. (2002) Endoplasmic reticulum stress-inducible protein, Herp, enhances presenilin-mediated generation of amyloid beta-protein. *Journal of Biological Chemistry*. 277, 12915-20.

Sambamurti K, Refolo LM, Shioi J, Pappolla MA, Robakis NK (1992) The Alzheimer's amyloid precursor is cleaved intracellularly in the trans-Golgi network or in a post-Golgi compartment *Annals of the New York Academy of Sciences* 674, 118-28.

Sastre M, Turner RS, Levy E (1998) X11 interaction with beta-amyloid precursor protein modulates its cellular stabilization and reduces amyloid beta-protein secretion *J Biol Chem* 273, 22351-7.

Sato N, Urano F, Yoon Leem J et al. (2000) Upregulation of BiP and CHOP by the unfolded-protein response is independent of presenilin expression *Nat Cell Biol* 2, 863-70.

Satoh J, Kuroda Y (2001) Nicastrin, a key regulator of presenilin function, is expressed constitutively in human neural cell lines *Neuropathology* 21, 115-22.

Sawamura N, Morishima-Kawashima M, Waki H et al. (2000) Mutant presenilin 2 transgenic mice - A large increase in the levels of A beta 42 id presumably associated with the low density membrane domain that contains decreased levels of glycerophospholipids and sphingomyelin *Journal of Biological Chemistry* 275, 27901-8.

Saxena MT, Schroeter EH, Mumm JS, Kopan R (2001) Murine notch homologs (N1-4) undergo presenilin-dependent proteolysis *J Biol Chem* 276, 40268-73.

Schellenberg GD, Bird TD, Wijsman EM et al. (1992) Genetic linkage evidence for a familial Alzheimer's disease locus on chromosome 14 *Science* 258, 668-71.

Scheuner D, Eckman C, Jensen M et al. (1996) Secreted amyloid beta-protein similar to that in the senile plaques of Alzheimer's disease is increased in vivo by the presenilin 1 and 2 and APP mutations linked to familial Alzheimer's disease [see comments] *Nature Medicine* 2, 864-70.

Schroeter EH, Kisslinger JA, Kopan R (1998) Notch-1 signalling requires ligand-induced proteolytic release of intracellular domain *Nature* 393, 382-6.

Schubert D, LaCorbiere M, Saitoh T, Cole G (1989) Characterization of an amyloid beta precursor protein that binds heparin and contains tyrosine sulfate *Proceedings of the National Academy of Sciences of the United States of America* 86, 2066-9.

Schwarzman AL, Singh N, Tsiper M et al. (1999) Endogenous presenilin 1 redistributes to the surface of lamellipodia upon adhesion of Jurkat cells to a collagen matrix *Proceedings of the National Academy of Sciences of the United States of America* 96, 7932-7.

Seeger M, Nordstedt C, Petanceska S et al. (1997) Evidence For Phosphorylation and Oligomeric Assembly of Presenilin 1 *Proceedings of the National Academy of Sciences of the United States of America* 94, 5090-4.

Seiffert D, Bradley JD, Rominger CM et al. (2000) Presenilin-1 and -2 are molecular targets for gamma-secretase inhibitors *J Biol Chem* 275, 34086-91.

Selkoe DJ (2001) Alzheimer's disease: genes, proteins, and therapy *Physiol Rev* 81, 741-66.

Shen J, Bronson RT, Chen DF, Xia WM, Selkoe DJ, Tonegawa S (1997) Skeletal and Cns Defects in Presenilin-1-Deficient Mice *Cell* 89, 629-39.

Sherrington R, Rogaev EI, Liang Y et al. (1995) Cloning of a gene bearing missense mutations in early-onset familial Alzheimer's disease [see comments] *Nature* 375, 754-60.

Siman R, Velji J (2003) Localization of presenilin-nicastrin complexes and gamma-secretase activity to the trans-Golgi network *J Neurochem* 84, 1143-53.

Slack BE, Nitsch RM, Livneh E, Kunz GM, Jr., Eldar H, Wurtman RJ (1993) Regulation of amyloid precursor protein release by protein kinase C in Swiss 3T3 fibroblasts *Annals of the New York Academy of Sciences* 695, 128-31.

Song WH, Nadeau P, Yuan ML, Yang XD, Shen J, Yankner BA (1999) Proteolytic release and nuclear translocation of Notch-1 are induced by presenilin-1 and impaired by pathogenic presenilin-1 mutations *Proceedings of the National Academy of Sciences of the United States of America.* 96, 6959-63.

Soriano S, Lu DC, Chandra S, Pietrzik CU, Koo EH (2001) The amyloidogenic pathway of amyloid precursor protein (APP) is independent of its cleavage by caspases *J Biol Chem* 276, 29045-50.

St George-Hyslop P, Haines J, Rogaev E et al. (1992) Genetic evidence for a novel familial Alzheimer's disease locus on chromosome 14 *Nat Genet* 2, 330-4.

Steiner H, Capell A, Pesold B et al. (1998) Expression of Alzheimer's disease-associated presenilin-1 is controlled by proteolytic degradation and complex formation *Journal of Biological Chemistry* 273, 32322-31.

Steiner H, Duff K, Capell A et al. (1999a) A loss of function mutation of presenilin-2 interferes with amyloid beta-peptide production and notch signaling *Journal of Biological Chemistry.* 274, 28669-73.

Steiner H, Pesold B, Haass C (1999b) An in vivo assay for the identification of target proteases which cleave membrane-associated substrates *FEBS Letters* 463, 245-9.

Steiner H, Winkler E, Edbauer D et al. (2002) PEN-2 is an integral component of the gamma-secretase complex required for coordinated expression of presenilin and nicastrin *J Biol Chem* 277, 39062-5.

Struhl G, Adachi A (1998) Nuclear access and action of notch in vivo *Cell* 93, 649-60.

Sudoh S, Kawamura Y, Sato S et al. (1998) Presenilin 1 mutations linked to familial Alzheimer's disease increase the intracellular levels of amyloid beta-protein 1-42 and its N-terminally truncated variant(s) which are generated at distinct sites *Journal of Neurochemistry* 71, 1535-43.

Takashima A, Sato M, Mercken M, Tanaka S, Kondo S, Honda T, Sato K, Murayama M, Noguchi K, Nakazato Y, Takahashi H. (1996) Localization of Alzheimer-associated presenilin 1 in transfected COS-7 cells. *Biochemical and biophysical research communications*. 227, 423-6.

Tanahashi H, Tabira T (1999) Isolation of human delta-catenin and its binding specificity with presenilin 1 *Neuroreport* 10, 563-8.

Tanzi RE, George-Hyslop PS, Gusella JF (1991) Molecular genetics of Alzheimer disease amyloid *Journal of Biological Chemistry* 266, 20579-82.

Tesco G, Kim TW, Diehlmann A, Beyreuther K, Tanzi RE (1998a) Abrogation of the presenilin 1 beta-catenin interaction and preservation of the heterodimeric presenilin 1 complex following caspase activation *Journal of Biological Chemistry* 273, 33909-14.

Tesco G, Kim TW, Diehlmann A, Beyreuther K, Tanzi RE (1998b) Abrogation of the presenilin 1/beta-catenin interaction and preservation of the heterodimeric presenilin 1 complex following caspase activation *J Biol Chem* 273, 33909-14.

Thinakaran G, Borchelt DR, Lee MK et al. (1996a) Endoproteolysis of Presenilin 1 and Accumulation of Processed Derivatives in Vivo *Neuron* 17, 181-90.

Thinakaran G, Teplow DB, Siman R, Greenberg B, Sisodia SS (1996b) Metabolism of the "Swedish" amyloid precursor protein variant in neuro2a (N2a) cells. Evidence that cleavage at the "beta-secretase" site occurs in the golgi apparatus *Journal of Biological Chemistry* 271, 9390-7.

Tirasophon W, Welihinda AA, Kaufman RJ (1998) A stress response pathway from the endoplasmic reticulum to the nucleus requires a novel bifunctional protein kinase/endoribonuclease (Ire1p) in mammalian cells *Genes Dev* 12, 1812-24.

Tomita S, Kirino Y, Suzuki T (1998) Cleavage of Alzheimer's amyloid precursor protein (APP) by secretases occurs after O-glycosylation of APP in the protein secretory pathway. Identification of intracellular compartments in which APP cleavage occurs without using toxic agents that interfere with protein metabolism *Journal of Biological Chemistry* 273, 6277-84.

Tomita S, Ozaki T, Taru H et al. (1999) Interaction of a neuron-specific protein containing PDZ domains with Alzheimer's amyloid precursor protein *J Biol Chem* 274, 2243-54.

Tomita T, Katayama R, Takikawa R, Iwatsubo T (2002) Complex N-glycosylated form of nicastrin is stabilized and selectively bound to presenilin fragments *FEBS Lett* 520, 117-21.

Uchihara T, el Hachimi HK, Duyckaerts C et al. (1996) Widespread immunoreactivity of presenilin in neurons of normal and Alzheimer's disease brains: double-labeling immunohistochemical study *Acta Neuropathologica* 92, 325-30.

Urban S, Freeman M (2002) Intramembrane proteolysis controls diverse signalling pathways throughout evolution *Curr Opin Genet Dev* 12, 512-8.

van de Craen M, de Jonghe C, van den Brande I et al. (1999) Identification of caspases that cleave presenilin-1 and presenilin-2. Five presenilin-1 (PS1) mutations do not alter the sensitivity of PS1 to caspases *FEBS Lett* 445, 149-54.

Van Gassen G, De Jonghe C, Pype S et al. (1999) Alzheimer's disease associated presenilin 1 interacts with HC5 and ZETA, subunits of the catalytic 20S proteasome *Neurobiol Dis* 6, 376-91.

Verdile G, Martins RN, Duthie M, Holmes E, St George-Hyslop PH, Fraser PE (2000) Inhibiting amyloid precursor protein C-terminal cleavage promotes an interaction with presenilin 1 *Journal of Biological Chemistry* 275, 20794-8.

Walter J, Capell A, Grunberg J et al. (1996) The Alzheimer's disease-associated presenilins are differentially phosphorylated proteins located predominantly within the endoplasmic reticulum *Molecular Medicine* 2, 673-91.

Walter J, Capell A, Hung AY et al. (1997a) Ectodomain phosphorylation of beta-amyloid precursor protein at two distinct cellular locations *J Biol Chem* 272, 1896-903.

Walter J, Grunberg J, Capell A et al. (1997b) Proteolytic processing of the Alzheimer disease-associated presenilin-1 generates an in vivo substrate for protein kinase C *Proceedings of the National Academy of Sciences of the United States of America* 94, 5349-54.

Walter J, Grunberg J, Schindzielorz A, Haass C (1998) Proteolytic fragments of the Alzheimer's disease associated presenilins-1 and -2 are phosphorylated in vivo by distinct cellular mechanisms *Biochemistry* 37, 5961-7.

Walter J, Schindzielorz A, Grunberg J, Haass C (1999) Phosphorylation of presenilin-2 regulates its cleavage by caspases and retards progression of apoptosis *Proceedings of the National Academy of Sciences of the United States of America* 96, 1391-6.

Walter J, Schindzielorz A, Hartung B, Haass C (2000) Phosphorylation of the beta-amyloid precursor protein at the cell surface by ectocasein kinases 1 and 2 *Journal of Biological Chemistry* 275, 23523-9.

Wang XZ, Harding HP, Zhang Y, Jolicoeur EM, Kuroda M, Ron D (1998) Cloning of mammalian Ire1 reveals diversity in the ER stress responses *Embo J* 17, 5708-17.

Weidemann A, Konig G, Bunke D et al. (1989) Identification, biogenesis, and localization of precursors of Alzheimer's disease A4 amyloid protein *Cell* 57, 115-26.

Weidemann A, Paliga K, Durrwang U et al. (1997) Formation of stable complexes between two Alzheimer's disease gene products: presenilin-2 and beta-amyloid precursor protein *Nature Medicine* 3, 328-32.

Weidemann A, Paliga K, Durrwang U et al. (1999) Proteolytic processing of the Alzheimer's disease amyloid precursor protein within its cytoplasmic domain by caspase-like proteases *Journal of Biological Chemistry* 274, 5823-9.

Wild-Bode C, Yamazaki T, Capell A et al. (1997) Intracellular generation and accumulation of amyloid beta-peptide terminating at amino acid 42 *J Biol Chem* 272, 16085-8.

Williams SE, Ashcom JD, Argraves WS, Strickland DK (1992) A novel mechanism for controlling the activity of alpha 2-macroglobulin receptor/low density lipoprotein receptor-related protein. Multiple regulatory sites for 39-kDa receptor-associated protein *J Biol Chem* 267, 9035-40.

Wolfe MS (2001) Presenilin and gamma-secretase: structure meets function *J Neurochem* 76, 1615-20.

Wolfe MS (2002) Secretase as a target for Alzheimer's disease *Curr Top Med Chem* 2, 371-83.

Wolfe MS, Citron M, Diehl TS, Xia W, Donkor IO, Selkoe DJ (1998) A substrate-based difluoro ketone selectively inhibits Alzheimer's gamma-secretase activity *Journal of Medicinal Chemistry* 41, 6-9.

Wolfe MS, Xia W, Ostaszewski BL, Diehl TS, Kimberly WT, Selkoe DJ (1999) Two transmembrane aspartates in presenilin-1 required for presenilin endoproteolysis and gamma-secretase activity *Nature* 398, 513-7.

Wolozin B, Iwasaki K, Vito P et al. (1996) Participation of presenilin 2 in apoptosis: enhanced basal activity conferred by an Alzheimer mutation *Science* 274, 1710-3.

Xia W, Ray WJ, Ostaszewski BL et al. (2000a) Presenilin complexes with the C-terminal fragments of amyloid precursor protein at the sites of amyloid beta-protein generation *Proc Natl Acad Sci U S A* 97, 9299-304.

Xia W, Zhang J, Ostaszewski BL et al. (1998) Presenilin 1 regulates the processing of beta-amyloid precursor protein C-terminal fragments and the generation of amyloid beta-protein in endoplasmic reticulum and Golgi *Biochemistry* 37, 16465-71.

Xia W, Zhang J, Perez R, Koo EH, Selkoe DJ (1997a) Interaction between amyloid precursor protein and presenilins in mammalian cells: implications for the pathogenesis of Alzheimer disease *Proc Natl Acad Sci U S A* 94, 8208-13.

Xia WM, Ostaszewski BL, Kimberly WT et al. (2000b) FAD mutations in presenilin-1 or amyloid precursor protein decrease the efficacy of a gamma-secretase inhibitor: Evidence for direct involvement of PS1 in the gamma-secretase cleavage complex *Neurobiology of Disease* 7, 673-81.

Xia WM, Zhang JM, Kholodenko D et al. (1997b) Enhanced Production and Oligomerization of the 42-Residue Amyloid Beta-Protein By Chinese Hamster Ovary Cells Stably Expressing Mutant Presenilins *Journal of Biological Chemistry* 272, 7977-82.

Yagi T, Takeichi M (2000) Cadherin superfamily genes: functions, genomic organization, and neurologic diversity *Genes Dev* 14, 1169-80.

Yang DS, Tandon A, Chen F et al. (2002) Mature glycosylation and trafficking of nicastrin modulate its binding to presenilins *J Biol Chem* 277, 28135-42.

Yasuda Y, Kudo T, Katayama T et al. (2002) FAD-linked presenilin-1 mutants impede translation regulation under ER stress *Biochem Biophys Res Commun* 296, 313-8.

Yu C, Kim SH, Ikeuchi T et al. (2001) Characterization of a presenilin-mediated amyloid precursor protein carboxyl-terminal fragment gamma. Evidence for distinct mechanisms involved in gamma -secretase processing of the APP and Notch1 transmembrane domains *J Biol Chem* 276, 43756-60.

Yu G, Chen F, Levesque G et al. (1998) The presenilin 1 protein is a component of a high molecular weight intracellular complex that contains beta-catenin *J Biol Chem* 273, 16470-5.

Yu G, Nishimura M, Arawaka S et al. (2000) Nicastrin modulates presenilin-mediated notch/glp-1 signal transduction and beta APP processing *Nature* 407, 48-54.

Zelenski NG, Rawson RB, Brown MS, Goldstein JL (1999) Membrane topology of S2P, a protein required for intramembranous cleavage of sterol regulatory element-binding proteins *J Biol Chem* 274, 21973-80.

Zhang JM, Kang DE, Xia WM et al. (1998a) Subcellular Distribution and Turnover of Presenilins in Transfected Cells *Journal of Biological Chemistry* 273, 12436-42.

Zhang W, Han SW, McKeel DW, Goate A, Wu JY (1998b) Interaction of presenilins with the filamin family of actin-binding proteins *Journal of Neuroscience* 18, 914-22.

Chapter VIII

THE ROLE OF VASCULAR RISK, BETA-AMYLOID METABOLISM, AND NEUROINFLAMMATION IN THE GENETICS OF LATE-ONSET ALZHEIMER'S DISEASE

Francesco Panza**, *Alessia D'Introno*, *Anna M. Colacicco*, *Cristiano Capurso*, *Anna M. Basile*, *Antonio Capurso* and *Vincenzo Solfrizzi

Department of Geriatrics - Center for the Aging Brain - Memory Unit
University of Bari
Policlinico - Piazza Giulio Cesare, 11
70124 Bari, Italy

INTRODUCTION

Alzheimer's Disease (AD), the most common primary neurodegenerative disorder in the elderly, is characterized by protein processing gone haywire and a rising cluster of toxic proteins inside the brain cells and in the intercellular spaces. The intraneuronal protein clusters are composed of paired helical filaments of hyperphosphorilated tau protein, called neurofibrillary tangles (NFT); whereas, extracellular protein clusters are formed mostly by the deposition of β-amyloid (Aβ). There are called senile plaques (SP) and appear long before NFT do. The creation of SP begins with the misprocessing of amyloid precursor protein (APP) and causes aggregates that are thought to initiate a pathogenic cascade ultimately leading to neuronal loss and dementia.

* Address correspondence to: Francesco Panza, MD, Department of Geriatrics - Center for Aging Brain - Memory Unit, University of Bari - Policlinico - Piazza Giulio Cesare, 11, 70124 Bari – Italy, Phone: + 39-80-5592685; Fax: + 39-80-5478633; E-mail: geriat.dot@geriatria.uniba.it

The clinical, neuropathological, and biochemical abnormalities of AD are virtually identical in either early onset familial AD or sporadic late onset AD, suggesting a common pathogenic pathway for both forms. Genetic analysis of the familial autosomal-dominant AD with early onset has led to the identification of disease-causing mutations in three genes: amyloid precursor protein (APP), presenilin1 (PS1) and presenilin2 (PS2) [1-3] (Table 1). These inheritance mutations most likely play a role in 50% of early onset familial AD cases. The common effect of all these mutations is increased production of Aβ. By contrast, the cause of the more common, sporadic, late-onset AD remains unknown. It seems clear that AD is a multifactorial disease, with several complex triggers, where environmental factors in conjunction with genetic mutations have to be considered. Yet attempts to identify environmental and genetic risk factors associated with AD have not been conclusive. The risk factors identified so far are intriguing but not completely illuminating.

Table 1. Gene Mutations in Familial Autosomal-Dominant AD with Early Onset.

Mutations	Effects on Aβ metabolism
Chromosome 21 (Down Syndrome)	Increased production of APP and Aβ
APP mutations (chromosome 21)	Aberrant production of APP and increased production of Aβ
PS-1 mutations (chromosome 14)	Increased production of Aβ
PS-2 mutations (chromosome 1)	Increased production of Aβ

APP = amyloid precursor protein
PS = presenilin
AD = Alzheimer's disease

APOLIPOPROTEIN E AND THE CURRENT SEARCH FOR DIFFERENT AD SUSCEPTIBILITY GENES

The autosomal-dominant forms of AD account for, at most, 5% of all AD cases; the remaining 95% are represented by sporadic forms, where no obvious inheritance pattern is seen. It turns out that other genetic or nongenetic factors chould be involved in a greater proportion of cases. So far, several environmental factors have been identified and correlated with a higher risk of sporadic AD, such as age, educational level, female gender, previous history of head injury, high blood pressure, and dietary factors. Numerous genes, as well, have been shown to increase susceptibility for sporadic AD, but that does not mean causality but predisposition to the development of the disease (Tables 2-3). Among these genetic risk factors, Apolipoprotein E (APOE) gene is the best-documented one [4]. APOE gene is located on chromosome 19 and occurs in three common alleles, ε2, ε3, and ε4. Having the ε4 allele may increase the risk for AD. Autopsy-confirmed studies reported that the frequencies of APOE ε4 allele vary from 0.33 to 0.40 in AD patients, whereas they range from 0.05 to 0.14 in healthy subjects [5]. In our recent study carried out in a Southern Italy population [6], we showed that the frequency of APOE ε4 allele in both late-onset AD patients and middle aged controls is underexpressed in relation to that of other European populations. In this study we provided a new finding that the APOE ε4 allele frequency decreases according to a geographic trend from Northern to Southern Europe in late-onset AD patients and normal, middle-aged adults. However, the strength of association of APOE ε4 with AD seems to be not influenced by the low prevalence of ε4 allele due to the geographic decreasing trend from Northern to Southern Europe. In fact, in our subsequent study [7], we confirmed the association between AD and APO ε4 allele, when the whole AD sample was examined. However, stratifying the whole sample in two subgroups in relation to age at onset of AD symptoms, we found an increased ε4 allele frequency in late-onset AD patients compared to controls, but this difference was not significant. This finding suggests that the decreasing trend of APOE ε4 allele from Northern to Southern Europe may influence the strength of association between the ε4 allele and sporadic AD, but only in relation to age. The geographic trend and increasing age may act synergistically in decreasing APOE ε4 allele frequency. Furthermore, the strength of the association between ε4 and sporadic AD attenuates with age. It has also shown a gene dose-dependent increase in risk of AD, such that subjects with two copies of ε4 allele have an earlier age of onset than those with one or no copies of ε4 allele. However, the inheritance of one or two APOE ε4 alleles does not predict AD with certainty [8]. This means that a person can have one or two APOE ε4 alleles and still not get the disease, and people who develop the disease may not have any APOE ε4 alleles. APOE ε4 alleles increases the risk of developing AD, but it does not cause the disease. It has been estimated that the APOE gene accounts for only 45-60% of the genetic risk for late-onset AD, suggesting that additional risk factors must be involved in the development of late-onset AD.

Table 2. Vascular Susceptibility Genes for Sporadic Late-Onset AD

Genes (polymorphism)	Involvement in vascular risk
APOE (chromosome 19; exon 4 112 and 158 polymorphism)	Effect on levels of total cholesterol, LDL-cholesterol, and apo B
APOE (promoter polymorphisms)	Regulation of quantitative expression of APOE
ACE (chromosome 17; intron 16 I/D polymorphism)	Effect on plasma ACE levels
MTHFR (chromosome 1; 677C/T polymorphism)	Effect on homocysteine plasma levels
NOS3 (chromosome 7; exon 7 G/A polymorphism)	Strong effect on vasodilatation
PON1 (chromosome 7; 192 A/G polymorphism)	Participation in the prevention of LDL oxidation
LRP1 (chromosome 12; exon 3 C/T and tetranucleotide repeat polymorphisms)	Regulation of proteinase and lipoprotein levels

APOE = apolipoprotein E
ACE = angiotensin converting enzyme
MTHFR = methyltetrahydrofolatereductase
NOS3 = nitric oxide synhase 3
PON1 = paraoxonase 1
LRP1 = low-density lipoprotein receptor-related protein 1
AD = Alzheimer's disease

Studies over the last several years have attempted to identify other candidate genes for late-onset AD. Pericak–Vance and co-workers performed a complete genomic screen study in late-onset familial AD and showed the first evidence for a new late-onset AD locus on the pericentromeric region of chromosome 12 [9]. A subsequent follow-up study detected evidence for linkage in a wider region of the same chromosome [10]. These findings were replicated by other studies in independent samples [11, 12], and by two full genome scans [13, 14]. All these studies strengthen the argument that an AD susceptibility gene maps on chromosome 12, although they highlighted different regions of maximum linkage. Two functional candidate genes located on chromosome 12 have received considerable attention: low density lipoprotein receptor-related protein 1 (LRP1) [15], and alpha-2-macroglobulin (A2M) [16]. However, more recently, research efforts have identified other genes located within the linkage region of chromosome 12 that could be plausible candidate genes for late-onset AD.

Table 3. Susceptibility Genes for Sporadic Late-Onset AD Involved in Aβ Metabolism

Genes (polymorphism)	Effects on Aβ metabolism
APOE (chromosome 19; exon 4 112 and 158 polymorphism)	Binding of APOE4 to soluble Aβ with an increase in fibril formation
APOE (promoter polymorphisms)	Regulation of quantitative expression of APOE
A2M (chromosome 12; 5bp Insertion/Deletion and exon 24 G/A polymorphisms)	Effect on Aβ deposition and fibril formation
LRP1 (chromosome 12; exon 3 C/T and tetranucleotide repeat polymorphisms)	Influence on the balance of Aβ synthesis and clearance
LBP-1c/CP2/LSF (chromosome 12; 3' UTR G/A polymorphism)	Interaction with proteins involved in Aβ cascade pathway
ACT (chromosome 14; signal peptide coding region A/T polymorphism)	Implication in the polymerization of Aβ
BChE (chromosome 3; G/A polymorphism, K variant)	Participation in the Aβ transformation process
BH (chromosome 17; C terminus A/G polymorphism)	Involvement in processing of APP
Cat D (chromosome 11; exon 2 C/T polymorphism)	Implication in the proteolytic cleavage of APP

A2M = α-2-macroglobulin
LRP1 = low-density lipoprotein receptor-related protein
LBP-1c/CP2/LSF = LPS binding protein-1c/Coat Protein 2/Late SV40 Factor
ACT = alpha 1-antichymotrypsin
BChE = butyrylcholinesterase
BH = bleomycin hydrolase
Cat D = cathepsin
AD = Alzheimer's disease

Apart from chromosome 12, genome wide screens and linkage studies have indicated evidence of linkage to other chromosomes. Pericak-Vance and co-workers reported linkage in regions of chromosomes 4, 6, 20 and, more significantly, 9 [9]. In their genome screen, Kehoe et al. also indicated evidence of linkage to chromosomes 6 and 9 [13]. Recently, linkage to region on chromosome 6, where the gene coding the Tumor Necrosis Factor-α (TNF- α) is located, has been found by Collins et al. in APOE ε4- positive late-onset AD families [17]. Strong evidence of linkage to a new region on chromosome 10 in late-onset AD has also been shown, housing a possible candidate gene for AD on this chromosome [13, 18-22]. A linkage region on the same chromosome 10 influencing age at onset of AD has been recently found by genomic screen in families with AD [23]. In a wide genomic linkage disequilibrium mapping study in Finnish late-onset AD patients, Hiltunen et al. reported a linkage disequilibrium region in the 13q12 chromosome region, which may encompass a new susceptibility gene involved in a sex-specific effect in late-onset AD [24]. The same authors replicated this finding in a subsequent study, and found seven additional loci on different chromosomes associated with AD [25]. Linkage regions to several chromosomes were also obtained by Myers et al., although the strongest evidence for linkage was to chromosome 10 [14]. Building on improving understanding of the genetics of AD, by either linkage studies and full genome screens or candidate studies, research presumably will continue to look for clues as to which genetic loci are associated with AD.

APOLIPOPROTEIN E AND AD: VASCULAR AND AMYLOID CASCADE HYPOTHESIS

As mentioned before, the APOE gene is so far the best-established genetic risk factor for late-onset AD. APOE protein is one of the major constituents in very low density lipoproteins and plays a key role in the transport of cholesterol and other lipids among various cells of the body. The importance of APOE in the central nervous system (CNS) became evident with the association of the ε4 allele of APOE with late-onset familial and sporadic AD [26]. In CNS and in the peripheral nervous system, APOE is thought to be implicated in mobilization and redistribution of cholesterol, in repair, growth, and maintenance of myelin and neuronal membranes during development and injury [27, 28]. In the brains of AD patients, APOE occurs in excess amounts and is co-localized with plaques.

The ways by which APOE ε4 increases the likelihood of developing AD are not known with certainty, but one explanation holds that the E4 isoform of the protein binds Aβ with a higher affinity than does E3 isoform [29]. APOE4 acts as a "pathological molecular chaperone" that binds to soluble Aβ and enhances β-pleated sheet formation and amyloid fibril stability, facilitating Aβ build-up in plaques, as supported by the fact that patients bearing one APOE ε4 allele have an increased number of SP and Aβ deposition [30].

Another explanation about the association of APOE with AD has been put forward in recent years, and relies on a vascular hypothesis. APOE could be implicated in AD pathogenesis through its involvement in atherosclerosis and vascular disease. The presence of APOE ε4 allele has been, in fact, associated with Coronary Artery Disease (CAD), and the development of atherosclerosis [31], presumably related to the higher levels of total cholesterol, low density lipoprotein (LDL)-cholesterol, and apolipoprotein B in subjects with the homozygous APOE ε4 genotype than in those ε2- or ε3-carriers. Moreover, there is increasing evidence that vascular risk factors are associated with AD, suggesting that AD and vascular disease can be causally related or share common environmental and genetic determinants.

Since APOE ε4 is clearly a risk factor for AD, whatever its mechanism in AD pathogenesis may be, an APOE test might appear to give people useful information about their risk for AD. However, to date, APOE genotyping is not recommended in diagnosis of AD, because its predictive value is poor and is not very sensitive nor specific [32]. APOE testing can be performed only in patients suspected of having AD, but not in healthy people or relatives of AD patients as a screening or predictive test. For a person with symptoms of dementia, APOE testing may offer a piece of evidence that the dementia is due to AD, and may add confidence to the clinical diagnosis [33]. In AD Centers, clinical diagnosis is correct over 90% of the time without APOE testing. When APOE genotyping is performed in combination with the clinical criteria for the disease, the specificity of the diagnosis is increased by approximately 4%.

Recently, it has been suggested that the quantitative expression of APOE alleles results from mutations in the promoter region of the gene. Two polymorphisms at sites –491 and –219 of the APOE promoter gene have been initially examined and found to produce variations in the transcriptional activity of the gene, most probably through differential binding of nuclear proteins [34]. The effects of both these polymorphisms on AD risk have been analyzed in different case-control studies with inconsistent results [35-44]. Another two polymorphisms have been identified in the APOE gene, respectively at –427 site of the promoter region and at –186 base pairs (bp) of the gene TATA box, within a consensus sequence of a potential transcriptional binding site (Th1/E47cs). The studies on the association among these last two APOE polymorphisms and sporadic AD have been contradictory [41, 45-51], whereas a linkage between the alleles of all the APOE regulatory region polymorphisms and the APOE coding region alleles have been generally found. These findings confirm that the APOE ε4 status is still the best predictor of risk in AD.

VASCULAR RISK FACTORS IN AD

AD and vascular disease share common genetic and non genetic risk factors. Non genetic factors include cholesterol, diabetes mellitus, atrial fibrillation, hypertension, serum APOE levels, and atherosclerosis [52]. High serum cholesterol during middle age or early old age seems to confer an increased risk of AD in old age [53]. Epidemiological studies showed that the onset of AD occurs earlier in APOE ε4-carriers with high serum cholesterol [54]. On the contrary, a cross sectional study reported an association between AD and lower cholesterol [55]. This finding was confirmed by our recent study [56], in which lower serum levels of cholesterol were found in AD patients. In the same study, we analyzed the relationship between sporadic AD and Lipoprotein(a) [Lp(a)], a LDL-like particle with apolipoprotein(a), that is believed to have atherogenic and thrombotic properties [57] and has been associated with cerebrovascular disease (CVD) as well as vascular dementia (VaD) [58, 59]. We found that Lp(a) serum levels were significantly associated, according to a nonlinear relationship, with an increased risk for AD, independently of APOE genotypes, and dependent on age.

Epidemiological and cross sectional studies have shown a link between hypertension and AD [60, 55]. Neuropathological evidence also linked AD and hypertension, describing a higher prevalence of SP and NFT in hypertensive patients without dementia than in normotensives [61]. Positive association between diabetes mellitus and AD has been reported in different longitudinal studies. In a Rotterdam study, diabetes mellitus was found to nearly double the risk of both VaD and AD, and the subjects who needed insulin treatment were at higher risk of dementia [62]. The Rotterdam study also showed a positive association among atrial fibrillation, a known risk factor for CVD and dementia, stronger with AD rather than VaD [63]. Various indicators of atherosclerosis have been related to AD. The prevalence of the disease appears to increase with the degree of atherosclerosis. An interaction between atherosclerosis and APOE has also been reported: subjects bearing at least one APOE ε4 allele had the highest risk of AD [64].

Serum APOE concentrations have been shown to modulate lipid metabolism [65], suggesting that APOE concentration might be a risk factor for CAD and cerebrovascular disease [66]. A role for serum APOE concentration has been also suggested in AD, although the data on the association among serum APOE levels and AD are controversial [67-69]. In a recent study performed in AD patients and age-matched healthy controls, centenarians, and young healthy adults, we found that the presence of APOE ε4 allele was associated with lower serum APOE levels, whereas the ε2 allele with higher levels [70]. The difference in serum APOE concentration among AD cases and age-matched controls was not statistically significant, suggesting not only that serum APOE levels are unrelated to AD, but that AD patients are somewhat protected from an age-associated increase in serum APOE levels. We also stressed the important role of the APOE locus in regulating serum APOE levels, and excluded the use of serum APOE levels as a biochemical marker for AD.

Among genetic candidate links between AD and vascular risk (Table 2), apart from the APOE gene, the renin angiotensin system (RAS) has been an attractive target. One of the key enzymes of the RAS is the angiotensin I-converting enzyme (ACE), a dipeptidyl carboxypeptidase that plays an important role in blood pressure regulation and electrolyte balance by hydrolyzing angiotensin I into angiotensin II, and inactivating bradykinin, a potent vasodilator. Besides being present as a membrane-bound enzyme on the surface of vascular endothelial cells, ACE also circulates in plasma. Circulating ACE levels show extensive interindividual variability and are highly genetically determined [71]. The ACE gene is located on chromosome 17, and an insertion/deletion (I/D) polymorphism, due to the presence or absence of a 287bp alu-type sequence in its 16th intron, has been shown to cosegregate with serum ACE levels and tissue ACE activities [72]. The physiological importance of the I/D polymorphism relies on the fact that subjects bearing the D allele have higher circulating and tissue ACE levels than those with I allele [73]. Homozygosity of ACE D allele has been linked to an increased risk for myocardial infarction, left ventricular hypertrophy [74], and in-stent restenosis after angioplasty [75]. More recently this polymorphism has been associated with an increased risk for development of sporadic late-onset AD. A number of studies considered ACE I allele as a risk factor for AD [76-78], while other studies in different populations found an association between ACE D allele and dementia [79], or did not detect any effect of ACE polymorphism [80-82]. This means that results on the role of the ACE gene in AD are so far not conclusive. In a very recent study [83], we investigated the association between ACE polymorphism and increased risk of AD in a Southern Italy population. We did not find any link between this polymorphism and AD, but the age at onset of AD patients with the ACE I/I genotype was lower than those with

ACE D/D genotype, although not statistically significant, suggesting that the presence of a ACE I allele might help in anticipating the onset of the disease without an increased risk of AD associated with this allele. What is noteworthy is the finding that, as with our previous results on APOE, ACE I allele frequency decreases according to a geographic trend from Northern to Southern Europe in AD patients and age-matched controls, possibly reflecting the different and conflicting patterns for association of ACE polymorphism and AD found in various studies.

The methyltetrahydrofolatereductase (MTHFR) gene has been considered another new plausible susceptibility candidate gene for AD, as it is involved in the metabolism of homocysteine. High homocysteine plasma levels (hyperhomocystinemia) have been considered an independent risk factor for CAD and stroke [84]. A common mutation in the gene (677C→T) has been identified that results in thermolability and mildly reduced activity of the encoded enzyme, and causes hyperhomocystinemia [85]. The question whether carrying the C→T mutation is a risk factor for VaD and AD has been addressed in different studies [86-92]. However, just one study reported an association with the MTHFR gene and senile dementia [92], although several data supported the connection between hyperhomocystinemia and cognitive decline and AD. It can be assumed that the increased levels of homocysteine observed in AD patients are an epiphenomenon of dementia rather than a cause of it.

The overlap between vascular disease and AD has put forward other genetic vascular risk factors likely involved in AD, such as nitric oxide synthase (NOS) 3, paraoxonase (PON) 1, and LRP1.

The NOS 3 gene, located on chromosome 7, encodes endothelial NOS which produces the majority of circulating nitric oxide, a factor with potent vasodilatory properties that has been implicated in various disorders including hypertension and myocardial infarction [93, 94]. The gene has a common structural polymorphism (G→A) in its exon 7 which has been reported to be associated with late-onset AD, independently from the APOE gene [95]. But subsequent studies in different populations failed to replicate this original finding [78, 96-101], so that, even if not excluded, this genetic polymorphism cannot be considered as a susceptibility marker for AD.

Two polymorphisms in the gene encoding PON1, [192 (R or Q) and 55 (M or L)], have been identified and associated with coronary artery disease [102, 103]. PON1 is an A-esterase with peroxidase-like activity present on the surface of high density lipoproteins (HDL) and participates in the prevention of LDL oxidation. Serum levels of PON1 are genetically determined and strongly influenced by the polymorphism (A→G) at the position 192 of the gene [104]. A significant decrease in PON1 activity has been reported in AD and VaD patients compared to the healthy control subjects, suggesting that a defect in this enzyme can play a role in the pathogenesis of AD and VAD [105]. In a study performed in AD, VAD and mild cognitive impairment patients, compared with healthy control subjects, serum PON1 activity has been shown to be a discriminating factor between AD and VAD [106]. The 192 polymorphism has also been reported as a possible reliable marker to distinguish patients with AD from patients with VAD and from healthy subjects, indicating that differences in 192 polymorphism distribution between AD and VAD might partially explain the significant difference in serum PON1 found in these two types of dementia [107]. Other association studies, if not numerous, did not find any link among PON1 192 polymorphism and AD or VAD [108-110]. Further studies are needed to investigate and clarify the hypothetical role of this polymorphism in dementia.

The LRP1 noted to be involved in vascular disorders is a large endocytic and multifactorial receptor that regulates proteinase and lipoprotein levels by their catabolism. The LRP1 gene is an attractive candidate gene for AD for several reasons. Beyond its involvement in lipid metabolism, LRP1 is the main APOE receptor in the brain, and binds APP and A2M [111, 112], all of which are proteins involved in AD pathogenesis. Further, LRP1 is expressed in immunoreactive SP, dystrophic neurites and reactive astrocytes [113, 114], and it is located on chromosome 12 within the AD linked region (9). A silent C→T polymorphism in the exon 3 of LRP1 gene has been identified and associated with late-onset AD in some studies [15, 115-118], while contradictory results [119-124], or just an association modulated by APOE ε4 allele and gender have been reported from others [125, 126]. Also for this gene polymorphism there are conflicting results which can be explained by a possible linkage disequilibrium with other causative polymorphisms or differences in genetic background between different populations. Another common polymorphism in the 5' region of the LRP1 gene, characterized by a tetranucleotide repeat, has been described. A few reports have shown evidence of an association between the tetranucleotide polymorphism and AD, with relatively low strength of the association, and with different alleles being associated with the disease [127-129]. Most studies, however, did not observe any link between the gene polymorphism and increased risk for the disease [117, 122, 125, 126, 130-132]. Although the idea that a genetic mutation in the LRP1 gene could influence the risk for AD remains a suggestive hypothesis because of several biological functions of the LRP1 protein, no clear evidence to date supports this possibility, after analyzing both polymorphisms.

Genetic Risk Factors in AD and Amyloid Cascade Hypothesis

The amyloid cascade hypothesis claims a central role of Aβ in formation of neurofibrillary lesions and in inducing the full range of AD pathology. Besides Aβ, several other proteins are associated with SP (Table 3), including complement proteins and inhibitors, clotting factors, APOE and lipoprotein receptors, proteases as cathepsins and trypsin, protease inhibitors as cystatins, alpha 1-antichymotrypsin (ACT), alpha 1-antitrypsin, A2M, growth factors and cytokines, cell adhesion molecules, and proteoglycans. The role of all these Aβ-binding factors in SP formation and AD pathogenesis, as well as the way by which they interact each other are still unknown and are under investigation. But, it can be assumed that polymorphisms in genes encoding some of these proteins may be good targets for researches, as they can increase susceptibility to AD. Although among all the factors that are involved in promoting Aβ deposition and fibril formation, APOE is again the best documented one although other loci likely linked to AD are being sought.

One of these genetic loci is the A2M gene. This gene is mapped on chromosome 12, near to the linkage region, and it contains two different polymorphisms defined, respectively, by a 5 bp insertion/deletion at the 5' splice site of exon 18 [133], and a G→A point mutation in exon 24 [134]. Both polymorphisms have been associated with sporadic AD [134-140]. With respect to the insertion/deletion polymorphism, it has been supposed that the deletion can result in an alternative splicing, or an increased stability of A2M mRNA, leading to higher levels of A2M with neurotoxic effect [141. Instead, the point mutation polymorphism has been suggested to alter protein function because it is near the thiolester site of the protein [134]. Nonetheless, the results obtained so far about a link between both of these polymorphisms and AD remain conflicting [142-149], so that an association with the disease can not be established with certainty.

As A2M, ACT has been held as an additional candidate gene potentially involved in AD pathogenesis. A common polymorphism in the ACT signal peptide coding region (A→T) has been reported and linked with late-onset AD, as it significantly modified the APOE ε4 gene dosage effect associated with AD [150]. While some reports found this polymorphism associated with the disease, either directly or in combination with APOE [151-154], other studies have failed to find similar results [155-159]. In context with the contradictory data reported in the literature, it can be concluded that, in spite of the specific affinity of ACT for Aβ and its implication in the polymerization of Aβ peptide in amyloid filaments, any effect on AD risk of the common mutation in ACT gene, if present, might be very small. More recently, Wang et al. have identified new mutations [5'UTR(A→G), Asp128Asn(G→A), Ser250Ser(C→T), Leu301Pro(T→C), Thr324Thr(A→G), G→A in intron 4, and 3'UTR C→A] in the ACT gene (161). An analysis of these mutations as well as of the known variants, Thr-17Ala(A→G), Lys76Lys(A→G) and Leu241Leu(G→A), all of which occur at the polymorphic level, showed that the codon 241*A allele and the codon 250*T allele were associated with protective effects against AD irrespective of the APOE ε4 status, and the codon 324*G allele was associated with a marginal protective effect. By contrast, the codon 76*G, codon 227*G and intron 4*G alleles were associated with a modest risk of AD. A linkage disequilibrium between the A allele of the signal peptide polymorphism and some of the previous mutations has been detected, suggesting that the non-random combination of risk and protective alleles may partially explain why the association studies regarding the ACT signal peptide coding region have been inconsistent [160].

Among all factors playing a role in the critical Aβ pathway, butyrylcholinesterase (BChE) and bleomycin hydrolase (BH) have been proposed to be associated with AD. Although, at present, the principal function of BChE is not fully understood, its activity is known to increase with age and to be higher in AD brains [161]. Furthermore, BChE is associated with the SP and NFT [162] and has also been recently shown to participate in the Aβ transformation process changing Aβ from a benign to an eventually malignant form [163]. There are at least seven genetic variants of the BChE gene, with the BChE K variant being the most common [164]. The K variant arises from a missense mutation (G→A) at the position 1615, which reduces the catalytic activity of the BChE enzyme. A recent report showed that the BChE K variant increases the risk of AD, through a synergistic enhancement of risk of APOE ε4 [165]. But, not all subsequent studies have confirmed this initial finding. Some workers found an association between BchE K and AD, either with or without synergy with APOE ε4, and in age-related manner [166-170], whereas others reported little or no evidence of any K-associated AD risk [171-178]. An increased risk of AD associated with the wild type BchE genotype in combination with APOE ε4 or a protective effect of the K variant against the disease has been also proposed [77, 179-181]. A recent meta-analysis, analyzing the role of BchE K in AD, has lead to the identification of a potentially high-risk group for AD: over 75 year old male carriers of both APOE ε4 and BChE K variant [182]. In this study the authors suggest that, when different studies show inconsistent results about a potentially susceptibility gene, the precise composition of a cohort and the definition of a relevant subset is crucial. To date, the association of BChE K variant and AD may be only provisionally defined.

Not much is else known about the BH gene and its plausible role in AD. Though the physiological role of the enzyme has yet to be determined, BH, which is a member of the papain superfamily cysteine proteases, has been thought to play a role in neurodegenerative disorders. BH has been purified from the brains of AD patients, and is involved in processing of APP. It is considered to be a β-secretase candidate, because of its ability to cleave a peptide encompassing the β-secretase cleavage site of APP [183]. The BH gene, located on chromosome 17, has a potentially biologically important polymorphism (1450A→G) resulting in an I433V conserved amino acid substitution in the C terminus which covers the active domain of the enzyme [184]. The original report that found a moderate association of the BH gene with a risk of sporadic AD [185], has been confirmed only once [186]. As other studies [91, 187-190] have challenged this finding, further biochemical and molecular analysis should be undertaken to clarify the contribution of this gene to AD.

Another enzyme which has been demonstrated to be found in AD brains, and is thought to be implicated in the proteolytic cleavage of APP, like BH, is cathepsin D (catD). Cat D is an intracellular aspartyl protease showing β γ–secretase activities, and a functional C→T polymorphism in exon 2 of the gene. This possibly influences pro-catD secretion and intracellular maturation of the enzyme, and has been identified and associated with an increased risk for AD [191, 192]. A significant impact of the catD polymorphism on Aβ levels in the cerebrospinal fluid of AD patients has also been found [193]. Nevertheless, other studies did support a role for the catD gene as a genetic risk factor in the development of AD [91, 194-200], and thus the significance of catD polymorphism in the pathogenesis of AD remains uncertain.

As mentioned above, LRP1, because of its faculty to interact with APP, bind and clear the APOE/Aβ and A2M/Aβ complex, as well as for its association with SP, can play a critical role in the intricate metabolic cascade that influences the balance of Aβ synthesis and clearance. This means that LRP1 might be involved in the development of AD in different ways, even if, to date, the studies on LRP1 gene polymorphisms do not highlight the association between this gene and AD.

The transcription factor LBP-1c/CP2/LSF (CP2) is another genetic locus which can be assumed to be involved in AD pathogenesis. Because it is located close to the LRP1 gene within the AD linkage region on chromosome 12, it controls the expression of several genes and interacts with proteins playing a role in Aβ cascade pathway [201-203], and regulates the activation of some viruses likely related to the disease [204, 205]. Recently, a biallelic polymorphism (G→A) in the 3' untranslated region (UTR) of the gene has been identified and implicated in AD susceptibility, with the 3'-UTR A allele being associated with a reduction in the risk of sporadic AD [206, 207]. The first two reports on the association of the CP2 polymorphism with AD are encouraging, but, obviously, additional investigations in different ethnic populations are needed to draw a conclusion about the role of this gene as a disease-modified risk factor.

GENETIC RISK FACTORS IN AD AND INFLAMMATORY HYPOTHESIS

It has been speculated in recent years that a possible trigger of AD might be brain inflammation. Signs similar to chronic inflammation have been found in brain regions affected by AD. Large numbers of activated microglia have been found, especially around SP, and many extracellular inflammatory molecules are associated with the amyloid deposits, which include complement proteins, complement inhibitors, acute phase reactants, growth factors, heat shock proteins, cystatins, cytokines, integrin adhesion molecules and other miscellaneous proteins. Retrospective epidemiological studies suggesting that intake of anti-inflammatory medications is protective against the development of AD, support the hypothesis that inflammatory mechanisms play a major part in the pathogenesis of AD. What is not certain about is whether this inflammation is a cause or an effect of the disease. However, if inflammation is a secondary response, it does not mean that AD inflammation is unimportant. On the basis of these considerations, several studies are attempting to identify polymorphisms in genes encoding inflammatory modulators and to evaluate the association with the disease, shedding light on this new hypothesis.

It is noteworthy that virtually all the inflammatory molecules, especially the major pro-inflammatory ones, such as interleukin (IL)-1, IL-6, IL-8, TNF-α, tumor growth factor (TGF)-β, are upregulated in the AD brain [208, 209]. The cytokines or chemokines upregulation appear to induce increased expression of Aβ which, by turn, seems to be capable of inducing the expression of cytokines and chemokines in the astrocytes, microglia, and in some cases, neurons, in a vicious cycle.

Several studies highlighted that the risk of AD might be substantially influenced by genetic polymorphisms in the inflammatory agents as IL-1 α, IL1-β, IL-6, TNF-α (Table 4). Recently, it has been reported that the C allele of IL-6 "variable number of tandem repeat polymorphism" (VNTR) delayed initial onset of AD and also decreased its risk per se [210, 211]. Another functional polymorphism (G→C) in the IL-6 gene promoter region (IL-6prom) has also arisen as a candidate for AD susceptibility, because it has an influence on the regulation of plasma IL-6 concentration [212]; but different results have been reported on the association of this polymorphism with AD [195, 213-215]. In one study, a strong linkage disequilibrium between the VNTR and promoter polymorphisms has been demonstrated which modifies the risk of AD [213].

Table 4. Inflammatory Susceptibility Genes for Sporadic Late-Onset AD

Genes (polymorphism)	Effects on inflammation
APOE (chromosome 19 – 112 and 158 polymorphism)	Influence on microglia expression of inflammatory modulators
IL-6 (chromosome 7 – VNTR and promoter region G/C polymorphisms)	Regulation of plasma IL-6 concentration
IL-1 A (chromosome 2 – 5' regulatory region C/T polymorphism)	Regulation of plasma IL-1 concentration
IL-1B (chromosome 2 – regulatory region T/C and exon 5 T/C polymorphisms)	
TNF-α (chromosome 6 – promoter and microsatellite region polymorphisms)	Influence on the transcriptional activity and secretion of the TNF-α

IL-6 = Interlukin
IL-1A and IL-1B = Interleukin-1 alpha and Interleukin-1 beta
TNF-α = Tumor necrosis factor
AD = Alzheimer's disease

Polymorphisms in the genes encoding the alpha and beta isoforms of IL-1 (IL-1A and IL-1B, respectively) have been also identified and their association with the occurrence and age at onset of sporadic AD has been tested. Some genetic studies underscore the relevance of IL-1 in AD pathogenesis, showing that homozygosity of allele 2 resulting from a specific polymorphism in the 5' regulatory region at –889 of IL-1A gene (a C-to-T transition designated as IL-1A -889 allele 2) at least triples AD risk, especially for an earlier age of onset [216-220]. A gene dose-dependent association of IL-1A[-889] allele 2 with AD has been recently proposed, but not restricted to AD patients of a particular age [221]. However, these findings have not been confirmed by subsequent studies, where no evidence of risk for AD with the IL-1A variant was found [222-225]. Interestingly, a very recent study, carried out in patients followed for 3.8 years, has shown that IL-1A –889 allele 1 accelerates the rate of cognitive decline in AD, supporting the notion that inflammation could be important in the clinical course of AD [226].

Two polymorphisms in the IL-1B gene have been reported to increase the risk of AD, and they are located at the +3953 position in exon 5, where T and C alleles exist, and at the -511 position of the regulatory region, again with T and C alleles. It was found that the T/T genotype for the -511 polymorphism is associated with a slightly increased risk for late-onset AD [217]. However, other two different studies did not confirm this finding, though an impact of this polymorphism on Aβ brain levels was detected, suggesting that it might have a pathophysiological influence on the disease process [224, 227]. One study reported that the +3953 T/T genotype frequency is increased in AD patients than in controls, and the combination of the +3953 IL-1B T/T genotype with homozygosity for allele 2 of the IL-1A –889 polymorphism enhances the odds ratio for developing AD [217].

Interactions between IL-1, ACT, and A2M have also been reported. Particularly, it has been shown that IL-1 released from microglia induces the astrocytes expression of ACT [228], and stimulate the A2M synthesis [229]. A study investigating the combined effects of ACT and IL-1B polymorphisms on the risk of AD showed that the concomitant presence of the ACT T/T and IL-1B T/T genotypes increases the risk of AD and decreases the age at onset of the disease [230].

Although an important pathogenic role for IL-1 as a driver of cytokine cascades in AD has been proposed, further studies are required to determine if the IL-1 gene polymorphisms might have any effect on the risk of AD or the rate of the disease progression, or, eventually, might influence the responses to other genetic or environmental risk factors for AD.

TNF-α is another appropriate candidate for influencing the etiology of AD, as elevated levels of this cytokine have been found in patients with AD. It has been postulated that this molecule is capable of inducing apoptosis in neurons by increasing production of reactive oxygen species [231]. Different polymorphisms, which seem to influence the transcriptional activity and secretion of TNF-α, have been detected. In a genome wide scan for AD genes at chromosome 6, where the TNF gene is mapped, three polymorphisms of the TNF-α gene, at position –308 (G→A designed as allele 1 and allele 2, respectively) and –238 (C→T designed as allele 1 and allele 2, respectively) of the promoter region, and in the microsatellite region (about 10.5 kilobases upstream of TNF) have been typed in late onset AD families [17]. The TNF-α microsatellite allele 2 was by itself significantly associated with AD, but the 2-1-2 haplotype for the -308, -238 and microsatellite polymorphisms was even more strongly associated with AD [17].

A significant increase in the age at onset with either the –308A allele 2, or the allele 2 of the microsatellite polymorphism has been found in a recent study [232]. This significant increase still remained when the previous two alleles were combined with the –238G allele1 to give an haplotype, suggesting a modifying effect of the TNF-α gene in AD, primarily on age at onset [232]. Another common polymorphism in the promoter region at the position –850 (C/T) has been associated with an increased risk of AD in subjects carrier of the APOE ε4 allele [233]. But, a most recent study failed to replicate this finding [234].

Other molecules which appear to be implicated in the pathogenesis of AD, as they likely play a role in the amyloid cascade pathway, can be considered as part of the brain inflammatory process, as well. They include ACT, A2M, and APOE itself. ACT is, in fact, a characteristic protein of the acute-phase inflammation and its levels rise fivefold or more during the acute-phase reaction. Aβ binding to ACT might induce in the brain multiple effects that favour the propagation of inflammation and the synthesis and assembly of neurotoxic Aβ [235]. A2M also functions as a clearance system for inflammatory proteins and behaves as a carrier of cytokines and growth factors and might regulate their availability and composition in the extracellular space [236]. Known to be upregulated at sites of inflammation, APOE has been assumed to influence microglia expression of several inflammatory modulators [237, 238], with an isoform-dependent effect [239].

In spite of inconsistent results from genetic studies, the findings of neuroinflammation in AD state the importance of inflammation in the pathogenesis of the disease. However, further genetic and biochemical studies are needed to unravel the role of inflammation in AD and clarify some questions which still remain unresolved: is the inflammatory response to Aβ primarily responsible for the origin of AD or does it represent only a consequence of other etiopathogenic mechanisms?

CONCLUSION

In recent years, it has become plain that genes play an important role in the development of AD. The ability of genetic studies to help unravel new clues is crucial to progress. Theoretical models of possible pathogenetic mechanisms of the disease suggest a primary role for the genetic factors divided into two main categories. First, the three genes in which mutations are known to result in early onset autosomal dominant familial AD (presenilins 1 and 2, and APP), account for only a small proportion of AD cases. Secondly, there are a number of genetic risk factors that might increase the risk of developing sporadic AD, the most common form of the disease. Links among different susceptibility genes and sporadic AD has been suggested in numerous studies, but the findings are not consistent, other than the APOE gene. Particularly, many genes with a precise role in β-amyloid metabolism and deposition (A2M, ACT, CP2, LRP1, BchE, catD, or BH) have been analyzed. On the basis of an overlap between vascular disease and AD, several vascular genetic risk factors (ACE, MTHFR, NOS3, or PON1 gene polymorphisms) have been studied, too. Finally, the findings of neuroinflammation in the disease suggested also an influence of inflammatory genetic factors in AD (IL-1 α, IL1-β, IL-6, TNF-α). To explain the inconsistent results from various studies on the role of different susceptibility genes in AD, several hypotheses can be advanced: regional and ethnic differences which may affect the strength of association between a specific susceptibility factor and the disease, or a linkage disequilibrium with another variation nearby or in the same gene conferring AD risk.

Understanding the importance of genetics in the occurrence and development of AD, analyses of large samples of subjects from different geographic and ethnic populations, and linkage or genome scan studies should be considered as strategies to identify new genetic risk factors for AD.

REFERENCES

[1] Goate A, Chartier-Harlin MC, Mullan M et al. Segregation of a missense mutation in the amyloid precursor protein gene with familial Alzheimer's disease. *Nature* 1991;349:704-6

[2] Sherrington R, Rogaev EI, Liang Y, et al. Cloning of a novel gene bearing missense mutations in early onset familial Alzheimer's disease. *Nature* 1995; 375:754-60.

[3] Rogaeva EI, Sherrington R, Rogaeva EA, et al. Familial Alzheimer's disease in kindreds with missense mutations in a gene on chromosome 1 related to the Alzheimer's disease type 3 gene. *Nature* 1998;376:775-8.

[4] Saunders AM, Strittmatter WJ, Schmechel D, et al. Association of apolipoprotein E allele ε4 with late-onset familial and sporadic Alzheimer's disease. *Neurology* 1993;43:1467-72.

[5] Nalbantoglu J, Gilfix BM, Bertrand P, et al. Predictive value of apolipoprotein E genotyping in Alzheimer's disease: results of an autopsy series and an analysis of several combined studies. *Ann Neurol* 1994;36:889-95.

[6] Panza F, Solfrizzi V, Torres F, et al. Decreased frequency of apolipoprotein E epsilon4 allele from Northern to Southern Europe in Alzheimer's disease patients and centenarians. *Neurosci Lett* 1999;277:53-6.

[7] Panza F, Solfrizzi V, Torres F, et al. Apolipoprotein E in Southern Italy: protective effect of e2 allele in early- and late-onset sporadic Alzheimer's disease. *Neurosci Lett* 2000;292:79-82.

[8] Apolipoprotein E genotyping in Alzheimer's disease. National Institute on Aging/Alzheimer's Association Working Group. *Lancet* 1996;347:1091-5.

[9] Pericak-Vance MA, Bass MP, Yamaoka LH, et al. Complete Genomic Screen in Late-Onset Familial Alzheimer Disease: Evidence for a New Locus on Chromosome 12. *JAMA* 1997; 278:1237-41.

[10] Scott WK, Grubber JM, Abou-Donia SM, et al. Further evidence linking late-onset Alzheimer disease with chromosome 12. *JAMA* 1999;281:513-4.

[11] Rogaeva E, Premkumar S, Song Y, et al. Evidence for an Alzheimer disease susceptibility locus on chromosome 12 and for further locus heterogeneity. *JAMA* 1998;280:614-8.

[12] Wu WS, Holmans P, Wavrant-DeVrieze F, et al. Genetic studies on chromosome 12 in late-onset Alzheimer disease. *JAMA* 1998;280:619-22.

[13] Kehoe P, Wavrant-De Vrieze F, Crook R, et al. A full genome scan for late onset Alzheimer's disease. *Hum Mol Genet* 1999;8:237-45.

[14] Myers A, Wavrant De-Vrieze F, Holmans P, et al. Full genome screen for Alzheimer disease: stage II analysis. *Am J Med Genet*. 2002;114:235-44.

[15] Kang DE, Saitoh T, Chen X, et al. Genetic association of the low density lipoprotein receptor-related protein gene (LRP), an apolipoprotein E receptor, with late-onset Alzheimer's disease. *Neurology* 1997;49: 56-61.

[16] Blacker D, Wilcox MA, Laird NM, et al. Alpha-2 macroglobulin is genetically associated with Alzheimer disease. *Nat Genet* 1998;19:357-60.

[17] Collins JS, Perry RT, Watson B Jr, et al. Association of a haplotype for tumor necrosis factor in siblings with late-onset Alzheimer disease: the NIMH Alzheimer Disease Genetics Initiative. *Am J Med Genet*. 2000;96:823-30.

[18] Zubenko GS, Hughes HB, Stiffler JS, et al. Related AA genome survey for novel Alzheimer disease risk loci: results at 10-cM resolution. Genomics 1998;50:121-8.

[19] Pericak-Vance MA, Grubber J, Bailey LR, et al. Identification of novel genes in late-onset Alzheimer' s disease. *Exp Gerontol* 2000;35:1343-52.

[20] Majores M, Bagli M, Papassotiropoulos A, et al. Allelic association between the D10S1423 marker and Alzheimer's disease in a German population. *Neurosci Lett* 2000;289:224-6.

[21] Bertram L, Blacker D, Mullin K, et al. Evidence for genetic linkage of Alzheimer's disease to chromosome 10q. *Science* 2000;290:2302-3.

[22] Ertekin-Taner N, Graff-Radford N, Younkin LH, et al. Linkage of plasma Abeta42 to a quantitative locus on chromosome 10 in late-onset Alzheimer's disease pedigrees. *Science* 2000;290:2303-4.

[23] Li YJ, Scott WK, Hedges DJ, et al. Age at onset in two common neurodegenerative diseases is genetically controlled. Am J Hum Genet 2002;70:985-93.

[24] Hiltunen M, Mannermaa A, Koivisto AM, et al. Linkage disequilibrium in the 13q12 region in Finnish late onset Alzheimer's disease patients. *Eur J Hum Genet.* 1999;7:652-8.

[25] Hiltunen M, Mannermaa A, Thompson D, et al. Genome-wide linkage disequilibrium mapping of late-onset Alzheimer's disease in Finland. *Neurology* 2001;57:1663-8.

[26] Saunders AM, Strittmatter WJ, Schmechel D, et al. Association of apolipoprotein E allele e4 with late-onset familial and sporadic Alzheimer's disease. *Neurology* 1993;43:1467-72.

[27] Ignatius MJ, Gebicke-Haerter PJ, Pitas RE, et al. Apolipoprotein E in nerve injury and repair. *Prog Brain Res* 1987;71:177-84

[28] Poirier J. Apolipoprotein E in animal models of CNS injury and in Alzheimer's disease. *Trends Neurosci*1994;17:525-30

[29] Strittmatter WJ, Weisgraber KH, Huang DY et al. Apolipoprotein E: high avidity binding to ß-amyloid and increased frequency of type 4 allele in late-onset familial Alzheimer's disease. *Proc Natl Acad Sci* U.S.A. 1993;90:1977-81.

[30] Berr C, Hauw JJ, Delaere P, et al. Apolipoprotein E allele epsilon 4 is linked to increased deposition of the amyloid beta-peptide (A-beta) in cases with or without Alzheimer's disease. *Neurosci Lett* 1994;178:221-4.

[31] Davignon J, Gregg RE, Sing CF. Apolipoprotein E polymorphism and atherosclerosis. *Arteriosclerosis* 1988; 8:1-21.

[32] American College of Medical Genetics/American Society of Human Genetics Working Group on ApoE and Alzheimer disease. Statement on use of apolipoprotein E testing for Alzheimer disease. *JAMA* 1995;274:1627-9.

[33] Mayeux R, Saunders AM, Shea S, et al. Utility of the apolipoprotein E genotype in the diagnosis of Alzheimer's disease. Alzheimer's Disease Centers Consortium on Apolipoprotein E and Alzheimer's Disease. *N Engl J Med*;338:506-11.

[34] Artiga MJ, Bullido MJ, Sastre I, et al. Allelic polymorphisms in the transcriptional regulatory region of apolipoprotein E gene. *FEBS Lett* 1998;421:105-8.

[35] Artiga MJ, Bullido MJ, Frank A, et al. Risk for Alzheimer's disease correlates with transcriptional activity of the APOE gene. *Hum Mol Genet* 1998;7:1887-92.

[36] Laws SM, Taddei K, Martins G, et al. The -491AA polymorphism in the APOE gene is associated with increased plasma apoE levels in Alzheimer's disease. *Neuroreport* 1999;10:879-82.

[37] Lambert JC, Berr C, Pasquier F, et al. Pronounced impact of Th1/E47cs mutation compared with -491 AT mutation on neural APOE gene expression and risk of developing Alzheimer's disease. *Hum Mol Genet.* 1998;7:1511-6.

[38] Song YQ, Rogaeva E, Premkumar S, et al. Absence of association between Alzheimer disease and the -491 regulatory region polymorphism of APOE. *Neurosci Lett* 1998;250:189-92.

[39] Chen L, Baum L, Ng HK, Chan LY, et al. Apolipoprotein E promoter and alpha2-macroglobulin polymorphisms are not genetically associated with Chinese late onset Alzheimer's disease. *Neurosci Lett* 1999;269:173-7.

[40] Casadei VM, Ferri C, Veglia F, et al. APOE-491 promoter polymorphism is a risk factor for late-onset Alzheimer's disease. *Neurology* 1999;53:1888-9.

[41] Zurutuza L, Verpillat P, Raux G, et al. APOE promoter polymorphisms do not confer independent risk for Alzheimer's disease in a French population. *Eur J Hum Genet* 2000;8:713-6.

[42] Roks G, Cruts M, Houwing-Duistermaat JJ, Dermaut B, et al. Effect of the APOE-491A/T promoter polymorphism on apolipoprotein E levels and risk of Alzheimer disease: The Rotterdam Study. *Am J Med Genet* 2002;114:570-3.

[43] Rebeck GW, Cheung BS, Growdon WB, et al. Lack of independent associations of apolipoprotein E promoter and intron 1 polymorphisms with Alzheimer's disease. *Neurosci Lett* 1999;272:155-8.

[44] Lambert JC, Araria-Goumidi L, Myllykangas L, et al. Contribution of APOE promoter polymorphisms to Alzheimer's disease risk. Neurology 2002;59:59-66.

[45] Artiga MJ, Bullido MJ, Frank A, et al. Risk for Alzheimer's disease correlates with transcriptional activity of the APOE gene. *Hum Mol Genet* 1998;7:1887-92.

[46] Lambert JC, Pasquier F, Cottel D, et al. A new polymorphism in the APOE promoter associated with risk of developing Alzheimer's disease. *Hum Mol Genet* 1998;7:533-40.

[47] Lambert JC, Berr C, Pasquier F, et al.Pronounced impact of Th1/E47cs mutation compared with -491 AT mutation on neural APOE gene expression and risk of developing Alzheimer's disease. *Hum Mol Genet* 1998;7:1511-6.

[48] Wang JC, Kwon JM, Shah P, et al. Effect of APOE genotype and promoter polymorphism on risk of Alzheimer's disease. *Neurology* 2000;55:1644-9.

[49] Lambert JC, Berr C, Pasquier F, et al. Pronounced impact of Th1/E47cs mutation compared with -491 AT mutation on neural APOE gene expression and risk of developing Alzheimer's disease. *Hum Mol Genet* 1998;7:1511-6.

[50] Beyer K, Lao JI, Gomez M, et al. The Th1/E47cs-G apolipoprotein E (APOE) promoter allele is a risk factor for Alzheimer disease of very later onset. *Neurosci Lett* 2002;326:187-90.

[51] Zill P, Engel R, Hampel H, Behrens S, et al. Polymorphisms in the apolipoprotein E (APOE) gene in gerontopsychiatric patients. *Eur Arch Psychiatry Clin Neurosci* 2001;251:24-8.

[52] Capurso A, Panza F, Solfrizzi V, et al. Fattori di rischio vascolari nella demenza. *Dementia Update* 1999;4:6-14 [Italian].

[53] Notkola IL, Sulkava R, Pekkanen J, et al. Serum total cholesterol, apolipoprotein E epsilon 4 allele, and Alzheimer's disease. *Neuroepidemiology* 1998;17:14-20.

[54] Jarvik GP, Wijsman EM, Kukull WA, et al. Interactions of apolipoprotein E genotype, total cholesterol level, age, and sex in prediction of Alzheimer's disease: a case-control study. *Neurology* 1995;45:1092-6.

[55] Kuusisto J, Koivisto K, Mykkanen L, et al. Association between features of the insulin resistance syndrome and Alzheimer's disease independently of apolipoprotein E4 phenotype: cross sectional population based study. *BMJ* 1997;315:1045-9.

[56] Solfrizzi V, Panza F, D'Introno A, et al. Lipoprotein(a), apolipoprotein E genotype, and risk of Alzheimer's disease. *J Neurol Neurosurg Psychiatry* 2002;72:732-6.

[57] Eaton DL, Fless GM, Kohr WJ, et al. Partial amino acids sequence of apolipoprotein(a) shows that it is homologous to plasminogen. *Proc Natl Acad Sci* USA 1987;84:3224-8.

[58] Zenker G, Koltringer P, Bone G, et al. Lipoprotein(a) as a strong indicator for cerebrovascular disease. *Stroke* 1986;17:942-5.
[59] Urakami K, Wada-Isoe K, Wakutani Y, et al. Lipoprotein(a) phenotypes in patients with vascular dementia. *Dement Geriatr Cogn Disord* 2000;11:135-8.
[60] Skoog I, Lernfelt B, Landahl S, et al. 15-year longitudinal study of blood pressure and dementia. *Lancet* 1996;347:1141-5.
[61] Sparks DL, Scheff SW, Liu H, et al. Increased incidence of neurofibrillary tangles (NFT) in non-demented individuals with hypertension. *J Neurol Sci.* 1995;131:162-9.
[62] Ott A, Stolk RP, van Harskamp F, et al. Diabetes mellitus and the risk of dementia: The Rotterdam Study. *Neurology.* 1999;53:1937-42.
[63] Ott A, Breteler MM, de Bruyne MC, et al. Atrial fibrillation and dementia in a population-based study. The Rotterdam Study. *Stroke.* 1997;28:316-21.
[64] Hofman A, Ott A, Breteler MM, Bots ML, et al. Atherosclerosis, apolipoprotein E, and prevalence of dementia and Alzheimer's disease in the Rotterdam Study. *Lancet.* 1997;349:151-4.
[65] Bohnet K, Pillot T, Visvikis S, Sabolovic N, et al. Apolipoprotein (apo) E genotype and apoE concentration determine binding of normal very low density lipoproteins to HepG2 cell surface receptors. *J Lipid Res* 1996;37:1316-24.
[66] Siest G, Pillot T, Regis-Bailly A, Leininger-Muller B, et al. Apolipoprotein E: an important gene and protein to follow in laboratory medicine. *Clin Chem* 1995;41:1068-86.
[67] Taddei K, Clarnette R, Gandy SE, Martins RN. Increased plasma apolipoprotein E (apoE) levels in Alzheimer's disease. *Neurosci Lett* 1997;223:29-32.
[68] Scacchi R, Gambina G, Ruggeri M, et al. Plasma levels of apolipoprotein E and genetic markers in elderly patients with Alzheimer's disease. *Neurosci Lett* 1999;259:33-6.
[69] Kuo YM, Emmerling MR, Bisgaier CL, et al. Elevated low-density lipoprotein in Alzheimer's disease correlates with brain abeta 1-42 levels. *Biochem Biophys Res* Commun 1998;252:711-5.
[70] Panza F, Solfrizzi V, Colacicco AM, Basile AM, D'Introno A, Capruso C, Sabba M, Capruso S, Capruso A. Apolipoprotein E (APOE) polymorphism influences serum APOE levels in Alzheimer's disease patients and centenarians. *Neuroreport* 2003; 14:605-8.
[71] Cambien F, Porier O, Lecerf L et al. Deletion polymorphism in the gene of angiotensin converting-enzyme is a potent risk factor for myocardial infarction. *Nature* 1992;359:641-644.
[72] Rigat B, Hubert C et al. PCR detection of the insertion/deletion polymorphism of the human angiotensin converting enzyme gene (DCP1) (dipeptidyl carboxypeptidase 1). *Nucleic Acid Research* 1992;20:1433.
[73] Tiret L, Rigat B, Visvikis S et al. Evidence, from combined segregation and linkage analysis, that a variant of the angiotensin I-converting enzyme (ACE) gene controls plasma ACE levels. *Am J Hum Gene*t 1992;51:197-205.
[74] Schunkert H. Polymorphism of the angiotensin-converting enzyme gene and cardiovascular disease. *J Mol Med* 1997;75:867-75.

[75] Amant C, Bauters C, Bodart JC, et al. D allele of the angiotensin I-converting enzyme is a major risk factor for restenosis after coronary stenting. *Circulation* 1997;96:56-60.

[76] Kehoe PG, Russ C, Mcllroy S, et al. Variation in DCP1, encoding ACE, is associated with susceptibility to Alzheimer disease. *Nat Genet* 1999;21:71-2.

[77] Mattila MK, Rinne JO, Roytta M et al. Dipeptidil carboxypeptidase 1 (DCP1) and butyrilcholinesterase (BCHE) gene interactions with Alzheimer's disease and Parkinson's disease with coexisting Alzheimer pathology. *J Med Genet* 2000;37:766-70.

[78] Alvarez R, Alvarez V, Lahoz CH et al. Angiotensin converting enzyme and endothelial nitric oxide synthase DNA polymorphisms and late onset Alzheimer's disease. *J Neurol Neurosurg Psychiatry* 1999;67:733-6.

[79] Richard F, Fromentin-David I, Ricolfi F, et al. The angiotensin I converting enzyme gene as a susceptibility factor for dementia. *Neurology* 2001;56:1593-5.

[80] Scacchi R, De Bernardini L, Mantuano E, et al. DNA polymorphisms of apolipoprotein B and angiotensin I-converting enzyme genes and relationships with lipid levels in Italian patients with vascular dementia or Alzheimer's disease. *Dement Geriatr Cogn Disord* 1998;9:186-90.

[81] Palumbo B, Cadini D, Nocentini G, Filipponi E, Fravolini ML, Senin U. Angiotensin converting enzyme deletion allele in different kinds of dementia disorders. *Neurosci Lett* 1999 28;267:97-100.

[82] Zuliani G, Ble' A, Zanca R, et al. Genetic polymorphisms in older subjects with vascular or Alzheimer's dementia. *Acta Neurol Scand* 2001;103:304-8.

[83] Panza F, Solfrizzi V, D'Introno A et al. Shifts in angiotensin I converting enzyme insertion allele frequency across Europe: implications in Alzheimer's disease risk. *J Neurol Neurosurg Psychiatry* 2003; 74: 1159-1161.

[84] Riggs KM, Spiro III A, Tucker K, et al. Relations of vitamin B-12, vitamin B-6, folate, and homocysteine to cognitive performance in the *Normative Aging Study*. Am J Clin Nutr 1996;63:306-14.

[85] Frosst P, Blom HJ, Milos R, et al. A candidate genetic risk factor for vascular disease: a common mutation in methylenetetrahydrofolate reductase. *Nat Genet* 1995;10:111-3.

[86] Chapman J, Wang N, Treves TA et al. ACE, MTHFR, Factor V Leiden and APOE polymorphisms in patients with vascular and Alzheimer's dementia. *Stroke* 1998; 29: 1401-4.

[87] Gussekloo J, Heijmans BT, Slagboom PE, et al. Thermolabile methylenetetrahydrofolate reductase gene and the risk of cognitive impairment in those over 85. *J Neurol Neurosurg Psychiatry* 1999;67:535-8.

[88] Pollak RD, Pollak A, Idelson M et al. The C677T mutation in the methylenetetrahydrofolate reductase (MTHFR) gene and vascular dementia. *J Am Geriatr Soc* 2000;48:664-8.

[89] Zuliani G, Ble' A, Zanca R, et al. Genetic polymorphisms in older subjects with vascular or Alzheimer's dementia. *Acta Neurol Scand* 2001;103:304-8.

[90] Brunelli T, Bagnoli S, Giusti B, et al. The C677T methylenetetrahydrofolate reductase mutation is not associated with Alzheimer's disease. *Neurosci Lett* 2001;315:103-5.

[91] Prince JA, Feuk L, Sawyer SL, et al. Lack of replication of association findings in complex disease: an analysis of 15 polymorphisms in prior candidate genes for sporadic Alzheimer's disease. *Eur J Hum Genet* 2001;9:437-44.
[92] Nishiyama M, Kato Y, Hashimoto M, et al. Apolipoprotein E, methylenetetrahydrofolate reductase (MTHFR) mutation and the risk of senile dementia--an epidemiological study using the polymerase chain reaction (PCR) method. *J Epidemiol* 2000;10:163-72.
[93] Uwabo J, Soma M, Nakayama T, et al. Association of a variable number of tandem repeats in the endothelial constitutive nitric oxide synthase gene with essential hypertension in Japanese. *Am J Hypertens* 1998;11:125-8.
[94] Hibi K, Ishigami T, Tamura K, et al. Endothelial nitric oxide synthase gene polymorphism and acute myocardial infarction. *Hypertension* 1998;32:521-6.
[95] Dahiyat M, Cumming A, Harrington C, et al. Association between Alzheimer's disease and the NOS3 gene. *Ann Neurol* 1999;46: 664-7.
[96] Crawford F, Freeman M, Abdullah L, et al. No association between the NOS3 codon 298 polymorphism and Alzheimer's disease in a sample from the United States. *Ann Neurol* 2000;47:687.
[97] Higuchi S, Ohta S, Matsushita S, et al. NOS3 polymorphism not associated with Alzheimer's disease in Japanese. *Ann Neurol* 2000;48:685.
[98] Sanchez-Guerra M, Combarros O, Alvarez-Arcaya A, et al. The Glu298Asp polymorphism in the NOS3 gene is not associated with sporadic Alzheimer's disease. *J Neurol Neurosurg Psychiatry* 2001;70:566-7.
[99] Singleton AB, Gibson AM, McKeith IG, et al. Nitric oxide synthase gene polymorphisms in Alzheimer's disease and dementia with Lewy bodies. *Neurosci Lett* 2001;303:33-6.
[100] Liou YJ, Hong CJ, Liu HC, et al. No association between the neuronal nitric oxide synthase gene polymorphism and Alzheimer Disease. *Am J Med Genet* 2002;114:687-8.
[101] Tedde A, Nacmias B, Cellini E et al. Lack of association between NOS3 poly morphism and Italian sporadic and familial Alzheimer's disease. *J Neurol* 2002;249:110-1.
[102] Serrato M, Marian AJ. A variant of human paraoxonase/arylesterase (HUMPONA) gene is a risk factor for coronary artery disease. *J Clin Invest* 1995;96:3005-8.
[103] Mackness B, Mackness MI, Arrol S, et al. Effect of the human serum paraoxonase 55 and 192 genetic polymorphisms on the protection by high density lipoprotein against low density lipoprotein oxidative modification. FEBS Lett 1998;423:57-60.
[104] Mackness B, Durrington PN, Mackness MI. Human serum paraoxonase. *Gen Pharmacol* 1998;31:329-36.
[105] Paragh G, Balla P, Katona E, et al. Serum paraoxonase activity changes in patients with Alzheimer's disease and vascular dementia. *Eur Arch Psychiatry Clin Neurosci* 2002;252:63-7.
[106] Dantoine TF, Debord J, Merle L, et al. Paraoxonase 1 activity: a new vascular marker of dementia? *Ann N Y Acad Sci* 2002;977:96-101.

[107] Dantoine TF, Drouet M, Debord J, et al. Paraoxonase 1 192/55 gene polymorphisms in Alzheimer's disease. *Ann N Y Acad Sci* 2002;977:239-44.

[108] Sodeyama N, Yamada M, Itoh Y, et al. No association of paraoxonase gene polymorphism with atherosclerosis or Alzheimer's disease. *Neurology* 1999;53:1146-8.

[109] Zuliani G, Ble' A, Zanca R, Munari MR, et al. Genetic polymorphisms in older subjects with vascular or Alzheimer's dementia. *Acta Neurol Scand* 2001;103:304-8.

[110] Pola R, Gaetani E, Flex A, et al. Lack of Association between Alzheimer's Disease and Gln-Arg 192 Q/R Polymorphism of the PON-1 Gene in an Italian Population. *Dement Geriatr Cogn Disord* 2003;15:88-91.

[111] Rebeck GW, Moir RD, Mui S, et al. Association of membrane-bound amyloid precursor protein APP with the apolipoprotein E receptor LRP. *Brain Res Mol Brain Res* 2001;87:238-45.

[112] Rebeck GW, Harr SD, Strickland DK, Hyman BT. Multiple, diverse senile plaque-associated proteins are ligands of an apolipoprotein E receptor, the alpha 2-macroglobulin receptor/low-density-lipoprotein receptor-related protein. *Ann Neurol* 1995;37:211-7.

[113] Tooyama I, Kawamata T, Akiyama H, et al. Subcellular localization of the low density lipoprotein receptor-related protein (alpha 2-macroglobulin receptor) in human brain. *Brain Res* 1995;691:235-8.

[114] Arelin K, Kinoshita A, Whelan CM, et al. LRP and senile plaques in Alzheimer's disease: colocalization with apolipoprotein E and with activated astrocytes. *Brain Res Mol Brain Res* 2002;104:38-46.

[115] Hollenbach E, Ackermann S, Hyman BT, Rebeck GW. Confirmation of an association between a polymorphism in exon 3 of the low-density lipoprotein receptor-related protein gene and Alzheimer's disease. *Neurology* 1998;50:1905-7.

[116] Lambert JC, Wavrant-De Vrieze F, et al. Association at LRP gene locus with sporadic late-onset Alzheimer's disease. *Lancet* 1998;351:1787-8.

[117] Kamboh MI, Ferrell RE, DeKosky ST. Genetic association studies between Alzheimer's disease and two polymorphisms in the low density lipoprotein receptor-related protein gene. *Neurosci Lett* 1998;244:65-8

[118] Baum L, Chen L, Ng HK, et al. Low density lipoprotein receptor related protein gene exon 3 polymorphism association with Alzheimer's disease in Chinese. *Neurosci Lett* 1998;247:33-6.

[119] Woodward R, Singleton AB, Gibson AM, et al. LRP gene and late-onset Alzheimer's disease. *Lancet* 1998;352:239-40.

[120] Beffert U, Arguin C, Poirier J. The polymorphism in exon 3 of the low density lipoprotein receptor-related protein gene is weakly associated with Alzheimer's disease. *Neurosci Lett* 1999;259:29-32.

[121] Hu CJ, Sung SM, Liu HC, et al. Genetic risk factors of sporadic Alzheimer's disease among Chinese in Taiwan. *J Neurol Sci* 2000;181:127-31.

[122] McIlroy SP, Dynan KB, Vahidassr DJ, et al. Common polymorphisms in LRP and A2M do not affect genetic risk for Alzheimer disease in Northern Ireland. *Am J Med Genet* 2001;105:502-6.

[123] Sanchez-Guerra M, Combarros O, Infante J, et al. Case-control study and meta-analysis of low density lipoprotein receptor-related protein gene exon 3 polymorphism in Alzheimer's disease. *Neurosci Lett* 2001;316:17-20.

[124] Perry RT, Collins JS, Harrell LE, et al. Investigation of association of 13 polymorphisms in eight genes in southeastern African American Alzheimer disease patients as compared to age-matched controls. *Am J Med Genet* 2001;105:332-42.

[125] Bullido MJ, Guallar-Castillon P, Artiga MJ, et al. Alzheimer's risk associated with human apolipoprotein E, alpha-2 macroglobulin and lipoprotein receptor related protein polymorphisms: absence of genetic interactions, and modulation by gender. *Neurosci Lett* 2000;289:213-6.

[126] Hatanaka Y, Kamino K, Fukuo K, et al. Low density lipoprotein receptor-related protein gene polymorphisms and risk for late-onset Alzheimer's disease in a Japanese population. *Clin Genet* 2000;58:319-323.

[127] Lendon CL, Talbot CJ, Craddock NJ, et al. Genetic association studies between dementia of the Alzheimer's type and three receptors for apolipoprotein E in a Caucasian population. *Neurosci Lett* 1997;222:187-90.

[128] Lambert JC, Chartier-Harlin MC, Cottel D, et al. Is the LDL receptor-related protein involved in Alzheimer's disease? *Neurogenetics.* 1999;2:109-13.

[129] Wavrant-DeVrieze F, Perez-Tur J, Lambert JC, et al. Association between the low density lipoprotein receptor-related protein (LRP) and Alzheimer's disease. *Neurosci Lett* 1997;227:68-70.

[130] Fallin D, Kundtz A, Town T, et al. No association between the low density lipoprotein receptor-related protein (LRP) gene and late-onset Alzheimer's disease in a community-based sample. *Neurosci Lett* 1997;233:145-7.

[131] Clatworthy AE, Gomez-Isla T, Rebeck GW, et al. Lack of association of a polymorphism in the low-density lipoprotein receptor-related protein gene with Alzheimer disease. *Arch Neurol* 1997;54:1289-92.

[132] Scott WK, Yamaoka LH, Bass MP, et al. No genetic association between the LRP receptor and sporadic or late-onset familial Alzheimer disease. *Neurogenetics* 1998;1:179-83.

[133] Matthijs G, Marynen P. A deletion polymorphism in the human alpha-2-macroglobulin (A2M) gene. *Nucleic Acids Res* 1991;19:5102.

[134] Poller W, Faber JP, Klobeck G, Olek K. Cloning of the human alpha 2-macroglobulin gene and detection of mutations in two functional domains: the bait region and the thiolester site. *Hum Genet* 1992;88:313-9.

[135] Blacker D, Wilcox MA, Laird NM, et al. Alpha-2 macroglobulin is genetically associated with Alzheimer disease. *Nat Genet* 1998;19:357-60.

[136] Alvarez V, Alvarez R, Lahoz CH, et al. Association between an alpha(2) macroglobulin DNA polymorphism and late-onset Alzheimer's disease. *Biochem Biophys Res Commun* 1999;264:48-50.

[137] Dodel RC, Du Y, Bales KR, Gao F, et al. Alpha2 macroglobulin and the risk of Alzheimer's disease. *Neurology* 2000;54:438-42.

[138] Liao A, Nitsch RM, Greenberg SM, et al. Genetic association of an alpha2-macroglobulin (Val1000lle) polymorphism and Alzheimer's disease. *Hum Mol Genet* 1998;7:1953-6.

[139] Tang G, Zhang M, Xie H, et al. Alpha-2 macroglobulin I1000 V polymorphism in Chinese sporadic Alzheimer's disease and Parkinson's disease. *Neurosci Lett* 2002;328:195-7.

[140] Zappia M, Cittadella R, Manna I, et al. Genetic association of alpha2-macroglobulin polymorphisms with AD in southern Italy. *Neurology* 2002;59:756-8.

[141] Kovacs DM. alpha2-macroglobulin in late-onset Alzheimer's disease. *Exp Gerontol* 2000;35:473-9.

[142] Rogaeva EA, Premkumar S, Grubber J, et al. An alpha-2-macroglobulin insertion-deletion polymorphism in Alzheimer disease. *Nat Gene.* 1999;22:19-22.

[143] Korovaitseva GI, Premkumar S, Grigorenko A, et al. Alpha-2 macroglobulin gene in early- and late-onset Alzheimer disease. *Neurosci Lett* 1999;271:129-31.

[144] Kovacs T, Cairns NJ, Lantos PL. Alpha-2-macroglobulin intronic polymorphism is not associated with autopsy-confirmed late-onset Alzheimer's disease. *Neurosci Lett* 1999;273:61-83.

[145] Nacmias B, Tedde A, Cellini E, et al. Alpha2-macroglobulin polymorphisms in Italian sporadic and familial Alzheimer's disease. *Neurosci Lett* 2001;299:9-12.

[146] Wavrant-DeVrieze F, Rudrasingham V, Lambert JC, et al. No association between the alpha-2 macroglobulin I1000V polymorphism and Alzheimer's disease. *Neurosci Lett* 1999;262:137-9.

[147] Gibson AM, Singleton AB, Smith G, et al. Lack of association of the alpha2-macroglobulin locus on chromosome 12 in AD. *Neurology* 2000;54:433-8.

[148] Higuchi S, Matsushita S, Nakane J, et al. Alpha2-macroglobulin gene polymorphisms show racial diversity and are not associated with Alzheimer's disease. *Neuroreport* 2000;11:1167-71.

[149] Wang X, Luedecking EK, Minster RL, et al. Lack of association between alpha2-macroglobulin polymorphisms and Alzheimer's disease. *Hum Genet* 2001;108:105-8.

[150] Kamboh MI, Sanghera DK, Ferrell RE, et al. APOE*4-associated Alzheimer's disease risk is modified by alpha 1-antichymotrypsin polymorphism. *Nat Genet* 1995;10:486-8.

[151] DeKosky ST, Aston CE, Kamboh MI. Polygenic determinants of Alzheimer's disease: modulation of the risk by alpha-1-antichymotrypsin. *Ann N Y Acad Sci* 1996;802:27-34.

[152] Yoshiiwa A, Kamino K, Yamamoto H, et al. alpha 1-Antichymotrypsin as a risk modifier for late-onset Alzheimer's disease in Japanese apolipoprotein E epsilon 4 allele carriers. *Ann Neurol* 1997;42:115-7.

[153] Thome J, Baumer A, Kornhuber J, et al. Alpha-1-antichymotrypsin bi-allele polymorphism, apolipoprotein-E tri-allele polymorphism and genetic risk of Alzheimer's syndrome. *J Neural Transm Park Dis Dement Sect* 1995;10:207-12.

[154] Ezquerra M, Blesa R, Tolosa E, et al. Alpha-antichymotrypsin gene polymorphism and risk for Alzheimer's disease in the Spanish population. *Neurosci Lett* 1998;240:107-9.

[155] Nacmias B, Tedde A, Latorraca S, et al. Apolipoprotein E and alpha1-antichymotrypsin polymorphism in Alzheimer's disease. *Ann Neurol* 1996;40:678-80.

[156] Fallin D, Reading S, Schinka J, et al. No interaction between the APOE and the alpha-1-antichymotrypsin genes on risk for Alzheimer's disease. *Am J Med Genet* 1997;74:192-4.

[157] Sodeyama N, Yamada M, Itoh Y, et al. Lack of genetic associations of alpha-1-antichymotrypsin polymorphism with alzheimer-type neuropathological changes or sporadic Alzheimer's disease. *Dement Geriatr Cogn Disord* 1999;10:221-5.

[158] Schwab SG, Bagli M, Papassotiropoulos A, et al. Alpha-1-antichymotrypsin gene polymorphism and risk for sporadic Alzheimer's disease in a German population.*Dement Geriatr Cogn Disord* 1999;10:469-72.

[159] Tang G, Jiang S, Zhang M, et al. Genetic association study between alpha 1-antichymotrypsin polymorphism and Alzheimer disease in Chinese Han population. *Am J Med Genet* 2000;96:133-5.

[160] Wang X, DeKosky ST, Luedecking-Zimmer E, et al. Genetic variation in alpha(1)-antichymotrypsin and its association with Alzheimer's disease. *Hum Genet* 2002;110:356-65.

[161] Perry EK. The cholinergic system in old age and Alzheimer's disease. *Age Ageing* 1980;9:1-8.

[162] Gómez-Ramos P, Bouras C, Moran MA. Ultrastructural localization of butyrylcholinesterase on neurofibrillary degeneration sites in the brains of aged and Alzheimer's disease patients. *Brain Res* 1994;640:17-24.

[163] Guillozet AL, Smiley JF, Mash DC, Mesulam MM. Butyrylcholinesterase in the life cycle of amyloid plaques. *Ann Neurol* 1997;42:909-918.

[164] Jensen FS, Nielsen LR, Schwartz M. Detection of the plasma cholinesterase K variant by PCR using an amplification-created restriction site. *Hum Hered* 1996;46:26-31.

[165] Lehmann DJ, Johnston C, Smith AD. Synergy between the genes for butyrylcholinesterase K variant and apolipoprotein E4 in late-onset confirmed Alzheimer's disease. *Hum Mol Genet* 1997;6:1933-1936.

[166] Wiebusch H, Poirier J, Sevigny P, Schappert K. Further evidence for a synergistic association between APOE epsilon4 and BCHE-K in confirmed Alzheimer's disease. *Hum Genet* 1999;104:158-63.

[167] Tilley L, Morgan K, Grainger J, et al. Evaluation of polymorphisms in the presenilin-1 gene and the butyrylcholinesterase gene as risk factors in sporadic Alzheimer's disease. *Eur J Hum Genet* 1999;7:659-63.

[168] Panegyres PK, Mamotte CD, Vasikaran SD, et al. Butyrycholinesterase K variant and Alzheimer's disease. *J Neurol* 1999;246:369-70.

[169] McIlroy SP, Crawford VL, Dynan KB, et al. Butyrylcholinesterase K variant is genetically associated with late onset Alzheimer's disease in Northern Ireland. *J Med Genet* 2000;37:182-85.

[170] Ghebremedhin E, Thal DR, Schultz C, Braak H. Age-dependent association between butyrylcholinesterase K-variant and Alzheimer disease-related neuropathology in human brains. *Neurosci Lett* 2002;320:25-8.

[171] Brindle N, Song Y, Rogaeva E, et al. Analysis of the butyrylcholinesterase gene and nearby chromosome 3 markers in Alzheimer disease. *Hum Mol Genet* 1998;7:933-935.

[172] Singleton AB, Smith G, Gibson AM, et al. No association between the K variant of the butyrylcholinesterase gene and pathologically confirmed Alzheimer's disease. *Hum Mol Genet* 1998;7:937-9.

[173] Crawford F, Fallin D, Suo Z, et al. The butyrylcholinesterase gene is neither independently nor synergistically associated with late-onset AD in clinic- and community-based populations. *Neurosci Lett* 1998;249:115-8.

[174] Russ C, Powell J, Lovestone S, Holmes C. K variant of butyrycholinesterase and late-onset Alzheimer's disease. *Lancet* 1998;351:881.

[175] Kehoe PG, Williams H, Holmans P, et al. The butyrylcholinesterase K variant and susceptibility to Alzheimer's disease. *J Med Genet* 1998;35:1034-5.

[176] Yamamoto Y, Yasuda M, Mori E, Maeda K. et al. Failure to confirm a synergistic effect between the K-variant of the butyrylcholinesterase gene and the epsilon4 allele of the apolipoprotein gene in Japanese patients with Alzheimer's disease. *J Neurol Neurosurg Psychiatry* 1999;67:94-6.

[177] Lee DW, Liu HC, Liu TY, et al. No association between butyrylcholinesterase K-variant and Alzheimer disease in Chinese. *Am J Med Genet* 2000;96:167-9.

[178] Kim KW, Jhoo JH, Lee JH, et al. Neither the butyrylcholinesterase K variant nor transferrin C2 variant confers a risk for Alzheimer's disease in Koreans. *J Neural Transm* 2001;108:1159-66.

[179] Hiltunen M, Mannermaa A, Helisalmi S, et al. Butyrylcholinesterase K variant and apolipoprotein E4 genes do not act in synergy in Finnish late-onset Alzheimer's disease patients. *Neurosci Lett* 1998;250:69-71.

[180] Laws SM, Taddei K, Fisher C et al. Evidence that butyrylcholinesterase K variant can protecet ageinst late-onset Alzheimer's disease. *Alz Rep* 1999;2:219-23.

[181] Alvarez-Arcaya A, Combarros O, Llorca J, et al. The butyrylcholinesterase K variant is a protective factor for sporadic Alzheimer's disease in women. *Acta Neurol Scand* 2000;102:350-3.

[182] Lehmann DJ, Williams J, McBroom J, Smith AD. Using meta-analysis to explain the diversity of results in genetic studies of late-onset Alzheimer's disease and to identify high-risk subgroups. *Neuroscience* 2001;108:541-54.

[183] Chang T, Abraham CR. A novel brain cysteine protease forms an SDS stable complex with the beta-amyloid precursor protein. *Ann N Y Acad Sci* 1996;777:183-8.

[184] Ferrando AA, Pendas AM, Llano E, et al. Gene characterization, promoter analysis, and chromosomal localization of human bleomycin hydrolase. *J Biol Chem* 1997;272:33298-304.

[185] Montoya SE, Aston CE, DeKosky ST, et al. Bleomycin hydrolase is associated with risk of sporadic Alzheimer's disease. *Nat Genet* 1998;18:211-2.

[186] Papassotiropoulos A, Bagli M, Jessen F, et al. Confirmation of the association between bleomycin hydrolase genotype and Alzheimer's disease. *Mol Psychiatry* 2000;5:213-5.

[187] Farrer LA, Abraham CR, Haines JL, et al. Association between bleomycin hydrolase and Alzheimer's disease in caucasians. *Ann Neurol* 1998;44:808-11.

[188] Namba Y, Ouchi Y, Asada T, et al. Lack of association between bleomycin hydrolase gene polymorphism and Alzheimer's disease in Japanese people. *Ann Neurol* 1999;46:136-7.

[189] Thome J, Gewirtz JC, Sakai N, et al. Polymorphisms of the human apolipoprotein E promoter and bleomycin hydrolase gene: risk factors for Alzheimer's dementia? *Neurosci Lett* 1999;274:37-40.
[190] Hu CJ, Sung SM, Liu HC, et al. Genetic risk factors of sporadic Alzheimer's disease among Chinese in Taiwan. *J Neurol Sci* 2000;181:127-31.
[191] Papassotiropoulos A, Bagli M, Feder O, et al. Genetic polymorphism of cathepsin D is strongly associated with the risk for developing sporadic Alzheimer's disease. *Neurosci Lett* 1999;262:171-4.
[192] Crawford FC, Freeman MJ, Schinka J, et al. The genetic association between Cathepsin D and Alzheimer's disease. *Neurosci Lett* 2000;289:61-5.
[193] Papassotiropoulos A, Lewis HD, Bagli M, et al. Cerebrospinal fluid levels of beta-amyloid(42) in patients with Alzheimer's disease are related to the exon 2 polymorphism of the cathepsin D gene. *Neuroreport* 2002;13:1291-4.
[194] McIlroy SP, Dynan KB, McGleenon BM, et al. Cathepsin D gene exon 2 polymorphism and sporadic Alzheimer's disease. *Neurosci Lett* 1999;273:140-1.
[195] Bhojak TJ, DeKosky ST, Ganguli M, Kamboh MI. Genetic polymorphisms in the cathespin D and interleukin-6 genes and the risk of Alzheimer's disease. *Neurosci Lett* 2000;288:21-4.
[196] Bertram L, Guenette S, Jones J, Keeney D, et al. No evidence for genetic association or linkage of the cathepsin D (CTSD) exon 2 polymorphism and Alzheimer disease. *Ann Neurol* 2001;49:114-6.
[197] Menzer G, Muller-Thomsen T, Meins W, et al. Non-replication of association between cathepsin D genotype and late onset Alzheimer disease. *Am J Med Genet* 2001;105:179-82.
[198] Matsui T, Morikawa Y, Tojo M, et al. Cathepsin D polymorphism not associated with Alzheimer's disease in Japanese. *Ann Neurol* 2001;49:544-5.
[199] Mateo I, Sanchez-Guerra M, Combarros O, et al. Lack of association between cathepsin D genetic polymorphism and Alzheimer disease in a Spanish sample. *Am J Med Genet* 2002;114:31-3.
[200] Bagnoli S, Nacmias B, Tedde A, et al. Cathepsin D polymorphism in Italian sporadic and familial Alzheimer's disease. *Neurosci Lett* 2002;328:273-6.
[201] Bing Z, Reddy SA, Ren Y, et al. Purification and characterization of the serum amyloid A3 enhancer factor. *J Biol Chem* 1999;274:24649-56.
[202] Lau KF, Miller CC, Anderton BH, Shaw P.C. Molecular cloning and characterization of the human glycogen synthase kinase-3beta promoter. *Genomics* 1999;60:121-8.
[203] Zambrano N, Minopoli G, de Candia P, Russo T. The Fe65 adaptor protein interacts through its PID1 domain with the transcription factor CP2/LSF/LBP1. *J Biol Chem* 1998;273:20128-20133.
[204] Dabrowski CE, Carmillo PJ, Schaffer PA. Cellular protein interactions with herpes simplex virus type 1 oriS. *Mol Cell Biol* 1994;14:2545-2355.
[205] Yoon JB, Li G, Roeder RG. Characterization of a family of related cellular transcription factors which can modulate human immunodeficiency virus type 1 transcription in vitro. *Mol Cell Biol* 1994;14:1776-85.

[206] Lambert JC, Goumidi L, Wavrant-De Vrieze F, et al. The transcriptional factor LBP-1c/CP2/LSF gene on chromosome 12 is a genetic determinant of Alzheimer's disease. *Hum Mol Genet* 2000;9:2275-2280.

[207] Taylor AE, Yip A, Brayne C, et al. Genetic association of an LBP-1c/CP2/LSF gene polymorphism with late onset Alzheimer's disease. *J Med Genet* 2001;38:232-3.

[208] Grammas P, Ovase R. Inflammatory factors are elevated in brain microvessels in Alzheimer's disease. *Neurobiol Aging*. 2001;22:837-42.

[209] Dickson DW, Lee SC, Mattiace LA, et al. Microglia and cytokines in neurological disease, with special reference to AIDS and Alzheimer's disease. *Glia* 1993;7:75-83.

[210] Papassotiropoulos A, Bagli M, Jessen F, et al. A genetic variation of the inflammatory cytokine interleukin-6 delays the initial onset and reduces the risk for sporadic Alzheimer's disease. *Ann Neurol* 1999;45:666-668.

[211] Bagli M, Papassotiropoulos A, Knapp M, et al. Association between an interleukin-6 promoter and 3' flanking region haplotype and reduced Alzheimer's disease risk in a German population. *Neurosci Lett* 2000;283:109-12.

[212] Fishman D, Faulds G, Jeffery R. et al. The effect of novel polymorphisms in the interleukin-6 (IL-6) gene on IL-6 transcription and plasma IL-6 levels, and an association with systemic-onset juvenile chronic arthritis. *J Clin Invest* 1998;102:1369-76.

[213] Bagli M, Papassotiropoulos A, Knapp M, et al. Association between an interleukin-6 promoter and 3' flanking region haplotype and reduced Alzheimer's disease risk in a German population. *Neurosci Lett* 2000;283k:109-12.

[214] Shibata N, Ohnuma T, Takahashi T, et al. Effect of IL-6 polymorphism on risk of Alzheimer disease: genotype-phenotype association study in Japanese cases. *Am J Med Genet* 2002;114:436-9.

[215] Pola R, Flex A, Gaetani E, et al. The -74 G/C polymorphism of the interleukin-6 gene promoter is associated with Alzheimer's disease in an Italian population. *Neuroreport* 2002;13:1645-7.

[216] Grimaldi LM, Casadei VM, Ferri C, et al. Association of early-onset Alzheimer's disease with an interleukin-1alpha gene polymorphism. *Ann Neurol* 2000;47:361-5.

[217] Nicoll JA, Mrak RE, Graham DI, et al. Association of interleukin-1 gene polymorphisms with Alzheimer's disease. *Ann Neurol* 2000;47:365-8.

[218] Du Y, Dodel RC, Eastwood BJ, et al. Association of an interleukin 1 alpha polymorphism with Alzheimer's disease. *Neurology* 2000;55:480-3.

[219] Rebeck GW. Confirmation of the genetic association of interleukin-1A with early onset sporadic Alzheimer's disease. *Neurosci Lett* 2000;293:75-7.

[220] Kolsch H, Ptok U, Bagli M, Papassotiropoulos A, et al. Gene polymorphisms of interleukin-1alpha influence the course of Alzheimer's disease. *Ann Neurol* 2001;49:818-9.

[221] Combarros O, Sanchez-Guerra M, Infante J, et al. Gene dose-dependent association of interleukin-1A [-889] allele 2 polymorphism with Alzheimer's disease. *J Neurol* 2002;249:1242-5.

[222] Ki CS, Na DL, Kim DK, et al. Lack of association of the interleukin-1alpha gene polymorphism with Alzheimer's disease in a Korean population. *Ann Neurol* 2001;49:817-8.
[223] Fidani L, Goulas A, Mirtsou V, et al. Interleukin-1A polymorphism is not associated with late onset Alzheimer's disease. *Neurosci Lett* 2002;323:81-3.
[224] Green EK, Harris JM, Lemmon H, et al. Are interleukin-1 gene polymorphisms risk factors or disease modifiers in AD? *Neurology* 2002;58:1566-8.
[225] Pirskanen M, Hiltunen M, Mannermaa A, et al. Interleukin 1 alpha gene polymorphism as a susceptibility factor in Alzheimer's disease and its influence on the extent of histopathological hallmark lesions of Alzheimer's disease. *Dement Geriatr Cogn Disord* 2002;14(3):123-7.
[226] Murphy GM Jr, Claassen JD, et al. Rate of cognitive decline in AD is accelerated by the interleukin-1 alpha -889 *1 allele. *Neurology* 2001;56:1595-7.
[227] Ehl C, Kolsch H, Ptok U, et al. Association of an interleukin-1beta gene polymorphism at position -511 with Alzheimer's disease. *Int J Mol Med* 2003;11:235-8.
[228] Das S, Potter H. Expression of the Alzheimer amyloid-promoting factor antichymotrypsin is induced in human astrocytes by IL-1. *Neuron* 1995;14:447-56.
[229] Bauer J, Weber W, Tran-Thi TA, et al. Murine interleukin 1 stimulates alpha 2-macroglobulin synthesis in rat hepatocyte primary cultures. *FEBS Lett* 1985;190:271-4.
[230] Licastro F, Pedrini S, Ferri C, et al. Gene polymorphism affecting alpha1-antichymotrypsin and interleukin-1 plasma levels increases Alzheimer's disease risk. *Ann Neurol* 2000;48:388-91.
[231] Talley AK, Dewhurst S, Perry SW, et al. Tumor necrosis factor alpha-induced apoptosis in human neuronal cells: protection by the antioxidant N-acetylcysteine and the genes bcl-2 and crmA. *Mol Cell Biol* 1995;15:2359-66.
[232] Perry RT, Collins JS, Harrell LE, et al. Investigation of association of 13 polymorphisms in eight genes in southeastern African American Alzheimer disease patients as compared to age-matched controls. *Am J Med Genet* 2001;105:332-42.
[233] McCusker SM, Curran MD, Dynan KB, et al. Association between polymorphism in regulatory region of gene encoding tumour necrosis factor alpha and risk of Alzheimer's disease and vascular dementia: a case-control study. *Lancet* 2001;357:436-9.
[234] Infante J, Llorca J, Berciano J, Combarros O. No synergistic effect between -850 tumor necrosis factor-alpha promoter polymorphism and apolipoprotein E epsilon 4 allele in Alzheimer's disease. *Neurosci Lett* 2002;328:71-3.
[235] Nilsson LN, Bales KR, DiCarlo G, et al. Alpha-1-antichymotrypsin promotes beta-sheet amyloid plaque deposition in a transgenic mouse model of Alzheimer's disease. *J Neurosci* 2001;21:1444-51.
[236] Feige JJ, Negoescu A, Keramidas M, Alpha 2-macroglobulin: a binding protein for transforming growth factor-beta and various cytokines. *Horm Res* 1996;45:227-32
[237] Laskowitz DT, Goel S, Bennett ER, Matthew WD. Apolipoprotein E suppresses glial cell secretion of TNF alpha. *J Neuroimmunol* 1997;76:70-4.

[238] Laskowitz DT, Matthew WD, Bennett ER, et al. Endogenous apolipoprotein E suppresses LPS-stimulated microglial nitric oxide production. *Neuroreport* 1998;9:615-8.

[239] Barger SW, Harmon AD. Microglial activation by Alzheimer amyloid precursor protein and modulation by apolipoprotein E. *Nature* 1997;388:878-81.

Chapter IX

ETHICS RESEARCH IN DEMENTIA: THE WAY FORWARD?

Julian C. Hughes*

Newcastle General Hospital,
Westgate Road,
Newcastle upon Tyne,
NE4 6BE, UK.

INTRODUCTION

Let me start by introducing the idea that we have been moving down a pathway in ethical research to do with dementia. In which case, having looked at where we have been, we might anticipate the path ahead. The idea of this pathway is supported by trends in the literature and, as I shall show, by underpinning developments in both the social psychology and philosophy of dementia care.

Although the amount of published literature on ethical issues in dementia is vast, the pathway can be simply sketched. Most of the literature has considered ethical issues from the perspective of professionals involved in dementia care. More recently we have seen a move to look more carefully at the ethical issues for carers of people with dementia from their perspective. I would anticipate, if this is where we are already, that we shall move to consider more seriously the views relating to ethics of the people with dementia themselves. The pathway, therefore, leads from professionals to carers to people with dementia.

In outline, this chapter will have the following four sections:

* Address for correspondence: Dr. Julian C. Hughes, Gibside Unit, Newcastle General Hospital, Westgate Road, Newcastle upon Tyne, NE4 6BE, UK. Tel: +44 (0)191 256 3300 Fax: +44 (0)191 219 5065 Email: jchughes @doctors.org.uk

1. I shall briefly review the type of concerns and the type of research that has appeared over many years from the perspective of professionals involved in dementia care. In passing, this will allow some consideration of the debate between Dworkin and Dresser that has recently influenced much thinking about dementia.
2. I shall then discuss research that pays attention to the views of carers.
3. This will lead me to consider the situated-embodied-agent view (the SEA view) of the person. Having the broader view of what it is to be a person with dementia, which the SEA view provides, suggests a response to the Dworkin-Dresser debate. It also suggests how differences in ethical judgements might be reconciled. Moreover, it points us towards the importance of taking the view of the person with dementia seriously. And, in doing this, it will demonstrate the importance of conceptual analysis, metaphysics even, not as a luxury, but as an inescapable aspect of what it is to understand the perspective of people with dementia in relation to ethical issues.
4. I shall then move on to consider research with people with dementia. The recent work of Sabat allows us to see how qualitative research with people with dementia raises both ethical and underlying philosophical issues.

The pathway from professionals to carers to the people with dementia themselves is clear and my first propaganda point is that we should push on with the movement down this path and take seriously the views relating to ethical issues of those with dementia. The pathway could, of course, have gone the other way and started with the perspective of people with dementia. The fact that it did not probably reflects deep-rooted issues surrounding social standing and power. There is something to be said about the way in which dementia – and Alzheimer's disease in particular – became a politically important issue at a certain time in response to scientific developments and the ageing of the population. [1] Not only did professionals have the advantage of knowledge, they also operated in a paternalistic milieu in which it was taken for granted that they would make benign decisions for those under their care. Medical ethics (as a distinct specialty) has emerged in this milieu and, even if it has tended to commend the notion of autonomy as an antidote to paternalism, it has reflected the professional framework. The understanding of such sociological trends, however, is not something to which I can directly contribute.

There is another movement going on along the pathway relating to ethics and dementia. It is a movement in our understanding of ethical issues relating to clinical practice. As I shall show, what emerges is the importance of our philosophical understanding of notions such as personhood. In addition, what seems evident is that the raw data in debates on ethical issues should come from people themselves, even if the interpretation of the data involves philosophical analysis. So progress in ethical research will come, I assert (and this is my second propaganda point), from a bringing together of qualitative research and metaphysics.

Professional Ethics

In this section I shall briefly review the type of research that has appeared from the professional perspective to do with ethical issues in dementia. My aim is not, however, to offer a review of the literature itself. Not only would that be an exhausting task, it is unnecessary from the point of view of my first propaganda point. Instead, all I need to do is establish that the literature has been vast and that it has been, almost exclusively, professionally oriented.

In a systematic search of the literature covering the period 1980-2000, we found 1297 items relating to ethical issues in dementia. [2] In the same study we also found that 77% of the articles mainly focusing on ethical issues (rather than considering such issues as a secondary matter) had appeared between 1990 and 2000. Moreover, the proportion of articles primarily focusing on ethical issues, as a percentage of the literature on dementia and ethics as a whole, has increased from 23.6% in 1991 to 56% in 2000. So there is little doubt that the literature is large and seems to be increasing.

The issues discussed in the literature cover a wide terrain. The broad categories that appeared in our literature review included the following: advance directives, difficult behaviour, surrogate decision-making, driving, issues around treatment, end-of-life issues, genetics, consent, relationships with professionals, quality of life, resource allocation, issues around research ethics and truth-telling, as well as other less specific categories. We found that four categories persisted in this literature: professional care, end-of-life issues, decision-making and treatment. In the remainder of this section I shall consider examples of recent literature in each of these domains, but the papers I shall consider are only intended to be indicative of the type of literature and discussion that has occurred in the professional literature.

Professional Care

Treloar and colleagues grasped an issue that had been scarcely mentioned previously in the literature: the use of covert medication in food and drink for those with dementia. [3] There is no doubt that this is an important ethical issue and one that concerns professional standards of care. Their finding, that 71% of residential, nursing home and in-patient units questioned in the south-east of England sometimes gave medicines covertly, started a much-needed debate. [4]

They proposed that, under "exceptional circumstances", it would be licit to give medication covertly to patients who lack capacity to consent to treatment, who would otherwise refuse medication. [5] They argued, first, that deception is not always wrong if truthfulness leads to suffering; and, secondly, that the "duty of care" should allow proven treatment to be given to relieve suffering even if this involves deception. The ethical principles at stake are beneficence and non-maleficence. Autonomy did not seem to be relevant because the circumstances envisaged were precisely those in which the patient's autonomy was severely circumscribed.

Many clinicians and many family carers would probably agree with the proposition put forward by Treloar et al. [6] It was certainly an issue that needed airing because of the risks involved to nursing staff, in particular, if they were found to have secreted medicine in food without proper authority. The point to note, however, in line with my first propaganda point, is that this very useful research is, none the less, entirely based on the views of professional carers.

Does this matter? Well, libertarians will certainly have concerns about what might constitute "exceptional circumstances". From the professional point of view, shortages of staff might be considered exceptional circumstances. If a man with dementia wanders half naked into the room of a female resident in a home, this might constitute exceptional circumstances, especially if the relatives of the female resident lodge a formal complaint. If a person with dementia is positively aggressive, this might amount to exceptional circumstances. In all such cases it is always possible that the scenario can be portrayed as *exceptional* and the use of covert medication, to calm the behaviour, will seem warranted.

However, it is in just such cases that attention should be paid to the broader factors that might influence the behaviour of a person with dementia. [7] The difficulty is, of course, that the appropriate skills to deliver psychosocial interventions for behavioural symptoms in dementia are not always available to individual homes or localities. In which case, say in the presence of violence, the circumstances can quickly look exceptional. The line between benign and malignant paternalism is thin. As in the case of wandering, where the use of electronic tagging might seem like a "quick fix", it is the instances at the margin that should alert us to the civil libertarian's point of view. [8]

There are now a number of theories in medical ethics that reflect its rootedness in the context of practical, day-to-day encounters. Narrative ethics, feminist ethics, communicative ethics, the re-emergence of casuistry and the emphasis on character in virtue ethics all point to the importance of relationships and particular contexts for real people in difficult situations. [9] Underpinning these difficult ethical decisions is our deep-seated inclination to respect persons as such. This suggests, however, a degree of flexibility, a willingness to enter into careful negotiations and to pursue a broad range of therapeutic interventions, which might disappear if the option of deception (i.e. giving covert medication) seemed too readily available, even in "exceptional circumstances".

The focus on the person, in this case the person with dementia, is exactly the attitude that my first propaganda point suggests. We know that professionals will often be inclined to use covert medication. Clinical experience suggests that many carers will also feel that this is appropriate. But what will individual people with dementia think? The short answer is that we do not know and we might feel it is too difficult to find out. In particular cases, however, it might be possible to negotiate, or to discern what seems most acceptable. In any event, if our attention is on the particular case, we should be more prone to consider alternative ways of managing difficult behaviour and more open to the possibility that the person with dementia might have something important to contribute to our understanding of the problem.

End-of-Life Decisions

In another useful and important study, Coetzee and colleagues reported on the attitudes of carers and old age psychiatrists towards the treatment of potentially fatal events in end-stage dementia. [10] A questionnaire (appropriately validated and tested for reliability) was sent to 148 carers and 34 clinicians, with significant differences being found between the two groups. Clinicians were less keen than the carers, on active treatment in potentially fatal events in end-stage dementia. The carers, meanwhile, set higher value on "patient-centred" issues, such as dying with dignity, the patient's best interests and wishes. The researchers concluded that more debate was required between clinicians and carers, especially since (in England and Wales) it is likely that legislation in the future will give more power to carers in these decisions.

What is not said, however, is that people with dementia themselves might have views on how they should be treated when they develop life-threatening conditions in the severer stages of dementia. For one thing, this sort of dilemma is exactly where it might be useful to know the person's view as set down in an advance refusal of treatment, or "living will". With all the appropriate caveats in place (namely that the advance directive should be clearly established, applicable to the current circumstances and made without undue pressure from others), advance directives are a way of ensuring the person with dementia has some say in his or her treatment.

This is not, however, the whole of the issue. After all, what I am suggesting is not that we should find out what people with dementia once wanted, but rather that we ought to try to discover what they want when they have dementia. We cannot, of course, wait until they are actually so ill that they cannot tell us their wishes, but there will often be scope during the course of the illness to find out their opinions.

It is worth noting, for instance, that – albeit families are almost always the best source of information concerning a person's likely preferences – informal carers do not always know what the wishes of the person for whom they stand proxy would be. Certainly this has been shown to be true in connection with research, where proxies have tended to be more protective than the person would have been him or her self. [11] Indeed, Coetzee et al is not the first study to show disagreement between relatives and physicians. In an earlier study it appeared that families were less inclined to make use of objective facts. [12] Instead they often based their decisions on a subjective overall impression. Similarly, Moe and Schroll showed that relatives were more likely to seek curative treatments, rather than just palliative measures. [13]

What has emerged in the research literature is a process. [14] The initial step is to try to ascertain the wishes of the person, even if he or she has dementia. The process moves on to consider the views of significant others (be they family or friends); and then to hear the thoughts of professional carers and physicians. The person with dementia remains at the centre of such a process. And from the uncertainties that surround the views of proxies (discussed above), it is hard to argue against the conclusion that this is as it should be.

Decision-Making

I now turn to a paper of impeccable methodology, which considered the difficulties of gaining informed consent to pursue research. [15] The researchers assessed patients with Alzheimer's disease and family caregivers for competency (or capacity) to consent to a pharmacological clinical trial. They found that 70% of the caregivers (without dementia) were unable to comprehend basic information about the study. This raised a question about whether carers could act as surrogates for patient consent. Similarly, 70% of the patients with Alzheimer's disease were unable to demonstrate a minimal understanding of the research procedures. People with a Mini-Mental State Examination (MMSE) score of less than 18 were rated as incompetent or marginally incompetent in 95% of cases.

One of their proposals, as an upshot of the research, was that "under the surveillance of properly empowered ethical committees, an exhaustive explanation of research methodology is not always an essential part of the relevant information to be presented to the participant". The immediate danger of such a conclusion is that it opens the door to a type of paternalism in research. As in other arenas, this paternalism is likely to be benign, most of the time. The worry, however, is that this might not always be true. On the other hand, this research suggests in any case that the present methods of gaining consent for research studies must be flawed. An earlier study had shown that 15 subjects, already enrolled (and, therefore, consented) in a drug trial, all failed to meet rigorous standards of consent. [16]

It might be, however, that the conclusion of Pucci et al [17] is absolutely right: in fact, gaining consent is not an algorithmic process, but is one that suggests embedded values and the importance of context. [18] Whether what is done in this regard is right or wrong will depend hugely on the protagonists involved and upon their innate dispositions or virtues. Nevertheless, whilst this might all be true, what Pucci et al does not show us are the views of people with dementia themselves. They might, after all, cry out to be spared the details of the research and say that they do, by and large, trust their physicians to make decisions such as these for them. But equally, they might express a desire instead to have things explained in a way that they *can* comprehend, in a way that *does* make sense to them on each occasion, even if they cannot recall it meanwhile. After all, if non-demented carers cannot themselves understand the information given to them, it starts to seem as if all research should be carried out without detailed consent being achieved beyond the benign paternalistic oversight of the research ethics committees. That would be an affront to the autonomy of us all, but why should people with dementia be treated with any less respect? Why should they not be treated with more respect and brought into the decision-making process in their own right? Indeed, such was the suggestion of Cotrell and Schulz ten years ago. [19]

Treatment

The issue of feeding people with severe dementia who seem to reject food has been a concern for many years. In a recent study of nursing and care staff, using focus groups, it was shown that fine judgements were being made about the usefulness of different means of feeding. [20] In terms of ethical principles, although there was some weight given to the principle of autonomy, this was countered by the commitment to care felt by the staff. It also appeared that local and personal attitudes counted for more than professional ethics. It is interesting to compare this study to a similar study, which appeared in the same journal eight years previously. [21] Again it appeared that nurses would change their decisions to feed or not to feed depending on local pressures. (This is not to suggest that the pressures were illicit, merely that consensus amongst the treatment team or discussions with the family appeared to be salient issues; in the same way, local cultural and personal attitudes were more salient than professional rules in the later study.) In the earlier study, whereas those who wished to feed the patients emphasized the sanctity of life, those who chose not to feed the patients ranked autonomy as important. In the later study, autonomy was given some weight, but this was balanced against the duty to care.

What we see, therefore, in this research is a clash of principles for those professionals working with people with dementia who appear unwilling to eat. Before commenting on this clash of principles, it is worth considering how the debate about feeding has become more pointed with the advent of percutaneous endoscopic gastrostomy (PEG) as a possible way around the person's unwillingness or inability to eat or drink. PEG feeding seems to offer a technical solution to the problem. An evidence-based review, however, suggested that there was no good evidence in favour of any form of tube-feeding in people with severe dementia for any of the cited, putative indications (Finucane et al 1999). [22] Indeed, the authors found numerous side effects for both nasogastric tube (NGT) and PEG feeding, some of which were fatal. This sort of evidence convinced Gillick that artificial feeding was inappropriate on ethical grounds in severe dementia. [23] In the UK at least, there seems to be a degree of consensus around this conclusion.

It is worth, however, expressing a word of caution. I have argued elsewhere that, using the notions of ordinary and extraordinary means (according to which one is not bound to pursue treatments that are not objectively proportionate to the chances of improvement), it can be asserted that the same treatment, namely PEG feeding, might be ordinary in one circumstance and extraordinary in another. [24] In other words, it is the context that determines whether or not something is licit or illicit. The context we are normally considering in a discussion of feeding people with severe dementia is that of terminal care, where the person's refusal to eat is seen as a natural part of their inevitable decline. But, even if it is the norm, this might not always be the case, so there can be no blanket rules against the use of artificial feeding in dementia.

To return to the studies of feeding people with severe dementia and the nurses' and carers' attitudes, my first propaganda point can again be displayed. This is in no way a criticism of these interesting and useful papers, but it is apparent that they have focused on the views of professional carers. The issue is, indeed, regarded as a professional one. There is an acknowledgement that the views of the family will have some impact on professional decisions, but the views of carers are not the interest of these studies. The views of the people with dementia are also referred to tangentially, because carers give some weight to the notion of autonomy. This is, nevertheless, weighed against other ethical principles that influence the decisions that have to be made. So, how should professionals deal with these clashes of principle?

The Dworkin-Dresser Debate

As a way of shedding light on this question, before concluding this section, I shall introduce a broader debate that has featured in the literature around dementia for some while. Dworkin initiated the debate with his distinction between *critical* interests and *experiential* interests. [25] He argued that both were important. Whereas, however, experiential interests were necessarily transient (reflecting the pleasure of an experience, such as listening to a particular piece of music or eating), critical interests had (on his view) more to do with the shape of our lives as a whole. Critical interests, to do with the importance of our families for instance, have some bearing on the overall meaning of our lives. Dworkin went on to argue that, in severe dementia, where a person is only open to experiential interests, because he or she does not have a view of critical interests, it is nevertheless the critical interests that should be given precedence, because these are the interests a person has in the shape of his or her life as a whole. What happens to the person with severe dementia will affect that overall shape. In making decisions, therefore, it should be critical interests that outweigh any more immediate experiential interests, since the latter will not affect the character of the person's life as a whole.

The response to Dworkin's arguments came in a paper by Dresser. [26] The debate has subsequently been couched in terms of the then-self and the now-self. The question becomes, should the critical interests of the then-self outweigh the experiential interests of the now-self? If I seem generally happy now, despite my dementia, should my chest infection be treated even though, before I had dementia, I stipulated that life with dementia would be unbearable and I would not wish to have treatment that might lengthen a period of undignified existence? Dresser was more inclined to give weight to the experiences of the person now, rather than allowing the person's previously expressed wishes to dominate.

A number of authors have responded to the Dworkin-Dresser debate. One subtle response has been that of Jaworska. [27] She has argued that, in thinking about how to respect autonomy in people with severe dementia (which is the underpinning aim of both Dworkin and Dresser), we should notice the importance of values. We should regard people with dementia as people who can value: this is the point of respecting their agency, through which they make their autonomous decisions. For Jaworska, a person's previously expressed, critical interests will be important as a way of understanding his or her values, but the person's values will also be expressed in the present by experiential interests.

Now this might give us some sort of purchase on the question of clashing principles. It allows us to say that the reason for trying to respect the autonomous wishes of people with severe dementia is because those wishes express the person's values. But the person's values are likely to be expressed both by things they did or said in the past, as well as by things they do or say now. There will have to be some weighing up here, but it is not inevitable that the process of weighing up will favour what was said in the past. Moreover, Jaworska's argument is intended to be critical of Dworkin's idea that the crucial thing is the shape of a person's life *as a whole*. Instead, it might well be that values change as one goes along, so that the shape of one's life does not have to be pre-determined by one's unchanging critical interests.

Treatment Issues Again

Taking a broader view of values in a person's life undercuts the dichotomy of the Dworkin-Dresser debate. It also helps to focus attention on the person with dementia. Of course, it might be said, the problem in severe dementia is precisely that the person's values are not apparent. This is what leads to the clash of principles. One possible response, which might be engendered by closer attention to the person with dementia, is to say that under the right circumstances the person's values might well be apparent. It may be that the refusal of food is itself an expression of a value. What is required is a careful checking that there are no other causes of food refusal. Are there indications of a depressive illness? What is the context of food refusal? Does it come as yet another indication of the steady decline in the person's state? Is it, that is, clearly part of the terminal illness, or an abrupt change? Could the refusal of food indicate some other pathology?

But if the refusal of food could only be ascribed to the person's terminal state, then there are grounds for saying that it indicates the person no longer values nourishment in the way he or she once did. This might seem to be disingenuous: perhaps we impute values where none exists. But after all, other than by outer behaviour (albeit usually by speech or the written word), how else do we fathom what a person values? Are there not grounds for regarding a person's actions as indicative of what is important? Is it not possible to understand the refusal of food in severe dementia (where this is part of the person's terminal decline, rather than the result of some other pathology) as a sign that the purposes for which nourishment is normally required no longer have relevance and, therefore, food is no longer something to be valued?

But let us return to the studies this section opened with, which considered the ethical views of professional carers of people with severe dementia who do not eat. Over against "autonomy" we had "commitment to care", [28] or "sanctity of life" [29] as the contrasting principles. If these represent the clash of principles, it should be remarked that they occur in the space of values. The reason for "caring", whatever else it might involve, must imply some sort of commitment to the person who is cared for and, by extension, a concern for what that person regarded as important or of value. The "sanctity of life" argument does not involve an unconditional determination to maintain life at all costs. It will involve a recognition that, at some stage, death is an inevitable event. It is an argument that clearly values life, but will also value death of a certain kind at a certain time. So the conflicting principles can be thought of as a debate within the domain of values. The exchange of views, that is, can be pursued using the same currency, where the currency is the language of shared values rather than clashing principles. And, again, the values of the person with dementia are likely to be centre-stage.

The conclusion of this section, therefore, is an affirmation of my first propaganda point, namely that we should pursue the path from the perspective of professionals to the perspective of people with dementia. We come closer to the perspective of people with dementia, however, by engaging with carers. It is to the perspective of carers on ethical issues in dementia that I now turn.

THE CARERS' VIEW

Of the 1297 items we found in the literature between 1980 and 2000 relating to ethics and dementia, 162 concerned family carers. [30] However, this literature is almost entirely written from the perspective of professionals. Hope and Oppenheimer considered the values embedded in the relationships between carers and the people they care for and noted that the obligation to help someone is discussed in "the language of morality: compassion, self-sacrifice, obligation, selfishness, guilt, blame, betrayal and abandonment". [31] What is required, if the carers' perspective (which may not be singular) is not inevitably going to be simply a reflection of the professional view, is a study that tries to view the ethical issues from that perspective.

In a study that has remained unique until recently, Pratt et al reported on the ethical views of family carers of people with dementia. [32] This came about from a questionnaire on caring that concluded with a general invitation to raise other issues that might increase the researchers' understanding of caring. There were 240 carers involved in the study. Of these, 216 answered the last question and 54% made comments that raised ethical concerns. The authors grouped these into rather broad categories. Thus, 42% concerned the responsibilities of being a carer. The issues raised were to do with sharing the care and the need to give care because of vulnerability and reciprocity. Reciprocity is the view that help is owed because the person needing help once helped the person now in a position to give help. The carers also noted conflicts with other obligations (29%), issues around finance (13%) and standards of care (13%). Three carers mentioned the importance of being able to discuss the diagnosis with the person with dementia at an early stage in the illness.

Despite the rather unique nature of the study, it is likely that the questionnaire underestimated the ethical problems that occur for family carers. Moreover, the issues were not pursued, nor were they subjected to finer-grained analysis. The themes that did emerge were, nevertheless, worthy of note. For instance, the notion of reciprocity has no equivalent in the professional literature when it refers to its own perspective on ethical issues in dementia.

Research elsewhere has involved carers, but often to seek answers to questions that arise in a professional context. As I have outlined above, there have been a number of studies looking at differences between carers and other groups with respect to decision-making for people with dementia. [33] Similarly, professionals have an interest in truth-telling and giving the diagnosis of dementia. Pinner has usefully reviewed these studies. [34] A most striking finding has been that only 17% of family members accompanying patients to a memory clinic thought that the person with dementia should be told the diagnosis; whereas 71% said they would wish to be told themselves. [35] Once people with dementia were asked, however, 70% indicated they would wish to know the diagnosis or to have more information. [36]

One interesting report, which does reflect the perspective of the family carer, concerns the case of Roswell Gilbert, who shot his wife because of her dementia. [37] Although this presents the narrative from the point of view of Roswell Gilbert, through transcripts from the court proceedings, the analysis is speculative and not based on direct conversations with him about the ethical issues involved. Hasselkus, in a piece of qualitative research, has shown how carers deal with the conflicting ethical principles that face them. [38] Our own research, indeed, suggests that qualitative research with carers, even when its main focus is not ethical, tends to throw up ethical issues more readily. [39] This is not surprising given that qualitative research typically reflects meaning. The raw data, what carers actually say, is more likely to show "the language of morality". [40] We concluded:

> "...when carers focus on issues which solely involve either the person with dementia or others (and not specifically themselves), the issues are largely those seen by professionals too. But when the carers involve themselves in their perspective, the ethical issues become less predictable and more varied than the professional literature seems to suggest." [41]

On this basis, we carried out a small study of carers, seeking to find out what the ethical issues were from their own perspective. [42] The qualitative study involved 10 family carers. The methodology was not rigorous (only one interview was tape-recorded, for example) and the sampling was poor. But the study was able to demonstrate that (from their perspective) the ethical issues for carers seemed (and were) different compared to the issues as they presented themselves to professionals. For example, public embarrassment is an ethical issue for carers. For professionals this might be regarded as "difficult behaviour". As such it can be approached using a variety of models and attempts can be made to manage it by pharmacological, behavioural or psychosocial means. But for the husband or wife it is an ethical issue: should I take him out at all if he is going to act in that way? How should I react if she does that? What is the right thing to do, given that things are now like this?

Our research allowed us to identify several key moral concepts that seemed relevant to carers. Carers made reference to their sense of duty. There is often no alternative, from the moral point of view, for the carers but to do what they have to do. This links to the notion of reciprocity. Carers stand in a different relationship (compared to the professional) to the person they care for, so things seem different. Many professionals will be well aware of the tremendous sense of guilt felt by carers at particular times (for example, when the person they care for has to be admitted to nursing care). But professionals might not grasp the strongly ethical nature of this guilt for the carers. It could be explained, from a professional perspective, as an understandable adjustment reaction. But for the carer it might be a defining ethical moment, upon which hangs the weight of promises solemnly made, a sense of duty and gratitude, along with the carer's moral standing in his or her own eyes (and the eyes of family and friends). No wonder, then, that some carers have to wait until breaking point before seeking extra help.

Carers also took account of the consequences of their actions. This allowed them, in some instances, to be more coercive, more anti-libertarian, than professionals would ever dare to be. Carers could tell lies to the person with dementia, if this made it easier for the person to accept help. One carer locked the person with dementia in his bedroom at night to prevent wandering and inappropriate urination elsewhere in the house. None the less, carers were very attuned to the needs and wishes of the people they cared for, sometimes disadvantaging themselves in order to accord with the previously expressed wishes or inclinations of the person with dementia. Equally, however, sometimes an emergency was encountered and a quick decision made in the knowledge that it might not have been completely in accordance with other decisions. For example, someone who had always resisted active medical intervention, on the grounds that this is what the person with dementia would have chosen, allowed her choking mother to be aspirated because of the apparent distress at the time. This illustrates the extent to which the carer is enmeshed in a context, which is not just medical and technical, but is also ethical and value-laden. The decisions of carers take place in this context.

In a similar way, several carers made it plain that they considered their best interests should be taken into account in judgements about the person with dementia. Some of the carers pointed out that their best interests and the best interests of the person with dementia were enmeshed. Professionals would normally say that they act solely in the best interests of their patients. Giving sedative medication is a good example of where it might be considered best for the patient *because* it is good for the carer. One carer, however, regarded the use of such medication as itself an ethical issue. Her question might have been construed as a technical question about the half-life of the drug and its adverse effects, whereas her real concern was whether it was right *at all* for her to be trying to keep her husband at home, which she could not do without the drug.

In our subsequent (ongoing), larger, qualitative study of ethical issues from the perspective of carers of people with dementia similar issues emerge, but the full results are awaited. Nevertheless, it does seem as if carers would value help with making ethical decisions. Barber and Lyness have also suggested that therapists (in their case family therapists) should be in a position to provide advice and support to people facing ethical issues. [43] Many professionals working with carers and people with dementia might doubt their ability to do this. Whilst it might well be true that some formal instruction in ethics would be beneficial, it is also true that much of what we do in clinical practice involves ethical decisions in any case. So this is, whether or not it is recognized as such, familiar territory. Careful negotiation around values and wishes, balancing possible outcomes, choosing between options where neither is considered good, all of these are bread and butter to clinical practice. How we might help carers facing ethical decisions looks little different from the key components in any good, reflective listening or counselling. We should seek to pick up ethical cues and reflect these back to the carer; we should overtly acknowledge the ethical nature of the difficulties they face; we should show ourselves willing to discuss matters of value as well as matters of fact; and we should have some grasp of alternative ethical viewpoints to allow us to have an informed discussion. The main component here is not a vast knowledge of ethical theory, but an understanding of the need to be (and how to be) with someone who is facing a difficult decision, which they might have to make themselves, but which they do not necessarily have to make alone.

Another thing that emerges in discussing ethical issues with carers is that there can be disagreements: some would always wish to tell the truth about concealed medication; others think it is legitimate not to do so. This raises a question about how professionals should deal with different ethical viewpoints, especially when the carer's decision is at odds with the views of the professional.

Before considering this question, however, it is appropriate to notice that we have moved some way down the path towards the perspective of the person with dementia. Talking about carers' views, as we have seen, leads to a more nuanced account of the ethical issues that arise in dementia, beyond purely professional concerns. Moreover, we are naturally led into the importance of the contextual relationship between the carer and the person with dementia. My first propaganda point suggests that research on ethical issues in dementia needs to move further in the direction of the perspective of people with dementia themselves. In this section, however, we have also seen the emergence of the second propaganda point, which stresses the importance of qualitative research as a means to understand ethical issues.

THE SITUATED-EMBODIED-AGENT

I shall now present a brief description of the situated-embodied-agent (SEA) view of the person. [44] This will allow me to discuss how it is that we might begin to reconcile different judgements by carers about ethical issues in dementia. Incidentally, it will also provide a response to the Dworkin-Dresser debate. But then, having achieved this, it should suggest that the perspective of people with dementia must be taken more seriously. Meanwhile, the discussion of personhood will have taken us into the realms of conceptual analysis and metaphysics, adding weight to the other aspect of my second propaganda point: not only do we need qualitative research to progress in medical ethics, we need metaphysics too.

The SEA view of the person with dementia stands in opposition to a view inherited from Locke, [45] but made fashionable in recent times by Parfit. [46] To be a person is, according to Parfit, to have psychological continuity and connectedness. This is not, at first blush, so outrageous. For we do set an enormously high store by our capacity for conscious thought. It is our ability to link up conscious states by memory that seems to ensure our personal identity. I am the same person tonight as I was this morning, I can claim, because (and insofar as) my conscious states this morning and this evening are not only connected, but also continuous. In which case, if there were *not* such continuity and connectedness, perhaps I would not be the same person. And, if the continuity and connectedness completely broke down, in dementia say, perhaps I could not be called a person at all.

The trouble with the Locke-Parfit view is that it takes too narrow a perspective on what it is to be a person. When this is applied to dementia, for instance, we are led in the direction of some decisions that seem counter-intuitive or worrying. We are led to the view that an advance directive made when the person had capacity might no longer be valid if the person now with dementia cannot be considered the same as the person who made the advance directive. [47] We are led to the view that people with dementia should not be regarded as persons at all. [48] Most people working with people with dementia would be keen to repudiate such views. Fortunately, the SEA view provides an alternative to the Locke-Parfit view and one that squares more readily with clinical experience in this field. [49] The roots of the SEA view are various, from Wittgenstein to Heidegger to Merleau-Ponty, and evident in many of the writings of the contemporary philosopher Charles Taylor. [50] I shall briefly describe its component parts.

One very obvious riposte, to those who stress that our inner states are defining for us as persons, is to point to our bodies. These also provide continuity and connectedness. There is an important sense in which our bodies are our natural way of representing our*selves* to the world. Certainly one philosopher has defended the idea that the body is the defining feature of personhood. [51] The body need not be regarded simply as a physical thing, giving concrete reality to our standing as persons. It is, after all, through the body that I engage with the world. The body, as it were, participates in the world. It is our way of being-in-the-world. And, hence,

> 'Being-in-the-world, for embodied subjects such as ourselves, involves the interplay of both our "embodiment" and our "subjectivity", the expression of our way of seeing the world in our bodily movements'. [52]

So, being an *embodied* agent itself involves being embedded in the world and links the inner self with the outer self. Indeed, being embodied - because of the way our bodies reflect our selves and also participate in the world - breaks down the distinction between the inner and the outer.

Being an agent, meanwhile, indicates the extent to which persons *as such* act on the world, can have intentions, form plans, can demonstrate their thoughts and interests. This aspect of personhood, it can be admitted, might – at some stage – be regarded as absent in people with severe dementia. At the extreme, agency is absent from anyone who succumbs to a terminal illness. At this stage everyone would suffer the final loss of agency that signals the end of the person's life. Can it be said, however, that the person with severe dementia, prior to the point at which he or she enters a terminal state, still maintains agency (even if he or she is totally dependent on carers for all personal needs, immobile, dysphasic and doubly incontinent)?

The argument would need more careful analysis than I can give here, but I can gesture at an argument that emphasizes the situated nature of the instinctual responses that people, even with severe dementia, might make – the grimaces and gestures, for instance. They would be *merely* grimaces and gestures if they were outside their inevitable context. This might sound as if it is *merely* the context, and the meaning it gives to these instinctual responses, that makes the actions into the acts of an agent. To this there are two replies: first, it is not that these responses are just actions, they are the embodied actions of this type of situated being; secondly, the context is bound itself by a requirement for rationality. It is, as it were, a context amidst contexts. If the carers were regarding the dead body of someone who had dementia as an agent, this would not be enough to guarantee that it was rational to do so. Instead, the context must fit with other contexts: there must be some rational coherence to what it is that we allow to indicate pleasure or pain. Certain sorts of response could not possibly indicate pleasure, nor could the non-response of a dead person. So being a situated and an embodied agent of this sort is enough, perhaps, to allow that people with severe dementia retain agency.

So what is it to be situated? Well, we are situated in our culture and history, in our personal narrative (which includes the psychological continuities highlighted by Parfit), in a social context of friends and family, in a moral space of virtues and values and in our spiritual sphere, whatever that might amount to for us personally. We are, that is, in a multifaceted and multi-layered way, deeply embedded as part of what it is to be the creatures that we are. The consequence is that we need to take a *whole* view of the person and recognize that we are inter-connected and inter-dependent.

A further consequence of this view of the person is that it provides a response to the Dworkin-Dresser debate. Being a situated-embodied-agent entails that I have a past and a present and that they both, in some sense, go to make up my identity as a person. This would not make decisions any easier, in fact it is likely to make them trickier, but that is deliberate, because decisions about real people, *qua persons*, need to be made with seriousness and the utmost concern. This entails recognition of the person's cultural, social, spiritual and moral embeddedness in a personal, but shared, context, along with his or her essential embodied agency. Given this context, even in severe dementia, I might have critical interests, [53] in the same way Jaworska suggested I might still value things. [54] But, equally, my experiential interests will themselves be shaping how my life should go now, however it was that I planned it might go in the past. The then-self and the now-self must be brought together to understand who it is that I am and, therefore, what it is that I might wish to do or how it is that I might wish to be treated.

Does all of this allow us to reconcile the different judgements made by carers about the ethical issues they face? I think it supports what would usually occur in clinical practice, namely that people would discuss and negotiate matters. However, we need, perhaps, to become more aware that we move in a space of values, many of which are shared. By being clear about the different perspectives on a particular dilemma, it becomes obvious exactly where values are shared and where they are in conflict. In many cases people will be valuing the same thing. It may be that I am telling the truth to my spouse with dementia (about the fact that she is going into respite), whereas you are not. But this is not necessarily because I value truth and you do not. It might be that we both value something else to do with our relationships with our spouses. Perhaps you avoid distressing your spouse by being less than honest and my spouse would be distressed because of the dishonesty. It might be that the thing we share is a virtue; that is, a disposition to care and protect our spouses from distress.

We might, of course, still disagree, but the SEA view of the person locates the discourse about what is morally justified in the broader context of shared values. Now, at some point, those values might be incommensurable. The SEA view of the person does not necessarily allow that *anything* goes. At some stage we might have to state that we simply cannot share a person's values. At some stage we might have to say that someone appears to us to be *wrong*, even if in most cases the SEA view will encourage common ground to be mapped out. Ultimate moral justification rests, perhaps, not on some particular firm foundation, but on the rational coherence of our view, where "rational coherence" is a function of the inherent need for our thoughts and experiences to share a certain nature, which incorporates values as well as facts about the world.

In this section I have briefly sketched the SEA view of the person, which encourages us to take a *whole view* of the person. It also locates us in the sphere of shared values, in which differences over ethical judgements to do with people with dementia can be carefully negotiated. This still allows room for substantive disagreement, where rational grounds must be adduced by appeal to the coherence of our shared values. This foray into conceptual analysis, in which we have discussed metaphysical notions around personhood, underpins our other ethical judgements and our attitudes towards people with dementia. It helps to demonstrate the importance of philosophy as a means of understanding our clinical and ethical judgements.

Not only do we need metaphysics to pursue ethical research, the SEA view stresses the numerous ways in which a person with dementia might participate in or contribute to research. If we take a broad view of the person with dementia, we are more likely to be cognizant of the ways in which a person *can* contribute, rather than of his or her cognitive defects. So, having seen how metaphysics can contribute to debates about dementia, I shall move on to consider how people with dementia can be involved in research.

RESEARCH AND PERSONS WITH DEMENTIA

Involving people with dementia in research is, in a way, a straightforward idea. But what I have in mind is trying to find out, as we have started to do with carers, how things seem *from their point of view* with respect to ethical issues. This is, therefore, not just a matter of having people with dementia complete questionnaires. Rather it involves really engaging with them, in order to understand them and what it is to be situated as a human being with dementia. Qualitative research will allow us to grasp, from their point of view, the meaning of situations that face people with dementia. As Bond says in his description of the phenomenological perspective, 'the meaning and quality of life is only meaningful through the subjective definitions of individuals'. [55] The perspective of individuals with dementia is increasingly being considered in research. The propaganda point, that the person with dementia has experiences, which can be understood, has been made repeatedly by Kitwood. [56] My propaganda point is that we need to understand the ethical issues that people with dementia face, from their point of view. As Haimes has suggested, much of the empirical work in the social sciences, whilst not setting out to investigate ethical issues, has none the less touched upon and revealed 'how ethics are "done" (identified, thought about, acted upon) in everyday life…'. [57] We have seen this, too, in our own review of qualitative literature to do with carers. [58] Nevertheless, there is every reason to believe that research in this field should not satisfy itself with ethical issues arising by serendipity.

One thing that quickly emerges in any discussion of ethical issues to do with dementia is a concern about the self. [59] Haimes also suggests that there is a similar trend in research to do with reproductive technologies. [60] In ethical parlance, designating someone a person usually implies some sort of moral standing, with the person being entitled to a certain amount of dignity and respect. This just highlights the close connection between ethical and philosophical theories. The need for metaphysics, therefore, is apparent. Indeed, we are driven to metaphysical thoughts as soon as we engage with ethical issues in dementia; and we encounter such ethical issues as soon as we engage with people with dementia or their carers. In the rest of this section, before concluding, I shall briefly allude to the work of Steve Sabat, which exemplifies the points I have been making.

In *The Experience of Alzheimer's Disease*, Sabat records his engagement with a number of people with dementia, sometimes over long periods. [61] All of the people portrayed in the book were moderately to severely impaired by their disease if judged by formal cognitive testing. But with all of them Sabat was able, despite their significant language problems, to initiate conversations over long stretches of time. He demonstrated that, whatever one might say about their abilities on formal cognitive testing, they were able *inter alia* to recall important facts, sequence, plan, negotiate complex social situations, express opinions on issues that ranged from recent events in their lives to politics and, in general, convey meaning. As Sabat states:

> 'No battery of standard neuropsychological tests and resulting numerical scores, no matter how extensive, can open the door to the [dementia] sufferer's interpersonal, social world, and to the reality of the person's psychological experience in that world'. [62]

Sabat has shown how people with dementia can communicate a great deal about the experience of the disease. The research is qualitative, with the conversations having been recorded and later analyzed, but the story (often movingly told) is also 'about a human relationship and the process of communication between one healthy person and one who was diagnosed with [dementia]'. [63]

Rather than offer a summary of Sabat's book, for my purposes it demonstrates the importance of the propaganda points I have been making. In having these conversations, in undertaking this sort of qualitative research, Sabat brings out, time and again, the ethical dimension of the experience of dementia. For instance, he talks of 'positioning', and the ways in which positioning can be for good or for ill (as in Kitwood's 'malignant social psychology' [64]).

Take, for example, the case of Dr. B, who had Alzheimer's disease. At one stage in Sabat's relationship with him, Dr. B felt that he should have had some sort of formal recognition of his participation in the research. This was in keeping with his background as someone who valued and had himself undertaken research. He wanted to be able, despite his communication difficulties, to show other people what it was that he was doing by pointing to something tangible. Dr. B made his feelings known and threatened to leave the project. Sabat makes the point that tests of cognitive function would not allow one to predict all of the abilities that Dr. B demonstrated during this incident. Such tests tend towards what Sabat arrestingly calls, "defectology"; for they tend to show up defects, but say nothing about retained abilities.

> 'Feeling slighted or feeling as though one has been treated in an undignified way requires a highly complex combination of functions involving memory, attention, emotion, and abstract thought – such as the idea of fairness. And, even though Dr. B could not dress himself, he was still able to assert, and work to maintain, his sense of proper pride, and to understand and ask for reciprocity'. [65]

This one small example, which was nevertheless a big issue for Dr. B, demonstrates a broad theme in the ethics of dementia care: the requirement that people are treated, despite dementia, with respect and dignity. It is also striking that this issue, one's place in a research project being recognized, is not the sort of issue one would normally expect to find in a book on ethical issues in dementia. But such issues quickly emerge when qualitative research is undertaken. There was a similarly everyday sort of ethical issue for one of the carers we saw, who faced a dilemma over whether or not to get workmen into her home to do something that the person with dementia would himself have done at one stage. [66] The ethical issue was the same for this carer with respect to her husband as it was for Dr. B: she did not wish to undermine his status and upset his self-esteem.

Not only does Sabat's qualitative research throw up ethical issues, it quickly reveals the extent to which these issues, and the very nature of dementia, require attention to underlying philosophical concerns. Thus, Sabat discusses the notions of language and communication, meaning, intention, understanding and selfhood. And thus, along with a variety of contemporary philosophers, he makes use of ideas drawn from Austin, James, Laing, Mead, Stern, Vygotsky and Wittgenstein. There is little doubt in Sabat's work that engagement with people with dementia not only raises ethical issues that are unique to their perspective, but also uncovers the philosophical (metaphysical even) underpinnings that shape our attitudes and reactions both to the ethical issues and to people with dementia. Sabat further shows how our attitudes towards such philosophical notions (such as selfhood) have practical implications:

> 'Paying heed to the many ways in which the selfhood of the [dementia] sufferer still exists as well as to the ways in which it still can exist and be maintained, can bring the afflicted person some measure of satisfaction'. [67]

CONCLUSION

In this chapter I have indicated and discussed some of the research that has frequently been carried out around ethical issues in dementia, largely generated by professionals. I have then considered research relating to family carers of people with dementia. This also tends to reflect professional concerns, but recently there have been attempts made to understand the ethical issues that arise for carers from their perspective. In passing, I noted that qualitative research encourages the emergence of ethical issues. But my suggestion has been that we need now to press on to find ways of engaging with people with dementia themselves, to understand ethical issues from their perspective.

Ethical issues in dementia have a tendency to bring into focus metaphysical debates about the self, as shown by the debate between Dworkin and Dresser. Meanwhile, research with carers reveals the possibility of ethical disagreement. The SEA view of the person with dementia gestures in the direction of an answer to the Dworkin-Dresser debate and suggests a possible way to reconcile different ethical judgements, given a basic commitment to rational coherence. From this discussion, it should be evident that qualitative research, as a way to understand the ethical issues that arise for people with dementia from their perspective, must be supported by good philosophical thought about metaphysical notions concerning personhood and what it is to be a being of this sort in the world. I have, thus, been able to support my two propaganda points:

- We need to move down the pathway, which started with professional concerns and moved to the carers' perspectives, to consider ethical issues as they arise for people with dementia from their perspectives;
- Progress in this type of ethical research will be enhanced by bringing together qualitative methodologies and metaphysical thought.

The trend in the direction of taking the person with dementia seriously is now well-established and ineluctable. Taking this seriously from the point of view of research in ethics is imperative, both because of the numbers of people with dementia and because, as Sabat and others have increasingly shown, our humanity depends upon it.

ACKNOWLEDGEMENTS

I must acknowledge debts to Dr Clive Baldwin, Professor Tony Hope, Professor Robin Jacoby and Sue Ziebland. Together we are involved in research, supported by the Alzheimer's Society, on ethical issues for carers of people with dementia, being undertaken at The Oxford Centre for Ethics and Communication in Health Care Practice (Ethox). In addition, I must thank Dr Andrew Fairbairn and Dr Stephen Louw from Newcastle. Professor Steve Sabat has significantly influenced my thoughts and been unstinting in his encouragement. All of these colleagues have discussed issues covered in this chapter with me and helped to develop my thoughts. Whilst my gratitude to them is huge, they have no responsibility for the deficiencies of the chapter, for which I alone am responsible. At the time of writing I am receiving support from a Wellcome Trust Short-Term Fellowship in Bioethics, which I must also acknowledge with grateful thanks.

REFERENCES

[1] Bond J. Sociological perspectives. In: Cantley C. ed. *A Handbook of Dementia Care.* Buckingham and Philadelphia: Open University Press; 2001:44-61.

[2] Baldwin C, Hughes J, Hope T, Jacoby R, Ziebland S. Ethics and dementia: mapping the literature by bibliometric analysis. *Int J Geriatr Psychiatry.* 2003;18:41-54.

[3] Treloar A, Philpot M, Beats B. Concealing medication in patients' food. *Lancet.* 2001;357:62-64.

[4] Treloar A, Beats B, Philpot M. A pill in the sandwich: covert medication in food and drink. *J R Soc Med.* 2000;93:408-411.

[5] See reference 3.

[6] See reference 3.

[7] Ballard CG, O'Brien J, James I, Swann A. *Dementia: Management of Behavioural and Psychological Symptoms.* Oxford: Oxford University Press; 2001.

[8] Hughes JC, Louw SJ. Electronic tagging of people with dementia who wander. *BMJ.* 2002;325:847-848.

[9] Hughes JC. Ethics and the psychiatry of old age. In: Jacoby R, Oppenheimer C, eds. *Psychiatry in the Elderly.* 3rd ed. Oxford: Oxford University Press; 2002:863-895.

[10] Coetzee RH, Leask SJ, Jones RG. The attitudes of carers and old age psychiatrists towards the treatment of potentially fatal events in end-stage dementia. *Int J Geriatr Psychiatry.* 2003;18:169-173.

[11] Muncie HL Jr, Magaziner J, Hebel JR, Warren JW. Proxies' decisions about clinical research participation for their charges. *J Am Geriatr Soc.* 1997;45:929-933.

[12] Silberfeld M, Grundstein-Amado R, Stephens D, Deber R. Family and physicians' views of surrogate decision-making: the roles and how to choose. *Int Psychogeriatr.* 1996;8:589-596.

[13] Moe C, Schroll M. What degree of medical treatment do nursing home residents want in case of life-threatening disease? *Age Ageing.* 1997;26:133-137.

[14] van der Steen JT, Muller MT, Ooms ME, van der Wal G, Ribbe MW. Decisions to treat or not to treat pneumonia in demented psychogeriatric nursing home patients: development of a guideline. *J Med Ethics.* 2000;26:114-120.

[15] Pucci E, Belardinelli N, Borsetti G, Rodriguez D, Signorino M. Information and competency for consent to pharmacologic clinical trials in Alzheimer disease: an empirical analysis in patients and family caregivers. *Alzheimer Dis Assoc Disord.* 2001;3:146-154.

[16] Agarwal MR, Ferran J, Ost K, Wilson KCM. Ethics of 'informed consent' in dementia research - the debate continues. *Int J Geriatr Psychiatry.* 1996;11:801-806.

[17] See reference 15.

[18] Hughes JC. Ethics and the anti-dementia drugs. *Int J Geriatr Psychiatry.* 2000;15:538-543.

[19] Cotrell V, Schulz R. The perspective of the patient with Alzheimer's disease: a neglected dimension of dementia research. *Gerontologist.* 1993;33:205-211.

[20] Wilmot S, Legg L, Barratt J. Ethical issues in the feeding of patients suffering from dementia: a focus group study of hospital staff responses to conflicting principles. *Nurs Ethics.* 2002;9:599-611.

[21] Norberg A, Hirschfeld M, Davidson B, et al. Ethical reasoning concerning the feeding of severely demented patients: an international perspective. *Nurs Ethics.* 1994;1:3-13.

[22] Finucane TE, Christmas C, Travis K. Tube feeding in patients with advanced dementia. *JAMA.* 1999;282:1365-1370.

[23] Gillick MR. Rethinking the role of tube feeding in patients with advanced dementia. *N Engl J Med.* 2000;342:206-210.

[24] See reference 9.

[25] Dworkin R. Life's Dominion. *An Argument about Abortion and Euthanasia.* London: Harper Collins; 1993.

[26] Dresser R. Dworkin on dementia: elegant theory, questionable policy. *Hastings Center Report.* 1995;25:32-38.

[27] Jaworska A. Respecting the margins of agency: Alzheimer's patients and the capacity to value. *Philosophy and Public Affairs.* 1999;28:105-138.

[28] See reference 20.

[29] See reference 21.

[30] See reference 2.

[31] Hope T, Oppenheimer C. Ethics and the psychiatry of old age. In: Jacoby R, Oppenheimer C, eds. *Psychiatry in the Elderly.* 2nd ed. Oxford: Oxford University Press; 1997:709-735.

[32] Pratt C, Schmall V, Wright S. Ethical concerns of family caregivers to dementia patients. *Gerontologist.* 1987;27:632-638.

[33] See references 11, 12 and 13.

[34] Pinner G. Truth-telling and the diagnosis of dementia. *Br J Psychiatry.* 2000;176:514-515.

[35] Maguire CP, Kirby M, Coen R, Coakley D, Lawlor BA, O'Neill D. Family members' attitudes toward telling the patient with Alzheimer's disease their diagnosis. *BMJ.* 1996;31:529-30.

[36] Marzanski M. Would you like to know what is wrong with you? On telling the truth to patients with dementia. *J Med Ethics.* 2000;26:108-113.

[37] Hanks RS, Settles BH. Theoretical questions and ethical issues in a family caregiving relationship. *J Appl Soc Sci.* 1988-89;13:9-39.

[38] Hasselkus BR. Ethical dilemmas in family caregiving for the elderly: implications for occupational therapy. *Am J Occup Ther.* 1991;45:206-212.
[39] Hughes JC, Hope T, Savulescu J, Ziebland S. Carers, ethics and dementia: a survey and review of the literature. *Int J Geriatr Psychiatry.* 2002;17:35-40.
[40] See reference 31.
[41] See reference 39.
[42] Hughes JC, Hope T, Reader S, Rice D. Dementia and ethics: the views of informal carers. *J R Soc Med.* 2002;95:242-246.
[43] Barber CE, Lyness KP. Ethical issues in family care of older persons with dementia: implications for family therapists. *Home Health Care Serv Q.* 2001;20:1-26.
[44] Hughes JC. Views of the person with dementia. *J Med Ethics.* 2001;27:86-91.
[45] Locke J. *An Essay Concerning Human Understanding* (1690). Woozley AD, ed. Glasgow: William Collins/Fount; 1964.
[46] Parfit D. *Reasons and Persons.* Oxford: Oxford University Press; 1984.
[47] Hope T. Personal identity and psychiatric illness. In: Griffiths AP. ed. *Philosophy, Psychology and Psychiatry.* Cambridge: Cambridge University Press; 1995:131-143.
[48] Buchanan A. Advance directives and the personal identity problem. *Philosophy and Public Affairs.* 1988;17:277-302.
[49] See reference 44.
[50] Taylor C. *Sources of the Self: The Making of the Modern Identity.* Cambridge: Cambridge University Press; 1989.
[51] Williams BAD. *Problems of the Self.* Cambridge: Cambridge University Press; 1973.
[52] Matthews E. *The Philosophy of Merleau-Ponty.* Chesham: Acumen; 2002.
[53] See reference 25.
[54] See reference 27.
[55] See reference 1, page 56.
[56] Kitwood T. *Dementia Reconsidered: The Person Comes First.* Buckingham: Open University Press; 1997.
[57] Haimes E. What can the social sciences contribute to the study of ethics? Theoretical, empirical and substantive considerations. *Bioethics.* 2000;17:89-113.
[58] See reference 39.
[59] Post SG. *The Moral Challenge of Alzheimer Disease: Ethical Issues from Diagnosis to Dying.* 2nd ed. Baltimore: Johns Hopkins University Press; 2000.
[60] See reference 57.
[61] Sabat SR. *The Experience of Alzheimer's Disease: Life Through a Tangled Veil.* Oxford: Blackwell; 2001.
[62] Ibid. p. 315.
[63] Ibid. p. 24.
[64] See reference 56.
[65] See reference 61 p. 143
[66] See reference 42.
[67] See reference 61 p. 308

Chapter X

DIAGNOSTIC CRITERIA FOR DEMENTIA, MILD COGNITIVE IMPAIRMENT AND ALZHEIMER'S DISEASE

A. Robles, T. Del Ser**, J. Alom*** and J. Peña-Casanova*****

* Division of Neurology, Hospital Clínico Universitario, Santiago de Compostela, Spain

** Section of Neurology, Hospital Severo Ochoa, Madrid, Spain

*** Section of Neurology, Hospital General Universitario, Elche, Spain

**** Section of Behavioural Neurology and Dementia, Instituto Municipal de Asistencia Sanitaria, Hospital del Mar, Barcelona, Spain

Alzheimer's disease (AD), the most frequent cause of dementia in occidental countries, is currently considered a clinicopathological entity defined by the association of a slowly progressive dementia and several histological lesions such as neuritic plaques and neurofibrillar tangles, exceeding the expected amounts of a healthy individual of the same age. This neurodegenerative disease gradually leads to a complete psychological and physical dependency and finally to death within one to two decades.

Although the degenerative process starts several years before the first symptoms appear [1-5], there are no reliable markers of this pre-clinical stage and clinical diagnosis cannot be established before the cognitive failure is present. Therefore, it is important to clarify the existing concepts of dementia and of mild cognitive impairment (MCI), as the stage previous to dementia, to better apply the diagnosis of AD.

On the other hand, we know at the present time much more about the clinical and neuropsychological profile, the structural and functional neuroimaging features, and the biological and genetical markers of other non-Alzheimer degenerative dementias. Furthermore, clinical diagnostic criteria for several of these dementing illnesses (frontotemporal dementia [6], dementia with Lewy bodies [7], progressive supranuclear palsy [8], multisystem atrophy [9], Creutzfeldt-Jakob disease [10-11], vascular dementia [12-15]) have been established, and we can also ascertain by genetic analysis the presence of some familial dementias, such as Huntington's disease. These new diagnostic procedures have enhanced the accuracy of the clinical identification of AD (concord with histological lesions) because now more "positive" AD features are gathered through anamnesis, neurological examination and neuropsychological tests, more diagnostic markers (genetic, biological and neuroimaging) are detected, and more "negative" data supporting the exclusion not only of reversible dementias, but also of other non-Alzheimer degenerative dementias, are collected.

Consequently, it is necessary to update the current clinical diagnostic criteria for AD in order to incorporate the present clinical knowledge, the new diagnostic markers and the recent clinical criteria of other dementias usually considered in differential diagnosis [16]. According to the most common current criteria, NINCDS-ADRDA [17] and DSM-IV [13], the diagnosis of AD is based on the evidence of a slowly progressive dementia and the exclusion of other possible causes which can be detected on the usual ancillary tests, for example hydrocephalus, chronic subdural haematoma, cerebral tumour, neurosyphilis, chronic deficiency of B12 vitamin or severe and persistent hypothyroidism. There is no specific consideration of non-Alzheimer degenerative dementias in these criteria, except for the general exclusion of other causes. Therefore, it can be expected that the specificity of the current criteria would be optimised if patients with a non-Alzheimer dementia would not fit the AD criteria. The Group of Behavioural Neurology and Dementia of the Spanish Society of Neurology (SEN) has recently published a proposal of new clinical diagnostic criteria for AD (SEN criteria) [18] using this new approach.

DEMENTIA

During the last years the most common current criteria of dementia (those of the American Psychiatric Association -DSM-IV [13], Table 1, and those of the World Health Organization —ICD-10 [15], Table 2) have been criticized for several reasons. Firstly, both of them include the presence of memory impairment as a mandatory feature of dementia. Nevertheless, in some frequent dementias as frontotemporal dementia, dementia with Lewy bodies and vascular dementia, memory failure can be mild or absent during the first stages of the disease or can be masked by other more prominent cognitive manifestations. On the other hand, behavioural disturbances can be an outstanding primary and specific manifestation of dementia, as happens in patients with frontotemporal dementia or dementia with Lewy bodies. Therefore, it seems appropriate to apply the same value to memory impairment, persistent behavioural symptoms, executive dysfunction and other cognitive disturbances as clinical diagnostic features of the syndrome of dementia.

Secondly, dementia can be diagnosed when there is a clear decline with respect to previous cognitive performance. To demonstrate this decline it is necessary to apply a neuropsychological exam that must be extent enough as to be sure of cognitive failure, using standardized tests and cut-off scores appropriate for the age and education level of the patient, taking into account their occupational activity. The examiner has to be experienced enough as to differentiate between the difficulty or inability of the patient to solve a neuropsychological test, or if the result of a low score is simply due to simulation, abulia, depression or other psychopathological conditions. To exclude mental retardation, it is also necessary to find out if the results depict an impairment with respect to the previous cognitive status, which can be achieved by asking a reliable informant or repeating periodically the neuropsychological examination.

Table 1. DSM-IV Criteria for the Diagnosis of Dementia (1.994) [13]

A.1:	Memory impairment
A.2:	At least one of the following:
	Aphasia
	Apraxia
	Agnosia
	Executive dysfunction
B:	Sufficient severity of A1 and A2 as to interfere with social or occupational functioning. The disturbance represents a decline from a previous level of functioning
C:	Deficits do not occur exclusively during the course of a delirium

Table 2. ICD-10 Criteria for the Diagnosis of Dementia (1.992) [15]

A:	A decline in memory (registration, storage and retrieval)
B:	A deterioration in judgement and thinking, in general processing of information
C:	Sufficient to interfere with everyday activities
D:	Normal level of consciousness. Possible concurrent episodes of clouding of conciousness
E:	Symptoms should have been present for at least 6 months

An essential condition to establish the diagnosis of dementia is that the cognitive failure must be severe enough to impair the usual social and occupational daily activities. When dementia is mild, it only affects the instrumental activities which are usual for the age and sociocultural environment of the patient and, when dementia is more severe, basic daily activities are also impaired.

Likewise, it would be wrong to specify a minimum duration of the disorder. ICD-10 [15] requires at least 6 months, but patients with some types of dementia (Creutzfeldt-Jakob disease, normal pressure hydrocephalus, chronic subdural haematoma, etc.) can develop the complete disorder in a shorter period. On the other hand, a transient delirium can last up to several weeks in some patients. Therefore, a minimum duration of evolution may be a useful additional criterion for epidemiological studies, but it is arbitrary in daily clinical practice, where early detection of dementia is increasingly more important. When the cognitive trouble begins, fluctuation in the arousal level typical of delirium can help to differentiate this syndrome from dementia.

The SEN criteria [18] to diagnose dementia can be seen in Table 3.

Dementia is a syndrome that can be produced by many different causes. Once we have reached the syndromic diagnosis it is necessary to find out an etiologic diagnosis. Currently, the task of finding the most probable cause of dementia relies on data taken from anamnesis, physical, neurological and neuropsychological examinations, and some complementary tests.

Table 3. SEN Criteria for the Diagnosis of Dementia [18]

I: Disturbance of at least two of the following cognitive areas:

a.	Attention / concentration	e.	Praxis
b.	Language	f.	Visuospatial functions
c.	Gnosia	g.	Executive functions
d.	Memory	h.	Behaviour

II: These alterations must be:

a. Acquired (decline of previous abilities of the patient), confirmed by a reliable informant or after repeated assessments.

b. Confirmed on neuropsychological assessment

c. Persistent during weeks or months, with normal level of consciousness.

III: These disturbances are sufficiently severe as to interfere with everyday social and occupational activities.

IV: The disorder does not alter the level of consciousness until the most advanced phases, although transient concurrent disturbances may occur.

MILD COGNITIVE IMPAIRMENT

Mild cognitive impairment (MCI) is a syndrome that consists of an acquired and long lasting alteration of one or more cognitive functions, different from a focal syndrome and not serious enough to fulfil the criteria of dementia. This syndrome has already been defined in DSM-IV criteria [13], as "mild neurocognitive disorder", and in ICD-10 [15], as "mild cognitive impairment".

In MCI, as in dementia, it is necessary to evidence the cognitive failure in a patient with normal alertness, using standard neuropsychological tests and appropriate cut-off points for the age and educational level of the subject, taking into account his or her usual labour activity. To exclude a slight mental retardation, we must be sure that alterations are acquired, either by asking a reliable informant or by performing periodic neuropsychological exams during several months or years. Patients with MCI, unlike those with dementia, keep enough compensating mental resources as to perform alone their instrumental activities of daily living, with no difficulty or only minimal limitations. The minimum duration of cognitive failure required to diagnose MCI cannot be precisely established, however it should extend at least for several months. It may be transient and reversible, or steadily persist with little variations for a long time, or progress and evolve to dementia without a clear transition point. MCI, as dementia, can be produced by many causes. The SEN criteria of MCI can be seen in Table 4.

Table 4. SEN Criteria for fhe Diagnosis of *Mild Cognitive Impairment* [18]

I:	Disturbance of one or more of the following cognitive areas:		
	a. Attention/concentration	e.	Praxis
	b. Language	f.	Visuospatial functions
	c. Gnosia	g.	Executive functions
	d. Memory		
II:	Alterations must be:		
	a. Acquired, meaning a decline in the previous abilities of the subject		
	b. Reported by the patient or a reliable informant		
	c. Confirmed in the neuropsychological assessment		
	d. Present during months and with normal consciousness.		
III:	The cognitive impairment interferes only minimally with instrumental or advanced activities of daily living.		
IV:	The cognitive disorder does not alter the level of consciousness.		

Alzheimer Disease

The definite diagnosis of AD, as a clinicopathological entity, can be established when the characteristic histological lesions of this disease are disclosed in the brain of a demented patient, usually at autopsy. The presence of one mutation in presenilin 1, presenilin 2 or amyloid protein precursor genes (chromosomes 14, 1 and 21 respectively) associated to the autosomal dominant form of AD, in a patient with familial dementia, also supports the diagnosis of AD with almost 100% certainty. However, more than 95% of AD patients have the sporadic form of the disease, and the physician must establish the diagnosis based on clinical data and supported by the available supplementary tests, which should be rationally selected. Regarding current knowledge about the manifestations of AD and other dementias, the Group of Behavioural Neurology and Dementia of the SEN proposed the SEN-criteria for the clinical diagnosis of AD that are presented in Table 5.

Table 5. SEN Criteria for the Clinical Diagnosis of Alzheimer Disease [18]

I. **DEMENTIA**

a) Onset in adult age
b) Insidious onset (months or years)
c) Slowly progressive
d) Early decline of memory and learning capacity, confirmed in the exam

II. **ABSENCE OF THE FOLLOWING FEATURES IN EARLY STAGES:**

a) Spontaneous parkinsonism
b) Gait unsteadiness and frequent falls
c) Cerebellar syndrome
d) Corticospinal syndrome
e) Visual hallucinations
f) Major depression
g) Outstanding behavioural disturbances

III. EXCLUSION OF OTHER CAUSES OF DEMENTIA

e) According to standard ancillary tests
a) Absence of a recent stroke (6 months)

IV. SUPPORTIVE DIAGNOSTIC FEATURES:

a) Impairment of naming at the beginning of dementia
b) Difficulties in verbal comprehension, categorial verbal fluency and visuospatial orientation in the initial stages
c) Presence of one or two $\varepsilon 4$ alleles of the apolipoprotein E (Apo E) gene
d) Atrophy of the hippocampal complex (temporomesial region) in structural neuroimaging, greater than that of the rest of the cerebral cortex, in the initial stage of dementia
e) Bilateral hypometabolism or hypoperfusion in cortical temporoparietal areas, in PET or SPECT
f) Reduction of the βA_{42} peptide and simultaneous increase of τprotein in cerebrospinal fluid

V. FEATURES THAT MAKE THE DIAGNOSIS UNLIKELY:

a) Predominance of difficulties in the expresive component of language with respect to the disturbance of comprehension and other semantic aspects
b) Severe bradypsychia in the initial stages
c) Outstanding and frequent cognitive fluctuations
d) Vertical gaze palsy
e) Urinary incontinence in the initial stage of dementia not due to urological causes
f) Atrophy (structural neuroimaging), or hypoperfusion or hypometabolism (functional neuroimaging), restricted to frontal lobes or/and temporal poles, in intermediate or advanced stages of dementia
g) Normal electroencephalogram, or quantitative electroencephalographic mapping, in the advanced stages of dementia

PROBABLE ALZHEIMER DISEASE:

Criteria I, II and III must be fulfilled and the items of V must be absent

POSSIBLE ALZHEIMER DISEASE:

All the features of I, II and III are present, except for either Ib, Ic or Id, or one or more items of V occur

DEFINITE ALZHEIMER DISEASE:

Probable or possible Alzheimer disease + neuropathologic criteria of AD, or Dementia
+ neuropathologic criteria of AD
+ absence of other neuropathologic alterations that might cause dementia, or Familial dementia
+ presence of one of the known mutations that can produce autosomal dominant AD (in presenilin 1 -chromosome 14-, presenilin 2 -chromosome 1- or the amyloid precursor protein -chromosome 21- genes)

MILD COGNITIVE IMPAIRMENT PROBABLY DUE TO INCIPIENT ALZHEIMER DISEASE

The manifestations described in I must be present, in a patient with "mild cognitive impairment"
The items of II and III must be present, and at least 1 of IVa – IVb – IVc, and at least 1 of IVd – IVe – IVf, andall items of V must be absent

COMBINED DEMENTIA:

Dementia
+ clinical and neuropathologic elements of at least two nosologic entities that might contribute to the appearance of the cognitive impairment

"ALZHEIMER DISEASE WITH CEREBROVASCULAR DISEASE"

Probable Alzheimer disease + evidence of cerebral vascular lesions in neuroimaging, or Dementia
+ neuropathologic criteria of AD + presence of concurrent cerebral vascular lesions

Section I

The dementia mentioned in Section I must fit the criteria shown in Table 3.

Although it is characteristic for AD dementia to start in adult age, the stated interval between 40 and 90 years is too narrow to include all cases with this disease [19-23]. In general, the first clinical manifestations are more frequent after the age of 65 in sporadic forms and more frequent before 60 in familial cases.

The clinical manifestations of AD usually appear insidiously. Occasionally, the relatives of the patient may remain unaware at the beginning, report the symptoms as subacute, and sometimes describe a presumed causal event. When the first symptoms are evident the underlying neuropathological process has probably gone on for several years and beyond the minimum threshold to be clinically noticed. However, in some patients another concurrent pathologic process (as for example a mild stroke) can accelerate this transition and the relatives can mistakenly associate the onset of the disease to this event, rather than being aware of the complete initial period.

The neurodegenerative process does not stop, which is why cognitive impairment increases as time goes by. There can be apparent plateaus, but a stationary or remittent evolution would make the diagnosis of AD doubtful.

Memory impairment is characteristic of AD and always appears at the beginning, except for some rare cases of focal AD, whose diagnosis may be impossible based only on clinical parameters.

Section II

Every dementing illness shows its more characteristic neurological and neuropsychological profiles during the early stages, although in some cases an unclear clinical picture with infrequent symptoms or atypical manifestations can appear. In order to diagnose AD, it is necessary to take into account both its most usual manifestations and those which are characteristic of other degenerative and non-degenerative dementias. Consequently, a non-iatrogenic parkinsonism at the first stages of cognitive decline is suggestive of dementia with Lewy bodies,[7] progressive supranuclear palsy [8] or subcortical vascular dementia, for example. An early asymmetric parkinsonism, sometimes with an "alien hand" syndrome, is probably due to corticobasal degeneration. When a patient with AD shows parkinsonian features they are usually symmetric and the disease is at the moderate or advanced stage. An unstable gait, as well as repeated falls during the first year of evolution, are usually due to progressive supranuclear palsy [8], normal pressure hydrocephalus or other subcortical brain diseases, but they are not early manifestations of AD. A cerebellar or/and corticospinal syndrome may be found in Creutzfeldt-Jakob disease [10-11], vascular or tumoral lesions, paraneoplastic syndrome, hydrocephalus or multiple system atrophy [9], as well as toxic, metabolic or iatrogenic alterations. Multiple system atrophy does not produce dementia at early stages [9], but may show mild memory disturbances and executive dysfunctions [24]. Visual hallucinations in a patient with early dementia without a previous history of psychosis or drug intake, and not taking medicines with a neurotropic effect, are one of the central features of dementia with Lewy bodies [7]. Outstanding alterations of behaviour, mood or personality constitute the principal manifestation of the first period of frototemporal dementia [6]. Anxiety, irritability, apathy, other personality changes, even mild delusions, are common in early stages of AD, but the progressive memory loss and the impairment of instrumental activities of daily living are always more relevant. They can also present a depressed mood, but not a serious depression with outstanding psychomotor inhibition. It is impossible to state accurately how long the first phase of a dementia lasts when these symptoms can make the diagnosis of AD questionable, but they should not be present at least during GDS (Reisberg's global deterioration scale) = 3 and 4 or CDR (Hughes' clinical dementia scale) = 0'5 and 1 stages.

Section III

To establish the clinical diagnosis of AD it is essential to perform at least some supplementary tests, in order to exclude other non-degenerative causes of dementia that can produce a clinical picture similar to that of AD. All patients with dementia must undergo a blood analysis, including complete blood count, ESR, glucose, cholesterol, triglycerides, urea, creatinine, uric acid, SGPT, GGT, alkaline phosphatases, Na^+, K^+, Ca^{++}, free T4, TSH, B12 vitamin, folic acid and luetic serological tests. Sometimes the abnormalities in these parameters may be only an aggravating element and not the primary cause of dementia. However, a diagnosis of dementia is in itself so serious that it justifies by far the expense involved in undertaking the above-mentioned analysis for all patients to guarantee the timely treatment of every possible reversible dementia. In any case, we always have to re-assess the patient after treatment, in order to ascertain if there is another underlying cause of dementia. The tests performed to detect syphilis are not mandatory in USA, where no cases of neurolues have been registered for more than 20 years [25], but they are necessary in Spain, as new cases are observed every year. Performing structural or functional brain neuroimaging has the same justification as the afore-mentioned analyses. One of these objectives is to detect the presence of vascular lesions, chronic subdural haematoma, neoplasm, hydrocephalus and other macroscopic lesions, which would prompt specific therapeutic measures which in turn might stabilize or even cure the dementia. Likewise, it is advisable to perform an electrocardiogram and a radiography of the chest, as the finding of a non-diagnosed arrhythmia, or a lung lesion indicative of systemic pathology or responsible for respiratory failure, can contribute to understanding the cognitive failure, and can point to the need for specific treatments.

Although the diagnostic efficiencies of some of the aforementioned tests are low, their systematic performance is important in order to detect most cases with a reversible dementia and also to keep homogeneous the diagnostic procedure undertaken in all patients.

Sometimes the anamnesis or the first examination raises the suspicion of an alternative diagnosis and the need for other specific tests, as for example an exhaustive immunological or haematological study, serological tests for HIV or other germs, cerebrospinal fluid analysis, search for specific genetic alterations, electroencephalogram (EEG) or quantitative EEG mapping, functional neuroimaging, thorough cardiovascular examination and, in exceptional cases, even brain or other tissue biopsy.

The effect of a stroke on cognitive functions, even though they might be reversible, can last several months. Therefore, a neuropsychological dysfunction noticed during the first months after a stroke, should not be attributed to AD. However, a remote antecedent of one or more strokes does not exclude the presence of AD, particularly when the patient has shown a proper cognitive function after the strokes and then a significant time later develops a progressive dementia with AD characteristics. When cerebrovascular disease can be verified through the presence of focal neurological signs as a consequence of previous strokes, or showing vascular lesions in neuroimaging or in a histological study, it is reasonable to think of a contribution of these lesions to the cognitive failure. On these occasions we can diagnose "AD with cerebrovascular disease", as was established in the NINDS-AIREN diagnostic criteria of vascular dementia [12].

Sections IV and V

AD is a heterogeneous entity. Several characteristics such as age of onset, clinical manifestations, rate of progression, the presence or not of genetic causal mutations or predisposing polymorphisms, and some biological and neuroimaging markers, as well as the topography and proportion of the different typical histopathologic lesions, are so heterogeneous that it is impossible to define a unique and absolute diagnostic guideline. However, as the clinical profile and the findings from supplementary tests are more close to common expectations, the more accurate the clinical diagnosis will be. In other words, it will be less probable that the histological diagnosis would be different from AD.

The chronology of the neuropsychological alterations observed in most patients with AD is well understood if we consider that the disease starts in the entorhinal cortex, and then spreads to the hippocampus and to the cortical association areas [2-4,26-28]. Since verbal and visuospatial information does not easily reach the limbic circuits of memory through the entorhinal cortex, the earliest and most characteristic clinical manifestation is difficulty in registering episodic information in memory, impeding any new learning. Therefore, cued memory tests with delayed recall time frames have shown a high diagnostic sensitivity and specificity [29-34]. The patients with a more selective impairment of the retrieving mechanisms (frontotemporal dementia, vascular dementia, ...) can recall more elements when we offer them a semantic cue, while patients with AD do not benefit from this prompt, because they have not been able to register any information. Generally speaking, when a patient does not show difficulty in new learning, the cause of their cognitive failure is not AD.

Selective attention and some executive functions may deteriorate early after memory impairment [35-38]. However, these alterations can also be present in other dementias, as vascular dementia [39], frontotemporal dementia [40] and dementia with Lewy bodies [41-43]. The presence of anomia, firstly selective for infrequent objects, an impairment of the semantic function and a visuospatial disorientation [44], in a non-advanced stage of dementia, are more characteristic of AD. A patient who reaches stage 4 of the GDS Reisberg scale should almost always obtain an abnormal score, according to their age and level of education, in the Boston naming and other similar tests. We can expect that language comprehension and category verbal fluency (semantic function) are worse than verbal fluency related to phonemic or lexical strategies [45], and the patient is disorientated, firstly in places that they have not visited frequently and then also in more familiar places. If a patient with an intermediate degree of cognitive failure can move alone throughout non-customary places, it is unlikely that he/she is suffering from AD. Additionally, a remarkable slowing of the mental processing is a typical neuropsychological characteristic of the subcortical lesions [46-47]. If bradypsychia is noteworthy when dementia is beginning it is improbable that cognitive failure is due exclusively to AD. Notable long lasting (non-sporadic) fluctuations of the cognitive functions, both between days and even within the same day, are characteristic of dementia with Lewy bodies, some vascular or metabolic dementias, and delirium, but not of AD.

Some neurological alterations associated to non-Alzheimer dementias were mentioned in section II. Reduction of vertical gaze, more often upward, is a clinical sign described in patients with diverse neurological diseases, some of them with dementia (dementia with Lewy bodies, corticobasal degeneration, frontotemporal degeneration, progressive subcortical gliosis, Huntington's disease, Creutzfeldt-Jakob disease, multi-infarct dementia) and in many healthy aged people as well. When this gaze trouble appears in a patient with a subcortical dementia, often starting by the downward component, progressive supranuclear palsy [8] is the first suspect. In any case, an evident paralysis of vertical gaze in a patient with cognitive failure is a finding that decreases the probability for AD to be the only underlying neuropathologic process. On the other hand, the presence of a neurological bladder incontinence during the initial phase of the dementia is a characteristic of normal pressure hydrocephalus, subcortical vascular dementia, some cases of dementia with Lewy bodies and other dementias with structural lesion or metabolic disfunction of the frontosubcortical region, but it is not a predictable manifestation of an incipient AD.

Some supplementary tests can offer valuable data for the differential diagnosis of degenerative dementias. The finding of a reduction of the hippocampal volume in structural neuroimaging when dementia is beginning, which is more evident than the cortical atrophy of the rest of the brain, has a sensitivity and diagnostic accuracy greater than 80% when referring to AD [48-50]. If we use computed tomography to see the hippocampus, a 15 to 20° caudal angle to the canthomeatal usual plane should be used [51-52]. Likewise, the finding of bilateral hypoperfusion or hypometabolism in the association parietotemporal areas, in functional neuroimaging (SPECT, PET), is a highly specific pattern (more than 80%) when it is observed at the initial phase of a progressive cognitive failure [52-57]. It can appear before the hippocampal atrophy is evident in structural neuroimaging, but its sensitivity is unfortunately low. If we apply magnetic resonance spectroscopy, the pattern of reduction of the NAA/Cr ratio and simultaneous increase of mI/Cr ratio can add strength to the mere morphologic observation of the brain, but its predictive values have not been determined yet [58] (NAA=N-acetyl-L-aspartic acid, Cr=creatine+ phosphocreatine, mI=myoinositol). When a dementia is progressive, the time when the test is performed and the rate of progression must be taken into account. So, the cortical atrophy observed in computed tomography or magnetic resonance can be non-specific when they are performed in the first phase of the dementia. However, a progression faster than expected in normal aging in a particular cerebral location can greatly assist to establish a proper diagnosis [59]. For instance, the atrophy (structural imaging), hypoperfusion or hypometabolism (functional imaging) that clearly increases in the frontal lobes or/and temporal poles, or appears exclusively in this location when dementia is intermediate or advanced, is more characteristic of frontotemporal degeneration [6] than of AD. The electroencephalogram of patients with AD shows a progressive slowing-down of background activity, and there is a progressive increase of delta and theta bands in the quantitative EEG mapping [60-63]. This electrophysiologic alteration is not specific to patients with AD, but it may be useful to differentiate them from other patients with normal bioelectrical activity, or with late onset alteration, as it happens in many cases of frontotemporal degeneration [6] and in patients with psychiatric trouble [64-66].

Among the numerous investigated biological markers of AD, the finding of a reduction of the βA_{42} peptide in cerebrospinal fluid and a simultaneous increase of τ protein is the parameter more consistently associated with AD since its earliest phase [67-68], although it is neither 100% sensitive nor 100% specific, it requires to perform a lumbar puncture, and it is still necessary to undertake more extensive research to determine its exact benefits [69].

More than 100 mutations that can give rise to the autosomal dominant form of AD must be searched for only in clearly hereditary cases [70], which are less than 5% of the total. Many of these familial cases are not carriers of any of these mutations, so we think there are more to be discovered. Some genetic traits facilitate the development of sporadic AD by promoting some elements of the pathogenic sequence of AD, as for example the formation or aggregation of the abnormal β-amyloid. Genotypes and genetic polymorphisms that predispose to develop AD have been identified in the genes responsible for Apo E [71-79] (chromosome 19), cystatin C [80-82].(chromosome 20), bleomycin hydrolase [83] and angiotensin converting enzyme (ACE) [84] (chromosome 17), α-1-antichymotrypsin [73] and presenilin-1 [85] (chromosome 14), α_2-macroglobulin [86-89] and the protein related to the low density lipoprotein -LRP-[90-95] (chromosome 12), the human leukocyte antigen complex -HLA-[73] (chromosome 6), the very low density lipoproteins -VLDL-[73] (chromosome 3), the interleukin 1 (IL-1) [96-96] (chromosome 2) and the cytochrome c oxidase (COX-c) [73, 98-99] (mitochondrial DNA), amongst others. At present we can consider them as risk factors, but not diagnostic markers. In the future it might be useful to search for those genotypes altogether [100], but for the moment only the presence of the ε4 allele of the ApoE gene has shown potential usefulness for differential diagnosis of patients with dementia. However, its low positive predictive value (0.1) [72] and its possible association to other non-Alzheimer dementias [101-104], means that this allele only supports the diagnosis of AD in patients with a clinically compatible dementia.

The fact of describing the supplementary tests that suggest or make unlikely the presence of AD does not mean that they all must be performed on every patient with dementia. Based on a cost effectiveness principle, the tests should be chosen according to the degree of difficulty in reaching a final diagnosis, the means we have available and the efficacy of the medication we would use to treat the suspected dementias included in our differential diagnosis. Nowadays we can early diagnose and treat total or partially reversible dementias. Therefore, this further highlights the necessity for all these patients to undergo a blood analysis and a neuroimaging test, as outlined above. Moreover, at present we have criteria available for the clinical diagnosis of vascular dementia and the principal non-Alzheimer degenerative dementias, whose treatment differs from that of AD. For instance, the proper treatment for AD is cholinesterase inhibitors [105-107], and probably for dementia with

Lewy bodies [108-111], vascular dementia [112-114] and dementias associated to Parkinson disease [115-119] as well, but not for frontotemporal dementia, as the cholinergic system is not involved [120]; memantine can be prescribed for patients with Alzheimer disease [121], and could also be useful for patients with vascular dementia [122], but there is no evidence of its value in subjects with other type of dementia; levodopa can be useful to treat parkinsonism in patients who have dementia with Lewy bodies [123], but not the late parkinsonism associated with AD and frontotemporal dementia; and neuroleptics should be used very cautiously in patients with dementia with Lewy bodies [124] (only atypical antipsychotics, and at lower doses than in other dementias). Furthermore, several neuroprotective treatments might decrease the rate of progression of the disease [125-133]. Taking into account these reflections we think that, when available, magnetic resonance is preferable to computed tomography for a better appraisal of the hippocampal dimensions or to detect small subcortical vascular lesions, and we could determine the Apo E genotype [72]. The remaining tests are only justified in particular cases where a definite diagnosis has not been reached through the first set of tests, or for an investigation purpose. However, as more efficacious medicaments are avalaible, more diagnostic markers (genetics, biological and functional neuroimaging) will become necessary to offer a greater chance of reaching the etiologic diagnosis of very early dementia, mild cognitive impairment, or even a preclinical stage. In any case, whatever the selected tests may be, they should appear in updated criteria, thus helping the physician to establish a definite diagnosis. These criteria should integrate new markers as they are discovered, taking into account their predictive value.

Probable Alzheimer's Disease

This term identifies the maximum degree of diagnostic certainty based on clinical criteria. To reach this diagnosis, apart from having a dementia, the patient must exhibit the specific characteristics that this syndrome shows in AD (I), including the most typical neuropsychological profile (difficulty to register new information in memory -Id), clinical signs of other types of dementia must be absent (II, V) and the minimum mandatory supplementary tests should exclude other causes of dementia (III) -Table 6.

Possible Alzheimer's Disease

This diagnosis is applied to patients whose most probable diagnosis is AD, in the physician's opinion, when they do not fulfil all the criteria for "probable AD". This diagnosis represents a high suspicion of AD, and not a collection of odds and ends where any dementia of uncertain origin can enter. That's why the diagnostic features of "probable AD" that can be absent are specifically listed (Table 6). They are features that, due to the known heterogeneity of AD, occasionally do not appear or are not present at the evolutionary moment when they are usually evident, or they reveal a significant alteration of a part of the brain that is seldom affected in typical patients. When the informant reports a rapid beginning of dementia (Ib), a faster progression than expected (Ic), little difficulty in retaining new information during the first phase (Id), as well as the presence of either of the items that "make unlikely the diagnosis", a diagnosis of AD would be possible if the rest of the manifestations do not fit the criteria of the other non-Alzheimer dementias. The remaining parameters that "support" or "make unlikely" the diagnosis can help the physician to establish a definite diagnosis.

Table 6. SEN Criteria for the Clinical Diagnosis of AD [18]

			PrAD dementia	PosAD dementia
I	a	Adult age	X	X
	b	Insidious onset (months or years)	X	(2)
	c	Slow progressive development (years)	X	(2)
	d	Early decline of memory/learning	X	(2)
II	a	No spontaneous parkinsonism in ISD	X	X
	b	No ataxia or frequent falls in ISD	X	X
	c	No cerebelous syndrome in ISD	X	X
	d	No corticospinal syndrome in ISD	X	X
	e	No visual hallucinations in ISD	X	X
	f	No major depression	X	X
	g	No outstanding behavioural disturbances in ISD	X	X
III	a	Exclusion of other causes, through standard tests[1]	X	X
	b	No strokes during the last 6 months (in ISD)	X	X
IV	a	Anomia for infrequent objects in ISD		
	b	Difficulties in verbal comprehension, categorial verbal fluency and visuospatial orientation in ISD or MSD		
	c	One or two $\varepsilon 4$ alleles in Apo E gene		
	d	Greater atrophy of temporomesial region (MR or CT)		
	e	Bilateral posterior TP hypoactivity (SPECT or PET)		
	f	βA_{42} decrease + τ increase, in cerebrospinal fluid		
V[3]	a	The expressive component of aphasia is predominant	X	
	b	Severe bradypsychia in ISD	X	
	c	Outstanding fluctuations of the cognitive functions	X	
	d	Vertical gaze palsy	X	
	e	No urologic urinary incontinence in ISD	X	
	f	Exclusively frontal and/or temporopolar atrophy (MR or CT) or hypoactivity (SPECT or PET) in MSD	X	
	g	EEG or qEEG normal at an ASD	X	

1. It is mandatory to perform in every patient at least a blood analysis, which must include blood count, ESR, glucose, cholesterol, triglycerides, urea, creatinine, uric acid, SGPT, GGT, alkaline phosphatases, Na^+, K^+, Ca^{++}, free T4, TSH, B12 vitamin, folic acid and luetic serological tests, as well as a test of structural neuroimaging (magnetic resonance or computed tomography of the brain), radiography of the chest and electrocardiogram. The remaining supplementary tests mentioned in other sections are optional.
2. Only one feature of those indicated with this epigraph is allowed to be absent.
3. This section describes manifestations that must be absent.

PosAD: Possible Alzheimer disease.
PrAD: Probable Alzheimer disease.
EEG: Electroencephalogram.
ISD: Initial stages of dementia.
MSD: Intermediate stages of dementia.
qEEG: Quantitative EEG mapping.
MR: Magnetic resonance.
SPECT: Single photon emission computed tomography.
CT: Computed tomography.
TP: Temporo-parietal.
ASD: Advanced stages of dementia.
PET: Positron emission tomography.

Definite Alzheimer's Disease

To establish this diagnosis it is necessary to verify the presence of the characteristic histopathological lesions of AD in the patient's brain. For the moment, AD is a clinicopathologic entity, so it is also necessary that the cognitive functions are impaired. When a patient does not fulfil the clinical criteria of AD (probable or possible), it is essential not only to confirm the presence of the histological lesions of AD (in an amount and extent sufficient enough to fulfil the neuropathologic criteria), but it is also necessary to exclude the presence of other lesions that could produce dementia.

When we face a familial case, the finding of a genetic mutation which can cause AD lets us establish the diagnosis without histological confirmation, because there are no reported cases with a mutation in APP, PS1 or PS2 genes and dementia due only to a non-Alzheimer disease.

Combined Dementia

The clinicopathological series of population-based samples of subjects [134], some of them obtained from very old patients [135], show that dementia is often due to the combined effect of two or more causal diseases, AD being included or not. Clinical and neuropathological research has usually centred on pure dementia, in spite of combined dementia being very frequent [134]. Although currently there are not suitable criteria for identifying the variants of combined dementia, even for the long term "mixed dementia" (AD with associated cerebrovascular disease), it is advisable that, when there is clinical or neuropathological evidence of two or more nosologic entities that might give rise to cognitive failure, a diagnosis of "combined dementia" be applied and the case should be considered as different from pure dementias.

Alzheimer's Disease with Cerebrovascular Disease

Frequently a patient fulfils the criteria for "probable AD", but also shows (in neuroimaging or neuropathological study) signs of cerebrovascular disease. In these patients, we can reasonably suspect a possible contribution of vascular lesions to the cognitive failure, despite thinking of AD as being the essential cause. These cases can be classified as "AD with cerebrovascular disease", in agreement with the term established in NINDS-AIREN criteria [12].

Mild Cognitive Impairment Probably Due to Incipient Alzheimer's Disease

The currently available diagnostic markers of AD are not sufficient to reach a certain preclinical diagnosis, but they may be present early enough as to let us know which patients with MCI have got a high probability of being in the first phase of an AD. With regard to the likelihood of a MCI to evolve into a typical AD, several reports point to the outstanding predictive value of the $\varepsilon 4$ allele of the Apo E gene [136-137], an increase of τ protein and a simultaneous decrease of βA_{42} in cerebrospinal fluid [138], a volume reduction of the hippocampal region in magnetic resonance [139-143], specially of the entorhinal cortex

[144], a higher myoinositol/creatine ratio in proton magnetic resonance spectroscopy [145-146], and bilateral hypoactivity of the temporoparietal cortex (PET, SPECT) [147-148], especially of the posterior cingulum [149]. Some authors have found the SPECT not useful to predict whether a patient with MCI is evolving to dementia [142, 150-152], and the other parameters are not 100% specific, so it is reasonable that a great approximation to the typical clinical profile of AD and the presence of some highly specific diagnostic markers (IVd or/and IVe or/and IVf) are required. (Table 7).

Table 7. Clinical Criteria for the Diagnosis of "Mild Cognitive Impairment Probably Due to Incipient Alzheimer Disease"

		Patient with MCI syndrome[1]	
I	a	Adult age	X
	b	Insidious onset (months or years)	X
	c	Slow progression	X
	d	Early decline of memory/learning	X
II	a	No spontaneous parkinsonism	X
	b	No ataxia or frequent falls	X
	c	No cerebelous syndrome	X
	d	No corticospinal syndrome	X
	e	No visual hallucinations	X
	f	No major depression	X
	g	No outstanding behavioural disturbances	X
III	a	Exclusion of other causes, through standard tests[2]	X
	b	No strokes during the last 6 months	X
IV	a	Anomia for infrequent objects	X (3)
	b	Difficulties in verbal comprehension, categorial verbal fluency and visuospatial orientation	X (3)
	c	One or two $\varepsilon 4$ alleles in Apo E gene[2]	X (3)
	d	Greater atrophy of temporomesial region (MR or CT)[2]	X (4)
	e	Bilateral posterior TP hypoactivity, and/or hypoactivity in posterior cingulate gyrus(SPECT or PET)[2]	X (4)
	f	βA_{42} decrease + τ increase, in cerebrospinal fluid[2]	X (4)
V[5]	a	The expressive component of aphasia is predominant	X
	b	Severe bradypsychia	X
	c	Outstanding fluctuations of the cognitive functions	X
	d	Vertical gaze palsy	X
	e	No urologic urinary incontinence	X

1. Mild cognitive impairment (MCI) is defined in Table 4.
2. The tests mentioned in Section III as mandatory for patients with dementia (Table 6, epigraph 1), as well as the remaining supplementary tests (IV.c, IV.d, IV.e, IV.f, IV.g), are currently optional in patients with MCI. However, the diagnosis of "mild cognitive impairment probably due to incipient Alzheimer disease" can be established only when all the tests required in Table 7 to fulfil the criteria have been performed.
3. The patient must fit at least one of the criteria indicated in this epigraph.
4. The patient must fit at least one of the criteria indicated in this epigraph.
5. This section describes manifestations that must be absent.

MCI: Mild cognitive impairment.
PET: Positron emission tomography.
MR: Magnetic resonance.
SPECT: Single photon emission computed tomography.
CT: Computed tomography.
TP: Temporo-parietal.

REFERENCES

[1] Grober E, Dickson D, Sliwinski MJ, Buschke H, Katz M, Crystal H et al. Memory and mental status correlates of modified Braak staging. *Neurobiol Aging* 1999; 20: 573-579.

[2] Braak H, Braak E. Evolution of neuronal changes in the course of Alzheimer's disease. *J Neural Transm Suppl* 1998; 53: 127-140.

[3] Braak H, Braak E. Diagnostic criteria for neuropathologic assessment of Alzheimer's disease. *Neurobiol Aging* 1997; 18: (suppl 4): S85-S88.

[4] Braak H, Braak E. Staging of Alzheimer's disease-related neurofibrillary changes. 1995; *Neurobiol Aging* 16: 271-278.

[5] Thal DR, Rüb U, Orantes M, Braak H. Phases of Aβ-deposition in the human brain and its relevance for the development of AD. *Neurology* 2002; 58: 1791-1800.

[6] Neary D, Snowden JS, Gustafson L, Passant U, Stuss D, Black S et al. Frontotemporal lobar degeneration. A consensus on clinical diagnostic criteria. *Neurology* 1998; 51: 1546-1554.

[7] McKeith IG, Galasko D, Kosaka K, Perry EK, Dickson DW, Hansen LA et al, for the Consortium on Dementia with Lewy bodies: Consensus guidelines for the clinical and pathologic diagnosis of dementia with Lewy bodies (DLB): Report of the consortium on DLB international workshop. *Neurology* 1996; 47: 1113-1124.

[8] Litvan I, Agid Y, Calne D, Campbell G, Dubois B, Duvoisin RC et al. Clinical research criteria for the diagnosis of progressive supranuclear palsy (Steele-Richardson-Olszewski syndrome): report of the NINDS-SPSP international workshop. *Neurology* 1996; 47: 1-9.

[9] Gilman S, Low P, Quinn N, Albanese A, Ben-Shlomo Y, Fowler C et al. Consenso sobre el diagnóstico de atrofia multisistémica. *Neurología* 1999; 14: 425-428.

[10] World Health Organization; emerging and other communicable diseases, surveillance and control. Global surveillance, diagnosis and therapy of human transmissible spongiform encephalopathies: report of a WHO consultation. Ginebra, Suiza, 9-11 de febrero de 1.998. WHO / EMC / ZDI / 98.9. INTERNET: http://www.WHO.org/emc-documents/tse/docs/ whoemczdi989.pdf

[11] Will RG, Zeidler M, Stewart GE, Macleod MA, Ironside JW, Cousens SN et al. Diagnosis of New variant Creutzfeldt-Jakob disease. *Ann Neurol* 2000; 47: 575-582.

[12] Román GC, Tatemichi TK, Erkinjuntti T, Cummings JL, Masdeu JC, García JH et al. Vascular dementia: Diagnostic criteria for research studies. Report of the NINDS-AIREN International Workshop. *Neurology* 1993; 43: 250-260.

[13] American Psychiatric Association. *Diagnostic and Statistical Manual of Mental Disorders*, 4th ed, Washington D.C., 1994.

[14] Chui HC, Victoroff JI, Margolin D, Jagust W, Shankle R, Katzman R. Criteria for the diagnosis of ischemia vascular dementia proposed by the State of California Alzheimer's Disease Diagnostic and Treatment Centers. *Neurology* 1992; 42: 473-480.

[15] World Health Organization. *The ICD-10 Classification of mental and behavioural disorders*. World Health Organization, Geneva, 1992.

[16] Reisberg B, Burns A, Brodaty H, Eastwood R, Rossor M, Sartorius N et al. Diagnosis of Alzheimer's disease. Report of an International Psychogeriatric Association Special Meeting Work Group under the cosponsorship of Alzheimer's Disease International, the European Federation of Neurological Societies, the World Health Organization, and the World Psychiatric Association. *Int Psychogeriatr* 1997; 9 (suppl 1): 11-38.

[17] McKhann G, Drachman D, Folstein M, Katzman R, Price D, Stadlan EM. Clinical diagnosis of Alzheimer's disease: Report of the NINCDS-ADRDA Work Group under the auspices of Department of Health and Human Services Task Force on Alzheimer's Disease. *Neurology* 1984; 34: 939-944.

[18] Robles A, Del Ser T, Alom J, Peña-Casanova J y Grupo Asesor del Grupo de Neurología de la Conducta y Demencias de la Sociedad Española de Neurología, con el refrendo del Comité Científico de la Sociedad Española de Neurología. Propuesta de criterios para el diagnóstico clínico del deterioro cognitivo ligero, la demencia y la enfermedad de Alzheimer. *Neurología* 2002; 17: 17-32.

[19] Kowalska A, Forsell C, Florczak J, Pruchnik-Wolinska D, Modestowicz R, Paprzycki W et al. A Polish pedigree with Alzheimer's disease determined by a novel mutation in exon 12 of the presenilin 1 gene: clinical and molecular characterization. *Folia Neuropathol* 1999; 37: 57-61.

[20] Wegiel J, Wisniewski HM, Kuchna I, Tarnawski M, Badmajew E, Popovitch E et al. Cell-type-specific enhacement of amyloid-beta deposition in a novel presenilin-1 mutation (P117L). *J Neuropathol Exp Neurol* 1998; 57: 831-838.

[21] von Strauss E, Viitanen M, De Ronchi D, Winblad B, Fratiglioni L. Aging and the ocurrence of dementia. Findings from a population-based cohort with a large sample of nonagenarians. *Arch Neurol* 1999; 56: 587-592.

[22] Ezquerra M, Carnero C, Blesa R, Oliva R. A novel presenilin 1 mutation (Leu166Arg) associated with early-onset Alzheimer disease. *Arch Neurol* 2000; 57:485-488.

[23] Ezquerra M, Carnero C, Blesa R, Gelpi JL, Ballesta F, Oliva R. A presenilin 1 mutation (Ser169Pro) associated with early-onset AD and myoclonic seizures. *Neurology* 1999; 52: 566-570.

[24] Vidailhet M, Bonnet AM, Agid Y. Critères cliniques de diagnostic des atrophies multi-systématisées. *Rev Neurol (Paris)* 1998; 154: 17-21.

[25] Knopman DS, DeKosky ST, Cummings JL, Chui H, Corey-Bloom J, Relkin N et al. Practice parameter: Diagnosis of dementia (an evidence-based review). Report of the Quality Standards Subcommittee of the American Academy of Neurology. *Neurology* 2001; 56: 1143-1153.

[26] Braak H, Braak E, Bohl J. Staging of Alzheimer-related cortical destruction. *Eur Neurol* 1993; 33: 403-408.

[27] Braak H, Braak E. Neuropathological staging of Alzheimer related changes. *Acta Neuropathol* 1991; 82: 239-259.

[28] Arnold SE, Hyman BT, Flory J, Damasio AR, van Hoesen GW. The topographical and neuroanatomical distribution of neurofibrillary tangles and neuritic plaques in cerebral cortex of patients with Alzheimer's disease. *Cereb Cortex* 1991; 1: 103-116.

[29] Buschke H, Kuslansky G, Katz M, Stewart WF, Sliwinski MJ, Eckholdt HM et al. Screening for dementia with the memory impairment screen. *Neurology* 1999; 52: 231-238.

[30] Knopman DS, Ryberg S. A verbal memory test with high predictive accuracy for dementia of the Alzheimer type. *Arch Neurol* 1989; 46: 141-145.

[31] Petersen RC, Smith GE, Ivnik RJ, Kokmen E, Tangalos EG. Memory function in very early Alzheimer's disease. *Neurology* 1994; 44: 867-872.

[32] Welsh KA, Butters N, Hughes JP, Mohs RC, Heyman A. Detection and staging of dementia in Alzheimer's disease. Use of the neuropsychological measures developed for the Consortium to establish a registry for Alzheimer's disease. *Arch Neurol* 1992; 49: 448-452.

[33] Welsh KA, Butters N, Hughes JP, Mohs RC, Heyman A. Detection of abnormal memory decline in mild cases of Alzheimer's disease using CERAD neuropsychological measures. *Arch Neurol* 1991; 48: 278-281.

[34] Davis PE, Mumford SJ. Cued recall and the nature of the memory disorder in dementia. *Br J Psychiat* 1984; 144: 383-386.

[35] Perry RJ, Watson P, Hodges JR. The nature and staging of attention dysfunction in early (minimal and mild) Alzheimer's disease: relationship to episodic and semantic memory impairment. *Neuropsychologia* 2000; 38: 252-271.

[36] Perry RJ, Hodges JR. Attention and executive deficits in Alzheimer's disease. A critical review. *Brain* 1999; 122: 383-404.

[37] Collette F, Van der Linden M, Salmon E. Executive dysfunction in Alzheimer's disease. *Cortex* 1999; 35: 57-72.

[38] Traykov L, Marcie P, Dalla Barba G, Boller F. La neuropsychologie de la maladie d'Alzheimer. *Rev Neurol (Paris)* 1999; 155 (supl. 4): S38-S43.

[39] Looi JC, Sachdev PS. Differentiation of vascular dementia from AD on neuropsychological tests. *Neurology* 1999; 53: 670-678.

[40] Perry RJ, Hodges JR. Differentiating frontal and temporal variant frontotemporal dementia from Alzheimer's disease. *Neurology* 2000; 54: 2277-2284.

[41] Connor DJ, Salmon DP, Sandy TJ, Galasko D, Hansen LA, Thal LJ. Cognitive profiles of autopsy-confirmed Lewy body variant vs pure Alzheimer disease. *Arch Neurol* 1998; 55: 994-1000.

[42] Salmon DP, Galasko D, Hansen LA, Masliah E, Butters N, Thal LJ et al. Neuropsychological deficits associated with diffuse Lewy body disease. *Brain Cogn* 1996; 31: 148-165.

[43] Galasko D, Katzman R, Salmon DP, Hansen L. Clinical and neuropathological findings in Lewy body dementias. *Brain Cogn* 1996; 31: 166-175.

[44] Price BH, Gurvit H, Weintraub S, Geula C, Leimkuhler E, Mesulam M. Neuropsychological patterns and language deficits in 20 consecutive cases of autopsy-confirmed Alzheimer's disease. *Arch Neurol* 1993; 50: 931-937.

[45] Monsch AU, Bondi MW, Butters N, Salmon DP, Katzman R, Thal LJ. Comparisons of verbal fluency tasks in the detection of dementia of the Alzheimer type. *Arch Neurol* 1992; 49: 1253-1258.

[46] Cummings JL, Benson DF. Subcortical dementia. Review of an emerging concept. *Arch Neurol* 1984; 41: 874-879.

[47] Brown RG, Marsden CD. 'Subcortical dementia': The neuropsychological evidence. *Neuroscience* 1988; 25: 363-387.

[48] Killiany RJ, Moss MB, Albert MS, Sandor T, Tieman J, Jolesz F. Temporal lobe regions on magnetic resonance imaging identify patients with early Alzheimer's disease. *Arch Neurol* 1993; 50: 949-954.

[49] Jack CR, Petersen RC, O'Brien PC, Tangalos EG. MR-based hippocampal volumetry in the diagnosis of Alzheimer's disease. *Neurology* 1992; 42: 183-188.

[50] Kesslak JP, Nalcioglu O, Cotman CW. Quantification of magnetic resonance scans for hippocampal and parahippocampal atrophy in Alzheimer's disease. *Neurology* 1991; 41: 51-54.

[51] Jobst KA, Smith AD, Szatmari M, Molyneux A, Esiri ME, King E et al. Detection in life of confirmed Alzheimer" disease using a simple measurement of medial temporal lobe atrophy by computed tomography. *Lancet* 1992; 340: 1179-1183.

[52] Jobst KA, Smith AD, Barker CS, Wear A, King EM, Smith A et al. Association of atrophy of the medial temporal lobe with reduced blood flow in the posterior parietotemporal cortex in patients with a clinical and pathological diagnosis of Alzheimer's disease. *J Neurol Neurosurg Psychiatry* 1992; 55: 190-194.

[53] Meltzer CC, Zubieta JK, Brandt J, Tune LE, Mayberg HS, Frost JJ. Regional hypometabolism in Alzheimer's disease as measured by positron emission tomography after correction for effects of parital volume averaging. *Neurology* 1996; 47: 454-461.

[54] Read SL, Miller BL, Mena I, Kim R, Itabashi H, Darby A. SPECT in dementia: Clinical and pathological correlation. *J Am Geriatr Soc* 1995; 43: 1243-1247.

[55] Claus JJ, van Harskamp F, Breteler MMB, Krenning EP, de Koning I, van der Cammen TJM et al. The diagnostic value of SPECT with Tc 99m HMPAO in Alzheimer's disease: A population-based study. *Neurology* 1994; 44: 454-461.

[56] Powers WJ, Perlmutter JS, Videen TO, Herscovitch P, Griffeth LK, Royal HD et al. Blinded clinical evaluation of positron emission tomography for diagnosis of probable Alzheimer's disease. *Neurology* 1992; 42: 765-770.

[57] Johnson KA, Holman L, Mueller SP, Rosen TJ, English R, Nagel JS, Growdon JH. Single photon emission computed tomography in Alzheimer's disease. *Arch Neurol* 1988; 45: 392-396.

[58] Miller BL, Moats RA, Shonk T, Ernst T, Woolley S, Ross BD et al. Alzheimer disease: Depiction of increased cerebral myo-inositol with proton MR spectroscopy. *Radiology* 1993; 187: 433-437.

[59] Jack CR, Petersen RC, Xu Y, O'Brien PC, Smith GE, Ivnik RJ et al. Rate of medial temporal lobe atrophy in typical aging and Alzheimer's disease. *Neurology* 1998; 51: 993-999.

[60] Almárcegui C, Pascual-Millán LF, Lorente-Lasala S, Bertol-Alegre V, Valdizán-Usón JR. Cartografía cerebral en pacientes con demencia tipo Alzheimer. *Rev Neurol* 1997; 25: 448-451.

[61] Duffy FH, McAnulty GB, Albert MS. Temporoparietal electrophysiological differences characterize patients with Alzheimer's disease: a split-half replication study. *Cereb Cortex* 1995; 5: 215-221.

[62] Passero S, Rocchi R, Vatti G, Burgalassi R, Battistini N. Quantitative EEG mapping, regional cerebral blood flow, and neuropsychological function in Alzheimer's disease. *Dementia* 1995; 6: 148-156.

[63] Miyauchi T, Hagimoto H, Ishii M, Endo S, Tanaka K, Kajiwara S et al. Quantitative EEG in patients with presenile and senile dementia of the Alzheimer type. *Acta Neurol Scand* 1994; 89: 56-64.

[64] Primavera A, Novello P. Quantitative electroencephalography in Parkinson's disease, dementia, depression and normal aging. *Neuropsychobiology* 1992; 25: 102-105.

[65] Kolibas E, Kesicky D. Moznosti pouzitia automatickej kvantitativnej analyzy elektroencefalogramu v diagnostike demencii. *Cesk Psychiatr* 1992; 88: 85-90.

[66] Brenner RP, Reynolds CF, Ulrich RF. EEG findings in depressive pseudodementia and dementia with secondary depression. Electroencephalogr *Clin Neurophysiol* 1989; 72: 298-304.

[67] The Ronald and Nancy Reagan Research Institute of the Alzheimer's association and the National Institute of Aging working group. Consensus report of the working group on: "Molecular and biochemical markers of Alzheimer's disease". *Neurobiol Aging* 1998; 19: 109-116.

[68] Andreasen N, Minthon L, Davidsson P, Vanmechelen E, Vanderstichele H, Winblad B et al. Evaluation of CSF-tau and CSF-Abeta42 as diagnostic markers for Alzheimer disease in clinical practice. *Arch Neurol* 2001; 58: 373-379.

[69] Galasko D. CSF tau and Aβ42: Logical biomarkers for Alzheimer's disease? *Neurobiol Aging* 1998; 19: 117-119.

[70] Post SG, Whitehouse PJ, Binstock RH, Bird TD, Eckert SK, Farrer LA et al. The clinical introduction of genetic testing for Alzheimer disease. An ethical perspective. *JAMA* 1997; 277: 832-836.

[71] National Institute on Aging / Alzheimer's Association Working Group. Apolipoprotein E genotyping in Alzheimer's disease. *Lancet* 1996; 347: 1091-1095.

[72] Myers RH, Schaefer EJ, Wilson PWF, D'Agostino R, Ordovas JM, Espino A et al. Apolipoprotein E ε4 association with dementia in a population-based study: the Framingham study. *Neurology* 1996; 46: 673-677.

[73] Sandbrink R, Hartmann T, Masters CL, Beyreuther K. Genes contributing to Alzheimer's disease. *Molec Psychiatry* 1996; 1: 27-40.

[74] Nalbantoglu J, Gilfix BM, Bertrand P, Robitaille Y, Gauthier S, Rosenblatt DS et al. Predictive value of apolipoprotein E genotyping in Alzheimer's disease: Results of an autopsy series and an analysis of several combined studies. *Ann Neurol* 1994; 36: 889-895.

[75] Tsai MS, Tangalos EG, Petersen RC, Smith GE, Schaid DJ, Kokmen E et al. Apolipoprotein E: risk factor for Alzheimer disease. *Am J Hum Genet* 1994; 54: 643-649.

[76] Corder EH, Saunders AM, Strittmatter WJ, Schmechel DE, Gaskell PC, Small GW et al. Gene dose of apolipoprotein E type 4 allele and the risk of Alzheimer's disease in late onset families. *Science* 1993; 261: 921-923.

[77] Saunders AM, Strittmatter WJ, Schmechel D, George-Hyslop PH, Pericak-Vance MA, Joo SH et al. Association of apolipoprotein E allele epsilon 4 with late-onset familial and sporadic Alzheimer's disease. *Neurology* 1993; 43: 1467-1472.

[78] Mayeux R, Stern Y, Ottman R, Tatemichi TK, Tang M, Maestre G et al. The apolipoprotein ε4 allele in patients with Alzheimer's disease. *Ann Neurol* 1993; 34: 752-754.

[79] Strittmatter WJ, Saunders AM, Schmechel D, Pericak-Vance MA, Enghild J, Salvesen GS et al. Apolipoprotein E: high-avidity to beta-amyloid and increased frequency of type 4 allele in late-onset familial Alzheimer disease. *Proc Natl Acad Sci USA* 1993; 90: 1977-1981.

[80] Crawford FC, Freeman MJ, Schinka JA, Abdullah LI, Gold M, Hartman R et al. A polymorphism in the cystatin C gene is a novel risk factor for late-onset Alzheimer's disease. *Neurology* 2000; 55: 763-768.

[81] Finckh U, von der Kammer H, Velden J, Michel T, Andresen B, Deng A et al. Genetic association of a cystatin C gene polymorphism with late-onset Alzheimer disease. *Arch Neurol* 2000; 57: 1579-1583.

[82] Beyer K, Lao JI, Gómez M, Riutort N, Latorre P, Mate JL et al. Alzheimer's disease and the cystatin C gene polymorphism: an association study. *Neurosci* Lett 2001; 315: 17-20.

[83] Papassotiropoulos A, Bagli M, Jessen F, Frahnert C, Rao ML, Maier W et al. Confirmation of the association between bleomycin hydrolase genotype and Alzheimer's disease. *Mol Psychiatry* 2000; 5: 213-215.

[84] Narain Y, Yip A, Murphy T, Brayne C, Easton D, Evans JG et al. The ACE gene and Alzheimer's disease susceptibility. *J Med Genet* 2000; 37: 695-697.

[85] Ezquerra M, Blesa R, Tolosa E, López-Pousa S, Aguilar M, Peña J et al. The genotype 2/2 of the presenilin-1 polymorphism is decreased in Spanish early-onset Alzheimer's disease. *Neurosci Lett* 1997; 227: 201-204.

[86] Myllykangas L, Polvikoski T, Sulkava R, Verkkoniemi A, Crook R, Tienari PJ et al. Genetic association of α_2–macroglobulin with Alzheimer's disease in a Finnish elderly population. *Ann Neurol* 1999; 46: 382-390.

[87] Marx J. New gene tied to common form of Alzheimer's. *Science* 1998; 281: 507-509.

[88] Blacker D, Wilcox MA, Laird NM, Rodes L, Horvath SM, Go RCP et al. Alpha-2 macroglobulin is genetically associated with Alzheimer disease. *Nature Genet* 1998; 19: 357-360.

[89] Liao A, Nitsch RM, Greenberg SM, Finckh U, Blacker D, Albert M et al. Genetic association of an alpha2-macroglobulin (Val1000lle) polymorphism and Alzheimer's disease. *Hum Mol Genet* 1998; 7: 1953-1956.

[90] Hyman BT, Strickland D, Rebeck GW. Role of the low-density lipoprotein receptor-related protein in beta–amyloid metabolism and Alzheimer disease. *Arch Neurol* 2000; 57: 646-650.

[91] Van Uden E, Carlson G, St George-Hyslop P, Westaway D, Orlando R, Mallory M et al. Aberrant presenilin-1 expression downregulates LDL receptor-related protein (LRP): is LRP central to Alzheimer's disease pathogenesis? *Mol Cell Neurosci* 1999; 14: 129-140.

[92] Lambert JC, Chartier-Harlin MC, Cottel D, Richard F, Neuman E, Guez D et al. Is the LDL receptor-related protein involved in Alzheimer's disease? *Neurogenetics* 1999; 2: 109-113.

[93] Beffert U, Arguin C, Poirier J. The polymorphism in exon 3 of the low density lipoprotein receptor-related protein gene is weakly associated with Alzheimer's disease. *Neurosci Lett* 1999; 259: 29-32.

[94] Hollenbach E, Ackermann S, Hyman BT, Rebeck GW. Confirmation of an association between a polymorphism in exon 3 of the low-density lipoprotein receptor-related protein gene and Alzheimer's disease. *Neurology* 1998; 50: 1905-1907.

[95] Kamboh MI, Ferrell RE, DeKosky ST. Genetic association studies between Alzheimer's disease and two polymorphisms in the low density lipoprotein receptor-related protein gene. *Neurosci Lett* 1998; 244: 65-68.

[96] Grimaldi LM, Casadei VM, Ferri C, Veglia F, Licastro F, Annoni G et al. Association of early-onset Alzheimer's disease with an interleukin-1 alpha gene polymorphism. *Ann Neurol* 2000; 47: 361-365.

[97] Nicoll JA, Mrak RE, Graham DI, Stewart J, Wilcock G, MacGowan S et al. Association of interleukin-1 gene polymorphisms with Alzheimer's disease. *Ann Neurol* 2000; 47: 365-368.

[98] Davis RE, Miller S, Gerrnstadt C, Ghosh SS, Fahy E, Shinobu LA et al. Mutations in mitochondrial cytochrome c oxidase genes segregate with late-onset Alzheimer disease. *Proc Natl Acad Sci* 1997; 94: 4526-4531.

[99] Hutchin T, Cortopassi G. A mitochondrial DNA clone is associated with increased risk for Alzheimer disease. Proc Natl Acad Sci 1995; 92: 6892-6895.

[100] Selkoe DJ. Translating cell biology into therapeutic advances in Alzheimer's disease. *Nature* 1999; 399 (suppl): A23-A31.

[101] Arai H, Higuchi S, Muramatsu T, Iwatsubo T, Sasaki H, Trojanowski JQ. Apolipoprotein E gene in diffuse Lewy body disease with or without co-existing Alzheimer's disease. *Lancet* 1994; 344: 1307.

[102] Pickering-Brown SM, Mann DMA, Bourke JP. Apolipoprotein E and Alzheimer's disease pathology in Lewy body disease and in other β-amyloid-forming diseases. *Lancet* 1994; 343:1155.

[103] Frisoni GB, Bianchetti A, Govoni S, Trabucchi M, Calabresi L, Franceschini G. Association of Apolipoprotein E E4 with vascular dementia. *JAMA* 1994; 271: 1317.

[104] Frisoni GB, Calabresi L, Geroldi C. Apolipoprotein E ε4 allele in Alzheimer's disease and vascular dementia. *Dementia* 1994; 5: 240-242.

[105] Giacobini E. Invited review: Cholinesterase inhibitors for Alzheimer's disease therapy: from tacrine to future applications. *Neurochem Int* 1998: 32: 413-419.

[106] Krall WJ, Sramek JJ, Cutler NR. Cholinesterase inhibitors: a therapeutic strategy for Alzheimer disease. Ann Pharmacother 1999; 33: 441-450.

[107] Jann MW. Pharmacology and clinical efficacy of cholinesterase inhibitors. *Am J Health Syst Pharm* 1998; 55 (suppl 2): S22-S25.

[108] McKeith I, Del Ser T, Spano P, Emre M, Wesnes K, Anand R et al. Efficacy of rivastigmine in dementia with Lewy bodies: a randomised, double-blinded, placebo-controlled international study. *Lancet* 2000; 356: 2031-2036.

[109] Querfurth HW, Allam GJ, Geffroy MA, Schiff HB, Kaplan RF. Acetylcholinesterase inhibition in dementia with Lewy bodies: results of a prospective pilot trial. *Dement Geriatr Cogn Disord* 2000; 11: 314-321.

[110] Shea C, MacKnight C, Rockwood K. Donepezil for treatment of dementia with Lewy bodies: a case series of nine patients. *Int Psychogeriatr* 1998; 10: 229-238.

[111] Samuel W, Caligiuri M, Galasko D, Lacro J, Marini M, McClure FS et al. Better cognitive and psychopathologic response to donepezil in patients prospectively diagnosed as dementia with Lewy bodies: a preliminary study. *Int J Geriatr Psychiatry* 2000; 15: 794-802.

[112] Erkinjuntti T, Kurz A, Gauthier S, Bullock R, Lilienfeld S, Damaraju CV. Efficacy of galantamine in probable vascular dementia and Alzheimer's disease combined with cerebrovascular disease: a randomised trial. *Lancet* 2002; 359: 1283-1290.

[113] Shua-Haim JR, Shua-Haim V, Comsti E, Ross JS. Donepezil (Aricept®) treatment of multi infarct dementia: The caregivers and clinical impression. *Am J Alzheimer's Dis* 2000; 15: 201-211.

[114] Moretti R, Torre P, Antonello RM, Cazzato G, Bava A. Rivastigmine in subcortical vascular dementia: an open 22-month study. *J Neurol Sci* 2002; 203-204: 141-146.

[115] Reading PJ, Luce AK, McKeith IG. Rivastigmine in the treatment of parkinsonian psychosis and cognitive impairment: preliminary findings from an open trial. *Mov Disord* 2001; 16: 1171-1174.

[116] Fabbrini G, Barbanti P, Aurilia C, Pauletti C, Lenzi GL, Meco G. Donepezil in the treatment of hallucinations and delusions in Parkinson's disease. *Neurol Sci* 2002; 23: 41-43.

[117] Aarsland D, Laake K, Larsen JP, Janvin C. Donepezil for cognitive impairment in Parkinson's disease: a randomised controlled study. J Neurol *Neurosurg Psychiatry* 2002; 72: 708-712.

[118] Bergman J, Lerner V. Successful use of donepezil for the treatment of psychotic symptoms in patients with Parkinson's disease. *Clin Neuropharmacol* 2002; 25: 107-110.

[119] Werber EA, Rabey JM. The beneficial effect of cholinesterase inhibitors on patients suffering from Parkinson's disease and dementia. *J Neural Transm* 2001; 108: 1319-1325.

[120] Francis PT, Holmes C, Webster MT, Stratmann GC, Procter AW, Bowen DM. Preliminary neurochemical findings in non-Alzheimer dementia due to lobar atrophy. *Dementia* 1993; 4: 172-177.

[121] Reisberg B, Windscheif U, Ferris SH, Hingorani VN, Stoeffler A, Moebius H-J. Memantine in moderately severe to severe Alzheimer's disease (AD): Results of a placebo-controlled 6-month trial. *Neurobiol Aging* 2000; 21 (suppl 1): S275.

[122] Orgogozo J-M, Rigaud A-S, Stöffler A, Möbius H-J, Forette F. Efficacy and safety of memantine in patients with mild to moderate vascular dementia. A randomized, placebo-controlled trial (MMM300). *Stroke* 2002; 33: 1834-1839.

[123] Geroldi C, Frisoni GB, Bianchetti A, Trabucchi M. Drug treatment in Lewy body dementia. *Dement Geriatr Cogn Disord* 1997; 8: 188-197.

[124] McKeith I, Fairbairn A, Perry R, Thompson P, Perry E. Neuroleptic sensitivity in patients with senile dementia of Lewy body type. *BMJ* 1992; 305: 673-678.

[125] Fricker J. From mechanisms to drugs in Alzheimer's disease. *Lancet* 1997; 349: 480.

[126] Oken BS, Storzbach DM, Kaye JA. The efficacy of Ginkgo biloba on cognitive function in Alzheimer disease. *Arch Neurol* 1998; 55: 1409-1415.

[127] Soholm B. Clinical improvement of memory and other cognitive functions by Ginkgo biloba: review of relevant literature. *Adv Ther* 1998; 15: 54-65.

[128] Sano M, Ernesto C, Thomas RG, Klauber MR, Schafer K, Grundman M et al. A controlled trial of selegiline, alpha-tocopherol, or both as treatment for Alzheimer's disease. The Alzheimer's disease cooperative study. *N Engl J Med* 1997; 336: 1216-1222.

[129] Flynn BL, Ranno AE. Pharmacologic management of Alzheimer disease, Part II: Antioxidants, antihypertensives, and ergoloid derivatives. *Ann Pharmacother* 1999; 33: 188-197.

[130] Regland B, Lehmann W, Abedini I, Blennow K, Jonsson M, Karlsson I et al. Treatment of Alzheimer's disease with clioquinol. *Dement Geriatr Cogn Disord* 2001; 12: 408-414.

[131] Melov S. '...and C is for Clioquinol' - the AbetaCs of Alzheimer's disease. *Trends Neurosci* 2002; 25: 121-124.

[132] Scott HD, Laake K. Statins for the prevention of Alzheimer's disease. *Cochrane Database Syst Rev* 2001; 4: CD003160.

[133] Aisen PS, Davis KL. The search for disease-modifying treatment for Alzheimer's disease. *Neurology* 1997; 48 (suppl 6): S35-S41.

[134] Holmes C, Cairns N, Lantos P, Mann A. Validity of current clinical criteria for Alzheimer's disease, vascular dementia and dementia with Lewy bodies. *Br J Psychiatry* 1999; 174: 45-50.

[135] Skoog I, Nilsson L, Palmertz B, Andreasson LA, Svanborg A. A population-based study of dementia in 85-year-olds. *N Engl J Med* 1993; 328: 153-158.

[136] Petersen RC, Smith GE, Ivnik RJ, Tangalos EG, Schaid DJ, Thibodeau SN et al. Apolipoprotein E status as a predictor of the development of Alzheimer's disease in memory-impaired individuals. *JAMA* 1995; 273: 1274-1278.

[137] Blesa R, Adroer R, Santacruz P, Ascaso C, Tolosa E, Oliva R. High apolipoprotein E epsilon 4 allele frequency in age-related memory decline. *Ann Neurol* 1996; 39: 548-551.

[138] Andreasen N, Minthon L, Vanmechelen E, Vanderstichele H, Davidsson P, Winblad B et al. Cerebrospinal fluid tau and Abeta42 as predictors of development of Alzheimer's disease in patients with mild cognitive impairment. *Neurosci Lett* 1999; 273: 5-8.

[139] Jack CR Jr, Petersen RC, Xu YC, O'Brien PC, Smith GE, Ivnik RJ et al. Prediction of AD with MRI-based hippocampal volume in mild cognitive impairment. *Neurology* 1999; 52: 1397-1403.

[140] De Leon MJ, Convit A, DeSanti S, Bobinski M, George AE, Wisniewski HM et al. Contribution of structural neuroimaging to the early diagnosis of Alzheimer's disease. *Int Psychogeriatr* 1997; 9 (suppl 1): 183-190.

[141] Convit A, De Leon MJ, Tarshish C, De Santi S, Tsui W, Rusinek H et al. Specific hippocampal volume reductions in individuals at risk for Alzheimer's disease. *Neurobiol Aging* 1997; 18: 131-138.

[142] Parnetti L, Lowenthal DT, Presciutti O, Pelliccioli GP, Palumbo R, Gobbi G et al. 1H-MRS, MRI-based hippocampal volumetry, and 99mTc-HMPAO-SPECT in normal aging, age-associated memory impairment, and probable Alzheimer's disease. *J Am Geriatr Soc* 1996; 44: 133-138.

[143] Xu Y, Jack CR Jr, O'Brien PC, Kokmen E, Smith GE, Ivnik RJ et al. Usefulness of MRI measures of entorhinal cortex versus hippocampus in AD. *Neurology* 2000; 54: 1760-1767.

[144] Du AT, Schuff N, Amend D, Laakso MP, Hsu YY, Jagust WJ et al. Magnetic resonance imaging of the entorhinal cortex and hippocampus in mild cognitive impairment and Alzheimer's disease. *J Neurol Neurosurg Psychiatry* 2001; 71: 441-447.

[145] Kantarci K, Jack CR Jr, Xu YC, Campeau NG, O'Brien PC, Smith GE et al. Regional metabolic patterns in mild cognitive impairment and Alzheimer's disease: A ^{1}H MRS study. *Neurology* 2000; 55: 210-217.

[146] Catani M, Cherubini A, Howard R, Tarducci R, Pelliccioli GP, Piccirilli M et al. (1)H-MR spectroscopy differentiates mild cognitive impairment from normal brain aging. *Neuroreport* 2001; 12: 2315-2317.

[147] Rapoport SI. Discriminant analysis of brain imaging data identifies subjects with early Alzheimer's disease. *Int Psychogeriatr* 1997; 9 (suppl 1): 229-235.

[148] Johnson KA, Jones K, Holman BL, Becker JA, Spiers PA, Satlin A et al. Preclinical prediction of Alzheimer's disease using SPECT. *Neurology* 1998; 50: 1563-1571.

[149] Okamura N, Shinkawa M, Arai H, Matsui T, Nakajo K, Maruyama M et al. Prediction of progression in patients with mild cognitive impairment using IMP-SPECT. *Nippon Ronen Igakkai Zasshi 2000*; 37: 974-978 (article in Japanese, abstract in Medline).

[150] McKelvey R, Bergman H, Stern J, Rush C, Zahirney G, Chertkow H. Lack of prognostic significance of SPECT abnormalities in non-demented elderly subjects with memory loss. *Can J Neurol Sci* 1999; 26: 23-28.

[151] Ishiwata A, Kitamura S, Nagazumi A, Terashi A. Cerebral blood flow of patients with age-associated memory impairment and the early stage of Alzheimer's disease. A study by SPECT using the ARG method. *Nippon Ika Daigaku Zasshi* 1998; 65: 140-147 (article in Japanese, abstract in Medline).

[152] Celsis P, Agniel A, Cardebat D, Demonet JF, Ousset PJ, Puel M. Age related cognitive decline: a clinical entity? A longitudinal study of cerebral blood flow and memory performance. *J Neurol Neurosurg Psychiatry* 1997; 62: 601-608.

Chapter XI

WHEN MEMORY FAILS: ASSESSMENT AND CARE OF PERSONS WITH ALZHEIMER'S DISEASE

Fay L. Bower
Chair, Department of Nursing
Holy Names College
Oakland, CA
Cyndi S. McCullough
Senior Consultant
HDR, INC.
Omaha, NE

INTRODUCTION

When memory fails it does not mean Alzheimer's disease (AD) is the problem. However, a decline in mental abilities including memory, language, and logical thinking that persists over time could indicate the person has AD, which is the most common form of dementia that affects over 4 million people in the US. By 2050, 14 million Americans are expected to have AD. In addition, AD is the fourth leading cause of death among adults, and one in 10 persons over 65 and nearly half of those over 85 have AD. More alarming is the fact that this number is increasing in people in their 40s and 50s. [1]

The impact of AD reaches far beyond those affected by the disease. Persons with AD cost Americans approximately $80-100 billion a year. "Neither Medicare nor any private health insurance covers the long-term type of care most patients need." [2] And more than 7 of every 10 persons with AD live at home which means the family is involved in the care of the person with AD. In fact, 75% of the home care is provided by family which costs an average of $12,500 per year paid out-of-pocket by the family. [3]

In this chapter the authors present the risk factors, signs and symptoms of AD, how assessment/diagnosis is determined, the kinds of care available and the impact of the setting on the life and performance of persons with AD.

Risk Factors

While the exact cause of AD is not known and there is no cure for the disease, there are many ways to assist in diagnosing of AD and halting the progression of the disease. One of the ways is to determine and control the risk factors for the development of the disease. For example, age, gender, family history, level of education, head injury, elevated blood pressure, and an inactive mind are all risk factors for AD. While there is little one can do about family history, age or gender there are ways to reduce the risk of AD related to blood pressure, brain injury, education, and an inactive mind. Keeping blood-pressure within normal limits is not only one way to reduce risk for AD, it is also a way to reduce risk for stroke, heart attack, and diabetes. Avoiding brain injury, which is usually the result of car or other accidents, is an important way to reduce risk for AD and many other kinds of health problems. And the latest research indicates education is a way to reduce risk for AD because it keeps the mind active.

Several large research studies of priests, nuns, and brothers have discovered cognitively stimulating activities reduce the risk of AD. The researchers of the Snowden study of nuns [4], which has been going on since 1993, found that low linguistic ability in early life has a strong relationship to poor cognitive functioning and dementia in late life. Nuns who showed signs of AD had consistently authored essays low in idea density and grammatical complexity 50 or more years earlier. In contrast, those nuns who were teachers and kept their minds active did not have symptoms of AD even though plaques and tangles, which indicate AD, were found in their brains on autopsy.

The Rush University study of priests, nuns and brothers has surfaced similar findings. [5] Seven hundred dementia-free participants age 65 and older were studied for 4.5 years with cognitive testing done each year. They found the frequency of participating in activities like listening to the radio, reading newspapers or magazines, reading books, playing games such a cards, checkers, crosswords or others puzzles and going to museums was related to a reduced risk for AD.

We know that as people grow older their chances for developing AD increase. There has been research to determine if other factors related to growing older affect the risk factor. Studies indicate there are other risk factors when coupled with growing older that do create an increased risk for AD. For instance, if there is a family history of AD and a personal history of depression, the risk of developing the disease increases. [6] Further according to Lopez and colleagues [7] the presence of cardiovascular disease, a history of alcohol abuse, and a history of depression with the onset of dementia hastens the time of death.

Studies have also been conducted on certain genes and their role in the development of AD. To date we know that the ApoE gene on chromosome 19 makes a substance that carries cholesterol in the bloodstream. We also know that ApoE appears to influence the exact age of onset of AD. [8] More research in this area is needed but it is clear we need to help people keep their cholesterol levels at normal range for this problem and for many other health reasons.

Mercury as a risk factor for the development of AD has also been studied. To date researchers have found no significant relationship between silver fillings in teeth with AD when the brain was studied on autopsy. [9] However, researchers continue to look for something in the air, soil or water that may have a relationship to the development of AD.

SIGNS AND SYMPTOMS OF AD

The decline in cognitive functioning is characterized by irretrievable memory loss and faulty reasoning. There are also personality and behavior changes. The relentless progression of AD from mild forgetfulness to the inability to function independently can be so subtle that it is not recognized until the individual is far into the disease process. To help people with dementia and their families recognize the warning signs of AD, the Alzheimer's Association has developed a list of ten common signs. Any one of them alone can be an indicator of AD.

1. Changes in mood or behavior. Rapid mood swings from calm to fears to anger for no apparent reason is a common warning sign that may indicate AD.
2. Changes in personality. A completely independent person may become extremely confused, very dependent on a family member or very fearful once they are diagnosed with AD.
3. Difficulty performing familiar tasks. Performing tasks that don't typically require much thought is often difficult for the person with AD. They might not remember how to use the vacuum, tie their shoes, make a phone call, or play a card game they were very familiar with.
4. Disorientation to time and place. Persons with AD can forget where they are, how they got there and/or where they are going. Although it is normal to forget where one is going sometimes, the person without AD can find their way home, the person with AD cannot.
5. Loss of initiative. Persons with AD may sleep or watch TV more than usual. They may not want to socialize as they usually do.
6. Memory loss. Doctors often can't distinguish between routine forgetfulness and the more serious memory problems of AD. While forgetting names and telephone numbers happens to most people, they will eventually remember them. When persons with dementia forget those things, they will probably not remember them later.
7. Poor or decreased judgment. Persons with AD may wear layers of clothes when it is warm or wear very little clothing when it is cold. They may also give large amounts of money to telemarketers or pay for home or car repairs that aren't needed.
8. Misplacing things. A person with AD might misplace things or put them in unusual places. A person with AD might put their checkbook in the refrigerator or their car keys in the cookie jar.

9. Problems with abstract thinking. Balancing a checkbook or paying bills may be too complicated to complete for the person with AD.
10. Problems with language. Forgetting simple words or substituting unusual words is another warning sign of AD. [10]

Symptoms of AD vary by person but in all cases they gradually worsen over time. Symptoms are categorized as mild, moderate and severe. Mild symptoms include confusion and memory loss, disorientation, withdrawal from social situations, general apathy, tendency to lose things, difficulty remembering the month or day of week, and changes in personality and judgment.

Moderate symptoms include difficulty with activities of daily living such as bathing and eating, sleeping, and recognizing family and friends. Other moderate symptoms include wandering and pacing, fear of bathing, hallucinations, inappropriate sexual behavior, violent behavior, and agitation or depression.

Severe symptoms include loss of speech, little appetite resulting in weight loss, loss of bladder and bowel control, loss of ability to walk, smile, or swallow, and inability to recognize people, places, and objects.

As the symptoms of AD increase, the demands placed on the caregiver also increase. As care becomes more physically demanding and more time-consuming, partial or full institutionalization is the only option. Medications can alter the progression of AD, therefore, it is important to recognize those early signs and symptoms so an appropriate treatment plan can be established.

Obtaining a Diagnosis

Assessment of the individual's physical, psycho-social and mental condition is essential both for making the diagnosis and for determining an appropriate care approach. It is also important for the assessments to occur early when the first indications of a problem are noticed. Many of the symptoms of AD are also present in other health conditions, so ruling out other conditions is the first step to obtaining a diagnosis of AD. Making observations, measuring physical performance, conducting a health history, and performing neuro-psychological testing and laboratory studies, are necessary in order to rule out other conditions.

Making Observations

While observation has not always been a consistently successful way to assess for AD, in studies conducted by Dennis, Furness, Lindesay, and Wright [11] and Sjobeck and Isacsson [12] the use of a structured tool and systematic observation proved to work as a way to gather data that leads to a diagnosis of AD. The trick to success appears to depend on whether the observer uses a structured tool and a systematic process.

Measuring Physical Performance

Assessing physical performance is also a useful way to differentiate AD from other conditions. In a study by Tappen, Roach, Buchner, Barry, and Edelstein [13] physical performance was measured using a six-minute walk. The researchers found that persons in the later stages of AD were not able to finish the walk due to the inability to follow commands. Van Someren and colleagues [14] examined sleep and sleep patterns and found that persons with higher levels of AD had more sleep disturbances. The researchers also found the activity level of persons with AD was significantly lower than the control group. Bliwise, Hughes, McMahon, and Kutner [15] found the patterns of relationships and the severity of the dementia can also be detected by observing the sleep/wakefulness ratio

Assessing eating behavior is another way to measure an individual's ability to function. Tully, Matrakas, Mir, and Musallam [16] found persons who demonstrated impairments in attention, construction, conceptualization, and memory had difficulty completing the task of eating. Another study by Durnbaugh, Haley and Roberts [17] found noise, environmental distractions, and motor agitation often caused persons with AD to play with their food and not eat. Clearly an assessment of mealtime behavior is important in order to determine the level of functional behavior and the nutritional needs of the person with AD.

Conducting a Health History

Completing a health assessment is an important component of the assessment of individuals suspected to have AD. But completeness of the assessment is probably the most important aspect of the health assessment. Completeness means the assessor must determine the physical, psycho-social and mental condition of the individual. The physical elements to be assessed include a head to toe review and an analysis of all the body's systems.

One of the sources for providing information about the psychosocial behavior of the individual who might have AD that must be included in the assessment is the family. Family can provide data about the individual's social interactions, functional abilities, cognitive reasoning, ability to stay focused and in touch with reality, and behaviors that are disruptive to others over time. They can also provide information about the prescription and non-prescription drug use.

Assessing the mental condition of the individual should include the use of several psycho-metric instruments, such as the Mini-Mental State Exam (MMSE), The Cognitive Assessment Screening Test (CAST), the Boston Naming test, Wechsler-Scale, and the Palui Test.

Measuring Neuropsychological Functions

There are many ways to measure neuropsychological functioning. However, the Mini Mental State Exam (MMSE) is an excellent tool for measuring memory, language skills, ability to do arithmetic, and other abilities related to brain functioning. Another and very easy and simple way to assess cognitive functioning is the "clock test." which was tested by

Paganini-Hill, Clark, Henderson, & Birge. [18] This test, which correlates with more detailed and time-consuming cognitive screening, can be administered by anyone. The individual suspected of having AD is asked to draw the face of a clock and to place the numbers and hands on the clock for a specific time. If there is cognitive dysfunction, the individual will place the numbers in the wrong places and/or not be able to place the hands in the proper angles for the specified time

The use of EEG as an assessment tool to assist in the diagnosis of AD has also been studied. Grusendorf [19] found EEG changes occur as the dementia of the person with AD progresses when measured by the Global Deterioration Scale (GDS). Correlating the EEG reading with the GDS provides a picture of the severity of the dementia.

Performing Laboratory and Imaging Tests

There are also a number of laboratory tests that help rule out AD, such as blood, urine, and spinal fluid tests to determine if there may be anemia, infections or liver, kidney, thyroid and/or vitamin deficiencies. Brain scans, such as, Magnetic Resonance Imaging (MRI) and Computive Tomography (CT), are also used to rule out tumors, atherosclerosis, stroke, and brain conditions. The latest research on the use of Positron Emission Tomography (PET) indicates it is a good way to determine whether there is normal activity in the posterior portion of the brain where language and memories are processed [20].

GETTING THE RIGHT CARE

While there is currently no cure for Alzheimer's Disease, there are many pharmacological and non pharmacological interventions, based on research, to relieve the symptoms of AD. These interventions can be used to improve cognitive function, lessen mood disturbances, reduce aggression and agitation, stabilize activity, correct sleep disturbances, prevent falls, and improve the individual's ability to perform the acts of daily living.

Improve Cognitive Function

Loss of memory and disturbances in judgment are often the first visible signs of AD. Drugs specifically designed to improve cognitive function are relatively new but have demonstrated some impressive results. Cholinesterase inhibitors, such as, Tacrine, Rivastigmine, Donepezil, and Galantamine have been on the market less than a decade and are still in the early stages of development. However, they have provided some reduction of symptoms of early-stage AD. [21] In 1993, these four drugs were approved for use by FDA. The first one, Tacrine (Cognex), is seldom prescribed now because of its history of many side effects. The other three have proved to be effective in improving memory and with few side effects. Unfortunately, these drugs are not effective for everyone and their effectiveness is limited to the early and middle stages of AD.

Filip and Kolibas [22] reported positive cognitive results from Selegiline, a monoamine oxidase inhibitor. Selegiline is thought to improve memory in the prefrontal areas of the brain. Ginko Biloba Special Extract EGb 761, a herbal alkaloid, has also been studied for its effectiveness as a drug to reduce memory loss. Results have been mixed [23].

Fischhof, Moslinger-Gehmayr, Herrmann, Friedman, & Rusmann [24] evaluated the effectiveness of Vincamine, an herbal alkaloid and found persons with AD had improved cognition. This improvement is thought to be the result of increased cerebral blood flow resulting in better utilization of oxygen and glucose in the brain. Continued research will give us more information about the benefits of these drugs and herbal alkaloids.

Lessen Mood Disturbances

Depression is a common symptom during the early stages of AD when the individual has some awareness and then later when greater deterioration of the brain occurs. Therapy to date has primarily been pharmacological with antidepressant drugs, such as Sertraline and selected serotonin reuptake inhibitors (SSRIs), which are the drugs of choice. Studies of the effectiveness of these drugs, however, indicate there is not enough evidence of their usefulness in relieving depression. Trappler and Cohen [25] who studied the effectiveness of SSRIs, found those individuals with major depression improved but those with central nervous system depression experienced less improvement. Magai, Kennedy and Gomberg [26] also found little improvement in depression for those persons with AD who took Sertraline. Clearly there is a need for more research in this area.

Reduce Aggression and Agitation

Many approaches/strategies have been tried, with varying success, to reduce the aggression and agitation displayed by persons with AD. Predominant has been the use of music, [27, 28, 29, 30] bathing, [31, 32] and massage. [33, 34, 35] Other approaches, such as bright light therapy, [36, 37] dog therapy, [38] mirror usage, [39] diverse activities [40] and altering visual barriers [41, 42] have also been used to reduce agitation and aggression. All of these interventions have demonstrated some degree of success but the question in each case has been whether the therapy was effective alone or whether the attention and interaction of the person providing the intervention was the real reason for a reduction in aggression and agitation. Clearly more study is needed.

Several pharmacological agents have been studied as interventions to control agitation and aggression. For example, Carbamazepine, an anticonvulsant, has been used to manage restlessness, verbal disruptive behaviors, and physical aggression with some positive results. [43] Valproate, another anticonsulsant, has also been tried as an agent to control dementia-related aggressive behavior [44]. And Risperidone, as an agent to control behavior disturbances, has also been used and evaluated. [45, 46, 47] As a result of the use and study of these pharmacological agents, Risperidone is now considered an effective treatment for both aggression and agitation and is the usual protocol for severe dementia.

Estrogen also been tested as a drug to control aggression and aggression. [48] While the results were impressive the studies were small so the researchers recommended further clinical trials be conducted to determine the long-term effects of Estrogen.

Stabilize Activity

Many interventions have been initiated for decreasing the wandering and pacing so common of persons with AD. Rather than pacing and wandering, which can result in agitation or simply sitting which can create stagnation and physical complications, constructive activities to change behavior have been tried. Hutchinson and Marshall [49] conducted an ethnographic study to determine the effectiveness of an activity kit that contained 20 therapeutic activities and found, for some, the activities facilitated connections but for others they were a burden. Another study by Teri and colleagues [50] demonstrated that a structured exercise programs can improve balance, flexibility, lower body strength and endurance. The researchers noted that familiarity with the routine was probably the most important aspect of the program.

Pharmacological agents have also been used to control activity. For example, Fluvozamine, an SSRI agent, has been used and evaluated to determine its effectiveness as a drug to control stereotypic movement. While the results were impressive more study is needed as these studies were small and without controls.

Correct Sleep Disturbances

The presence of sleep disturbances is another symptom used to rule out or validate the diagnosis of AD. Natural light and daytime activity levels have been found to influence the rest- activity rhythm disturbances in persons with AD. Von Someren and his colleagues [51] found nighttime arousals and noise levels in nursing homes contributed to the rhythm disturbances experienced by the institutionalized patients. Other researchers [52] found higher levels of dementia and greater dependency on a caregiver were associated with more disturbed sleep. An additional important finding is that age, gender, and psychoactive medication use were not associated with sleep disturbances.

Measuring sleep disturbances can be difficult. However, one successful method to measure sleep disturbances is to use the Actillume, as it measure both activity and illumination exposure. [53] The Actillume is worn on the wrist and continuously and unobtrusively monitors the patient's sleep-wake cycles.

Prevent Falls

There has been little research on ways to prevent falls by demented persons. However, one study by Meddaugh, Friedenberg, and Knisley [54] that was conducted in an SCU for individuals with AD, found that residents who wore treaded socks to bed at night experienced fewer falls. The reduction in the number of falls was not significant, but the reduction in the number of falls due to slipping in urine was. This simple intervention coupled with prompted voiding has proved to be a useful and successful way to manage potentially harmful situations.

Improve Acts of Daily Living

Approaches aimed at improving dressing, eating, feeding, and incontinence to improve functioning have been studied with positive results. Rogers and his colleagues [55] used behavioral rehabilitative interventions with residents and staff in five nursing homes. The residents showed increased independence with dressing and the staff reduced the amount of assistance given to the resident when behavioral interventions were used.

The use of soothing music coupled with skill training has proved to be a good way to increase the AD individuals' ability to feed themselves, as well as, to increase their food intake. [56, 57] Amella [58] examined the relationship between caregiver interaction during mealtime and the proportion of food consumed by older residents with dementia and concluded that when dementia patients fail to meet adequate nutritional standards, clinicians should examine the interactions between the patient and caregiver during mealtimes. Others [59, 60] echo her suggestion.

LeClerc and Wells [61] introduced a content methodology process to enhance the feeding abilities of people with AD who experienced ideational apraxia. Nurses were able to develop interventions to enhance and maintain the feeding abilities in this group of patients when they used the content methodology.

Many persons with AD have incontinence, which is often accompanied by embarrassment and leads to infections. One successful solution that has been studied is prompted voiding. [62, 63, 64] The best aspect of this approach is that it is easy to do and costs very little. A scheduled program for toileting is especially helpful for those who are physically immobile, unable to communicate needs, as well as, for staff who are extremely busy.

Approaches for managing patients with AD exist, however as Gugel [65] so aptly states, "Despite the fact that research supports the effectiveness of behavioral interventions for specific behavioral problems related to AD, there is not widespread use of these strategies in nursing home settings" (p. 867).

Impact of the Setting

Care for the person with Alzheimer's disease occurs in many settings ranging from the home to institutional care, with the approach to care being different both in scope and cost. Additionally, the healthcare settings for person with AD are categorized as three types: special care units (SCUs), residential care special dementia units RC-SDU), and group living facilities (GLF). Researchers have examined all three and have compared them in an attempt to determine which setting is best for the person with AD. The results are inconsistent but enlightening.

Special Care Units

The Joint Commission on Accreditation of Healthcare Organizations (JCAHO) defines the ideal AD unit as one that has an alarm for wanderers; a home-like environment with soft-colors and no-shadow lighting; a specially trained staff; activities to stimulate physical, cognitive and social skills; and a way to involve family in the care. [66] SCUs were developed to meet the JCAHO standards but have not always been able to do so. Some researchers were able to demonstrate improved patient outcomes and family satisfaction with the SCU experience. [67, 68] Others [69, 70] have compared the behavior of persons with AD in SCUs with those in traditional units and found no difference in their rate of functional decline. These researchers concluded the SCU experience is no better but more likely a label used as a marketing tool and a reason to charge a higher rate for care.

An earlier study by Volicer & colleagues [71] compared SCU residents to those in traditional units and found those in SCUs often were less exposed to aggressive medical interventions. Sloane and colleagues [72] discovered low levels of agitation in the SCU were related to a combination of factors: the physical environment, staff treatment activities, low rates of restraint use, small unit size, and fewer numbers of co-morbid conditions. More study in this area is clearly needed.

Studies that have compared staff behavior in SCUs with staff behavior in traditional units revealed staff who worked in SCUs were less stressed. [73] Another comparison study that focused on the goals of AD care of staff in SCUs and traditional units found the staff in the SCUs focused more on reducing agitation and anxiety/disruptive behavior, and the number and amount of sedatives taken than their nursing home counterparts. [74]

Residential Care Facilities

The focus of residential care facilities is on personal rather than medical care. [75] Residential care facilities offer a less intensive level of service. Wandering, resisting help with Acts of Daily Living (ADLs), and verbal abuse are the most common behavioral problems with residents in residential care special dementia programs (RC-SDP). [76] Sloane and colleagues [77] determined there is less disorientation, anxiety, and agitation in residents in small home-like residential care environments. However, Innes and Surr, [78] discovered residential facilities were meeting the physical care but not the psychosocial care needs of the patients.

Group Living Facilities

When group living facilities were compared with nursing home settings, the researchers found living conditions had minimal effects on cognitive function and the capacity to complete activities of daily living. [79] They concluded it is possible to care for severely demented patients in group living facilities.

While many disturbing behavioral problems of those in the early stages of AD can be partially managed by the care setting/environment, cost and scope of the care must be considered when selecting the care setting. Obviously more research is needed before we will be able to determine the best environment for helping the person with AD stay as functional as possible and at an affordable cost.

CONCLUSIONS

The assessment, diagnosis and care of persons with AD are currently hot topics due to the projected incidence and prevalence of AD. Much research is being conducted but there remains a need for much more. Even though there is a great deal of evidence-based knowledge about ways to counsel, treat, and care for persons with AD, much more is needed. This chapter contains the most current data on the subjects presented but care providers need to watch the growing body of knowledge about AD and the best ways to provide care as the research being conducted is vast and diverse. Also presented in this chapter is the beginning body of knowledge about the appropriate setting for persons with AD and the cost of that care so families have the information, based on research, they need to make informed decisions. Not included in this chapter is what we know about caregiver burden and the strategies that decrease that burden.

REFERENCES

[1] Alzheimer's Association (n.d.). *Statistics about Alzheimer's Disease*. Retrieved on February 5, 2003. http://www.alz.org/AboutAD/Statistics.htm

[2] Alzheimer's Association (n.d.). *Statistics about Alzheimer's Disease*. Retrieved on February 5, 2003. http://www.alz.org/AboutAD/Statistics.htm

[3] Snowdon, D. A., Greiner, L. H., & Markesbury, W. R. (2000). Linguistic ability early in life and the neuropathology of Alzheimer's disease and cerebrovascular disease: Findings from the nun study. *Annals of the New York Academy of Sciences, 903,* 34-8.

[4] Azar, B. (2002). Use it or lose it? More research suggests that mental activity may stave off the symptoms of Alzheimer's disease. *Monitor on Psychology, 33*(5). Retrieved on March 16, 2003 from http://www.apa.org/monitor/may02/useit.html

[5] Butt, Z. A. & Strauss, M. E. (2001). Relationship of family and personal history to the occurrence of depression in persons with Alzheimer's Disease. *American Journal of Geriatric Psychiatry, 9*(3), 249-54.

[6] Lopez, O. L., Becker, J. T., Klunk, W., Saxton, J., Hamilton, R. L., Kaufer, D. I., Sweet, R. A., Cidis Meltzer, C., Wisniewski, S., Kamboh, M. I., & Dekosky, S. T. (2000). Research evaluation and diagnosis of possible Alzheimer's disease over the last two decades: II. *Neurology, 55*(12), 1863-9.

[7] Morris, C. M., Benjamin, R., Leake, A., McArthur, F. K., Candy, J. M., Ince, P. G., Torvik, A., Bjertness, E., & Edwardson, J. A. (1995). Effect of apolipoprotein E genotype on Alzheimer's disease neuropathology in a cohort of elderly Norweigans. *Neuroscience Letters, 201*(1), 45-7.

[8] Saxe, S. R., Wekstein, M. W., Kryscio, R. J., Henry, R. G., Cornett, C. R.,Snowdon, D. A. Grant, F. T., Schmitt, F. A., Donegan, S. J., Wekstein, D. R., Ehmann, W. D., &

Markesbery, W. R. (1999). Alzheimer's Disease, dental amalgam and mercury. *Journal of the American Dental Association 130*(2), 191-99.

[9] Ten warning signs of Alzheimer's disease (2002). Retrieved on February 4, 2003 from http://www.alz.org/AboutAD/10Signs.html

[10] Dennis, M., Furness, L., Lindesay, J., & Wright, N. (1998). Assessment of patients with memory problems using a nurse-administered instrument to detect early dementia and dementia subtypes. *International Journal of Geriatric Psychiatry, 13*(6), 405-9.

[11] Sjobeck, B., & Isacsson, A. (1995). Ability of a trained primary healthcare nurse to discriminate dementia from other psychogeriatric disorders. *International Psychogeriatrics, 7*(1), 9-16.

[12] Tappen, R. M., Roach, K. E., Buchner, D., Barry, C., & Edelstein, J. (1997). Reliability of physical performance measures in nursing home residents with Alzheimer's disease. *Journal of Gerontology: Medical Sciences, 52A*(1), M52-5.

[13] van Someren, E. J., Hagebeuk, E. E., Lijzenga, C., Scheltens, P., de Rooij, S. E., Jonker, C. Pot, A., Mirmiran, M., & Swaab, D. F. (1996). Circadian rest-activity rhythm in Alzheimer's disease. *Biological Psychiatry, 40*(4), 259-70.

[14] Bliwise, D. L., Hughes, M., McMahon, P. M., & Kutner, N. (1995). Observed sleep/wakefulness and severity of dementia in an Alzheimer's disease special care unit. *Journal of Gerontology: Medical Sciences, 50*(6), M303 6.

[15] Tully, M. W., Matrakas, K. L., Muir, J., & Musallam, K. (1997). The Eating Behavior Scale. A simple method of assessing functional ability in patients with Alzheimer's disease. *Journal of Gerontological Nursing, 23*(7), 9-15.

[16] Durnbaugh, T., Haley, B., & Roberts, S. (1996). Assessing problem feeding behaviors in mid-stage Alzheimer'' disease. *Geriatric Nursing, 17*(2), 63-7.

[17] Panganini-Hill, A., Clark, L. J., Henderson, V. W., & Birge, S. J. (2001). Clock drawing: Analysis in a retirement community. *Journal of the American Geriatrics Society, 49*(7), 941-7.

[18] Grusendorf, P. E. (1994). EEGs in cognitive stages of Alzheimer's –type dementia. *Journal of Neuroscience Nursing, 26*(1), 42-6.

[19] Stevens, L. M. (2001). Alzheimer's disease. *The Journal of the American* Medical Association, 286, 2194. Retrieved on February 2, 2003 from http://www.medem.com/MedLB/article_detaillb.cfm?article_ID=ZZZMOSHHTC&sub_c...

[20] Lamb, H. M., & Goa, K. L. (2001). Rivastigmine. A pharmacoeconomic review of its use in Alzheimer's disease. Pharmacoeconomics, 19(3), 303-18.

[21] Farlow, M. R., Hake, A., Messina, J., Hartman, R., Veach, J., & Anand, R. (2001). Response of patients with Alzheimer's disease to rivastigmine treatment is predicted by the rate of disease progression. Archives of Neurology, 58(3), 417-22.

[22] Bullock, R. (2002). New drugs for Alzheimer's disease and other dementias. British Journal of Psychiatry, 180, 135-9.

[23] Filip, V., & Kolibas, E. (1999). Selegiline in the treatment of Alzheimer's disease: a long-term randomized placebo-controlled trial. *Journal of Psychiatry and Neuroscience, 24*(3), 234-43.

[24] Schreiter Gasser, U., & Gasser, T. (2001). A comparison of cholinesterase inhibitors and ginkgo extract in treatment of Alzheimer dementia. *Fortschritte der Medzin. Originalien, 119*(3-4), 135-8.

[25] LeBars, P. L., Velasco, F. M., Ferguson, J. M., Dessain, E. C., Kieser, M., & Hoerr, R. (2002). Influence of the severity of cognitive impairment on the effect of the Ginkgo biloba extract EGb 761 in Alzheimer's disease. *Neuropsychobiology, 45*(1), 19-26.

[26] Fischhof, P. K., Moslinger-Gehmayr, R., Herrmann, W. M., Friedmann, A., & Rubmann, D. L. (1996). Therapeutic efficacy of vincamine in dementia. *Neuropsychobiology, 34*(1), 29-35.

[27] Trappler, B., & Cohen, C. I. (1998). Use of SSRIs in "very old" depressed nursing home residents. *American Journal of Geriatric Psychiatry, 6*(1), 83-9.

[28] Magai, C., Kennedy, G., Cohen, C. I., & Gomberg, D. (2000). A controlled clinical trial of sertraline in the treatment of depression in nursing home patients with late-stage Alzheimer's disease. *American Journal of Geriatric Psychiatry, 8*(1), 66-74.

[29] Clark, M. E., Lipe, A. W., & Bilbrey, M. (1998). Use of music to decrease aggressive behaviors in people with dementia. *Journal of Gerontological Nursing, 24*(7), 10-7.

[30] Gerdner, L. A. (2000). Effects of individualized versus classical "relaxation" music on the frequency of agitation in elderly persons with Alzheimer's disease and related disorders. *International Psychogeriatrics, 12*(1), 49-65.

[31] Ragneskog, H., Kihlgren, M., Karlsson, I., & Norberg, A. (1996). Dinner music for demented patients: Analysis of video-recorded observations. *Clinical Nursing Research, 5*(3), 262-277.

[32] Sambandham, M., & Schirm, V. (1995). Music as a nursing intervention for residents with Alzheimer disease in long-term care. *Geriatric Nurse, 16*(2), 79-83.

[33] Martin, L. S., Morden, P., & McDowell, C. (1999). Using the towel bath to give tender care in dementia: A case example. *Perspectives, 23*(1), 8-11.

[34] Namazi, K. H., & Johnson, B. D. (1996). Issues related to behavior and the physical environment: Bathing cognitively impaired patients. *Geriatric Nursing, 17*(5), 234-8.

[35] Rowe, M., & Alfred, D. (1999). The effectiveness of slow-stroke massage in diffusing agitated behaviors in individuals with Alzheimer's disease. *Journal of Gerontological Nursing, 25*(6), 22-34.

[36] Kim, E. J., & Buschmann, M. T. (1999). The effect of expressive physical touch on patients with dementia. *International Journal of Nursing Studies, 36*(3), 235-43.

[37] Snyder, M., Egan, E. C., & Burns, K. R. (1995a). Efficacy of hand massage in decreasing agitation behaviors associated with care activities in persons with dementia. *Geriatric Nursing, 16*(2), 60-3.

[38] Snyder, M., Egan, E. C., & Burns, K. R. (1995b). Interventions for decreasing agitation behaviors in persons with dementia. *Journal of Gerontological Nursing, 21*(7), 34-40.

[39] Dawson, P. (1999). Bright light treatment for people with Alzheimer's disease. *Perspectives, 23*(1), 25-6.

[40] Lyketsos, C. G., Lindell Veiel, L., Baker, A., & Steele, C. (1999). A randomized, controlled trial of bright light therapy for agitated behaviors in dementia patients residing in long-term care. *International Journal of Geriatric Psychiatry, 14*(7), 520-5.

[41] Churchill, M., Safaoui, J., McCabe, B. W., & Baun, M. M. (1999). Using a therapy dog to alleviate the agitation and desocialization of people with Alzheimer's disease. *Journal Psychosocial Nursing and Mental Health Services, 37*(4), 16-22.

[42] Tabak, N., Bergman, R., & Alpert, R. (1996). The mirror as a therapeutic tool for patients with dementia. *International Journal of Nursing Practice, 2*(3), 155-159.

[43] Sival, R. C., Vingerhoets, R. W., Haffmans, P. M., Jansen, P. A., Ton Hazelhoff, J. N. (1997). Effect of program of diverse activities on disturbed behavior in three severely demented patients. *International Psychogeriatrics, 9*(4), 423-30.

[44] Dickinson, J. I., McLain-Kark, J., & Marshall-Baker, A. (1995). The effects of visual barriers on exiting behavior in a dementia care unit. *The Gerontologist, 35*(1), 127-30.

[45] Namazi, K. H., Rosner, T. T., & Calkins, M. P. (1989). Visual barriers to prevent ambulatory Alzheimer's patients from exiting through the emergency door. *The Gerontologist, 29*(5), 699-702.

[46] Tariot, P. N., Erb, R., Leibovici, A., Podgorski, C. A., Cox, C., Asnis, J., Kolassa, J., & Irvine, C. (1994). Carbamazepine treatment of agitation in nursing home patients with dementia: A preliminary study. *Journal of American Geriatric Society, 42*(11), 1160-6.

[47] Lott, A. D., McElroy, S. L., & Keys, M. A. (1995). Valproate in the treatment of behavioral agitation in elderly patients with dementia. *Journal of Neuropsychiatry, 7*(3), 314-9.

[48] Goldberg, R. J., & Goldberg, J. (1997). Risperidone for dementia-related disturbed behavior in nursing home residents: a clinical experience. *International Psychogeriatrics, 9*(1), 65-8.

[49] Kopala, L. C., & Honer, W. G. (1997). The use of Risperidone in severely demented patients with persistent vocalizations. *International Journal of Geriatric Psychiatry, 12*(1), 73-7.

[50] De Deyn, P. P. & Katz, I. R. (2000). Control of aggression and agitation in patients with dementia: Efficacy and safety of risperidone. *International Journal of Geriatric Psychiatry, 15*(S1), S14-S22.

[51] Shelton, P. S., & Brooks, V. G. (1999). Estrogen for dementia-related aggression in elderly men. *American Pharmacotherapy, 33*(7-8), 808-12.

[52] Hutchinson, S. A. & Marshall, M. (2000). Responses of family caregivers and family members with Alzheimer's disease to an activity kit: An ethnographic study. Journal of Advanced Nursing, 31(1), 44-50.

[53] Teri, L., McCurry, S. M., Buchner, D. M., Logsdon, R. G., LaCroix, A. Z., Kukull, W. A., Barlow, W. E., & Larson, E. B. (1998). Exercise and activity level in Alzheimer's disease: A potential treatment focus. *Journal of Rehabilitation Research and Development, 35*(4), 411-9.

[54] van Someren, E. J., Hagebeuk, E. E., Lijzenga, C., Scheltens, P., de Rooij, S. E., Jonker, C. Pot, A., Mirmiran, M., & Swaab, D. F. (1996). Circadian rest-activity rhythm in Alzheimer's disease. *Biological Psychiatry, 40*(4), 259-70.

[55] Bliwise, D. L., Hughes, M., McMahon, P. M., & Kutner, N. (1995). Observed sleep/wakefulness and severity of dementia in an Alzheimer's disease special care unit. *Journal of Gerontology: Medical Sciences, 50*(6), M303 6.

[56] Ancoli-Israel, S., Clopton, P., Klauber, M. R., Fell, R., & Mason, W. (1997). Use of wrist activity for monitoring sleep/wake in demented nursing-home patients. *Sleep, 20*(1), 24-7.
[57] Meddaugh, D. I., Friedenberg, D. L., & Knisley, R. (1996). Special socks for special people: Falls in special care units. *Geriatric Nursing, 17*(1). 24-6.
[58] Rogers, J. C., Holm, M. B., Burgio, L. D., Granieri, E., Hsu, C., Hardin, J. M., & McDowell, B. J. (1999). Improving morning care routines of nursing home residents with dementia. *Journal of American Geriatric Society, 47*(9), 1049-57.
[59] Forbes, D. A. (1998). Strategies for managing behavioural symptomatology associated with dementia of the Alzheimer type: A systematic overview. *Canadian Journal of Nursing Research, 30*(2), 67-86.
[60] Forbes, D., & Strang, V. (1997). Managing the symptoms of individuals with Alzheimer's disease. *AARN News Letter, 53*(10), 7-9.
[61] Tappen, R. M. (1994). The effect of skill training on functional abilities of nursing home residents with dementia. *Research in Nursing and Health, 17*(3), 159-65.
[62] Amella, E. J. (1999). Factors influencing the proportion of food consumed by nursing home residents with dementia. *Journal of the American Geriatrics Society, 47*(7), 879-85.
[63] Coyne, M. L., & Hoskins, L. (1997). Improving eating behaviors in dementia using behavioral strategies. *Clinical Nursing Research, 6*(3), 275-90.
[64] McGillivray, T., & Marland, G. R. (1999). Assisting demented patients with feeding: Problems in a ward environment. A review of the literature. *Journal of Advanced Nursing, 29*(3), 608-14.
[65] LeClerc, C. M., & Wells, D. L. (1998). Use of a content methodology process to enhance feeding abilities threatened by ideational apraxia in people with Alzheimer's-type dementia. *Geriatric Nursing, 19*(5), 261-7.
[66] Adkins, V. K., & Mathews, R. M. (1997). Prompted voiding to reduce incontinence in community-dwelling older adults. *Journal of Applied Behavioral Analysis, 30*(1), 153-6.
[67] Skelly, J., & Flint, A. J. (1995). Urinary incontinence associated with dementia. *Journal of American Geriatrics Society, 43*(3), 286-94.
[68] Hutchinson, S. A., Leger-Krall, S., & Skodol-Wilson, H. (1996). Toileting: A biobehavioral challenge in Alzheimer's dementia care. *Journal of Gerontological Nursing, 22*(10), 18-27.
[69] Gugel, R. N.(1994). Behavioral approaches for managing patients with Alzheimer's disease and related disorders. *Medical Clinics of America, 78*(4), 861-7.
[70] Joint Commission on Accreditation of Healthcare Organizations (1994). *Standards and survey protocol for dementia special care units.* Oakbrook Terrace: Il: Author.
[71] Maas, M. (1988). Management of patients with Alzheimer's Disease in long term care facilities. *Nursing Clinics of North America, 23*(1), 57-68.
[72] Ronch, J. (1987). Specialized Alzheimer's Units in nursing homes: Pros and cons. *American Journal of Alzheimer Care and Research, 2*,10-19.
[73] Phillips, C. D., Sloane, P. D., Hawes, C., Koch, G., Han, J., Spry, K., Dunteman, G., & Williams, R. L. (1997). Effects of residence in Alzheimer's disease special care units on functional outcomes. *Journal of American Medical Association, 278*(16), 1340-4.

[74] Swanson, E. A., Maas, M. L., & Buckwalter, K. C. (1994). Alzheimer's residents' cognitive and functional measures: special and traditional care unit comparison. *Clinical Nursing Research, 3*(1), 27-41.

[75] Volicer, L., Collard, A., Hurley, A., Bishop, C., Kern, D., & Karon, S. (1994). Impact of special care units for patients with advanced Alzheimer's disease on patients' discomfort and costs. *Journal of the American Geriatric Society, 42*(6), 597-603.

[76] Sloane, P. D., Mitchell, C. M., Preisser, J. S., Phillips, C., Commander, C., & Burker, E. (1998). Environmental correlates of resident agitation in Alzheimer's disease special care units. *Journal of American Geriatric Society, 46*(7), 862-9.

[77] Maas, M. L., Swanson, E., Specht, J., & Buckwalter, K. C. (1994). Alzheimer's special care units. *Nursing Clinics of North America, 29*(1), 173-94.

[78] Kane, R. A., Jordan, N., & Grant, L. A. (1998). Goals for Alzheimer's care in nursing homes: What kind of differences do special care units expect to make? *Journal of Health and Human Services Administration, 20*(3), 311-32.

[79] McCoy, J. L., & Conley, R. W. (1990). Surveying board and care homes: Issues and data collection problems. *The Gerontologist 30*(2), 147-53.

[80] Davis, K. J., Sloane, P. D., Mitchell, C. M., Preisser, J., Grant, L., Hawes, M. C., Lindeman, D., Montgomery, R., Long, K., Phillips, C., & Koch, G. (2000). Specialized dementia programs in residential care settings. *The Gerontologist, 40*(1), 32-42.

[81] Sloane, P. D., Mitchell, C. M., Preisser, J. S., Phillips, C., Commander, C., & Burker, E. (1998). Environmental correlates of resident agitation in Alzheimer's disease special care units. *Journal of American Geriatric Society, 46*(7), 862-9.

[82] Innes, A., & Surr, C. (2001). Measuring the well-being of people with dementia living in formal care settings: The use of Dementia Care Mapping. *Aging and Mental Health, 5*(3), 258-68.

[83] Wimo, A., Adolfsson, R., & Sandman, P. O. (1995). Care for demented patients in different living conditions. Effects on cognitive function, ADL-capacity and behavior. *Scandinavian Journal of Primary Health Care, 13*(3), 205-10.

Chapter XII

PATIENTS WITH DEMENTIA AND THEIR CAREGIVERS IN TAIWAN

Jong-Ling Fuh
The Neurological Institute
Veterans General Hospital – Taipei
Taipei, Taiwan 112

ABSTRACT

The percentage of Taiwanese aged 65 years and older has been increasing over the past 20 years, from 4.1% in 1980 to to 8.6% in 2000. Studies on the Taiwan population have shown that the prevalence of dementia is approximately 1.7-4.4% among elderly people, and that the most common cause of dementia is Alzheimer's disease. The lower prevalence rate might be due to simple lifestyles in elderly Chinese, selective higher mortality, and lower prevalence of the APOE4 allele in the Chinese population. The evaluation of dementia derives from several reliable and valid assessment tools for cognitive and behavioral evaluation of demented patients, which were developed in Western countries and currently available in Taiwan. These tools are not only useful for clinical evaluation but also offer a method for possible cross-cultural studies. The majority of the elderly population in Taiwan is illiterate; however, because of the obligatory education requirement in Taiwan (6 years since 1943 and 9 years since 1968), it is expected that the prevalence of illiteracy among the elderly will decrease substantially with time. Nevertheless, the assessment of dementia must still consider illiteracy as factor, in addition to language and cultural factors. Aberrant motor behavior was the most frequently recorded behavior of Taiwanese dementia patients, whereas euphoria was the least recorded. A spouse, daughter-in-law, or other adult family member tends to provide home care for most of Taiwan's patients with dementia, and this burden of care is an increasing problem in Taiwan. The symptoms most frequently reported to be severely distressing to caregivers were aberrant motor activity, anxiety, agitation, and delusions. In contrast to caregivers in the United States, Taiwanese caregivers do not report being bothered to any great extent by the patient's depression. The mental status of dementia patients was the most significant variable affecting caregivers' attitudes toward nursing home placement. In highly urbanized areas, primary caregivers emphasized family manpower resources available for caregiving at home as a determining factor affecting the decision to use nursing home care.

INTRODUCTION

The current population in Taiwan is 23 million persons. Austronesian aborigines inhabited the country before the Han Chinese entered the area, but because the aboriginal population was low, the Han Chinese (made up of Fukienese and Hakka peoples from the southeast coast of China and more recent immigrants from various parts of China) have dominated Taiwan's population growth. Many people (69%) in Taiwan live in large metropolitan areas.

The population of older persons (≥ 65 years) in Taiwan increased at average annual growth rate of 4.5% over the past 10 years [1]. In contrast, the whole population increased at a rate of only 0.9% during this period. The percentage of older persons in the total population has risen continuously over the past 20 years, from 4.1% in 1980 to 6.1% in 1990 to 8.6% in 2000 [1]. The aging index, defined as the number of persons aged 65 and over per the persons aged 14 and under, increased dramatically from 21.7% in 1989 to 43.2% in 2002. The declining birth rate and increasing life expectancy in older persons has resulted in an increasing burden on care facilities and services in Taiwan. Because the prevalence of dementia doubles every 5 years after the age of 60 years [2], dementia has become a major public health problem in Taiwan.

Older Taiwanese generally tend to be undereducated, and in 2001 the illiteracy rate among men and women ≥ 65 years old was 8.6% and 42.0%, respectively. This discrepancy may be attributed to the past education tradition in Chinese society of placing less importance on education for females. Even if the women were able to attend school, they usually did not receive the same quality and quality of education as men, especially in rural regions. However, an obligatory education requirement of 6 years has been in effect in Taiwan since 1943; this requirement was increased to 9 years in 1968. These requirements have significantly changed the educational conditions in Taiwan, particularly for women. At the end of 2000, 50% of university and college graduates and 29% of graduate school graduates were women; 2 decades earlier, these figures were 36% and 16%, respectively.

The average life expectancy in 2000 was 78.3 and 72.6 years for women and men, respectively. In 2001, 75% of men aged 65 and older were married, compared to only 48.4% of older women. Forty-seven percent of older women were widows, and most of them received financial assistance from their children. These older women deserve special concern in Taiwan.

EPIDEMIOLOGICAL STUDIES OF DEMENTIA IN TAIWAN

Prevalence and Incidence

Several epidemiological studies have shown that the prevalence of dementia in Taiwan is between 1.7% and 4.4% in subjects ≥ 65 years of age [3-8] (Table 1). All of these studies showed that the prevalence of dementia increases with age and is higher among women than among men. The prevalence of dementia in Taiwan was quite similar to that reported in the studies conducted in mainland China, which reported a range from 1.1% to 4.6% [9-12]. Nevertheless, the reported prevalence rates of dementia in Europe and the US are higher, ranging from 5% to 10% [13-17].

Table 1. Prevalence of Dementia among Persons ≥ 65 Years in Studies Conducted in Taiwan

Authors, Year	Site	Sample size	Prevalence of dementia (%)	Predominant type of dementia
Rin H, 1987 [3]	Rural	1586	1.7%	Vascular dementia
Liu HC, 1988 [7]	Rural/Urban	1469	2.0%	Alzheimer's disease
Yip PK, 1991[4]	Urban	1038	1.9%	Not available
Liu HC, 1993[6]	Rural	1764	2.6%	Alzheimer's disease
Liu CK, 1993[8]	Urban	1016	4.3%	Alzheimer's disease

The subject of dementia and ethnicity has generated interest recently. The conclusion that there are ethnic differences in dementia is quite controversial because it is difficult to compare the findings of these studies due to the differences in methodology and diagnosis. If such ethnic differences do exist, they may be due to racial genetic factors, shared cultural practices, or common environmental factors. The low prevalence of dementia in persons of Chinese descent might be due to underreporting of data, selective high mortality rate, or the lower prevalence of the apolipoprotein E (ApoE) 4 allele in Chinese population.

Both the DSM-IIIR [18] and DSM-IV [19] require that the diagnosis of dementia fulfill the criterion of significant impairment in social or occupational functioning. However, because elderly Chinese are frequently freed from household responsibilities, their family members may not identify the decline until the condition is severe. Therefore, the prevalence of dementia might be underreported. Ross et al found that more than 60% of the subjects identified as having dementia via a survey either were not recognized by their family informants to have a memory problem or were not medically evaluated for this problem [20]. Because these study subjects were Japanese-American and Japanese culture is known for its respect for the elderly, the investigators hypothesized that family members of subjects with dementia denied the mild cognitive problem because of this cultural tradition. Similar to the Japanese culture, Chinese is known for respect of elders, and Taiwanese families may also fail to recognize or report mild cognitive deficiencies. In addition, the traditional Asian populations have low expectations of older persons and treat the memory decline as a normal part of the aging process. If epidemiological surveys rely mostly on the informants' report, they might underestimate the prevalence of dementia. The 2 studies [8,11] that used extensive cognitive testing reported higher dementia rate among Chinese population, but we can not rule out the possibility that the higher prevalence rate was due to the higher false-positive rate of these extensive cognitive tests in lower educational populations.

Two population-based studies in Taiwan reported mortality rates ranging from 32% to 48% in patients with dementia [6, 21]. These rates were higher compared with Western reports. Since the prevalence proportion is a function of disease incidence and disease survival, the selective higher mortality in patients with dementia might produce a lower prevalence in Taiwan.

Because incidence reflects the true rate of disease occurrence, comparing the incidence rates among different populations might provide us with more accurate information regarding the risk factors. The annual incidence of dementia among those aged ≥ 65 in Taiwan is 1.3%, and increases with age from 0.77% for 65- to 74-year-olds to 6.19% for persons aged 85 years or older [21]. The incidence of dementia in Taiwan is similar to that in mainland China (1.2%) [22], but lies on the lower end of the range reported in Western countries (1.3-2.5%) [23-27]. It is interesting that another 2 incidence studies from Asia, one from Japan [28] and one from India [29], also report lower rates of dementia. This implies that a difference in the incidence of dementia might exist between the East and West. APOE genotype is currently the strongest and most consistent risk factor for nonfamilial Alzheimer's disease (AD) [30-34]. Genotypes containing the 4 allele are associated with an increased risk of AD in many ethnic groups, including the Chinese population [35]. The frequency of 4 allele was lower among the Chinese population (4.8-11.0%) [35-38] compared with Western populations (9.0% to 16.5%) [31-34]. The lower frequency of ε4 allele might be one factor contributing to the lower prevalence of dementia in Taiwan.

Type of Dementia

With the exception of 1 study in Beijing [9], AD was the most common cause of dementia in community-based studies in Chinese society [6,7,8], as in Western countries. Two hospital-based studies found higher frequencies of vascular dementia (VaD) than AD [39,40]. One community study showed that women predominated in the AD group but males predominated in the VaD group [8]. Some authors attributed this discrepancy to the fact that stroke patients were more likely to be brought to hospitals. It is not certain whether AD is the leading cause of dementia in Taiwan at present [39, 40]. Since neuroimaging plays a critical role in the diagnosis of VaD, the lower ratio found in the community study might be due to the lack of brain imaging data. The higher mortality of patients with VaD compared with that of patients with AD might also contribute partly to it [21].

Screening Tools for Dementia in Taiwan

Most of the instruments used for screening Chinese population are adapted from the original versions developed in the West. One of the major challenges to studying dementia in Chinese communities was to select a screening instrument for dementia that was translated in the local dialect, culturally appropriate, and suitable for testing in both illiterate and literate individuals. It has been suggested that questions from the dementia assessment tools should be modified to culturally appropriate circumstances and scoring methods should be maintained as in the original version [41]. Because, many elderly persons in Taiwan are illiterate, the assessment of dementia has to consider illiteracy as factor in addition to the other language and cultural factors. In this chapter, we introduce 2 commonly used screening tools for dementia in Taiwan. One is an objective test, the Mini-Mental State Examination (MMSE), and the other is a subjective test, the Informant Questionnaire on Cognitive Decline in the Elderly (IQCODE).

The Mini-Mental State Examination

The MMSE is the screening instrument used most widely for detecting dementia [42]. Many versions of the MMSE are available in various languages. The MMSE is currently the most popular screening instrument for dementia in Taiwan. Several Chinese versions of the MMSE have been developed and validated [43,44,45]. Although most versions preserve the original structure, some differences exist in terms of neuropsychological and procedural aspects. For example, in 1 of the Taiwanese versions, a novel 7-character Chinese phrase was used for the original repetition phrase "no ifs, ands, or buts," and "hand it back to me" was used instead of "put it on the floor" for the last part of the 3-step command were used [44]. In the Chinese version of the MMSE, 2 of the items were modified [45]. The repetition phrase "no ifs, ands, or buts" was substituted by a famous Chinese alliteration "44 stone lions" and "say a sentence" was substituted for "write a sentence."

Although only the reading and writing items in the MMSE seem clearly related to formal schooling, some studies showed that education affected performance on practically all items except naming and registration [44, 46]. The effects of ethnicity on the MMSE performance are controversial. One study that compared the MMSE performance in Finland and China showed that mean scores were similar after considering the education level [46]. Nevertheless, the performances on individual items were significantly different in these two populations. It was not sure if this was due to the education or cultural factors.

The Informant Questionnaire on Cognitive Decline in the Elderly

The IQCODE is a 26-item questionnaire that asks the informant about cognitive changes in everyday cognitive functions during the previous 10 years [47, 48]. The IQCODE has also been translated into languages other than English, and several studies have proved that its cross-cultural application is good [48,49]. Educational level, residency in rural or urban region, occupational levels, and gender are all possible confounding factors for the objective screening instruments of dementia. In contrast, IQCODE score has little correlation with education or premorbid ability level. In our previous study, the IQCODE was found to perform better than the MMSE as a screening test for dementia in a population with a large variation in educational background [48]. Nevertheless, the performances of both tests were not different in the illiterate group. Therefore, the performance of the IQCODE and MMSE might be no different among subjects with the same educational background, but the IQCODE performs better in a society where the variation in educational levels is great, like in most Asian countries [46, 48]. The major concern of the use of IQCODE was that this questionnaire assumes that the informants are objective and honest in their rating, and variations from this will alter the results.

NEUROPSYCHIATRIC SYMPTOMS

In addition to cognitive disturbances, psychiatric symptoms are very common among patients with dementia. Hwang et al reported a higher frequency of many behavioral disturbances in psychiatric inpatients with AD in Taiwan compared with western countries [50]. However, most studies in Taiwan could not support this result [51,52]. It is very difficult to perform a comparative investigation of behavioral disturbances in patients with dementia. The studies were conducted in different clinical settings, and psychiatric inpatients might have higher frequency of behavioral disturbance; however, the outpatient samples, especially the neurological clinic samples, did not show a higher frequency. Besides this, the definition of behavioral disturbances and the variable type of behavior were different among studies. Some behavioral disturbances are related to the cognitive impairment [50, 53], therefore the levels of cognitive impairment of the recruited patients in studies influence the prevalence of behavioral disturbance.

Although it was hypothesized that Chinese subjects would have more severe dementia at the time of presentation because they seek medical care only after they experience behavioral changes, this hypothesis was not been proved [51]. In terms of the manifestation of neuropsychiatric symptoms, a transcultural study showed that Chinese caregivers reported anxiety and delusions more frequently than whites, and whites reported appetite changes and apathy more frequently than the Chinese sample [51]. Since the same method was used for the dementia patients, genetic or sociocultural factors might play a role in these differences. In addition, different prevalences of various neuropsychiatric symptoms might exist in different ethnic groups, and cultural or genetic factors might also influence the other neuropsychiatric manifestations in the agitated patients with dementia. We studied 3 ethnic groups - Taiwan, Italy and the US - and found all groups had a high rate of agitation manifestation among the dementia patients [54]. However, agitation was significantly associated with hallucinations in Taiwanese patients and apathy in Italian patients, implying that the underlying neurobiologic change was important for the manifestation of agitation in dementia patients since all the different ethnic groups had high rate of agitation. The sociocultural factor might be superimposed to the neurobiologic change because the manifestations of agitation in dementia patients were different among different ethnic groups.

In our study, we found a lower prevalence (44%) of apathy in Taiwanese patients with dementia than in those previously reported in white populations (72%) [55, 56]. Chinese culture does not evaluate passive behavior in an older person as being negative. The interpretation of behavioral changes is culturally dependent, and caregivers might report apathy less frequently than in other ethnic groups. Nevertheless, euphoria was the least frequently recorded behavior among all the ethnic groups, suggesting that some behaviors were due to a common underlying neuropathy, but others might be more related to cultural or environmental factors.

CAREGIVERS' BURDEN

Most of the elderly population (89.5%) in Taiwan lives with their families, and only a few older Taiwanese live on their own. It is customary in Taiwan that adult children look after their parents, and Chinese cultural emphasizes filial obligations to provide for and look after parents. There were lower scores for caregiver burden in Taiwanese caregivers of dementia patients compared with that for Western caregivers. Taiwanese caregivers might accept the responsibilities for older persons and cope well with behavioral problems in dementia patients [52].

The sword has 2 sides. The filial obligation also has a negative effect on the caregiver burden, especially for the daughters-in-law [57]. According to Chinese tradition, daughters-in-law are expected to take care of their husband's parents, and these women are usually more depressed compared with the adult children caregivers [58]. In Taiwan, it is not uncommon that daughters-in-law have conflicts with their mothers-in-law. As expected, these daughters-in-law who were caregivers complained more about the burden of care when their mothers-in-law became demented [59]. Spouse caregivers were more depressed than adult children caregivers, just like in Western countries [58, 60]. The relationships of caregivers might face different difficulties. Most of the spouse caregivers are older, and it is difficult for them to help with the patient's daily activities. The adult children caregivers usually complain of economic and time constraints because they have to take care of 2 families.

In a previous study of dementia patients in the US [61], the caregivers' distress was most often due to the depression-related behaviors of the dementia patients. In Taiwan, caregivers are most often distressed by disruptive behaviors of the dementia patient, followed by anxiety, agitation, and delusions [52]. Besides the behavioral problems, the caregivers are also bothered by patients waking up at night and by incontinence [62]. Since the dementia patients are elderly, they usually have other medical illness. Handling health problems of patient is also a difficult task for caregivers [63].

The caregiver burden increases as the disease progresses [64]. In our previous study, the caregivers did not learn to adapt the distress but rather through a wear-and-tear process [64]. It is not the demands of care per se that directly impact the caregiver's burden, but how much the caregiver is involved in the caregiving situation that produces caregiver burden [57]. Increased use of emotion-focused coping strategies by the caregiver was related to more burdens, and increased use of problem-focused coping was related to fewer burdens [57, 64].

The lower the educational level of caregivers, the higher the caregiver burden [64]. Caregivers tend to be economically disadvantaged and often don't know how to find support from society. Helping these caregivers should be one of the major priorities for health care policy-makers in Taiwan.

NURSING HOME PLACEMENT

In Western countries, approximately 50% of patients with dementia are nursing home residents [65]. Institutionalization can relieve the family caregivers' burden. It is debatable whether institutionalization is the best interest of the society, dementia patients, and their families [66]. In a survey of Taiwanese caregivers of patients with dementia [67], 28% of caregivers anticipated institutionalization. The acceptance of institutionalization among the patients with moderate to severe stages of dementia was close to the rate observed in Western countries [66].

Urbanization also has significant effect on nursing home placement [68]. In a highly urbanized metropolitan area, the willingness to use nursing placement is much higher compared with rural regions. In rural areas of Taiwan, many children still lived with their parents even they married. However, family support is relatively weaker in urban areas. The metropolitan caregivers concern the quality of care in nursing home more than the filial obligation. The mental status of demented patient and the manpower of the family available for caregiving are 2 important factors affecting the caregivers' attitude toward the nursing home placement for the patients [68]. As the tendency of the industrialization and Westernization in the cities of Taiwan, the caregivers will show similar attitude for nursing home placement as the Western caregivers in the future.

In Taiwan, the availability of long-term care has greatly increased since the passage of legislation in August 1993. It was estimated that about 2% of persons over 65 years were currently institutionalized in nursing homes in Taiwan [69]. Two recent studies showed that nursing home placement for demented patients is cheaper than home-based care [70, 71]

Besides filial obligation, the concern over the quality of care is the main reason that the caregivers are unwilling to consider nursing home placement. A study found that most of the residents in nursing homes in Taiwan had poor mental and physical function, and that about half were cognitively impaired [72]. Many nursing home residents complained that life in the nursing home was boring. They remain primarily inside the institution once they are admitted, and seldom have contact with the outside world and usual social life, except for the occasional visits from relatives. Therefore, most people have a negative impression of nursing homes in Taiwan.

Besides the quality of care, the caregivers of patients with dementia in Taiwan also consider the accessibility to nursing home services as an important factor for choosing nursing home placement [73]. This is because they can visit their relatives more frequently and can take them during holiday.

Surprisingly, there was no correlation between the number of nursing home staff per resident and the prevalence of selected clinical outcomes in 1 quality-of-care study conducted in Taiwan [74]. Nevertheless, level of satisfaction with nursing home care was positively correlated with the number of nurses and assistants [74]. Most of the nursing homes in Taiwan don't have full-time physicians. Since the nursing home system is new to Taiwan society, continuing education for the nursing home staff is an important factor to improve the quality of care.

END-OF-LIFE CARE

Caregivers usually have to make surrogate judgments for dementia patient who are at the later stage of their diseases. In the traditional culture, it is considered taboo to discuss issues related to death with the elderly. Therefore, only a few caregivers were aware of the patients' attitudes toward end-of-life care in Taiwan [67].

By comparison with Western countries, Taiwanese caregivers expressed a relatively low acceptance rate of cardiopulmonary resuscitation (CPR) refusal [67]. The caregivers usually were lacking CPR knowledge. The tradition of filial obligation also contributed to the low CPR refusal rate, as persons believe the best way to show respect for aged patients is by doing everything possible to keep them alive, regardless of the significance or goal behind the treatment. This concept is not only found in Taiwan but also in Japan. In a transcultural study, Japanese physicians adopted an aggressive stance toward the treatment of their critically ill patients but declined such treatment for themselves; this finding is not apparent for Japanese-American physicians [75]. This ambivalence reflects a similar attitude.

CONCLUSION

The impact and burden of dementia will be exacerbated in the future as the population ages, and the development of culturally appropriate evaluation tools is important in Taiwan. The need for long-term care will increase with progressive industrialization and Westernization in Taiwan. The health policy-makers should pay more attention to the burden among the caregivers of dementia patients.

REFERENCES

[1] Anonymous: *Demographic Facts of Taiwan and Fu-Chen Area, seasonal report,* Taipei: Department of Statistics, The Ministry of the Interior of the Republic of China, 2002

[2] Hendrie HC. Epidemiology of dementia and Alzheimer's disease. *Am J Ger Psychiatry* 1998; 6:S3-18.

[3] Rin H, Huang MG, Tseng MC. Prevalence of elderly dementias in Taipei area. Proc Ann Meeting Soc Neurol Psychiatry, *ROC* 1987:24.

[4] Yip PK, Shyu TI, Lee JY, et al: Prevalence of dementia in the elderly in an urban district of Taipei. *Acta Neurol Sin* 1992; 1:347-354.

[5] Liu HC, Lin KN, Wang SJ, et al: Assessing cognitive abilities and dementia in a predominantly illiterate population of older individuals in Kinmen. *Psychol Med* 1994; 24:1-8.

[6] Liu HC, Fuh JL, Wang SJ, et al. Prevalence and subtypes of dementia in a rural Chinese population. *Alzheimer Dis Assoc Disord* 1998; 12:127-134.

[7] Liu HC, Lin KN, Teng EL, et al. Prevalence and subtypes of dementia in Taiwan: a community survey of 5297 individuals. *J Am Geriatr Soc* 1995; 43:144-149.

[8] Liu CK, Lin RT, Chen YF, et al. Prevalence of dementia in an urban area in Taiwan. *J Formos Med Assoc* 1996; 95:762-768.

[9] Li G, Shen YC, Chen CH, et al. An epidemiological survey of age-related dementia in an urban area of Beijing. *Acta Psychiatr Scand* 1989; 79:557-563.

[10] Li G, Shen YC, Chen CH, et al. A three-year follow-up study of age-related dementia in an urban area of Beijing. *Acta Psychiatr Scand* 1991: 83:99-104.

[11] Zhang M, Katzman R, Salmon D, et al. The prevalence of dementia and Alzheimer's disease in Shanghai, China: impact of age, gender and education. *Ann Neurol* 1990; 27:428-437.

[12] Wang W, Wu S, Cheng X, et al. Prevalence of Alzheimer's disease and other dementing disorders in an urban community of Beijing, China. *Neuroepidemiology* 2000; 19:194-200.

[13] Bachman DL, Wolf PA, Linn R, et al. Prevalence of dementia and probable senile dementia of Alzheimer type in the Framingham study. *Neurology* 1992; 42:115-119.

[14] Copeland JR, Dewey ME, Wood N, et al. Range of mental illness among the elderly in the community. Prevalence in Liverpool using the GMS-AGECAT package. *Br J Psychiatry* 1987; 150:815-823.

[15] Hendrie H. Epidemiology of dementia and Alzheimer's disease. *Am J Geriatr Psychiatry* 1998; 6(suppl): S3-18.

[16] Ravaglia G, Forti P, Maioli F, et al. Education, occupation, and prevalence of dementia: findings from the Conselice study. *Dement Geriatr Cogn Disord* 2002; 14:90-100.

[17] Stevens T, Livingston G, Kitchen G, et al. Islington study of dementia subtypes in the community. *Br J Psychiatry* 2002; 180:270-276.

[18] American Psychiatric Association: *Diagnostic and statistical manual of mental disorders* 3rd ed, rev. Washington, DC: American Psychiatric Association Press, 1987.

[19] American Psychiatric Association. *Diagnostic and Statistical Manual of Mental Disorders.* 4th ed. Washington, DC: American Psychiatric Association Press; 1994.

[20] Ross GW, Abbott RD, Petrovitch H, et al. Frequency and Characteristics of Silent Dementia Among Elderly Japanese-American Men: The Honolulu-Asia Aging Study. *JAMA* 1997; 277:800-805.

[21] Liu CK, Lai CL, Tai CT, et al. Incidence and subtypes of dementia in southern Taiwan: impact of socio-demographic factors. *Neurology* 1998; 50:1572-1579.

[22] Zhang M, Katzman R, Yu E, et al. A preliminary analysis of incidence of dementia in Shanghai, China. *Psychiatry Clin Neurosci* 1998; 52 (Suppl):S291-294.

[23] Letenneur L, Commenges D, Dartigues JF, Barverger-Gateau P. Incidence of dementia and Alzheimer's disease in elderly community residents of southwestern France. *Int J Epidemiol* 1994; 23:1256-1261.

[24] Bickel H, Cooper B. Incidence and relative risk of dementia in an urban elderly population: findings of a prospective field study. *Psychol Med* 1994; 24:179-192.

[25] Ganguli M, Dodge HH, Chen P, Belle S, DeKosky ST. Ten-year incidence in a rural elderly US community population: the MoVIES Project. *Neurology* 2000; 54:1109-1116.

[26] Anonymous. The incidence of dementia in Canada. The Canadian Study of Health and Aging Working Group. *Neurology* 2000; 55:66-73.

[27] Clarke D, Morgan K, Lilley J, et al. Dementia and 'borderline dementia" in Britain: 8-year incidence and post-screening outcomes. *Psychol Med* 1996; 26:829-835.

[28] Yoshitake T, Kiyohara Y, Kato I, et al. Incidence and risk factors of vascular dementia and Alzheimer's disease in a defined elderly Japanese population: the Hisayama Study. *Neurology* 1995 45: 1161-1168

[29] Chandra V, Pandav R, Dodge HH, et al. Incidence of Alzheimer's disease in a rural community in India: The Indo–US Study. *Neurology* 2001; 57:985-989

[30] Saunders A, Schmader K, Breitner J, et al. Apolipoprotein E epsilon 4 allele distributions in late-onset Alzheimer's disease and in other amyloid-forming diseases. *Lancet* 1993; 342:710-711.

[31] Myers RH, Schaefer EJ, Wilson PWF, et al. Apolipoprotein Eε4 association with dementia in a population-based study: the Framingham study. *Neurology* 1996; 46:673-677.

[32] Kuusisto J, Koivisto K, Kervinen K, et al. Association of apolipoprotein E phenotype with late onset Alzheimer's disease: population based study. *BMJ* 1994; 309:636-638.

[33] Hyman BT, Gomez-Isla T, Briggs M, et al. Apolipoprotein E and cognitive change in an elderly population. *Ann Neurol* 1996; 40:55-66.

[34] Evans DA, Beckett LA, Field TS, et al. Apolipoprotein Eε4 and incidence of Alzheimer's disease in a community population of older persons. *JAMA* 1997; 277:822-824.

[35] Hong CJ, Liu TY, Liu HC, et al. ε4 allele of apolipoprotein E increase risk of Alzheimer's disease in a Chinese population. *Neurology* 1996; 46:1749-1751.

[36] Kao JT, Hsu WS, Tasi KS. Apolipoprotein phenotyping methodology and population frequency of Taiwan. *J Biomed Lab Sci* 1994; 6:73-79.

[37] Hallman DM, Boerwinkle E, Saha N, et al. The apolipoprotein E polymorphism: a comparison of allele frequencies and effects in nine population. *Am J Hum Genet* 1991; 49:338-349.

[38] Katzman R, Zhang MY, Chen PJ, et al. Effects of apolipoprotein E on dementia and aging in the Shanghai survey of dementia. *Neurology* 1997; 49:779-785.

[39] Liu HC, tsou HK, Lin KN, et al. Evaluation of 110 patients with dementia: a prospective study. *Acta Neurol Scand* 1991; 84:421-425.

[40] Liu CK, Lin RT, Howang SL, et al. Types of dementia in Taiwan-a prospective study. *Kao-Hsiung I Hsueh K'O Hsueh Tsa Chih* 1992; 8:290-298.

[41] Auchus AP, Chen CPLH. Asia regional meeting of the international working group for the harmonization of dementia drug guidelines: meeting report. *Alzheimer Dis Assoc Disord* 2001; 15:66-68.

[42] Folstein MF, Folstein SE, McHugh PR. 'Mini-Mental State'. A practical method for grading the cognitive state of patients for the dementia. *J Psychiatr Res* 1975; 12:189-198.

[43] Salmon DP, Riekkinen PJ, Katzman R, et al. Cross-cultural studies of dementia: a comparison of mini-mental state examination performance in Finland and China. *Arch Neurol* 1989; 46:769 –772.

[44] Liu HC, Teng EL, Lin KN, et al. Performance on a dementia screening test in relation to demographic variables: study of 5297 community residents in Taiwan. *Arch Neurol* 1994; 51:910-915.

[45] Salmon DP, Riekkinen PJ, Katzman R, et al. Cross-cultural studies of dementia: a comparison of Mini-Mental State Examination performance in Finland and China. *Arch Neurol* 1989; 46:769-772.

[46] O'Connoer DW, Pollitt PA, Treasure FP, Brook CP, Reiss BB. The influence of education, social class and sex on Mini-Mental State scores. *Psychol Med* 1989; 19:771-776.

[47] Jorm AF, Scott R, Cullen JS, MacKinnon AJ. Performance of Informant Questionnaire on Cognitive Decline in the Elderly (IQCODE) as a screening test for dementia. *Psychol Med* 1991; 21:785-790.

[48] Fuh JL, Teng EL, Lin KN, et al. The Informant Questionnaire on Cognitive Decline in the Elderly (IQCODE) as a screening tool for dementia for a predominantly illiterate Chinese population. *Neurology* 1995; 45:92-96.

[49] Law S, Wolfson C. Validation of a French version of an Informant-Based Questionnaire as a screening test for Alzheimer's Disease. *Br J Psychiatry* 1995; 167:541-544.

[50] Hwang JP, Yang CH, Tsai SJ, Liu KM. Behavioral disturbances in psychiatric inpatients with dementia of the Alzheimer's type in Taiwan. *Int J Geriatr Psychiatry* 1997; 12:902-906.

[51] Chow TW, Liu CK, Fuh JL, et al. Neuropsychiatric symptoms of Alzheimer's disease differ in Chinese and American patients. *Int J Geriatr Psychiatry* 2002; 17:22-28.

[52] Fuh JL, Liu CY, Wang SJ, Wang HC, Liu HC. Revised Memory and Behavior Problems Checklist in Taiwanese patients with Alzheimer's disease. *Int Psychogeriatr* 1999; 11:181-189.

[53] Hwang JP, Tasi SJ, Yang CH, Liu KM, Lirng JF. Persecutory delusions in dementia. *J Clin Psychiatry* 1999; 60:550-553.

[54] Fuh JL, Mega MS, Binetti G, et al. A transcultural study of agitation in dementia. *J Geriatr Psychiatry Neurol* 2002; 15:171-174.

[55] Fuh JL, Liu CK, Mega MS, Wang SJ, Cummings JL. Behavioral disorders and caregivers' reaction in Taiwanese patients with Alzheimer's disease. *Int Psychogeriatr* 2001: 13:121-128.

[56] Mega MS, Cummings JL, Fiorello T, Gornbein J. The spectrum of behavioral changes in Alzheimer's disease. *Neurology* 1996; 46:130-135.

[57] Chou KR, LaMontagne LL, Hepworth JT. Burden experienced by caregivers of relatives with dementia in Taiwan. *Nurs Res* 1999; 48:206-213

[58] Fuh JL, Wang SJ, Liu HC, Liu CY, Wang HC. Predictors of depression among Chinese family caregivers of Alzheimer's patients. *Alzheimer Dis Assoc Disord* 1999; 13:171-175.

[59] Heok KE, Li TS. Stress of caregivers of dementia patients in the Singapore Chinese family. *Int J Geriatr Psychiatry* 1997; 12:466-469.

[60] Schulz R, O'Brien AT, Bookwala J, Fleissner K. Psychiatric and physical morbidity effects of dementia caregiving: prevlalence, correlates and causes. *Gerontologist* 1995; 35:771-791.

[61] Teri L, Truan P, Logsdon R, et al. Assessment of behavioral problems in dementia: the Revised Memory and Behavior Problems Checklist. *Psychol Aging* 1992; 7:627-631.

[62] Tiang LY, Mao CL, Chou CF, Chen RC, Lin HC. Caregiver burden of demented elderly and related factors: an exploratory study. *J Nurs* 1992; 39:89-98. (in Chinese)

[63] Shyu YI, Yip PK, Chen RC. Caregiving experiences of family caregivers of elderly persons with dementia in northern Taiwan. Kaohsiung *J Med Sci* 1996; 12:50-61.

[64] Fuh JL, Wang SJ, Liu HC, Wang HC. The caregiving burden scale among Chinese caregivers of Alzheimer's patients. *Dement Geriatr Cogn Disord* 1999; 10:186-191.

[65] Fratiglioni L, Forsell Y, Torres HA, Winblad B. Severity of dementia and institutionalization in the elderly: prevalence data from an urban area in Sweden. *Neuroepidemiology* 1994; 13:79-88.

[66] Montgomery RJV, Kosloski K. A longitudinal analysis of nursing home placement for dependent elders cared for by spouses vs adult children. *J Gerontol* 1994; 49:S62-S74.

[67] Chen WT, Wang SJ, Lu SR, Fuh JL. Which level of care is preferred for end-stage dementia? Survey of Taiwanese caregivers. *J Geriatr Psychiatry Neurol* 2002; 15:16-19.

[68] Chiu L, Shyu WC, Liu YH, Wang SP, Chang TP. Factors determining the attitudes of family caregivers of dementia patients toward nursing home placement in Taiwan: comparisons between urban and semiurban areas. *Public Health Nurs* 2001; 18:281-291.

[69] Wu SC. Health and long-term care for the elderly. In Yaung Cl (ed): *Preventive medicine.* Public Health Foundation of KP Chen, 1997.

[70] Chiu L, Tang KY, Shyu WC, Chang TP. Cost comparisons between family-based care and nursing home care for dementia. *J Adv Nurs* 1999; 29:1005-1012.

[71] Chiu L, Shyu WC. Estimation of the family cost of private nursing home care versus home care for patients with dementia in Taiwan. *Chang Gung Med J* 2001; 24:608-614.

[72] Wu SC, Ke D, Su TL. The prevalence of cognitive impairment among nursing home residents in Taipei, Taiwan. *Neuroepidemiology* 1998; 17:147-153.

[73] Chiu L, Tang KY, Liu YH, Shyu WC, Chang TP. Willingness of families caring for victims of dementia to pay for nursing home care: results of a pilot study in Taiwan. *Journal of Management in Medicine* 1998; 12:349-360.

[74] Yeh SH, Sehy YA, Lin LW. The quality of nursing home care in Taiwan. *J Gerontol Nurs* 2002; 28:13-21.

[75] Asai A, Fukuhara S, Lo B. Attitudes of Japanese and Japanese-American physicians towards life sustaining treatment. *Lancet* 1995; 346:356-359.

INDEX

G

H

I

O

P